AUTOMOTIVE ENGINEERING AND LITIGATION

Volume 1

AUTOMOTIVE ENGINEERING AND LITIGATION
Volume 1

Edited by George A. Peters, J.D., P.E.
and Barbara J. Peters, J.D.
Peters and Peters
Attorneys at Law
Santa Monica, California

 Garland Law Publishing
New York & London

Director of Editing and Production: **Ruth Adams**
Production Editor: **Geoffrey Braine**

15 14 13 12 11 10 9 8 7 6 5 4 3 2 1

Library of Congress Cataloging in Publication Data
Main entry under title:

Automotive engineering and litigation.
  Bibliography: p.
  Includes index.
  1. Products liability—Automobiles—United
States. 2. Automobile industry and trade—Law
and legislation—United States. 3. Trial practice
—United States. 4. Automobile engineering.
I. Peters, George A. II. Peters, Barbara J., 1950–
KF1297.A8A97 1984   346.7303′82   83-16542
ISBN 0-8240-6100-4 (v. 1) 347.306382

Published by Garland Law Publishing
136 Madison Avenue, New York, New York 10016

Printed in the United States of America

Contents

II

HAZARD IDENTIFICATION

9 Recreational Vehicles   177

Laurie N. Solomon

III

ACCIDENT ANALYSIS

10 Multiple Causation   215

Sheldon C. Plotkin

11 Metallurgical Failures: Analysis of Structural Fractures Relative to Accident Causation   229

David K. Felbeck

IV

HUMAN FACTORS AND BIODYNAMICS

15 Visibility Problems in Nighttime Driving   383

Paul L. Olson and Michael Sivak

V

RISK REDUCTION

19 How Safe Is Reasonable?   555

*Kenneth A. Solomon, Charles L. Batten,
and Charles E. Phelps*

20 Warnings in Automotive Systems   575

Lorna Middendorf

21   Product Recall and Recall Prevention   595

John J. Wargo

22   System Safety Engineering   611

Rex B. Gordon

VI

DISCOVERY AND SETTLEMENT

25   Effective Claims Handling   671

Joseph O. Kern

26   Structured Settlements (Periodic Payments)   693

Edmund A. McGinn

VII

TRIAL AND APPEAL

29 Expert Testimony by Engineers   735

Barbara J. Peters

30 Significant Verdicts   747

George A. Peters

Preface

The automotive vehicle industry has had a profound influence on modern civilization. Consider what it must have been like prior to the introduction of personal automobiles, trucks and buses, motorized earth-moving and construction equipment, lift trucks and gantry cranes, riding lawn mowers and off-road vehicles, self-propelled guns and military tanks, trains and aircraft, and the guided vehicle systems in automated manufacturing and business enterprises. Self-propelled vehicles have spawned roadways and expressways across the landscape, fostered the development of parking lots and the design of structures that accommodate motor vehicles, enabled suburban growth and development to occur, and provided enormous employment opportunities in ancilliary, supporting, and service industries. This has all occurred in a relatively short time, dating from the use of steam power, 200 years ago, to drive a wheeled military vehicle. About 100 years ago, the horseless carriage, with its electric and gasoline engines, kindled the inventive creativity that transformed agrarian societies into progressive industrial and commercial entities. The benefits included unlimited opportunities for individual prosperity, enjoyment of life, and the fulfillment of many of the basic needs of modern mankind.

Obviously, the character of modern industrial civilization has been greatly shaped by the motor vehicle. It is increasingly apparent that the merging of national and world marketplaces has had a dramatic effect on the character of the automotive industry. New marketing forces became manifest at about the same time that radical technological developments had matured and could be applied in the design, manufacture, and testing of automotive vehicles. In addition, concepts of vigorous self-regulating entrepreneurship in the management of automotive enterprises and in automotive product engineering have gradually yielded to the coercive pressures of governmental regulation and court-imposed financial liabilities for failure to conform to externally mandated standards and criteria relating to environmental health and safety. Reindustrialization has been accompanied by a reconceptualization of the role of the human participants in the unfolding drama of the automotive industry. In essence, this means that automotive engineering as a professional discipline has been faced with greater challenge, accelerated transition, and new creative opportunities that could benefit both the automotive industry and the general public.

The scope of automotive engineering has become vastly broadened. In the past, the individual engineer was often assigned a narrowly defined job specialty or semidedicated function with tasks that progressed in an evolutionary manner. His job or function may *now* include system engineering responsibilities, obligations to understand or work in a multidisciplinary setting, pressures to deal with accessible information resources in a rapid cost-effective manner for decision-making purposes, and the necessity to perform a wider range of increasingly sophisticated work tasks. For example, the design engineer's intentions and directions as to product use are no longer paramount and controlling. Instead, the design engineer must be able to obtain and utilize objective and specific knowledge of actual field use, product misuse and abuse, and conformance to operating and maintenance instructions. Can he predict field failure modes and select desirable design or procedural remedies prior to user injury or property loss? Does he properly perceive his role relative to designing to avoid foreseeable misuse? Does he possess an adequate and appropriate understanding of the scientific principles of human factors engineering to deal with human misuse problems? Does he understand the legal concepts of product design or manufacturing "defects" and the "failure" to warn, test, instruct, or recall? Can he utilize computer-aided design and manufacturing processes, the advantages of flexible automation, and available collateral information sources to solve design, development, and customer problems? Such questions illustrate the broader scope and increasing complexity of the role of the individual automotive engineer.

The purpose of *Automotive Engineering and Litigation* is to provide an overview of the concepts and information now necessary for the practice of automotive engineering. The information provided is comprehensive in nature, reflecting the wide range of concepts that impinge upon this field of endeavor. It is a multidisciplinary approach to the topic matter and, perhaps as a result, presents differing opinions and sometimes criticism intended to be constructive. It is meant to be utilitarian so that future problems can be confronted realistically and effectively resolved. Whatever "problems" that have existed or will exist should not obscure the tremendous contributions that have been and will be made by an industry having significant beneficial social impact.

There is sufficient detail so that each volume is both a tutorial and a reference handbook. These volumes are useful to those who wish to plan and perform relevant scientific and medical research. They are practical primers for lawyers who wish to better understand the state-of-the-art of the automotive industry and how to deal with automobile-related claims and lawsuits. Engineers will benefit by reading the sections written by lawyers, since every engineer should anticipate some future connection with a lawsuit. These books should be extremely helpful to those who supply products or provide technical services for the automotive industry. They could foster understanding among the various government auto industry regulators and legislators. They should provide better "insight" for those insurance underwriters, claims adjusters, and loss control engineers who deal with automobiles, trucks, and other vehicles. Above all, they provide information not otherwise available to those automotive engineers faced with the challenge to "upgrade or perish" and those wishing to actively participate in what seems to be the "renaissance" of the automobile industry.

I

DESIGN
CONSIDERATIONS

It is appropriate to begin this book with an introduction to some of the basic design concepts relating to automotive vehicles. Thus Section 1, Fuel System Design, is a logical starting point because the ultimate source of energy is the fuel that is transformed into motive power by the vehicle's engine. Some of the more common fuel system hazards include stuck throttles, carburetor backfires, engine stalling, and fuel-fed fires. Recognition of such possible hazards is prerequisite for the formulation of preventive design remedies and appropriate testing.

Electrical and electronics system design (Section 2) is an area of considerable competitive vigor, where dramatic changes and added functions are occurring in terms of automotive design engineering. There are obvious benefits in terms of fuel economy, vehicle performance, driver convenience, passenger safety, reliability growth, and consumer interest. Design considerations should include system reliability enhancement, selection of fail-safe features or components, avoidance of the introduction of new hazards, and overall risk minimization. The design opportunities are fascinating and hold great promise in the immediate future.

Section 3, Hitches and Hydraulic Systems, presents an interesting historical review of the development of an automotive equipment system intended for off-road use. It illustrates the progressive nature of design improvements, notes how the automotive engineer attempts to meet changing requirements, and describes some of the operating safety considerations. Similarly, Section 4, Steering Trailers, illustrates the establishment of desirable design criteria, the development of equipment to meet those criteria, and a comparison of various design alternatives. The hitch is of a different type, to meet different (on road) requirements (including the resolution of recognized safety problems).

Section 5, Modifications, Maintenance, and Repairs, provides information on what happens after the vehicle leaves the original equipment manufacturer. This is an area too frequently overlooked, often given cursory attention, and generally underestimated in terms of impaired vehicle safety. Automotive design engineering may occur for the "after market," sometimes in a sophisticated fashion and sometimes to the despair of the original vehicle manufacturer.

1

Fuel System Design

JAY A. BOLT, P.E., P.C.
Professor of Mechanical Engineering
University of Michigan
Ann Arbor, Michigan

The author has degrees from Michigan State University, Purdue University, and the Chrysler Institute of Engineering. He has been engaged in teaching and research relating to automotive engineering and internal combustion engines at the University of Michigan for more than 40 years. His industrial experience includes employment at Chrysler Corporation and the Bendix Corporation on fuel metering and control of engines. He has been a consultant to both the Ford Motor Company and General Motors Corporation on engine development activities. He is a registered professional engineer, a Fellow of both the Society of Automotive Engineers and the American Society of Mechanical Engineers, and a member of the Institution of Mechanical Engineers of England. Professor Bolt may be contacted at 311 W.E. Lay Automotive Laboratory, North Campus, University of Michigan, Ann Arbor, Michigan 48109 (313-764-4256).

I. INTRODUCTION

The components of a vehicle fuel system include the following:

1. A tank to provide safe storage for the fuel, in an amount necessary for reasonable convenience and range for nonstop travel.
2. Lines or ducts to convey the fuel between the several components, and ultimately to the engine.
3. Filters and/or strainers to prevent foreign material from stopping the flow or causing harm to the system.
4. Necessary pumps to provide fuel flow to the engine at the correct pressure.
5. Means to prevent fuel vapor from escaping to the atmosphere, to prevent air pollution, and for safety.
6. A carburetor or alternate device to supply fuel-air mixture of the correct proportions for combustion in the engine cylinders.

A complete automotive fuel system is illustrated in Figure 1–1.

II. GASOLINE ENGINES AND DIESEL ENGINES

Gasoline engines are piston-type or positive-displacement machines that utilize either a two-stroke or four-stroke cycle. Passenger cars today use four-stroke-cycle engines almost without exception, which provide a power or firing impulse from each cylinder every two revolutions of the crankshaft. Most gasoline engines utilize a carburetor to mix thoroughly the gasoline and air in the correct proportions to form a combustible gaseous mixture. Other fuels are commonly used, including liquified petroleum gas (LPG), natural gas (mainly methane), and the alcohols.

An electrical ignition system is a requirement for these engines to supply a properly timed spark to each cylinder to initiate combustion, which must be accomplished thousands of times per minute for the typical automobile multicylinder engine when running on the highway.

A necessary characteristic of all fuels used in a gasoline engine, or as more broadly labeled, a spark-ignited engine, is that the fuel be readily vaporized from the liquid to gaseous state.

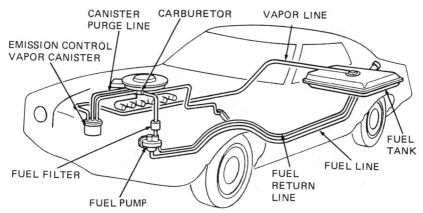

CANISTER   CARBURETOR   VAPOR LINE
PURGE LINE

EMISSION CONTROL
VAPOR CANISTER

FUEL
TANK

FUEL LINE

FUEL FILTER

FUEL
RETURN
LINE

FUEL PUMP

Figure 1-1 Complete automotive fuel system (Courtesy of the Ford Parts and Service Division, Ford Motor Company, Dearborn, Michigan.)

In contrast, the diesel engine is able to burn heavier and less volatile fuels, which is one of the merits of the diesel engine. These less volatile fuels are safer to handle and use than gasoline, and they have more energy per gallon.

The compression ratio is the ratio of the volume of the cylinder charge before compression divided by the charge volume at the end of the compression stroke. The diesel engine uses a much higher compression ratio than does the gasoline engine, commonly as high as 24 to 1. This high compression of the air charge results in a compressed air temperature high enough to ignite the fuel when injected into this hot-air charge. Thus, the need for an electric spark and the ignition system of the gasoline engine is eliminated. The compression ratio of the gasoline engine is limited to less than about 10 to 1 by auto-ignition, or the tendency of the fuel to self-ignite.

As was said by one famous engineer, amplified somewhat, "The main difference between a gasoline engine (spark-ignition) and a diesel engine (compression-ignition) is that in the diesel engine you inject some fuel into a cylinder full of fire, whereas in the gasoline engine you inject a spark into a cylinder full of fuel mixture."

Reference 1 (and others) provide abundant material for more detailed study of internal combustion engines (see page 19).

III. FUEL CHARACTERISTICS AND COMBUSTION

Vehicles most commonly use liquid hydrocarbon fuels, composed of carbon and hydrogen, because:

1. They have a high energy content per unit of weight and volume and thus provide maximum range of travel between refueling.
2. There is a relatively abundant supply of hydrocarbon fuels (derived from petroleum) and their cost is relatively low.
3. They are easily transported and handled on the vehicle.

Gasoline is the most commonly used fuel for passenger vehicles. It is often defined as the fraction of petroleum constituents having boiling points between about 100°F and 400°F. Various additives are used to make it most suitable for gasoline engines.

The following characteristics are important:

1. *Specific Gravity.* This refers to the weight in relation to water: this value is about 0.7. Gasoline weighs about 6 pounds per gallon.
2. *Volatility.* This refers to the ease with which the liquid will vaporize. In general, the lower the molecular weight of a hydrocarbon fuel, the more readily it will vaporize. For example, methane, CH_4, the lightest hydrocarbon, usually exists in the gaseous state. It is the principal constituent of natural gas. Gasoline must have a sufficient amount of light molecules to make it vaporize readily so that an engine can be started cold on a cold day. Gasoline, like other liquids, vaporizes more readily at reduced pressure (for example, at high altitude) and higher temperature.
3. *Flash Point and Fire Points.* These refer to the minimum temperature at which the fuel will vaporize sufficiently to start or maintain fire if a flame is passed over the liquid fuel surface, under controlled test conditions. Both are mainly a measure of the volatility of the fuel, and for gasoline will be in the region of 0°F.
4. *Ignition Temperature.* This refers to the minimum temperature that a fuel and air mixture must reach

before it will auto-ignite, or start to burn spontaneously without the aid of an ignition source such as a spark. The ignition temperature of gasoline is relatively high, in excess of 1000°F.

Diesel fuels usually have an ignition temperature lower than 1000°F, considerably lower than gasoline. Gasoline is so much more hazardous because it is much more volatile, or it vaporizes much more easily than does diesel fuel. Diesel fuel is less volatile and has higher flash and fire points than gasoline.

5. *Octane Number.* Octane number is a measure of the resistance of a fuel to knocking, or auto-igniting, in a spark-ignited engine. The cetane number, in contrast, is a measure of the ease of compression-ignition of a diesel fuel. High cetane number of the diesel fuel will cause less combustion noise in the diesel engine.

6. *Combustion.* It requires approximately 15 pounds of air to burn 1 pound of gasoline or other hydrocarbon fuel. This ratio, of about 15 to 1, is referred to as the chemically correct or stoichiometric ratio.

There are limits to the ratio of fuel to air which can be ignited and burned. A ratio of about 8 pounds of air per pound of fuel vapor is about the rich limit; about 22 to 1 is near the lean limit of flammability of homogeneous gaseous hydrocarbon fuel and air mixtures.

It is commonly and correctly stated that only fuel vapors burn. In other words, the liquid fuel must become a vapor before it can be burned. When flame is observed above a pan of cold liquid gasoline, or diesel fuel, one is observing the combustion of vapors above the liquid pool that have mixed with air to form a flammable mixture.

If a space is filled with a uniform mixture of fuel vapor and air that is within the limits of flammability, very rapid combustion of the volume of mixture will occur if a spark or flame is applied to the mixture. Such rapid combustion is referred to as an explosion, which causes a sudden increase in pressure or volume, depending on whether it is in a sealed container. This is the nature of combustion in the cylinder of a gasoline engine, which causes an increase in pressure. This pressure, acting upon a moving piston, produces a force moving through a distance, which constitutes work.

IV. THE PRINCIPAL COMPONENTS OF A VEHICLE FUEL SYSTEM USING A CARBURETOR

A. Tank for Storage

Fuel tanks are most commonly made of sheet steel with a noncorroding surface coating, although plastic materials are now in common use. It must have a convenient filler pipe that permits quite rapid filling and have a cover or cap. A line that draws fuel from near the bottom of the tank supplies fuel on its way to the engine. The tank will also usually include the mechanism of a float and electric circuit that provides a signal for a fuel gauge on the instrument panel. Fuel tanks on newer vehicles are vented through a carbon cannister to prevent loss of vapor to the atmosphere.

The fuel tank should be in as safe a location as possible and as remote and separated from the passenger compartment as is practical. As an example, most front-wheel drive cars now have the fuel tank forward of the rear axle and under the passenger compartment floor. This provides as much protection as is practical from collisions. No part of the fuel system should pass through the passenger body compartment.

B. Fuel Lines and Filters

The fuel lines are usually made of steel and are placed alongside the frame or other structural members to provide protection from mechanical injury and from heat. Flexible rubberlike materials are used where relative motion must be accommodated—for example, where the fuel line leaves the vehicle frame structure and goes to an engine-mounted fuel pump.

Filters or strainers are used to remove foreign materials that may plug the system, damage parts, or prevent proper operation of the system. Filters may consist of a screen, sintered and porous metal, or pleated specially treated paper. They are often located on the suction pipe in the fuel tank, at the inlet to the fuel pump, or at the carburetor inlet. Plugging of these filter elements will cause the engine to stop.

C. Fuel Pumps

A fuel pump for an automobile engine fitted with a carburetor is usually mounted on the forward portion of the engine, and as low as practical. It is most commonly driven by a spring-loaded arm that is caused to move up and down by an eccentric on the engine camshaft. This reciprocating motion actuates a flexible pumping diaphragm.

Greater detail concerning this type of engine-driven pump can be found in Reference 1.

Fuel pumps driven by small electric direct-current motors are also commonly used to supply fuel pressure to the fuel system. These are usually installed in or near the fuel tank and are normally electrically powered when the ignition switch is turned on. Fuel injection systems also very commonly incorporate electric-motor-driven fuel pumps in or near the fuel tank. Commercial vehicles and buses also commonly use tank pumps because the delivery line must be longer and for other reasons. An advantage of these tank-mounted pumps is that the fuel is kept under pressure from the tank to the engine, which reduces the likelihood of interruption of flow due to vapor formation in the fuel lines. On the other hand, the hazards from leakage are greater.

The fuel pump delivers fuel to the carburetor at a pressure which is usually near 5 lbs/in^2.

D. The Carburetor

The function of the engine carburetor is to mix in proper proportions the fuel and air and thus provide a combustible mixture to the engine cylinders. This is a difficult task, since the air to be metered is a gas and the gasoline is a liquid when metered or measured. Further, different engine operating conditions require different mixture ratios of fuel to air, and a good carburetor must provide for such changes with precision. The carburetor also includes the throttle valve, which is the device that controls the amount of fuel and air mixture that goes to the engine and thus controls the engine power output.

Figure 1-2 shows the main metering and enrichment system of a typical float carburetor, although greatly simplified for easy understanding of the main elements. The principal parts have been labeled.

Fuel is admitted at about 5 pounds per square inch of pressure through a fuel supply inlet pipe (usually fitted with an inlet fuel filter). A float needle valve and float maintain a constant level of fuel in the float chamber, which is essential. This float chamber must be kept at atmospheric pressure and is usually vented to the air inlet below and after the air

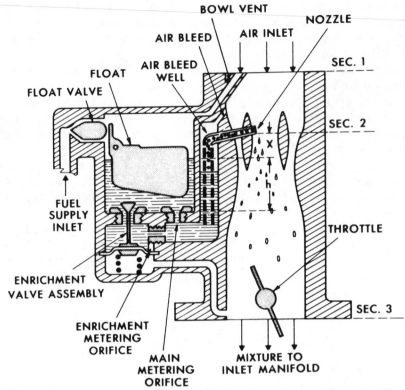

Figure 1-2 Main metering and enrichment system of a float carburetor. (Reprinted from J. A. Bolt and M. Boerma, SAE paper 660119, 1966, with permission of the Society of Automotive Engineers, Warrendale, PA.)

cleaner and silencer. The flow of air through the restricted air passage (labeled SEC. 2 in Figure 1-2), or venturi, results in increased air velocity and a reduced pressure. This reduced air pressure at the venturi section draws in fuel from the main metering jet. This fuel mixes with the air to provide the proper fuel-to-air mixture ratio. At full throttle, or maximum power, an additional enrichment valve and jet are opened that provide a richer mixture for maximum power and help suppress engine knock.

Under engine idling conditions there is not sufficient suction at the airflow venturi to draw the fuel into the airstream. Therefore, carburetors have a separate idling fuel supply system. This is seen in Figure 1-3, which shows the idling system of the carburetor of Figure 1-2. At idling conditions a high vacuum or suction exists at the throttle valve; thus means are provided to supply and control the discharge of fuel at the edge of the throttle valve. An idle-mixture adjusting screw is necessary to adjust the idle mixture to the need of the particular engine. On modern carburetors the amount of this adjustment is severely restricted in an effort to control exhaust pollutants and avoid tampering. There is also an adjustment of the degree of closing of the throttle valve that serves as an idle engine speed adjustment.

A choke valve (not shown) at the air inlet to the carburetor is ordinarily used to permit enrichment of the mixture for cold starting the engine. This is necessary since at very

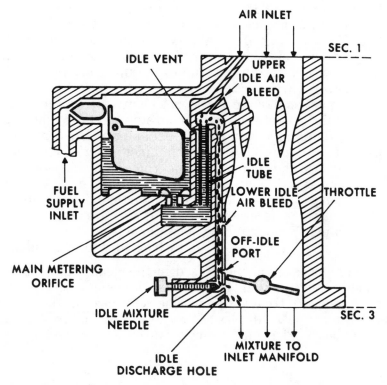

Figure 1-3 Idle fuel flow system of a float carburetor. (Reprinted from J. A. Bolt and M. Boerma, SAE paper 660119, 1966, with permission of the Society of Automotive Engineers, Warrendale, PA.)

cold temperatures only a small fraction of the fuel vaporizes and additional fuel must be supplied to insure sufficient fuel vapor to obtain a combustible vapor mixture with the air for starting.

The mixture of fuel and air is usually heated in the intake manifold leading to the cylinders, so that most of the fuel for a hot engine will be vaporized by the time it is trapped in the cylinders by the closing of the inlet valve, which follows the induction stroke.

E. The Air Cleaner

The air inlet to the carburetor is fitted with a quite large sheet metal container, which has the following functions:

1. To remove dirt, bugs, and gritty material from the air entering the engine system, which can be very harmful and cause excessive engine wear.
2. To act as an air-intake system silencer. The intake system noise can be very loud and annoying since the flow is intermittent due to the unsteady flow of the several cylinders.
3. To act as a flame arrestor. The mixture in the intake manifold between the carburetor and the cylinders is a flammable mixture of fuel and air. If the mixture is ignited, as will be explained later, combustion occurs, and flame can issue from the carburetor inlet. This is commonly referred to as a backfire. It can be a source of fire under the hood, particularly if gasoline-wetted surfaces are present. It can also be dangerous to personnel standing near the carburetor. Backfire has been the cause of many tragic personal accidents.

The air cleaner element used in the cleaner assembly is commonly a circular part having a filter element consisting of pleated specially treated paper. The references at the end of this chapter show examples of this assembly. The unit should properly be called an air cleaner, silencer, and flame arrester.

V. FUEL INJECTION EQUIPMENT

Fuel injection for engines refers to the means or the equipment for injecting fuel into the engine air supply, either in the intake manifold or directly into the cylinder. For diesel engines the fuel must be injected directly into the combustion chamber or cylinder. For such compression-ignition engines the fuel must be injected directly into the high pressure existing in the cylinder at the end of the compression stroke, since the timing of the burning depends upon the fuel injection timing. This is a difficult task and requires precision equipment that is expensive and complex.

For many years various fuel injection devices have been made and used on some gasoline engines. In this case the injection system must function as a substitute for a conventional carburetor, provide for both the metering of the fuel and air, and mix them. This also proves to be a difficult task.

A typical gasoline engine electronic fuel injection system (EFI) is shown in Figure 1-4, together with a listing of the principal components.

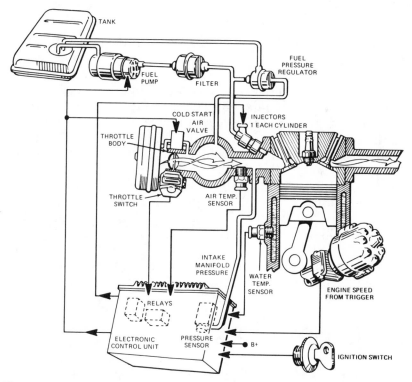

Figure 1-4 Typical electronic fuel injection system, with parts labeled. (Reprinted from *Automotive Engineering*, Vol. 84, No. 2, February 1976, p. 19, with permission of the Society of Automotive Engineers, Warrendale, PA.)

The principal advantages of a gasoline injection system over a carburetor usually claimed are:

1. Delivery of the fuel through nozzles usually at a point in the intake manifold near the inlet valve. Thus the problems of a flammable mixture of wet fuel and air in the intake manifold are eliminated, and greater equality of the fuel-to-air mixture to each cylinder can be achieved.
2. Improved starting, idling, and warm-up conditions, due mainly to improved fuel vaporization, and in some cases overcoming an engine tendency to stall at or near idle.
3. Maintaining the fuel under higher pressure throughout the system and thus avoiding vapor loss, such as occurs from carburetors in hot weather, especially from the float bowl, which must be maintained at atmospheric pressure.

Although all the above are very important objectives, they prove rather difficult to achieve, and the necessary equipment is usually more expensive than a carburetor.

On the other hand, present exhaust emission requirements place many additional requirements upon the carburetor functions, together with very precise metering. As these requirements multiply, there are increasing advantages in going to electric controls, and these electronic controls are most easily incorporated into modern fuel injection systems. Their use will without doubt increase in the future.

Injection systems also require fuel pumps, commonly placed in or near the fuel tank, to maintain higher fuel pressures than are necessary for carburetors. These pumps commonly deliver the fuel to the fuel injection nozzles at about 30 lbs/in^2 of pressure for spark-ignited engines.

VI. DIESEL FUEL SYSTEM

The injection system for a diesel engine must provide for injecting fuel at very high pressure (many thousands of pounds per square inch of pressure) into highly compressed heated air near the end of the compression stroke of the engine. The fuel must be injected at the correct time because the injection controls the time of ignition and burning, and the fuel must be finely atomized to assist very rapid vaporization and combustion in the cylinder.

The fuel injection system to accomplish this usually consists of a high-pressure piston pump, a fuel line, and a nozzle that injects finely atomized fuel into the hot compressed-air charge in the engine cylinder. As part of this system, there must also be a supply tank, an auxilliary fuel pump, and one or more fuel filters. Diesel injection systems must be kept free of dirt of all kinds. Therefore, a very high quality of fuel filtering is essential.

The injection system for the compression-ignition (diesel) engine should accomplish the following:

1. Discharge the correct quantity of fuel from the nozzles for each load and speed of the engine. This involves equal amounts from each nozzle on successive cycles and from the nozzles in the several cylinders.
2. Begin the injection at the proper time near the end of the compression stroke, since this controls the timing of the beginning of combustion.
3. Control the rate of injection of the fuel, since this has an important influence on the rate of pressure rise and maximum combustion pressure attained in the cylinder.
4. Form a nozzle fuel spray pattern that will aid in distributing the fuel throughout the air charge.
5. Break up the fuel into very small drops to increase the fuel surface area for rapid vaporization.
6. Provide means for filtering the fuel, and be as insensitive to dirt as possible.

A. Classification of Diesel Injection Systems

A great variety of diesel injection equipment has been developed, and it is somewhat difficult to make even most of them fall into a few classifications. However, a classification is helpful, and the following general types are predominant:

1. *Individual Pump System.* In this system each nozzle is supplied by its own injection pump unit.
2. *Distributor System.* In this arrangement a single injection pump meters and controls the time of injection for all the nozzles. This is accomplished by having the

pump joined in sequence to each of the nozzles by means of a distributor unit.

All of these fuel systems include a supply tank, filters, and a low-pressure boost pump to supply clean fuel to the high-pressure pumping system. The injection system pressures are high (from 3000 to 30,000 psi), and the plungers and other moving parts must be very closely fitted to avoid leakage and to insure precise metering.

VII. FUEL TANKS

A vehicle fuel tank should provide for the following:

1. Be of sufficient size for reasonable nonstop trips.
2. Be so located to minimize the chances of impact or crushing of the tank during a collision. As an example, most modern front-drive vehicles place the fuel tank in front of the rear axle of the vehicle and under the sheet metal floor of the car. This provides a space well protected from rear, front, and side collisions.
3. The filler pipe must be of sufficient size for rapid filling, and the filler cap should not extend beyond the vehicle exterior sheet metal. It should be as protected from injury as practical.
4. The space and surfaces adjacent to the fuel tank should not present sharp edges or projections that might tear or puncture the tank.
5. The tank should be corrosion resistant to avoid leakage, provide long life, and avoid solid accumulation.
6. No part of the fuel system should pass through the passenger space.

If a nearly full fuel tank is crushed or compressed in a collision, very high pressures are built up, which, if there is a break in the tank wall, can cause fuel to be sprayed great distances, often with tragic results. Almost nothing burns more intensely than a stream or jet of gasoline. Sources of ignition are commonly present due to sparks caused by steel scraping on steel or pavement during a collision or due to disturbed electrical wiring that causes electrical sparks. Either can readily ignite gasoline vapor and air mixtures.

VIII. FUEL SYSTEM PROBLEMS AND HAZARDS

A. Stuck Throttle

One of the most common reasons given for automobile accidents is the claim that the "throttle stuck open." If the throttle stays in the open position, the vehicle accelerates rapidly due to high power output of the engine. It is also common that the driver is so busy steering the car to avoid objects that the driver fails to shut off the ignition switch, which is the obvious thing to do. An accident usually follows. Some of the causes of actual "stuck throttles" are:

1. The accelerator pedal, which actuates the throttle, is moved to the closed position by a return or closing spring or springs. If these become disengaged, become weak, or are not the proper part for the vehicle, the throttle may not be pulled to the closed position.
2. Unusual friction may develop in the throttle shaft due to metal warping or damage to the carburetor throttle bearings or due to improper fitting. There may also be friction in the actuating linkage to the foot pedal or interference due to floor rugs or other objects. Icing is also a possibility.

B. Backfires in the Induction System

The carburetor supplies a flammable mixture of gasoline and air that fills the pipes that connect the carburetor to the intake valves of the cylinders. This piping system is called the intake manifold. If the mixture ratio in a cylinder is very rich or lean when ignited by a spark plug in a cylinder, the charge may continue to burn until the intake valve again opens for the next induction stroke. In this case the burning charge in the cylinder ignites the charge in the intake manifold. This causes a sudden burning of the contents of the intake manifold, and flame will commonly be seen coming out of the carburetor inlet. This is usually accompanied by a loud popping noise. It is the purpose of the intake air silencer and flame arrester to prevent this fire from getting into the engine compartment. Most automobile service manuals now have a caution to not operate the engine without the cleaner–silencer–flame arrestor properly installed. Failure to have this part installed has been the source of many fires and personal injury burns.

C. Stalling of Engine

Stalling, or stopping, of the engine from an idling or light-load condition is a common complaint. There are a multitude of conditions that can cause such stalling. It is also agreed that this can be a safety hazard and problem, since stalling of a vehicle on the highway can lead to a great variety of accident situations. Among the common reasons for stalling of an engine are the following, but it is by no means a complete list:

1. Idle speed set too low.
2. Idling fuel/air mixture not correct. There is only limited adjustment for this mixture on recent carburetors.
3. Malfunctions in the carburetor, such as dirt or varnish accumulation or a stuck choke valve.
4. Mechanical defects in the engine, such as leaky valves, poor compression, misfiring of spark plugs. Other mechanical malfunctions can also cause stalling.
5. Failures in the electronic ignition system now in common use on vehicles, or in older types of ignition systems.

In general, stalling of the engine, or stopping from an idling condition, or when accelerating, is a quite common problem, one that can be due to a great variety of malfunctions.

D. Fuel Tank and Fuel System Fires

Whenever the fuel tank space is invaded, fuel is likely to be ejected due to increased fuel pressure built up in the tank. If the tank is punctured or torn by sharp adjoining objects, fuel is likely to be thrown in many directions, and the opportunities for fire of the very volatile gasoline are great. Federal Motor Vehicle Safety Standard (FMVSS) 301 was developed to give some criteria of a fuel system to resist fuel spillage under collision circumstances. These tests consist of front and rear barrier impact tests and roll-over tests. Under the conditions of these carefully specified tests, the federal standard calls for a minimum loss of fuel during and after the impact. Failure to pass FMVSS 301 is commonly due to puncturing or tearing of the fuel tank or to separation of the parts that comprise the fuel inlet system. For example, many vehicles have used rubber hose sections and hose clamps in the tank filler pipe assembly, both for ease of assembly and to provide desirable flexibility in the system. However, these clamped joints often separate during a collision, or the rubber may burn out.

Another important aspect of fuel tank fires caused by rear impacts is sufficient stiffness of the vehicle structure so that the doors will not be jammed in the closed position and thus prevent rapid escape of the passengers.

To meet FMVSS 301, most cars now use a nonreturn spring-loaded valve incorporated into the fuel inlet connection to the carburetor (commonly incorporated into the fuel filter element) to avoid spilling the contents of the carburetor fuel bowl.

In summary, an important aspect of fuel system design is to make it in such a way that spillage in a collision and resulting fire is a minimum and the location of the components is such that the maximum possible time is provided for escape of the passengers if fire occurs. As much provision as is practical should be made so passengers can easily and quickly escape from a burning vehicle.

REFERENCES

1. W. H. Crouse, *Automotive Mechanics*, 7th ed. New York: McGraw-Hill, 1975.
2. W. H. Crouse, *Automotive Engine Design*. New York: McGraw-Hill, 1970. (Excellent reference.)
3. *Complete Car Care Manual*. Pleasantville, N.Y.: Reader's Digest, 1981. (Good elementary book, with exceptionally good color pictures of equipment.)
4. C. F. Taylor, *The Internal Combustion Engine in Theory and Practice*, 2nd ed., Vols. I and II (paperbacks). Cambridge: MIT Press, 1977.
5. E. F. Obert, *Internal Combustion Engines and Air Pollution*. New York: Intext, 1973.
6. T. Baumeister (ed.), *Marks Standard Handbook for Mechanical Engineers*, 8th ed. New York: McGraw-Hill, 1978. (Section on Internal Combustion Engines, by Bolt, Cole, Mirsky, and Patterson, pp. 9-78 to 9-119.)

2

Electrical and Electronic Design Considerations

DIANE M. COPTY, J.D.
Ford Motor Company
Dearborn, Michigan

Diane M. Copty joined Ford Motor Company in 1979 and is currently a Supervisor in the Powertrain Electrical and Electronic Products Engineering Executive Engineering Group of the Product Engineering Office, Electrical and Electronics Division. Her responsibilities include design of microprocessor-based special function modules, preparation of engineering specifications, tracking of warranty/ reliability, and analysis of product returns. Prior to this, the author worked in the Electronic Engine Controls Subsystem and Applications and Safety and Reliability Engineering Departments of Ford. She began her work career in 1972 at General Motors Corporation working in various areas including engineering computer applications, test and development, and vehicle assembly. She holds a B.S.E.E. from Michigan Technological University and a J.D. from the University of Detroit. She is a member of the State Bar of Michigan, the American Bar Association, and the Society of Women Engineers. In conjunction with her engineering and law background, Ms. Copty has worked with the law firm of Philo, Atkinson, Steinberg, Walker, and White (Detroit) on nonautomotive product liability/ personal injury cases. She also maintains a general law practice at 25730 Castlereigh Drive, Farmington Hills, Michigan 48018 (313-476-4710).

I. INTRODUCTION

The electrical and electronic aspects of automotive vehicles will be discussed separately. The electronics subsection includes instrumentation/vehicle controls and engine management/power train controls. The electrical subsection, titled Wiring, addresses gauge, circuit protection, fiber optics, and miscellaneous information. Citations, secondary sources, and an extensive general reference list are included at the end of the section.

II. ELECTRONICS

A. Introduction

Electronics exhibit a phenomenon referred to as infant mortality. Translated, this means the component will either fail very early or continue on to exceed the expected vehicle life, which is typically ten years. To "weed out" the units that will fail early in vehicle life, manufacturers subject the components to stringent production line testing with a burn-in period usually included.

Electronics are being utilized in four major automotive areas: (1) instrumentation, (2) engine management/power train controls, (3) vehicle controls, and (4) entertainment. "By 1985 many electronically assisted vehicle functions will have evolved as standard equipment. So much so, that by then, the cost of electronics is reckoned to take up between 10 and 15% of the total cost of the car."[1]

B. Instrumentation and Vehicle Controls

Mechanical displays are being replaced by electronic instrument clusters. The various display technologies available include:

1. Light-emitting diodes (LEDs)
2. Gas discharge
3. Electroluminescence
4. Vacuum fluorescence
5. Liquid crystal

None of these technologies has proven to be dominant. All allow use of solely digital display or, the more likely combination, of analog/digital information display. Electronic instrument clusters provide an opportunity to go beyond the conventional warning lights to display full driver diagnostic information on fluid levels (oil, coolant, transmission, and brake fluids), brake pad wear, bulb failures, fuel economy and other dynamic engine function information (air-to-fuel ratio measurements, temperatures, and pressures), and pollution control system parameters (exhaust gas recirculation valve operation and catalytic converter efficiencies).

The technology that forms the basis of these developments is the microprocessing chip, using either large-scale integrated (LSI) chips—those containing 15,000 to 20,000 components—or very large-scale integrated (VLSI) chips—those containing 50,000 to 100,000 components.

National Semiconductor's COP 400 microprocessor is the base for a trip computer called Compucruise. Information on fuel flow and vehicle speed are transmitted to the microprocessor, which can perform 44 individual functions, and more features can be added using external temperature sensors. Utilizing the total system, the driver is able to activate speed control, monitor fuel economy (thus determining the most fuel-efficient driving speed and the effect of tires—pressure, type), and interrogate the vehicle for tune-up or repair times. The Compucruise also indicates time, distance, or fuel available for a previously determined trip based on current rate of fuel consumption, calculated and updated once a second.

Cadillac's Trip Computer, first marketed on the Seville in 1978, provided information to the driver on average and instantaneous mpg, average trip speed, elapsed time, driving range, remaining miles to destination, estimated arrival time, digital clock, engine rpm, engine coolant temperature, and microprocessor system voltage.

Ford Motor Company markets two systems: the Tripminder and the Message Center. In addition to the trip functions, there is a system checkout that is interactive with the driver. It checks headlamps, brake lights, oil pressure, and system voltage.

Chrysler introduced a fully electronic instrument panel, in the 1981 Imperial, that displays the usual safety, reminder, and engine function information with the addition of elapsed time, trip mileage, average speed, driving range, and average and instantaneous mpg.

A study[2] evaluating the effect of several formats of electronic/electro-optical display (with emphasis on the speedometer) concluded that the digital speedometers were read more accurately and quickly. Overall, they were also preferred. There are a number of factors involved in the optimization of instrumentation. These include size, brightness, update rate, and color.

The majority of the electronic instrumentation is applied to the higher vehicle lines, due to the high cost of development and installation. Reliability problems were experienced during the initial year of production of many of the systems. As manufacturers have gained experience, the reliability of the instrumentation has significantly improved. Wider application rates will reduce the cost, thus providing the technology to lower line vehicles.

With the increasing number of microprocessor-based products on vehicles, the establishment of a data communications link appears to be quite likely. The three major sophisticated systems are the instrumentation, engine control, and trip computer modules. While there are several others, they are lower function modules that transfer or receive only one or two pieces of information. Examples include cooling fan control, air suspension, shift indicator light, keyless entry, automatic headlamps, speed control, memory seat, automatic highway headlamp dimming, and deceleration fuel shutoff.

Linking the three major systems will provide new customer features such as:

- Setting a favorite speed control setpoint through the buttons on a trip computer.
- Customer selection of the gauge content of the electronic instrument cluster.
- Expanded monitoring of vehicle warnings, including "predictive" warnings based on functional degradation.
- More meaningful warnings, including warning seriousness and suggested actions (computational gauges).
- Fuel economy, hazard, and shift information feedback to a customer as a result of his operating habits and based on real-time performance.

In addition to customer features, a communications link will provide new engineering opportunities such as:

- A central vehicle location for nonvolatile and keep-alive memory.
- Redistribution of the microprocessor burden through the use of shared function processing.

- Enhanced diagnostics using coordinated module inter-action and instrumentation display capabilities.
- Minimum system tearup, retroactively to incorporate short lead-time competitive features.
- A simple means for low-speed I/O module expansions.

Cathode-ray-tube (CRT) display systems are another source of driver information now being developed. The future data center (Figure 2-1) is a multifunction CRT information center being developed by Ford Motor Company that displays data and control panels on its screen at the touch of a finger. Its unique feature is a satellite-navigation system that pin-points a car's location on a map display (shown in the close-up at the *upper right*). An experimental car with a 7-inch whip antenna has received latitude and longitude signals from an orbiting Transit satellite. The car's position is then updated between the 90-minute satellite passes, using its odometer and a magnetic flux gate that senses the earth's magnetic field.

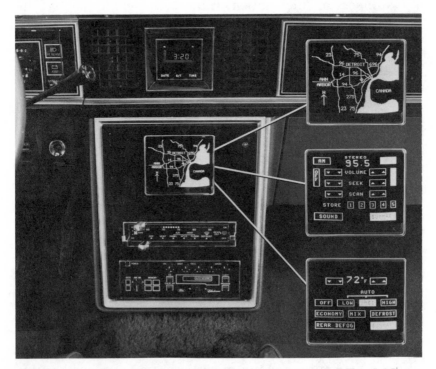

Figure 2-1 The future data center. (Courtesy of Ford Motor Company, Dearborn, Michigan.)

Other available panel displays include a radio control panel (close-up *center right*) and an automatic temperature control panel (close-up *bottom right*). Travel data, clock, and calendar panels also can be displayed. When the desired panel has been called up, the motorist touches the appropriate area of the screen to display information or control vehicle functions.

Voice synthesis is being used to warn and alert drivers to vehicle functions/conditions, such as "Door is ajar," "Headlamps are on," "Key is in the ignition." Beyond this, manufacturers are developing systems that respond to simple verbal commands. At a May 1982 news conference, Ford demonstrated a model that responded to headlamp and antenna commands. At the 1982 Tokyo Motor Show, Nissan Motors displayed a vehicle that allowed disabled persons to adjust seating position, operate windshield wipers, or turn on lights simply by talking into a computer console. Additionally, the car obeys in whatever language the command is given. Steering is by foot pedal. Nissan also claims it has the technology to develop a vehicle that drives itself on the basis of voice-actuated commands.

A new feature of electronic instrument clusters is automatic display brightness that makes instruments readable even in bright daylight, which has been a significant problem. A photo-optical sensor is located in the instrument panel. Through its measurements the brightness level is adjusted.

A new vehicle control offering is an automatic day/night mirror that changes from day to night position automatically when bright lights are aimed at the vehicle's rear window, then returns to the day position when bright light is removed.

A new antitheft system goes beyond flashing the headlights and taillights and sounding the horn intermittently—it disables the starter if unauthorized entry of a locked car is attempted.

Electronic suspension controls provide new electronic control concepts for ride and handling performance. This might also include load leveling features.

C. Engine Management/Power Train Controls

Electronic engine controls fall into two basic types—(1) feedback carburetors and (2) fuel injection. These two types of systems perform essentially the same function of delivering an air/fuel mixture to the engine. However, the similarity ends there. The feedback carburetor systems have a restricted range of authority, and in most cases if the system does not control spark, the vehicle will run without the processor, or with one that has failed. This is the case with Ford Motor Company's MCU system. The more prevalent failure is a shorted output driver transistor in the module that would put the vehicle in a rich air/fuel mode. The vehicle will drive better but experience a degradation in fuel economy.

The General Motors C-3 system (Figure 2–2) was used as standard on GM's gasoline-powered 1981 model cars. The solid-state microprocessor on-board computer is connected to sensors that monitor oxygen in the exhaust, engine speed, coolant temperature, engine load, and throttle setting. With information received from these sensors, it controls an electro-mechanical carburetor, or fuel injection in some cases, and the distributor. The computer constantly adjusts the air/fuel ratio and the spark timing.

Electronic fuel injection is quickly becoming the preferred fuel-metering system. Based on an Arthur D. Little, Inc., survey performed for the Bendix Corporation, as yet unpublished, fuel injection systems are being used primarily as an image item as opposed to function in meeting pollution and fuel economy requirements.

Fuel injection systems operate with a greatly expanded range of authority. A failure in the system will, with great probability, affect the vehicle operation ranging from a mild degradation in drive and/or fuel economy to stumbles, stalls, no-starts, and rich fuel failures (which would probably overheat and permanently damage the catalytic converter). To avoid most of these drive problems, General Motors' Cadillac Motor Car Division pioneered the software technique of "value substitution." If a sensor, such as the coolant sensor, should fail, the computer's diagnostic routines would detect it. Based on the readings from other areas of the system, a nominal coolant temperature value will be substituted into the computer software. A "check engine" light will illuminate, telling the driver to have the vehicle serviced. Due to the value substituted, the vehicle will continue to operate, although it may be at a reduced level. This has been referred to as "limp home capability."

The tremendous challenge facing both the auto industry and the consumer is the servicing of these electronic vehicles. On-board diagnostics, either continuous or on-demand, have been included in the software. The servicing industry, whether

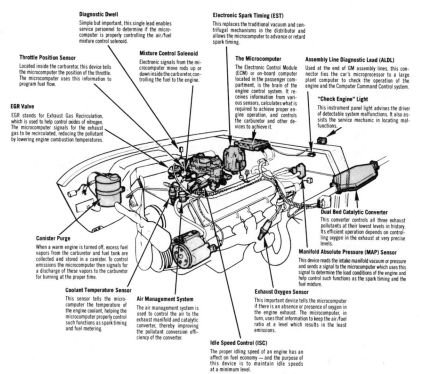

Diagnostic Dwell
Simple but important, this single lead enables service personnel to determine if the microcomputer is properly controlling the air/fuel mixture control solenoid.

Electronic Spark Timing (EST)
This replaces the traditional vacuum and centrifugal mechanisms in the distributor and allows the microcomputer to advance or retard spark timing.

Throttle Position Sensor
Located inside the carburetor, this device tells the microcomputer the position of the throttle. The microcomputer uses this information to program fuel flow.

Mixture Control Solenoid
Electronic signals from the microcomputer move rods up or down inside the carburetor, controlling the fuel to the engine.

The Microcomputer
The Electronic Control Module (ECM) or on-board computer located in the passenger compartment, is the brain of the engine control system. It receives information from various sensors, calculates what is required to achieve proper engine operation, and controls the carburetor and other devices to achieve it.

Assembly Line Diagnostic Lead (ALDL)
Used at the end of GM assembly lines, this connector ties the car's microprocessor to a large plant computer to check the operation of the engine and the Computer Command Control system.

"Check Engine" Light
This instrument panel light advises the driver of detectable system malfunctions. It also assists the service mechanic in locating malfunctions.

EGR Valve
EGR stands for Exhaust Gas Recirculation, which is used to help control oxides of nitrogen. The microcomputer signals for the exhaust gas to be recirculated, reducing the pollutant by lowering engine combustion temperatures.

Dual Bed Catalytic Converter
This converter controls all three exhaust pollutants at their lowest levels in history. Its efficient operation depends on controlling oxygen in the exhaust at very precise levels.

Canister Purge
When a warm engine is turned off, excess fuel vapors from the carburetor and fuel tank are collected and stored in a canister. To control emissions the microcomputer then signals for a discharge of these vapors to the carburetor for burning at the proper time.

Manifold Absolute Pressure (MAP) Sensor
This device reads the intake manifold vacuum or pressure and sends a signal to the microcomputer which uses this signal to determine the load conditions of the engine and help control such functions as the spark timing and the fuel mixture.

Coolant Temperature Sensor
This sensor tells the microcomputer the temperature of the engine coolant, helping the microcomputer properly control such functions as spark timing and fuel metering.

Air Management System
The air management system is used to control the air to the exhaust manifold and catalytic converter, thereby improving the pollutant conversion efficiency of the converter.

Exhaust Oxygen Sensor
This important device tells the microcomputer if there is an absence or presence of oxygen in the engine exhaust. The microcomputer, in turn, uses that information to keep the air/fuel ratio at a level which results in the least emissions.

Idle Speed Control (ISC)
The proper idling speed of an engine has an affect on fuel economy — and the purpose of this device is to maintain idle speeds at a minimum level.

Figure 2-2 A typical 1981 GM computer command control system. (Courtesy of General Motors Corporation, Detroit, Michigan.)

dealerships or independent garages, is struggling to learn these new systems. The great difficulty is not in repair but, as always, in diagnosis. The common belief is the diagnostic service code generated by the vehicle's computer will tell the mechanic exactly what is wrong. This is not possible. A fouled spark plug may cause the computer to react with the same service code as a rich fuel failure. This happens because the spark plug problem manifests itself the same way an engine would reveal a rich air/fuel mixture. The computer only knows from reading its sensors that there is too much fuel.

The service technician is requested to verify that the usual mechanical things (listed in the shop manual) are checked before beginning the diagnostic routines for electronic engine controls. Reference to vehicle service manuals is recommended, especially those put out by Cadillac, which have consistently been the best in the industry for explanations of theories of operation.

III. WIRING

A. Gauge

Wiring gauge (sizing, related to cross-sectional area) must be selected to provide sufficient current carrying capacity for all modes of usage. The algebraic relationship

$$V = IR$$

where V = voltage, I = current flow or amperage, and R = resistance to current flow, governs simple direct current (DC) circuits. This is referred to as Ohm's law in electrical engineering.

In many of today's automotive convenience items, such as intermittent windshield wipers and instrument panel light dimming, the variation of speed or lighting intensity is accomplished by varying the resistance. System voltage remains essentially constant; therefore, the current must vary to keep the equation, noted above, balanced.

Operating the intermittent wipers at the slowest speed corresponds to the lowest resistive setting, thus inducing the highest current in the wiring harness. This current can be further increased by the system effects of a tacky windshield surface (which would be foreseeable at a slow speed of operation as a small amount of moisture reaches the windshield).

Standardized industrial charts list gauge in relation to I, R, and V. Once the system's electrical characteristics have been determined, which is the difficult engineering task, it is a simple matter of referencing a table for gauge size.

When an insufficient gauge size has been selected, circuit overload could lead to damaged wiring and/or components. In the extreme case, an electrical fire could begin (this is not the only cause of electrical fires).

B. Circuit Protection—Fusible Links

The designed function of a fuse is to interrupt current flow in an electric circuit whenever the current exceeds the safe design value for the circuit. Under such a condition, failure to interrupt, or "open," a circuit may result in serious damage to the connecting wires and/or components. The heat developed by the abnormal current in the various resistive parts of the circuit is the cause of the destructive action. The heating effect of current in a resistance is proportional to the square of the current, to the resistance, and to the time the current flows (this is known as Joule's law). Insulation may be damaged even though the current is not large enough to develop sufficient heat to melt any of the conducting parts of the circuit. It is therefore necessary to include a protective device in electric circuits to interrupt the current under abnormal conditions. A fuse should be designed as the weakest link connected in series with the circuit.

Various switches utilized in the automotive instrument panel, such as windshield wiper, headlamp, heating/cooling, and defog/defroster, have copper circuit tracks to an edgecard-type connector. If the circuit protection is not properly located, the copper track may be the first weakest link encountered and will thus serve as the fusible link. These switches must be replaced—repair is not advised.

C. Fiber Optics

In the future, fiber optics with a single, multiplexed signal bus are likely to be used to carry sensor and actuator signals as a replacement for the wiring harness. Transmissions, using fiber optics, are immune to electromagnetic interference and have the safety feature of not causing or being affected by electrical disturbance. Also, a greater amount of information is transmitted with respect to cable weight. Fiber optics offer increased reliability and cost and weight reduction, although problems are still present with interconnections.

The design objectives for optical fibers are:

- Maximize light transfer into the core of the fiber—maximize numerical aperture (N.A.).
- Minimize light loss in traveling through the fiber—minimize attenuation (dB/km).
- Control the effects of bending—control bending losses.

There are three basic types of fiber optic interconnections: (1) connectors, (2) splices, and (3) couplers. They are used to join sources and/or detectors to the fiber, beam split and combine light for interferometers, provide fiber-to-fiber inter-connections, and accomplish each of these functions with minimum reflection and insertion loss. The connector is a demountable joint between two fibers. The splice is a fused or potted joint between two fibers. The coupler redistributes energy between two or more fibers.

Connector and splice losses can be classified in two ways:

1. Intrinsics—which are due to variations in fiber manufacturing characteristics not mechanically correctable. Examples are mismatches in core area, numerical aperture, and profile.
2. Extrinsics—which are due to fiber end preparation or mechanical mating. Examples are end separation, angular misalignment, and lateral offset.

The requirements for coupling are:

1. Bring the cores sufficiently close for energy distribution to overlap.
2. Adjust the extent and degree of overlap to achieve desired coupling ratio.
3. Make the coupling rugged and insure constant coupling with temperature.

Satisfactory techniques for forming low-loss, single-mode splices and couplers are currently available; however, current connector technology is inadequate for repeated low-loss interconnects.

D. Miscellaneous

Federal Motor Vehicle Safety Standard (FMVSS) No. 215, Exterior Protection, Passenger Cars (effective September 1, 1972) requires passenger cars to withstand barrier and pendulum impacts of 5 mph front and rear, without damage to lighting, fuel, exhaust, cooling, and latching systems. From the viewpoint of wiring, this means the wiring must be selected with sufficient insulation protection and routed in such a manner as not to sustain damage that would prevent the lighting system from functioning properly. The mandate, that wiring not be damaged, serves an additional purpose of removing a potential spark source for ignition in the case of a rear crash with fuel spillage. (Most vehicles have inertia switches that open on impact to terminate electrical power flow to the fuel pump.)

CITATIONS

[1]D. Brown, "Ideas for Car Computer-Controls: And Their Realisation." *Automotive Engineer*, Vol. 5, No. 5, October/November 1980, p. 29.

[2]G. R. W. Simmonds, M. Galer, and A. Baines, "Ergonomics of Electronic Displays." SAE paper 810826. Warrendale, PA.: Society of Automotive Engineers, 1981.

SECONDARY SOURCES

I. Electronics

1. M. H. Westbrook, "Developments in Automotive Electronics." *Automotive Engineer*, Vol. 4, No. 4, August/September 1979, pp. 19–23.
2. L. Middendorf, "Automotive Human Factors Today." *Proceedings of the Fifth International System Safety Conference* (Denver: July 27–31, 1981). Newport Beach, CA.: System Safety Society, Vol. 1, Part II, 1981.
3. M. Scanlon, "Electronics: The Future Is Now." *Ward's Auto World*, November 1981, pp. 44–49.

II. Wiring

1. C. E. Skroder and M. S. Helm, *Circuit Analysis by Laboratory Methods*. Englewood Cliffs, N.J.: Prentice-Hall, 1946, 1955, Chapters 3 and 7.

REFERENCES

1. J. McElory, "The 80s Standards Force Move to Electronic Engine Controls." *Automotive Industries*, Vol. 159, October 1979, pp. 105–107.
2. F. J. Gawronski, "Ford Brain Makes Service Easier." *Automotive News*, December 15, 1980, p. E14.
3. J. McElory, "Designers Handbook Electronics." *Automotive Industries*, Vol. 159, March 1979, pp. 55–58.
4. R. F. Schaden and V. C. Heldman, *Product Design Liability*. New York: Practising Law Institute, 1982.
5. K. Ross and M. J. Foley, *Product Liability of Manufacturers: Prevention and Defense 1981*. New York: Practising Law Institute, 1981.

6. G. A. Peters, *Product Liability and Safety*. Washington, D.C.: Coiner Publications, 1971.
7. A. S. Weinstein, A. D. Twerski, H. R. Piekler, and W. A. Donaher, *Product Liability and the Reasonably Safe Product: A Guide for Management, Design, and Marketing*. New York: Wiley, 1978.
8. *Third International System Safety Conference* (October 17–21, 1977): G. H. Robinson, "Human Performance in Accident Causation: Toward Theories on Warning Systems and Hazard Appreciation," pp. 55–69; and O. C. Lindsey, "Hazard Analysis for Software Systems," pp. 907–918. Newport Beach, CA.: System Safety Society, 1977.
9. "Product Liability—Its Growing Business Importance." *Automotive Engineering*, Vol. 84, No. 10, October 1976, pp. 30–32, 74. (Based on SAE paper 760702, "Product Liability—Its Effect on the Manufacturer–Distributor Relationship," by R. D. Tomlinson.)
10. "Products Liability: An Engineering Curriculum Subject?" *Automotive Engineering*, Vol. 86, No. 10, October 1978, pp. 72–73. (Based on SAE paper 770619, "Product Safety—A Prime Consideration in Expanded Design Criteria for Engineering Education and Practice," by L. C. Peters; and paper 780381, "Products Liability—Bringing the Interaction of Society and Technology into Engineering Education," by J. F. Thorpe.)
11. P. C. Nelson, "Product Liability—Its Effect on Industry." *Automotive Engineering*, Vol. 82, No. 10, October 1974, pp. 44–45, 71.
12. A. H. Rubenstein and J. E. Ettlie, "Federal Stimuli to Development of New Technology by Suppliers to Automobile Manufacturers." March 1978. (U.S. Department of Transportation sponsored study.)
13. R. J. Fosdick, "Product Liability—Can the Bomb Be Defused?" *Automotive Industries*, Vol. 157, September 15, 1977, pp. 27–32.
14. "EEC-I + 3-Way = EEC-II." *Automotive Engineering*, Vol. 86, No. 8, August 1978, pp. 49–54. (Based on SAE paper 780119, "A Practical Application of Microprocessors in the Automotive Environment," by G. Cilibraise; paper 780203, "Ford Three-Way Catalyst and Feedback Fuel Control System," by R. E. Seiter and R. J. Clark; paper 780211, "Temperature Sensors for Electronic Engine Control Systems," by J. E. Acker; paper 780213, "Application of a Crankshaft Position Sensor to Control Engine Timing," by J. C. Cook II; and paper 780214, "The First Production Automotive Capacitive Pressure Sensor," by G. M. Marx and R. L. Bell.)
15. "Systems Engineering Applied to Engine Control." *Automotive Engineering*, Vol. 86, No. 10, October 1978, pp. 88–91.
16. M. B. Kearney, J. R. Shreve, and W. A. Vincent, "Microprocessor Based Systems in the Automobile: Custom Integrated Circuits Provide an Effective Interface." SAE paper 810160. Warrendale, PA.: Society of Automotive Engineers, 1981.

17. M. Veneziano and T. Spoto, "EMI-RFI Software Filtering." SAE paper 810175. Warrendale, PA.: Society of Automotive Engineers, 1981.
18. A. D. Nielsen, "Electronic Component Testing and Design Practices for EMC." SAE paper 820816. Warrendale, PA.: Society of Automotive Engineers, 1982.
19. R. L. Waddell, "Automotive Electronics: The Black Box Comes of Age." *Ward's Auto World,* November 1980, pp. 23–26.
20. W. R. Iverson, "Ford Drives to 16-Bit Processor." *Electronics,* June 2, 1982, pp. 54–56. (See also "There's a CRT in Ford's Cockpit," p. 54.)
21. M. Scanlon, "Electronics: The Future Is Now." *Ward's Auto World,* November 1981, pp. 44–49.
22. M. H. Westbrook, "Developments in Automotive Electronics." *Automotive Engineer,* Vol. 4, August/September 1979, pp. 19–23.
23. "Dashboard Navigator." *Science Digest,* July 1982, p. 24.
24. M. Stepanek, "But Does Your Car Listen Well?" *The Detroit Free Press,* May 26, 1982, Section F, p. 1.
25. D. Brown, "Ideas for Car Computer-Controls: and Their Realisation." *Automotive Engineer,* Vol. 5, No. 5, October/November 1980, pp. 29–30.
26. L. Givens, "Engineering Highlights of the 1981 Automobiles." *Automotive Engineering,* Vol. 88, No. 10, October 1980, pp. 51–74.
27. "Designers Handbook." *Automotive Industries,* Vol. 159, March 1979, pp. 55–58.
28. "Electronics Growth Seen Continuing and Accelerating." *Automotive News,* November 24, 1980, pp. 24, 26.

3

Hitches
and Hydraulic Systems

W. JOHN FOXWELL
Mechanical Engineering Consultant
Troy, Michigan

The author started his career with Ford of Britain in 1936 as a student. Entering the Engineering Department in 1939, he designed military vehicles and tractors during World War II and progressed to Executive Engineer—Tractors in 1954. In 1962 he was transferred to Troy, Michigan, where he became Chief Engineer of Ford Tractor Operations—Worldwide in 1964. A holder of numerous patents, he started his own design service, specializing in farm tractors, in 1975. He is a Chartered Engineer in the United Kingdom, being a Fellow of the Institution of Mechanical Engineers and the Institution of Agricultural Engineers. He is also a member of the Society of Automotive Engineers and the American Society of Agricultural Engineers. The author may be reached at 2557 Lake Charnwood Boulevard, Troy, Michigan 48098 (313-879-0173).

I. INTRODUCTION

Early plows were carried on their own wheels and were pulled by tractors from their drawbars. At the end of a furrow, the operator pulled on a rope that tripped a mechanism in a box-type lift in one of the wheels. This raised the plow bottom, thus allowing turning at the headland. The operator would reverse the procedure at the beginning of each new furrow, and the plow bottoms would be sucked into the ground until the preset depth was reached.

Tractors with these pull-type implements were not very maneuverable: they could not be backed up into tight corners and they required a large headland for turning. Little or none of the plow's weight was carried on the tractors, which meant that the tractors were heavy to provide the necessary weight needed on the driving wheels for traction.

II. THE THREE-POINT HITCH

Harry Ferguson's pioneering efforts, in Britain in the early twenties, to find a way to make the plow and tractor one unit succeeded in the mid-thirties and culminated in 1939 with the introduction of the Ford–Ferguson 9N model tractor. For the first time a system, combining a light tractor with an integral three-point hitch, using matching light implements employing no ground engaging wheels of their own, was manufactured for the general farm market. This small 25-horsepower tractor was fitted with an adjustable wide front axle and the relatively new pneumatic tires on all wheels. The 9N Ford–Ferguson tractor with the new three-point hitch completely revolutionized the tractor industry by outperforming much larger machines (Figure 3-1). Only in the North American corn belt was the tractor's acceptance delayed. Here the high-clearance tricycle tractors remained in vogue because they could be adapted to carry front- and side-mounted cultivators for hoeing between the corn rows and then adapted in the fall to carry a two-row corn picker. Finally, in the early sixties, with the advent of chemical weed control and the multirow corn headers on the combine harvester, the need for the high-clearance tricycle tractor was eliminated. Today, practically all tractors have wide front axles and a three-point hitch and there appears to be no limitation to their size.

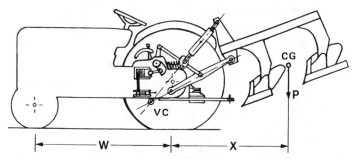

Figure 3-1 A tractor with a two-furrow mounted plow. (W) Wheelbase of tractor (inches), (X) distance from rear axle to CG of plow (inches), (P) weight of plow (pounds), (VC) virtual center of hitch links, and (CG) center of gravity of the plow (pounds). Note that the plow is shown without disc coulters and skimmers.

The three-point hitch is probably one of the most underrated innovations in this or any other century. It is to the farm tractor what a chuck is to a drilling machine. It allows a multitudinous array of equipment and implements to be carried on the tractor to the work site and provides complete flexibility between the tractor and implement in work.

The hitch consists of two lower links, each just under 3 feet long and attached at their front ends, by ball joints, low down on either side of the rear axle housing of the tractor (Figure 3-2). This allows the links to be angled vertically from just above ground level at their rear ends, which contain another ball joint for attachment to the implement, to about 3 feet above the ground while allowing a reasonable degree of sideways movement. A shorter, single top link is mounted centrally to the tractor near the top and rear of the rear axle housing, again with a ball joint, thus allowing the link to have a considerable vertical movement and limited side movement. A ball joint at the rear of the link allows it to be attached to the implement and retained by a cotter pin. The top link attachment hole on the implement is positioned vertically above the lower link balls. The upper link is normally made in three pieces. The two end pieces, with the balls, have an external threaded portion of opposite hand to each other that engage in a center piece that has internal right- and left-hand threads to suit. By manually turning the center piece, the link

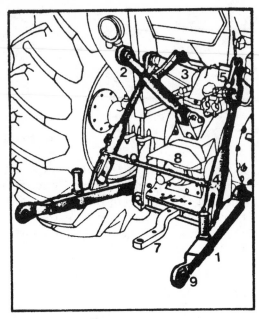

Figure 3–2 A three-point hitch, drawbar, and PTO. (1) Lower link, (2) top link, (3) lift arm, (4) lift rod, (5) leveling box, (6) sway block, (7) drawbar, (8) PTO with guard, (9) flexible end, and (10) flexible tie strap.

shortens or lengthens to adjust the pitch of the implement in work.

Ideally, when an implement is attached to a tractor in its normal working position, such as a plow at 8 inches depth, the lower links, when viewed from the side, should be parallel with the ground or with the rear balls no higher than 2 inches above the front ones (see Figure 3–3). The rear ball of the top link is normally 18 inches or a little more above the rear balls of the lower links, and its front ball is attached to the tractor in a lower position so that the top link slopes down toward the tractor at an angle between 10 and 15 degrees. If theoretical lines could be extended from the lower links and the top links, at the working depth of the implement, they should ideally converge at a point just behind the front axle and about 15 to 18 inches above the ground. This point is known as the virtual center (VC) of the hitch. The virtual center varies as the implement is being raised or lowered by the hitch.

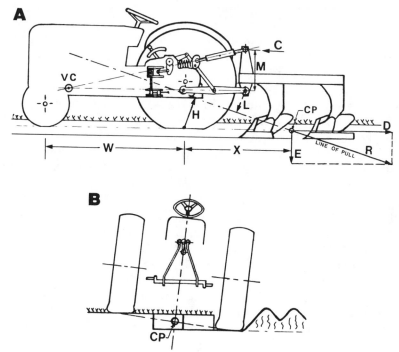

Figure 3-3 (**A**) A tractor plowing with top link control system. (W) Wheelbase (inches), (E) excess downward weight (pounds), (R) resultant pull (pounds), (H) height of the line of pull above the tire contact point (inches), (L) distance of the line of pull below the lower link rear balls (inches), (D) draft of plow (pounds), (M) plow mast height (inches), (CP) center of pressure of soil on plow, (VC) virtual center of the links, (C) compression force on top link (pounds) equals RL/M. Weight (in pounds) added to rear tires equals RH/W + E. (**B**) A rear view of tractor and plow in A. The plow has two 16-inch furrows and is plowing 8 inches deep. Notice that the cross-shaft of the plow is cranked to compensate for the tilt of the tractor, which has its right tires in a furrow. For plows with more than two furrows the tires on the tractor would be set wider to keep the CP on the center of the tractor.

It is important that the position outlined above is conformed to as far as possible because the configuration of the links keeps the implement parallel to the ground for minor changes in depth when draft control corrections are made, as will be explained later. The rear of the plow raises higher than its front end in the transport position, thus allowing clearance with the ground when traveling over unlevel land. When the plow is being lowered it penetrates the earth more quickly because the shares are at an angle to it at entry.

The plow is being pulled from the virtual center (see Figure 3-3A) until it reaches its desired depth through oil being trapped in the hydraulic lift cylinder. When this happens the virtual center no longer applies and the line of pull acts on the tractor (as shown in Figure 3-3A) at H inches above the tire contact point with the ground.

An additional important point to note is that, when viewed from above (Figure 3-4) the lower links converge toward the tractor so that when the pull of an implement is acting on each link they want to straighten out, causing an inward load at their rear ends. The loads cancel each other out and the implement trails smoothly and centrally behind the tractor.

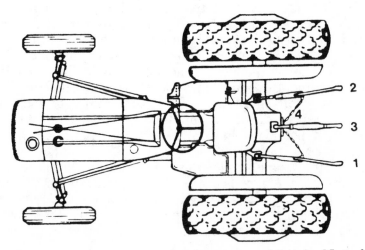

Figure 3-4 A plan view of a tractor and hitch. Note how lower links 1 and 2 theoretically converge at point C, which should be just behind the front wheels. Top link 3 is on the center line of the tractor. Check chains are shown at 4. They permit some side sway of the links in the working position and tighten up to prevent sway in transport.

III. THE HYDRAULIC SYSTEM

Thus far only the main members of the hitch have been mentioned, the top link and the two lower links. How does the hydraulic system raise and lower the links and keep the implement raised above the ground or at its desired depth in the ground? We shall use the Ford–Ferguson 9N model tractor as our example. A piston pump was mounted in the drive line between the transmission and rear axle and driven by the power take off shaft (PTO), which passed through it. The pump sucked oil from the axle housing and passed it through a simple valve to a single acting ram cylinder mounted in a housing that was bolted over the axle drive gears (see Figure 3-5). The piston in the cylinder activated a connecting rod attached at its rear end to a crank arm. The connecting rod had spherical ball joints at each end. The crank arm was mounted centrally in the housing on the center line of the tractor in the plan view and splined to a robust cross-shaft that extended out on both sides of the housing. Lift arms, 9 inches long, were splined to each end of the cross shaft. A lifting rod, attached by a universal type yoke to each lift arm, was fastened to each lower link by a clevis pin halfway along each link.

With the links in a lowered position, the operator, when standing on the ground, could raise the links by hand because the connecting rod front ball only contacted a spherical socket in the piston. This meant that the hydraulic system relied on the weight of the implement to lower itself into work and only provided the force to lift it out of work, hence the definition— single acting.

A manual control lever was connected by internal linkage to the control valve, and it was mounted in a quadrant where it would remain in the position selected by the operator. A large, heavy helical coil spring was positioned between the top link and the lift housing in such a way that when the tractor was plowing with the shares in the ground, the force to overcome the soil resistance would pull backward around the ball ends of the lower link and cause the top link to move forward and deflect the spring in proportion to the draft force (see Figure 3-3A). The top link was in compression, and the lower links were in tension. A medium load moved the spring halfway, and a severe load would compress it to its fullest extend, which was about half an inch. A series of levers connected the manual lever to the spring and valve so that when the draft

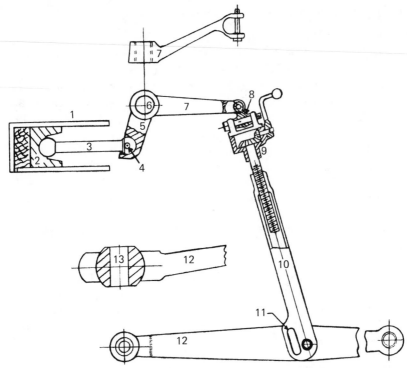

Figure 3-5 Lift linkage components: (1) Hydraulic cylinder, (2) piston, (3) connecting rod, (4) retaining pin, (5) crank arm, (6) cross shaft, (7) lift arm, (8) universal yoke, (9) leveling box assembly, (10) lift rod assembly, (11) sway slot for wide implements, (12) lower link, and (13) lower link ball.

load of the plow coincided with the position of the lever in the quadrant set by the driver, the control valve would shut off the oil leaving the cylinder, and the trapped oil would hold the plow at that height. If the draft force increased because of harder ground, the spring would compress more and open the valve so that oil entered the cylinder and raised the plow. This would result in lowering the draft force on the plow, causing less compression on the spring and thus shutting off the valve.

Similarly, less resistance in softer ground would reduce the draft force and lower the plow until the valve shut off again. This is called a "correction," and when plowing, the valve would correct about once a second, and the depth of the plow would vary up and down from its desired depth by about three-quarters of an inch. This variation was acceptable because of the gains achieved, such as less slip in the hard spots, more even speed, less engine lugging, and the ability to keep going. In addition, it made possible a lighter tractor and a lighter implement with outstanding maneuverability.

In the late fifties, as tractors became larger and could carry heavier plows, the top link draft control system that worked well with the shorter two-furrow and three-furrow light plows would not work at shallower depths when larger and heavier plows were used. For a while this situation was held at bay by giving the spring the capability of sensing a limited tension load as well as compression loads. This extended the use of top link draft control to light four-furrow plows and two-furrow reversible plows (Figure 3-6).

Large tractors are equipped with lower link draft control, which is practically insensitive to implement weight and length because the rear ball of the top link becomes the fulcrum point around which the draft forces react. Its greater distance above the ground ensures that the line of pull will pass beneath it for all implements capable of being fully mounted to the three-point hitch (Figure 3-6).

Lower link draft control is much costlier than top link control because the loads in the lower link are greater. As a result many small tractors will continue to be fitted with top link systems.

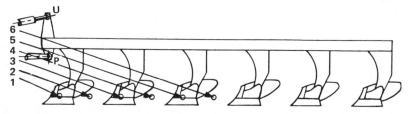

Figure 3-6 Mounted plows (one to six furrows). Approximate lines of pull are compared when plowing moist, stubble land. All plows would work with a lower link control system because all the lines pass below point U. Only the one-, two-, and three-furrow versions have their lines of pull passing well below point P and they would work well with an upper link control system. The four-furrow version would be marginal in opening a furrow with the upper link control system.

IV. TYPES OF HYDRAULIC SYSTEMS

As would be expected, the modern tractor's hydraulic system is more refined than that of the Ford–Ferguson 9N. First of all, a variety of pumps are used, and practically all are either mounted on the engine so that they are available to operate the hydraulic system even when the tractor is at a standstill, or they are driven from an independent engine-driven shaft in the transmission. Some pumps are constant displacement, such as the gear-type and fixed swashplate piston pumps. Others have variable output that are automatically controlled by the demand on them. All systems have refinements to control the smoothness of the lift during raising and lowering. Some tractors have one large pump that controls other functions, such as power steering, power brakes, the PTO, remote cylinders, and hydrostatic front-wheel drives. Others employ separate pumps for these functions, including the remote valves.

An implement is fully mounted when all three links are utilized. However, only the two lower links are used with semimounted implements (see Figure 3-7). A semimounted plow is attached, at its front end, to the two lower links and its rear end is carried on a wheel with runs in the furrow and is raised and lowered by a separate remote cylinder operated by its own control valve. When these plows are draft controlled, only the front end of the plow raises and lowers.

Let us look at the action of a mounted implement on the three-point linkage. Here an automatic compensating cut-off effect is always present because when a lifting correction is called for, the loads in the top and lower links both reduce, thus tending to cancel the correction. With the removal of the top link with semimounted implements, this self-compensation effect does not apply, and a plateau must be established above the datum point to cut off the signal before it becomes too large and unacceptable for good depth control. This is done on most tractors by feeding a separate position control signal, actuated by a cam or linkage on the lift cross-shaft and selected by a separate lever from the normal manual control lever, to cut off the upward correction before it can get too extreme. Some tractors merely have a latch with three or four definite positions. Others have an infinitely positioned lever mounted side by side with the main draft control lever so the signals controlled by each can be intermixed by the operator at will.

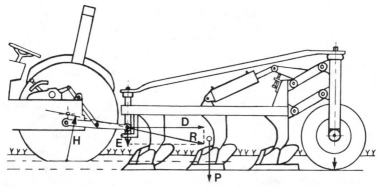

Figure 3-7 A semimounted plow (lower link control system). The plow is attached only to the two lower links of the tractor. The plow is pivoted at its front end and a link steers the rear wheel to enable tighter turns to be made at the headland. Normally, a semimounted plow would not have less than five furrows. There is not that much of the plow's weight transferred to the rear axle as with a mounted plow, because some of its weight is carried on its rear tires. During lowering in the ground, the line of pull goes through the front end of the links. When oil is trapped in the cylinder to hold the plow at its depth, the line of pull passes through the rear balls as shown. Load transfer to the rear tires equals HR/W + E.

This is particularly useful when performing fine grading work with a rear-mounted blade during landscaping.

Apart from reacting to varying draft loads, the hydraulic system will also compensate for minor leakage in the system as long as the engine is running. In transport, the implement will remain in its raised position even under the heaviest of shock loads because the pump will replace oil lost through leakage from seals or from pressure relief valves, which help to protect the various parts from damage. When the engine is stopped, slow leakage, if present, can cause the implement to lower slowly to the ground. No damage will accrue to the tractor, but the implement might damage something left under it. Therefore, when left unattended, the implement should be lowered to the ground. Of course, no one should ever work on an implement without first safely lowering it to the ground.

V. PULL-TYPE IMPLEMENTS

Many implements are too large to be mounted on the tractor or even semimounted. These are known as "pull-type" implements. They are pulled from the tractor's drawbar and have their own rubber-tired wheels to transport them to the work site and to hold the implement to the preselected depth in the field (see Figure 3-8). The lifting of the implement is controlled by a standard ASAE double-acting remote cylinder (Figure 3-9). More than one cylinder is needed if the implement is very large. Remote valves for the cylinders are added to the tractor, sometimes as many as four, with their own control levers. Each valve feeds into a quick-release coupler mounted conveniently to the rear end of the tractor so that the remote hydraulic hoses can be coupled and uncoupled easily by the operator. The couplers have the capability of releasing the hoses should the driver accidentally drive off after uncoupling the implement from the drawbar and forget to uncouple them (Figure 3-10). Pull-type implements are preset to a desired depth by a mechanical stop or a clamp on the cylinder rod. Therefore, the depth cannot be adjusted easily in the field, and the tractor has to be powerful enough not to stall or spin out in the tough spots or where traction is momentarily poor. Very wide implements are made with wings that fold up for road transport or for going through gates; these are also operated by hydraulic cylinders.

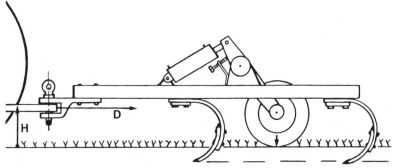

Figure 3-8 A chisel plow (pull type). For space consideration, a small chisel plow is shown attached by a pin to the tractor's drawbar. Most pull type implements exert little or no downward weight on the drawbar. Weight transfer to the rear axle is only DH/W.

Figure 3-9 The remote cylinder is connected to the rear wheel of a semimounted plow.

VI. CONTROL SYSTEM FOR BOTH MOUNTED AND PULL-TYPE IMPLEMENTS

Top and lower link draft control systems have been explained for mounted and semimounted implements. There is still another system that controls, not by signaling a load in the links, but by signaling the torque in the drive line of the tractor. This is the Load Monitor system offered on the medium Ford tractors, and it foreshadows things to come in the future. A small mechanical cylindrical device, about 5 inches long and 5 inches in diameter, is positioned in the tractor's drive line between the transmission and rear axle (Figure 3-11). Disk springs inside the unit push against balls placed in inclined ramps in such a way that when a twisting load or

Figure 3-10 Remote hose couplers. The hose is being connected to the tractor by an operator.

torque is applied to the unit, its outer sleeve moves backward and forward. This movement acts in the same way on the control valve as the movement of the top link draft control spring does. Depending on the depth setting of the manual control lever, the torque corresponding to the pull required to move the implement in the ground will balance out and control its depth. Greater load on the tractor and implement will cause the engine to respond, and the torque will increase, shorten the control device, and lift the implement until status quo similar to the linkage-sensitive systems is reached.

There are several differences between the systems, foremost of which is the insensitivity of the torque control system to the method by which the implement is attached to the tractor, i.e., whether it is mounted, semimounted, or pulled from the drawbar. With mounted implements the line of draft has no relationship to the ends of the links, as it does for top link control or lower link control. Therefore, the length and overhanging weight of the implement is not important. Further, the capability of extending automatic depth control to pull-type implements is achieved by bringing the remote cylinders or the implements under the control of the torque unit in the same manner that the hydraulic lift cylinder is controlled.

The torque control system, in addition to sensing the draft load of the implement, also senses the rolling resistance of the tractor as it propels itself over the ground. On stubble land these forces can be as much as one-third of the draft forces and 50 percent on cultivated loam.

Rolling resistance increases and the draft force lessens on softer ground. The opposite occurs on harder land. Therefore, because the torque control system is sensing both draft and rolling resistance, the combined variation, during a correc-

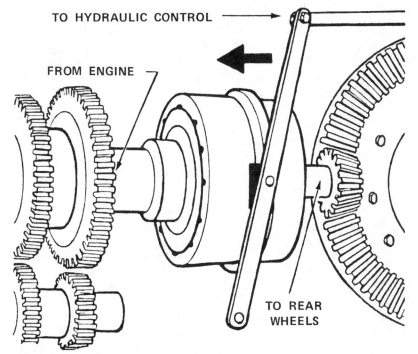

Figure 3-11 A torque-sensing unit. Mounted between the transmission and rear axle, it operates the hydraulic system valve to control the depth of the implement.

tion, is less of a change than the draft force alone. This results in less fluctuation of both engine speed and wheelslip, but more important is the fact that the depth of work is more constant than with a link-sensing system.

A tractor requires more power to climb an incline in a field. With a normal pull-type implement this means that its depth must be set so that the engine will not stall in negotiating the incline. The load-sensing system allows the implement to be set deeper on the level because it will be raised sufficiently on the incline to maintain engine revolutions.

For heavy tillage operations the torque control system is ideal, but it is not suitable for operating light grader blades, as used in landscaping, because the draft forces can be lower than the rolling resistance. For this reason the Ford tractors that have the torque sensing device maintain the top link load sensing systems for landscaping work.

VII. FUTURE TRENDS

The revolution and reliability of solid-state electronic devices and microprocessors will enable tractor implement engineers to monitor and control the performance of agricultural machines in ways not yet thought possible. Programmable remote cylinders will automatically set the depth or position of pull-type implements, allowing smaller and less powerful tractors to be used with resulting savings in time and efficiency. The next five years will see some exciting developments.

VIII. INTERCHANGEABILITY OF IMPLEMENTS AND TRACTORS

The hitch dimensions of the original Ford–Ferguson 9N tractor have been jointly standardized by the American Society of Agricultural Engineers (ASAE) and the Society of Automotive Engineers (SAE) as a Category I hitch. Over the years three larger categories have been added. The respective identification numbers of these standards are ASAE S217.0 (SAE J715), and they cover the categories I, II, III, and IV.

Some of the large hitches are designed to handle implements of a smaller category. This enables a big tractor to be used for chore work around the farm instead of standing idle.

To prevent the lower links of the hitch from swaying and hitting the tires when the tractor is moving, a chain is attached from the tractor to each lower link. Each chain has sufficient length to allow some sideways movement in the lowered position but none in the raised position.

Chains cannot be used with lower link control systems because the links move forward and backward. Instead, sway blocks, against which the links rub, are used.

IX. WEIGHT TRANSFER OF MOUNTED IMPLEMENTS

It is not good practice to overload a tractor's carrying capacity by attaching a too heavy implement to the three-point hitch. All of the implement's weight is behind the rear axle and the seesaw effect causes weight from the front axle to be removed and transferred to the rear axle. The implement's weight is also being carried on the rear axle (see Figure 3-1). The amount of weight taken off the front and added to the rear axle is equal to P times X divided by W. The total amount of weight added to the rear axle is $PX/W + P$.

It is important to make sure that there is sufficient weight left on the front axle for safe steering control in the field and on the road. The seesaw effect of the implement's weight can cause the rear tire loads to exceed the industry standards.

X. ATTACHMENT DEVICES

As tractors and implements get larger, it is impossible for one man to move them about when attaching them to the tractor. Devices are available to overcome this. Many lower links are designed with flexible ends that can be unlatched by the driver and extended a few inches to enable him to connect them to the implement. Backing up the tractor will lock the ends in place (see Figure 3-12).

Other devices take the form of quick couplers (Figure 3-13). These are special frames attached to the ends of the three-point hitch. Specially designed hooks and pawls can be released prior to backing up to an implement. When the implement is coupled, the pawls release to hook the implement firmly to the coupler. A standard has been developed to ensure interchangeability and the number is ASAE 278.6 (SAE J909).

Figure 3-12 A lower link with flexible ends facilitates attaching an implement to the lower links.

XI. DRAWBARS

Drawbars are attached beneath the rear of the tractor and project rearward beyond the tires. Some are fixed in one position. Others can be adjusted to one side or the other off the tractor's center line and most are adjusted for height. Large tractors have freely swinging drawbars that move from side to side to reduce the turning circle at the headland. Front drawbar attachments are available on some tractors for special operations.

The relative position of the drawbar to the PTO and the three-point hitch is important and standard dimensions have been developed for each. This ensures that any implement can be fitted to any tractor and perform properly. The PTO shaft guards are designed to fit any implement and tractor combination whether attached to the hitch or the drawbar. A pull-type baler is shown in Figure 3-14, ready to be attached to a tractor with PTO drive and drawbar. Note how the guard completely covers the universal joints and shafts.

Figure 3-13 A quick hitch allows the tractor to be backed directly to the implement-attaching points without dismounting from the tractor.

XII. GOOD AND BAD PRACTICES

When an implement is mounted to the three-point hitch, the top link causes it to be a very safe combination. It is practically impossible to achieve a rear overturn when the implement is in the ground. However, it is a very different matter when the implement is being transported, because its overhanging weight can reduce the front axle loading to the point where the front wheels leave the ground. Low axle weight for short and level journeys at slow speed might be tolerated if the operator is aware of the situation but not if rough ground with bumps and holes is to be crossed. The back of the implement might snag on something and with the front wheels off the ground, the tractor may veer to one side and run into a ditch or an obstacle with dire results.

Figure 3-14 A PTO shaft on a baler. The baler's guarded PTO drive is ready to be coupled to the tractor.

Easily attached cast iron front ballast weights are available for all tractors and should be taken on and off as implements are changed. Rear wheel weights are also available and should be added or removed to maintain safe tire loads with different implements. Liquid ballasting of the rear tires is almost always necessary and tables are published on what different sized tires can hold.

It is bad practice to use a tractor to pull out tree stumps and hard-to-move vehicles that may have become bogged down. Winches are available that can be quickly mounted on the tractor for these operations. If, in a dire emergency to save a life, the tractor has to be used, the chain should always be hitched to the drawbar to prevent backward overturning. The chain should never be hitched to the top link bracket or other high points on the tractor. The height of the reaction of the overturning couple is measured from where the tire contacts the ground and not from the center of the axle shaft. A chain attached to the top link exerts a couple on the tractor at least 2.5 times greater than if it was coupled to the drawbar.

Another bad practice is to shim up the tractor's relief valve to enable the lift to handle a heavy implement. This can cause the front axle to leave the ground, overload the rear tires, and perhaps fail a load-carrying member and cause the implement to drop.

Linch pins are used to retain the implement to the three-point hitch and should be replaced by ones recommended by the manufacturer. They become very highly stressed when the implement sways from side to side in transport and make-shift ones can easily fracture and cause an implement to become detached from the hitch.

Similarly, drawbar pins used with pull-type implements should comply with the recommended size and material speci-fications. Undersized ones should never be used.

Power take-off shields have been developed over the years to the point where they completely cover the moving parts of the drive. They are easy to install and maintain in working condition. It is good practice to inspect them carefully each time an implement is connected to the PTO shaft. Large tractors have two PTO speeds, one of 540 rpm for older and smaller implements and another of 1000 rpm for newer and larger implements. Different splined shafts are interchanged on the tractor in order to prevent the wrong implement from being hooked up. On no occasion should a 540 rpm implement be adapted to run at the 1000 rpm speed.

Sometimes PTO driven machinery clogs up and stops turning. To free a blocked implement, the tractor should be stopped, the PTO drive disengaged, the transmission put into neutral, the parking brake set, and the engine shut off before dismounting to free the blockage. In the case of a mounted implement it should also be lowered to the ground.

Hydraulic hoses that work with the cylinders of pull-type equipment should comply with the manufacturer's recom-mended specifications. They should be the correct length so that they are not stretched or chaffed as the implement and tractor move relative to each other in work.

Conditions in agriculture vary so much from day to day and from farm to farm that no one set of instructions is right for all occasions. The tractor manufacturer makes equipment available for all kinds of usage and selecting the ones best adapted for a range of conditions is important. Consultation with the dealer can be very helpful in this regard.

Regular maintenance and inspection are also necessary for safe and efficient operation.

XIII. CONCLUSION

This section has covered the general principles of how tractors and implements behave in combination. References are given on how hydraulic systems and valves work; standards, many of which are in worldwide use, are also referenced.

Each tractor has controls (see Figure 3–15) that are positioned and function in a little different way from others. All tractors and implements have operator's manuals when they are sold, and these should be studied by all drivers and kept

Figure 3-15 Typical hydraulic lift and remote valve controls in the cab of a 4WD tractor.

with the machines at all times. Control functions are clearly explained, and decals on the machines indicate what each control is for and the direction in which it operates.

Modern developments enable one man to hitch large implements to tractors by himself even though they weigh many tons.

It is hoped that these brief descriptions will give all those who come into contact with farm equipment a better understanding of the principles involved, resulting in greater efficiency and safety.

REFERENCES

1. W. J. Foxwell, "Maximizing the Drawbar Horsepower of Farm Tractors." Akron Rubber Group, paper, January 1975.
2. C. Frazer, *Harry Ferguson Inventor and Pioneer*. London: Camelot Press, reprinted 1973.
3. *Agricultural Engineers Yearbook, 1982–1983*, 29th ed. St. Joseph, MI.: American Society of Agricultural Engineers, 1983. (Contains copies of all the standards cited in the article as well as other useful information on tractor and implement performance and Nebraska Tractor Tests.)
4. J. Hobbs and H. Hesse, "Electric–Hydraulic Hitch Control for Agricultural Tractors." SAE paper 801018. Warrendale, PA.: Society of Automotive Engineers, 1980.
5. "Farm Equipment Hydraulics," Six-Part Series. *Implement and Tractor Magazine*, July 15, 1982.
6. H. L. Stewart and J. M. Storer, *ABC's of Hydraulic Circuits*. Indianapolis: Howard W. Sams, 1973.
7. *Tractor Shop Service Manuals*. Overland Park, KS.: Intertec.
8. *Product Data File*, 1983 Annual. Overland Park, KS.: Intertec.
9. *Red Book*, 1982 Annual. Overland Park, KS.: Intertec. (Includes specifications for farm tractors.)
10. *Fluid Power Data Book*, 5th ed. Dallas: Womack, 1981.

Appendix: List of Standards

STANDARD	SUBJECT
ASAE S295.2 (SAE J709d)	Covers Category I, II, III, and IV hitches.
ASAE S320 (SAE J909)	Covers Category O hitch for lawn and garden tractors up to 20 horsepower.
ASAE S203.10 (SAE J1170) ASAE S205.2 (SAE J722) ASAE S207.10 (SAE J721) ASAE S331.3 ASAE S297.1	Covers rear PTO drives and drawbars.
ASAE S298	Covers lawn and garden tractor drawbars.
ASAE S370.10	Covers 2000 rpm PTO shafts for lawn and garden tractors.
ASAE S201.4 (SAE J716)	Covers hydraulic remote cylinders.
ASAE S295.2 (SAE J709d)	Covers agricultural tire loadings, torque factors, and inflation factors.
ASAE S346.1 (SAE J884)	Covers liquid ballast tables for drive tires for agricultural machines.
ASAE S349.1 (SAE J283)	Covers a method to measure hydraulic lift force.

Copies of these standards can be obtained from:

The American Society of Agricultural Engineers
2950 Niles Road
St. Joseph, MI 49085
(616) 429-0300

and

The Society of Automotive Engineers, Inc.
400 Commonwealth Drive
Warrendale, PA 15096
(412) 776-4841

4

Steering Trailers

N. ROYCE CURRY
President, Auto Steering Trailers Limited
Oakville, Ontario, CANADA

*N. Royce Curry was educated in New Zealand. He studied
automotive diesel mechanics at Rotorua Technical Trade
School, graduating in 1960. While at school he worked for
the International Harvester Company of New Zealand, and
from 1960 until 1973 he was affiliated with International
Harvester in various capacities in London (U.K.), Ontario
(Canada), Durban (South Africa), and Auckland (New
Zealand). For example, he served as Assistant Supervisor
for Farm Equipment and Dealer Education in the United
Kingdom and as Assistant Supervisor of Industrial
Equipment and principal Heavy Truck Sales Representa-
tive for Canada. In 1973 he established Auto Steering
Trailers Limited in order to develop his patented Steering
Systems for transport trucks and trailers. These systems
involve such patented products as the ASTL Self Steering
Axle, Dual Wheel Kingpin type steering axles, Self Steering
"B" dollies, Self Tracking axles, and Tandem and Tri-Axle
Self Tracking Bogies. He is a member of SAE, CAPMA,
CMA, CFIB, and OTA. Curry is Chief Executive Officer
of Auto Steering Trailers Limited and its Manager of
Engineering. He may be contacted at Auto Steering
Trailers Limited, 316 Wyecroft Road, Oakville,
Ontario L6K 2G7, Canada (416-842-0010).*

I. THE DOUBLE DRAWBAR DOLLY CONCEPT

For the past several years, Auto Steering Trailers Limited (ASTL) has been involved in the development of steering systems for truck trailers. One area of our research and development involves the double drawbar converter gear for double and triple trailer configurations and for full trailer dollies (Figure 4-1). As a result of the promising outcome in the initial development work, we decided to pursue this area vigorously. We found that several configurations were necessary if all the needs of the trucking industry were to be met. Some of the preliminary design criteria established by ASTL were as follows:

1. Prevent dolly jackknife
2. Maintain good weight distribution of doubles
3. Reduce structural problems of B-trains
4. Simplify backing
5. Increase hitch safety
6. Reduce off-tracking
7. Tighten up intervehicle distances
8. Maintain fleet integration
9. Comply with bridge laws
10. Improve roll stability

ASTL had as its *first* goal the elimination of dolly jackknife. Other designs do not have this as their prime concern, so those dollies may continue to manifest "wiggle," "will be difficult to back up," and may perpetuate dolly jackknife! Further problems can be expected in attempting to have the design for double drawbar converter gear meet all of the applications required, especially where large intervehicle distances are concerned. For example, the design of full trailers and converter gear is dictated by "bridge laws" in each Canadian province or state in the United States.

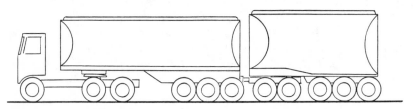

Figure 4-1 A double trailer.

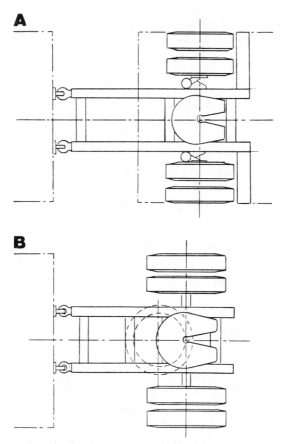

Figure 4-2 Two basic models for double drawbar converter gear developed by ASTL: (A) the ASTL "B" Dolly, and (B) the ASTL Turntable Dolly.

ASTL developed two basic models to meet these requirements, *neither of which will jackknife.* They are shown in Figure 4-2.

II. HSRI REPORT

The operation of double trailers in Michigan proved beyond doubt the need to improve the hitch design for doubles. Valuable data was compiled by the University of Michigan Highway Safety Research Institute (HSRI) that pointed out the problem of yaw amplification and instability threshold with double tanker trailers: "The greatest amplification occurs between the leading and the following trailers, peak lateral acceleration was 2.5 times greater than at the tractor with these doubles."[1] With a tractor semitrailer tanker, the trailer remained stable up to 0.49 G of acceleration, while the double tanker using a conventional dolly had to be restricted to 0.17 G for fear of rollover.

By using the four-point hitch or "C" train design, it was possible to achieve a 50 percent improvement in pup trailer stability, according to HSRI. Reducing the possibility of dolly jackknife by eliminating one hinge point from a train configuration is, therefore, in the best interest of the trucking industry and the traveling public, especially where hazardous goods are concerned.

Several designs are available that can assist the commercial fleet, private carrier, or owner–operator in improving train stability (some of these are subsequently described).

III. COMPARISON OF "A" AND "B" DOLLIES

A simple comparison points out the major difference between an "A" and "B" dolly (Figure 4-3). Whether a turntable (western ring) or 5th wheel is used, a double-pivot "A" dolly is still able to jackknife, whereas it is impossible to jackknife the "B" dolly. Use of ASTL Self Steering axles reduces tire scrub-

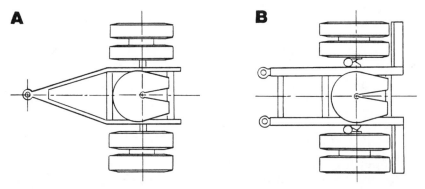

Figure 4-3 A side-by-side comparison of (A) an "A" dolly, and (B) a "B" dolly.

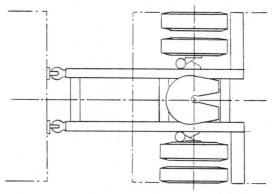

Figure 4-4 The ASTL "B" Dolly.

bing and gives improved off-tracking performance. Additional safety is provided by using two hitches instead of one. The rigid attachment and steering axle of the B-dolly is the major component in the design and prevents dolly jackknifing.

IV. "C" TRAIN STEERING DOLLY

The ASTL "B" Dolly (Figure 4-4) was designed specifically to eliminate yaw instability at the dolly and to improve the stability of the pup trailer, while still offering the flexibility of "A" dollies. Integration is reasonably straightforward. Axle spreads up to 3.5 meters (138 inches) are recommended.

A conventional Reyco or Hutch suspension is used in conjunction with an ASTL Self Steering axle. The double drawbar hitch prevents dolly jackknife and maintains good roll stability of the pup trailer.

V. C-TRAIN TURNTABLE DOLLY

With the ASTL Turntable Dolly (Figure 4-5) or conversion dolly, yaw is prevented by the typical double drawbar hitch. A conventional rigid axle is set behind the turntable and gives a caster effect. The turntable or western ring is fitted with a fail-safe lock and pneumatic stabilizer for dampening. Conventional "A" dolly components may be used to fit a turntable

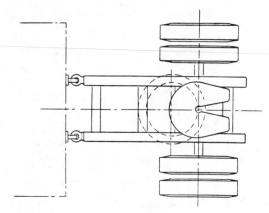

Figure 4-5 The ASTL Turntable Dolly.

dolly kit. Drawbar lengths are designed to suit axle spreads up to 3.5 meters (138 inches). With this design of dolly steering, angles of up to 30° can be achieved.

VI. FORCED STEERING DOLLY

The ASTL Forced Steering Dolly (Figure 4-6) is unique in that it prevents yaw in the same way a Skid-Steer does. Steering is transmitted to the axle through two steering arms from a double drawbar hitch in this patented product. The operator is able to steer the dolly in reverse, making backing the same for the full trailer as with a semitrailer,

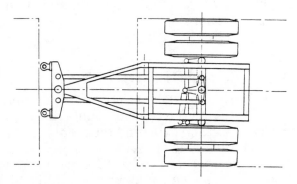

Figure 4-6 The ASTL Forced Steering Dolly.

a big advantage in close quarters. ASTL Forced Steering Dollies were developed especially for full trailers having large intervehicle distances (5 meters plus) and multi-axle configurations.

VII. GOODBYE DOLLY

The Goodbye Dolly (Figure 4-7) also eliminates yaw and is a good approach in applications where the dolly can be lost to the pup since it is permanently attached to the lead trailer. It may also be necessary to use at least one air suspension in order to maintain equalization when the dolly is moved up under the lead trailer and sliding can be a problem.

VIII. PIGGYBACK TRAIN

Probably the best known train design is the Canadian Piggyback or "B" Train (see Figure 4-8). It is a good approach to transporting hazardous goods. Some problems can be expected with weight distribution, tire damage, and frame stress. Flexibility and integration are also major problems for this train design.

IX. HSRI FOUR-POINT HITCH DOLLY

The University of Michigan four-point hitch (Figure 4-9) was designed to eliminate yaw and contribute to the stability of the pup trailer. These results stemmed from the testing of

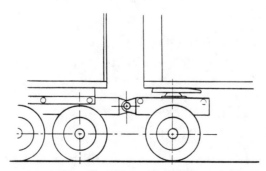

Figure 4-7 The Goodbye Dolly (or sliding dolly).

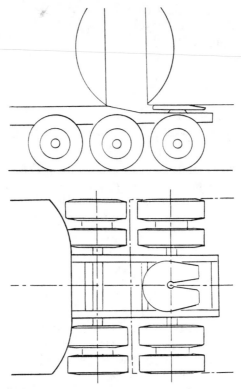

Figure 4-8 Side and top views of the Canadian Piggyback "B" train.

Fruehauf double bottom tankers. Horrendous tire scuffing and frame stress problems seem to be evident with this design.

X. TRAPEZOIDAL DOLLY

The trapezoidal dolly (Figure 4-10) is an attempt to reduce yaw instability, and achieves this within the drawbar geometry. This design does not prevent dolly jackknife, however; therefore, it is off the mark when considering the need for improved stability. Trailer "wiggle" is still evident with this design, backing is a problem, and with longer drawbars a tendency toward increased yaw instability exists. Major problems can be expected due to nonfailsafe hitch design.

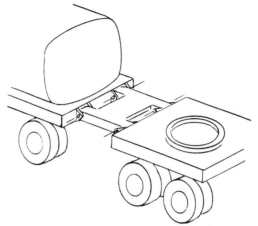

Figure 4-9 The HSRI four-point hitch.

XI. SKID-STEER DOLLY

The Skid-Steer dolly (Figure 4-11) is an admirable attempt to eliminate the problems of yaw instability, but it fails to solve the problem of articulation. Large forces can be expected at the drawbar, and high tire wear is directly related to axle spreads. In some cases, a self steering axle is substituted for the rigid axle. However, this approach is also hindered by the lack of the high steering angle required (30° minimum).

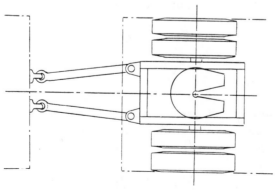

Figure 4-10 The trapezoidal dolly.

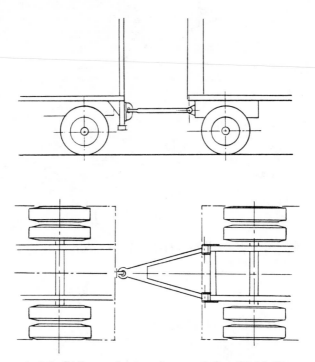

Figure 4-11 Side and top views of the Skid-Steer dolly.

XII. CROSS STEER DOLLY

The cross steer dolly (Figure 4-12) is an attempt at eliminating yaw instability at the expense of maneuverability. Tracking is also restricted due to reverse rotation; the drawbar attachment is unusual; and three hinge points are used, making this design possibly more prone to jackknifing and not of failsafe design.

XIII. INTEGRATION

Many fleets have large numbers of dollies for double and triple trailers, and it would cause major logistical problems if the new dolly selected could not be integrated into these fleets satisfactorily. The ASTL designs provide for easy integration in several ways:

    1. Conversion dollies make it possible to change existing "A" dolly parts over to the double drawbar kit.

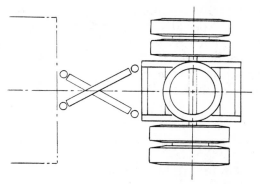

Figure 4-12 The cross steer dolly.

2. The addition of a reach to new B-dollies enables their utilization with existing single hitch trailers.
3. Three-point hitch attachment at the trailer provides for both A- and B-dollies during the process change-over.
4. ASTL also makes tag-axle B-dollies similar to Jifflox for truck/trailer applications using the steerable axle and double drawbar arrangement.

Recommended specifications on double drawbar hitch ICC bumper arrangements should be followed (Figure 4-13). Hitches

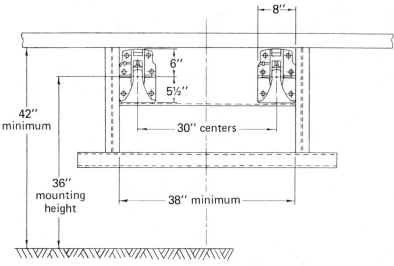

Figure 4-13 ASTL-ICC bumper requirements.

should be of at least 60,000 pound tensile strength and capable of withstanding a 20,000 pound vertical load on the latch assembly. Drawbar eyes at least $2^{7}/_{16}$ inches in diameter mounted on 30-inch centers should be used, and care should be taken in selecting fastener systems—Grade 5 bolts to be considered a minimum.

XIV. EQUALIZATION

Many states have a mandatory requirement that equalization between axles be maintained. In the case of "B" dollies, a means of maintaining dolly pitch is provided in order to avoid loading the lead trailer hitch and to maintain good weight distribution. With the Goodbye Dolly design an air suspension may be required in order to achieve this. The Canadian Piggyback "B" train design will require additional axles in order to take care of overloading and weight distribution problems.

XV. RETROFIT OR CONVERSION

The laws governing the use of doubles are changing to allow for larger gross vehicle weight, in accordance with prescribed axle spreads. This is bringing about a change in intervehicle distances. Thus, it is an ideal time to upgrade existing "A" dolly equipment to the double drawbar or "B" dolly design.

A word of caution: Not every application is ideally suited to the double drawbar concept as far as axle spreads are concerned. Thus, anyone contemplating changing to the double drawbar should speak to those manufacturers having knowledge in this area before proceeding.

ASTL recommends B-dollies for up to 100-inch tongue length or 3.5-meter axle spread without special engineering. For 5-meter (197-inch) axle spreads or longer, forced steering dollies are suggested. Fixed axle double drawbar dollies are NOT recommended except in very close (54 inches to 72 inches) axle spreads.

XVI. STEERING AND BRIDGE LAWS

Some jurisdictions call for steer axles or axles that articulate in the manner of a steering axle in applications where spreads are more than 65 inches. In the case of a double drawbar dolly, a steering axle is required for spreads over 65 inches in order to avoid increased hitch loads and frame stress and to meet those regulations.

This is a matter of further study by the National Research Council of Canada, the University of Michigan Highway Safety Research Institute, and the Ontario Ministry of Transportation and Communication.

XVII. CONCLUSION

Every fleet superintendent, private carrier, and owner operator should take a hard look at his rigs and count the number of articulated joints. If there are two hinge points between any set of doubles, it is advisable that plans be made to eliminate one hinge on all future purchases and that a conversion program be initiated. If the operator is buying new equipment, he should begin to implement ways to upgrade the equipment's specs accordingly and work at ways to convert existing units to piggyback trains, Goodbye Dolly, or B-dolly converters. *If you are operating "A" dolly rigs now, you're only as safe as your driver is professional.*

If you are a manufacturer of double and triple trailers and you do not recognize the continuing defect inherent in the "A" dolly and upgrade your engineering to B-dolly designs, you are exposing your corporation to potential product liability.

If you are now running triples using "A" dollies, you are risking the potential loss of one-third of the revenue generated by these combinations by exposing your business to either possible nonallowance of triples or a halt to their needed and obviously desirable expansion.

The National Research Council of Canada is conducting extensive research involving the stress and stability factors surrounding the use of ASTL B-dollies, and several papers will be presented to SAE describing their safety advantages.

CITATIONS

[1]R. Ervin, P. S. Fancher, T. E. Gillespie, C. B. Winkler, and A. Wolfe, *Ad Hoc Study of Certain Safety Related Characteristics of Double Bottom Tankers.* Report No. UM-HSRI-78-18. Ann Arbor: Highway Safety Research Institute, University of Michigan, 1978.

5

Modifications, Maintenance, and Repairs

REUBEN P. VOLLMER
and
CORY L. GRAY
Vollmer-Gray Engineering Laboratories
Long Beach, California

Reuben P. Vollmer received an Associate of Applied Science degree in Metallurgy in 1959 and a Bachelor of Science degree in Mechanical Engineering in 1961 from the Milwaukee School of Engineering. He gained substantial experience in failure analysis, test engineering, and metallurgical evaluation over the next several years until becoming the Director of Experimental Mechanics for Truesdail Laboratories. He founded Vollmer Engineering Laboratories in 1970 and has been engaged in consultation on accidents and other losses since that time. Vollmer is a registered professional engineer and an authority in the field of vehicle defect analysis.

Cory L. Gray received his Bachelor of Science degree in Engineering from the University of California at Los Angeles in 1957 and a Master of Science in Mechanical Engineering from the University of Southern California in 1963. He is a registered professional engineer with over

25 years of engineering experience in development, analysis, and testing of mechanical and electrical products, plus basic research in structures, dynamics, and safety. Gray joined Vollmer Engineering Laboratories in 1973 and became a partner in 1977. He has analyzed hundreds of defect-related vehicle accidents of all types. The Vollmer-Gray Engineering Laboratories are located at 1403 West Gaylord Street, Long Beach, California 90813 (213-437-6468).

I. INTRODUCTION

Improper modifications, maintenance, and repairs have been identified as factors in the occurrence or severity of many vehicle accidents. Therefore, the possibility of such defects should be considered carefully when attempting to analyze the causes and results of a traffic accident. General areas of consideration should include individual components, component integration with the rest of the vehicle, service diagnosis and inspection, and workmanship of repairs.

Vehicle effects can play a part in any segment of an accident sequence. Typically, the initiation of a vehicle-related accident represents a breakdown in the driver's ability to control the actions of the vehicle. In these cases, the designed-in accident avoidance capabilities of the vehicle have been diminished or entirely lost prior to its involvement in a collision. During a collision, vehicle factors may affect the severity of property damage or bodily injury. The same can be said for the period following a collision when the vehicle moves to its point of rest.

The ways in which modifications, maintenance, and repairs play a part in the overall accident sequence are too numerous to list individually. Some important examples, however, are given in the following material.

II. MODIFICATIONS

Modifications are those changes to a vehicle that make it different from the originally designed and manufactured configuration. Some modifications are performed at the direction of the manufacturer to correct deficiencies discovered after the vehicle was built. Those modifications that have been the subject of recall campaigns are listed periodically by the U.S. Department of Transportation.[1] At the present time, it is also possible to obtain recall information by telephone using the "Auto Safety Hotline" (800) 424-9393. Dealers sometimes modify vehicles while they are under their control in order to make them more salable or at the request of the buyer. Most often, however, modifications are undertaken by owners or their mechanics in an attempt to enhance the vehicle's performance, capacity, ride comfort, or appearance. Some modifications, if properly accomplished, do achieve the desired goal of improving on the original design. Typically, however, modifications are performed in a manner that reduces the integrity of the overall vehicle. Any modification to the as-built vehicle should be assessed in the context of available information to determine if it may have been a factor in an accident.

A commonly encountered passenger car modification involves replacement of the rims and/or tires with nonstandard or nonoptional sizes. This has been known to produce adverse handling and stability characteristics, especially in front-wheel-drive cars. Oversize tires may also interfere with portions of the vehicle body under severe loading or cornering conditions. This can damage the tires and affect handling. Recreational vehicles are often modified at the time of purchase with large tires and rims that aggravate stability problems in vehicles which already have high centers of gravity. After-market rims are ordinarily chosen for appearance, with no regard to the strength, the durability, or the effects of offset on steering characteristics and wheel bearing loads.

Tires must be compatible with the rims upon which they are mounted. If the tires are too narrow in section width, the chance of a rim "dig in" causing an upset is increased. Tubeless tires that are either too narrow or too wide for the rims may lose their seal under heavy cornering loads. An improper mix of tire types, such as radial-ply tires on the front wheels and bias-ply tires on the rears, can cause undesirable handling effects and loss of control. The proper tire and rim sizes for most vehicles can be found in the *Year Book of the Tire and Rim Association, Inc.*[2] and the *Tire Guide.*[3]

Peer-group pressure has led to classes of vehicle modifications having no real basis in safety or performance. Suspension, wheel, and tire modifications are common examples. Nearly always, these modifications will degrade the vehicle handling characteristics and reduce the ability of the driver to avoid accidents.

Modifications often found in customized vans can lead to bodily injury during the collision and postcollision phases of an accident. Many times vans, trucks, and recreational vehicles are equipped with after-market auxiliary fuel tanks that have been installed in vulnerable locations, poorly supported, or with exposed fuel line routing which greatly increases the hazard of fire during a collision. Furniture and cabinetry installed in customized vans is rarely secured well enough to resist impact loads. Loose items flying about inside a vehicle during a collision have produced bodily injuries directly related to the defective modifications. Large "picture windows" installed in vans are hazardous in at least two ways: (1) the removal of body material to provide window openings reduces the structural integrity; (2) then, the large openings that appear when the windows break out during collisions become avenues for occupant ejection. It has long been known that ejection from a vehicle is statistically related to increased injury potential. Add-on CB radios and electric trailer brake controls under the instrument panel have been the cause of many lower extremity injuries in collisions.

The vehicle operating controls are the link between the operator and the machine. Any modification of the controls must be viewed as a potential breakdown in the ability of the operator to control the vehicle. Some after-market variations include the addition of an automatic throttle control and replacement of the standard steering wheel with one of substantially smaller diameter. The small steering wheel has the additional shortcoming of concentrating chest impact loads during a frontal collision. Operating controls designed to accommodate the handicapped represent another major category of control modification with special problems.

The federal government has, for many years, required manufacturers to provide equipment for protection of vehicle occupants during collisions. Vehicle owners have occasionally modified their vehicles by removing or defeating these safety measures. Examples include removal of seatback head rests, restricting the movement of collapsible steering columns, and addition of protrusions inside the passenger compartment. In the last category, it is not uncommon to see a compass mounted on a dashboard or a heavy mirror on a sun visor. Steering column collapse can be dangerously limited by clamping instruments to the column between the steering wheel and the instrument panel.

III. MAINTENANCE

Maintenance refers to vehicle servicing that is required to prevent failure. Production vehicles are supplied with an owner's manual that ordinarily details the required maintenance schedule to be followed for optimum performance and durability. The procedures should be reasonable in cost and should be detailed in shop manuals available to mechanics not directly associated with dealers. Service operations should be reasonably obvious to a trained mechanic.

The need for nonscheduled maintenance must be determined by the operator of the vehicle. The operator, for example, would ordinarily be responsible for determining that windshield wiper blades needed to be replaced. The need for tire replacement can also be determined easily by visual inspection. Proper inspection, care and servicing of tires is described in the *Care and Service of Passenger Car Tires*.[4] If the vehicle is being maintained on a regular basis, then a trained mechanic should point out tire wear and other incipient failures such as cracked accessory drive belts, worn suspension bushings, or loose wheel fasteners.

Accidents have occasionally been produced or aggravated by incomplete maintenance operations. In one instance, a service station attendant failed to replace the cover over a brake master cylinder reservoir after checking the fluid level. After a few days of normal operation, all brake fluid was completely lost from the reservoir, and the service brakes were rendered ineffective. Brake fluid loss was produced by a combination of sloshing and normal geysering from the small ports in the bottoms of the reservoir chambers. Another example of incomplete maintenance procedures that has been observed several times is the failure to replace the cap on a fuel filler pipe after fueling a vehicle. The result of this oversight can be catastrophic if a vehicle overturns for any reason. The actual upset of the vehicle may not produce serious injuries, but the potential for a postaccident fire is greatly increased due to the inevitable fuel spillage. Other defective maintenance includes contamination of the brake fluid or power steering fluid as the result of dirt particles dropped in during fluid level checks. Checking the engine oil level can also introduce contamination to the lubricant, but that is usually not as serious a problem since there is a strainer in the oil pickup and engine oil is filtered. However, on many vehicles if the engine oil dipstick is not firmly replaced after checking the level, air will be allowed to leak into the crankcase and upset the air/fuel ratio entering the engine. This can cause engines to run roughly and even stall. When a vehicle stalls on the roadway, there is the potential for a rear-end collision from following traffic. A final example of defective maintenance that has produced property damage is the careless placement of a grease rag on an engine exhaust manifold during service operations. After traveling for a while, the exhaust manifold can reach temperatures sufficient to ignite such a grease rag, and the fire can spread to other parts of the engine compartment, producing large-scale damage.

Maintenance on a motorcycle is extremely important for trouble-free and safe riding. Maintenance-sensitive areas include tires, steering, and drive chain. Tires worn low are more susceptible to punctures resulting in loss of control. On motorcycles with ball bearings in the fork stem, galling and deformation of the balls or races may occur, leading to stability problems and possible "speed wobble." Swing-arm bushing wear can also increase the probability of wobble. Inadequate lubrication of the drive chain and/or sprocket misalignment can cause chain failure, with resultant possible rear wheel lockup.

IV. REPAIRS

Repairs are generally made to a vehicle, after a malfunction has occurred, to restore its original operating characteristics. The repairs should be accomplished so that unneeded parts and work are not included but that all repairs, and servicing that is affected by the repairs, are performed. Proper diagnosis by the repairing mechanic is one of the most significant services the mechanic can render. The dishonest mechanic who inflates the list of repairs only makes the motoring public skeptical of the need for repairs, leaving the vehicle owner vulnerable to an accident. A written explanation of the reason additional work was performed should be provided. Any parts removed should be returned to the owner for a fair determination of the need for replacement.

Most accidents that are defect-related are caused by improper repairs. Defects in both the parts and the workmanship of repair must be considered. Oftentimes, components not directly associated with the repaired item must be removed to gain access to the item being repaired. Improper reassembly alone can be the cause of an accident.

The ability to stop is the single most important accident-avoidance capability of a vehicle. For this reason, failure of the braking system is often suspected in motor vehicle collisions. Studies, such as the one reported in SAE paper 770115,[5] have found that brake failure is the most common problem that can be related to defective postmanufacturing servicing. Since the brake system is one of the more complex mechanical subsystems on a vehicle, it is highly sensitive to servicing errors. In addition, the brake system requires more maintenance and servicing throughout the life of the vehicle than any of the other controls.

The brake system is probably the most deceptive of the vehicle control systems to diagnose. Oftentimes, past repairs did not include the portion of the system that ultimately failed and caused an accident. For example, if a vehicle has a hydraulic system with contaminated brake fluid, the hydraulic cylinder bores may well be corroded and rough except where the piston seals normally slide. When brake lining material is replaced in the course of normal maintenance, the thicker material will cause the operating pistons to move to a new location. The hydraulic piston seals will then be sliding back and forth in a corroded area. Over a period of time, this may cause the seals to fail. In that case, the mechanic has done nothing intentional to alter the hydraulic system, but he has lacked the proper diagnosis of a defective condition at the time of repairs. The effect of his error in diagnosis may not be readily apparent. If the internal bore of a hydraulic cylinder is corroded and the seals are in good condition, it may take several thousand miles of driving before the seals are actually worn or abraded to the point of seal failure. When this happens, the service brake pedal gradually moves to the floor until, under even light braking effort, the driver finds the pedal at the floor with no brakes. At that point, he may not be able to stop his vehicle in time to avoid striking some object.

The condition of the brake fluid in the master cylinder reservoir can be used to evaluate the condition of the internal components of the hydraulic system. A significant accumulation of sludge at the bottom of the master cylinder reservoir is indicative of worn seals and corroded pistons and cylinder bores. The commonly used brake fluids are hygroscopic. When the brake fluid becomes sufficiently contaminated with water, certain adverse conditions develop. The primary adverse effects are a reduction in fluid boiling point and an increase in the corrosion of metal components in the hydraulic system.

The use of inadequate or improper brake lining friction material may result in premature brake fade, which is a loss of braking capability with an increase in brake temperature. Different friction materials have different sensitivities to temperature fade. For this reason, brake linings are coded according to the requirements given in SAE J866a,[6] and the coding is printed on the edge of the friction material. Replacement of the brake linings on one side of the vehicle should be accompanied by replacement on the other side, using linings with the same temperature characteristics in order to maintain brake balance. Some brake system designs use different lining materials for each of two shoes in a set. In such cases, the proper position of each shoe is determined by a color code marked on the edge in accordance with SAE J659.[7] The installer must contour the brake linings to fit the diameter of the drums in drum brake systems. Lack of contouring or improper contouring can lead to brake fade or lockup on one or more wheels. This can have an adverse effect on the ability of the driver to control the vehicle.

Brake drums must be inspected for dimensional irregularities and for hard spots, which can form under very high temperatures. A drum with irregular dimensions can often be brought into tolerance by turning. The maximum diameter to which a drum may be turned is indicated on the drum. A brake drum with hard spots must be replaced since it cannot be repaired by turning. Hard spots appear as small blue, brown, or yellow spots on the inside diameter. Failure to replace such a drum usually results in wheel lockup when the brakes are applied subsequent to repairs.

Omission of needed repairs can also be considered improper repair work. For example, when servicing wheel assemblies, it is necessary to correct any leakage of lubricant into the area that may contaminate the brakes. This could mean the installation of new lubricant seals or even wheel bearings. Brake springs that show evidence of corrosion cracking or excessive heating should be replaced at the time the brake shoes are replaced. The self-adjusting mechanism of drum brake assemblies should be replaced if there is damage or excessive wear. Existing brake fluid in the system should be flushed out to avoid operation with contaminated fluid. Most manufacturers now recommend changing brake fluid once per year. An alert mechanic should also be able to detect deterioration of brake hoses. Most brake hoses will appear cracked on the surface in a relatively short period of service. However, when the cracks penetrate the outer rubber sheath into the fabric reinforcement, it is time to change a hose. Any additional work of this type can be justified, but it may be opposed by the owner of the vehicle for economic reasons. In such cases, good business procedure requires that the mechanic make note on the invoice that recommended repairs were declined.

The use of incorrect parts in the repair of brake systems, and other systems for that matter, has been observed to cause accidents. As an example, in some vehicles, disc brakes and drum brakes are optional designs. However, the brake master cylinder for each system is different, and replacement using the wrong master cylinder will result in a brake failure.

The incidence of incorrect or damaged parts being installed during repairs is substantially greater if the parts are not new. During collision repairs, major subassemblies (such as body clips, engines, transmissions, rear axle assemblies and steering gears) are more often than not obtained from wrecked vehicles rather than the manufacturer. Many of these parts are not adequately inspected by the mechanic and may be damaged at the time they are installed. This can lead to engine failure and gear lockup among other hazardous results.

In performing many repair operations on a vehicle, it is necessary to remove the wheels. The potential for defective workmanship then exists when the wheels are reinstalled. If the hub has been removed from the spindle, it must be replaced without contaminating the bearings and with proper bearing adjustment. The cotter pin securing the spindle nut must be installed. Then, failure to tighten the wheel fasteners sufficiently may lead to loss of a wheel, which generally means loss of vehicle control.

When replacing, or in some cases repairing, an engine, the control, fuel, and exhaust connections are separated. Carelessness in reassembling these connections can create fire hazards, throttle control sticking, or exhaust leaks. Both over and under tightening fuel line connections has led to fuel leaks and fires in the engine compartment. Bending a metal fuel line out of the way during certain servicing operations will stretch flexible rubberized-hose line couplers in vehicles so equipped. Failure of the mechanic to realign the metal fuel line and coupler will leave the flexible hose segment under strain. This will greatly accelerate the aging process of the rubber and can cause early failure with the associated fire hazard.

Engine exhaust systems are often in need of repair after a vehicle has been in service for a few years. Defective repairs are usually in the form of incompletely welded or bolted piping connections. Resulting exhaust leaks may allow carbon monoxide to concentrate under the occupied areas of a vehicle or within the trunk. Then, with an unfavorable combination of openings and air circulation, the toxic gas can enter the occupant space. Even without a carbon monoxide hazard, leakage of hot exhaust gases can generate fire damage inside the vehicle and fluid boiling in adjacent brake lines. Brake fluid boiling due to heating from mislocated exhaust pipes will produce loss of effective braking at the wheels being served by the affected brake system. With subsequent cooling and brake fluid condensation, evidence of a brake failure may disappear.

V. DOCUMENTATION

The first indication that an accident may be defect-related is often a driver or witness report of unusual vehicle operating characteristics. These sources or an investigating officer may provide information that can guide the investigator to uncover a vehicle defect. Collateral information relating to the vehicle history in terms of modifications, maintenance, and repairs should then be assembled.

Physical evidence at the accident scene is often helpful in determining the characteristics of the vehicle's performance immediately prior to the accident. If the investigation is begun soon enough after the accident, that evidence may be obtainable at the scene. Otherwise, it may be necessary to rely on reports that others have made documenting the physical evidence. It may have been reported that there was a steering failure. However, skid marks at the scene showing locked rear wheels could be more indicative of a seized engine or gear train that caused loss of control than a steering defect. Similarly, tire marks showing that one of the tires was flat on the roadway may also be significant when a steering failure is reported. The existence of four-wheel locked skid marks extending for some distance and terminating at a point of impact will usually rule out total brake failure. Measurement of skid mark length and width at the accident site may be important in determining which wheel of which vehicle made each mark. The type and pattern of skids should be documented and photographed. This will allow an analyst to discriminate between braking, cornering, and broadside skids.

Before attempting to inspect a vehicle involved in an accident, it is necessary to obtain permission from the owner or controlling party. To make an accurate assessment of vehicle defects, the postaccident condition of the vehicle should be properly documented. This includes photographs and measurements of the significant damage. It is especially important to show the effects of collision damage on the vehicle component or subsystem in question. Information such as the vehicle identification number, date of manufacture, odometer reading, license number, and, of course, the date and location of the inspection should be recorded. A listing of the vehicle equipment such as engine, transmission, tires, brake type, type of steering, etc., is important. Vehicle equipment modifications must be noted, and service stickers placed on the doors, door frames, or engine compartment surfaces should not be overlooked.

The existence of any warnings or limitations having to do with the vehicle or modifications should be determined. A review of the owner's manual may bring to light warnings and admonitions that bear on a defect, failure, or misuse of the vehicle. Other warnings may have been implicit in publications such as a "Consumer Information" report required for each vehicle. Modifying-component warnings may have existed at the point of sale or on a package. Components themselves should be examined for warnings or limitations imprinted on the units.

Details of the actual inspection procedure will vary with the nature of the suspected defect under investigation. A general procedural outline for inspecting brakes, steering systems, suspension systems, tires and wheel assemblies can be found in Part 570 of the *Federal Motor Vehicle Safety Standards*.[8] Usually, a more detailed examination of the subject area will be required.

Any evidence that is removed from the vehicle should be adequately identified, documented, and stored so that others may also have the benefit of analyzing that evidence. If others do inspect the evidence, it should also be done with the permission of the owner or controlling party. The evidence should not be transferred or destroyed without the use of adequate documentation and receipts.

CITATIONS

[1]*Safety Related Recall Campaigns for Motor Vehicles and Motor Vehicle Equipment, Including Tires* (published quarterly). Washington, D.C.: Department of Transportation, National Highway Traffic Safety Administration.

[2]*Year Book of the Tire and Rim Association, Inc.* (published annually). Akron, OH.: Tire and Rim Association.

[3]*Tire Guide* (published annually). Syosset, N.Y.: Bennett Garfield.

[4]*Care and Service of Passenger Car Tires.* Washington, D.C.: Rubber Manufacturers Association, 1971.

[5]M. R. Appleby, L. J. Bintz, and P. E. Keen, Jr., "Incidents Caused by Vehicle Defects—Analysis of Their Characteristics." SAE paper 770115. Warrendale, PA.: Society of Automotive Engineers, 1977.

[6]"Friction Identification System for Brake Linings and Brake Blocks for Motor Vehicles—SAE J866a. SAE Recommended Practice." *SAE Handbook* (published annually). Warrendale, PA.: Society of Automotive Engineers.

[7]"Color Code for Location Identification of Combination Linings of Two Different Materials or Two Shoe Brakes—SAE J659. SAE Recommended Practice." *SAE Handbook* (published annually). Warrendale, PA.: Society of Automotive Engineers.

[8]"Vehicle in Use Inspection Standards." *Federal Motor Vehicle Safety Standards*, Part 570. Washington, D.C.: U.S. Government Printing Office, 1973 (Subpart A), 1974 (Subpart B).

II

HAZARD
IDENTIFICATION

The identification and resolution of possible hazards is a difficult process for many reasons. Within an industry, who will have the fortitude to identify and list hazards if the process could be perceived as having some adverse impact on a particular product, service, or company? The hazard proponents may be challenged as being akin to consumer advocates, but those who depreciate the hazard, lower its estimated risk, or profess the reasonableness of assessed danger may be viewed as company loyalists and industry protectors. Those proponents outside the industry may be disparaged or ignored as lacking appropriate knowledge and industry experience.

There are always questions as to accident causation or the courts would not be filled with parties disputing the facts, inferences, and expert opinions in regard to who or what was "at fault" according to known legal definitions. Assuming there is a "hazard," it may be a personal and subjective decision as to the "reasonableness" of the "risk" created for the producer and someone else's (the user's) willingness to accept the "danger." Any quantitative prediction of the risk, associated with a particular hazard, may be considered as a speculative overestimate or may be argued as patently too conservative because there always exists insufficient valid supporting data for such estimates. Yet, hazards must be identified, in some manner, and treated in a rational fashion if there are to be any corrective or preventive measures seriously considered and effectively implemented. Thus, there should be some open discussion of possible hazards, in a book such as this, to indicate how informed individuals, representative of various disciplines and experiences, perceive and conceptualize hazards that may exist in automotive vehicles.

Seat belts are intended to reduce injuries associated with certain hazards, such as occupant ejection, in foreseeable or expected automobile collisions. Do the seat belts create new hazards or injuries? Can such safety devices be improved? Can their use be mandated to improve their effectiveness? The first section of this part (Section 6) discusses some significant seat-belt data and draws some important inferences. Seat belts are one form of occupant restraint or protective device that is being used in most automobiles and an increasing proportion of trucks, buses, and special-purpose vehicles.

Carbon monoxide should be recognized as a potential safety problem. Section 7 describes the sources of carbon monoxide in automotive vehicles, why it merits special concern, how to investigate the likely causes of carbon monoxide poisoning, and what the design engineer could do to reduce the risk of injury. There is a commentary on vehicle fires, the hazards that are created, and the precautions that could be taken during the automotive vehicle design process. The list of possible hazards could extend to rubber adhesion problems in tires, the mounting of multipiece rims, and the many other descriptors that have accumulated in various recall programs. Historical failure modes provide the kind of experience that is useful in predicting and avoiding future hazards.

Crane accidents have provided a unique source of experience, relative to the identification of hazards, that has wide applicability in the field of automotive engineering. There are general principles involved in accident causation, regardless of philosophical biases that serve only to vary the degree of emphasis as to cause and cure. Section 8 on Crane Design Hazard Analysis reflects "real-world" hazard identification, recommended product improvements, and suggested "on-site" procedural measures that could be taken to reduce injuries. It is hazard identification based on on-site accident investigation and analysis that has been repeated many times during the past 30 years. A historically reinforced form of hazard recognition tends to create strong opinions, litigation, and contested advocacy as to appropriate countermeasures.

A review of hazard identification, relating to the automotive industry arena, would not be complete if the consumer advocate viewpoint were omitted, since this form of advocacy has had a significant effect on the automotive industry. Hazards have been identified from consumer complaints, consumer-oriented investigations, and aggressive analyses of legislative and regulatory proposals. Hazards have been given dramatic emphasis, persistent media attention, and have carried the threat of governmental rule making, standards formulation, and recall negotiation. Section 9, Recreational Vehicles, illustrates how such hazard identification may yield information of value and to which those in the automotive industry must pay heed or ignore at their own peril. Perhaps, giving attention to all sources of information on all possible hazards can be of more value to the automotive engineer than limiting his attention to those sources of his own selection, since each and every source may have inherent limitations or special access to pertinent information, some conceptual or self-interest bias, and some selective filtering or enhancement of facts. Without full knowledge, the wisdom of the automotive engineer may be found wanting. Hazard identification is too important to leave in the hands and minds of only one entity.

6

Seat-Belt-induced Injuries

FELIX H. WALZ, M.D.
and
ULRICH ZOLLINGER, M.D.
Institute for Forensic Medicine
University of Zurich
Zurich, Switzerland

*Dr. Felix H. Walz is a Deputy Medical Examiner and
Lecturer on forensic medicine (particularly forensic
biomechanics) at the University of Zurich, Switzerland. He
has done postgraduate work at the Institute of Forensic
Medicine (University of Zurich and St. Gallen, Switzerland),
the General Motors Research Center (Warren, Michigan),
and the Cantonal Hospital at Winterthur (Switzerland). He
is interested in the influence of accident mechanics on
pathomorphology of trauma, especially the way the wearing
of seat belts affects the injuries of car occupants; the wearing
of safety helmets, the injuries of two-wheel riders; and the
design of a car's front end, the injuries of pedestrians. He has
written 50 papers on these topics in German or English and
has been awarded several prizes for his contributions to
traffic safety. Currently, he is conducting a field study and
experimental tests of car-to-pedestrian impacts using
dummies and cadavers. Walz is a member of national and
international road safety committees and a member of
several editorial advisory boards.*

Dr. Ulrich Zollinger is a Deputy Medical Examiner and Lecturer on forensic medicine at the University of Zurich, Switzerland. He has done postgraduate work in surgery, internal medicine, forensic medicine, and surgical and anatomical pathology at hospitals and institutes in Switzerland and the United States. He was awarded a traffic safety prize in Switzerland in 1979 and one in Germany in 1980 for his dissertation on the inverse effects of wearing seat belts. He is interested in general forensic pathology, particularly in the influence of seat belts and sudden coronary death. Both authors may be contacted at the Institute of Forensic Medicine, University of Zurich, 8028 Zurich, Switzerland (01141-257-2850).

I. INTRODUCTION

The effectiveness of properly worn seat belts, in general, is sufficiently substantiated to date. According to literature reviews by Robertson[1] and Friedel,[2] *an overall protection rate of 20 to 50 percent can be assumed.* Similar figures are mentioned by the HUK-Verband (the West German motor vehicle insurance association).[3] Seat belts exhibit their highest efficiency in frontal collisions, with a reduction rate of 50 to 75 percent.[4-9] Good occupant protection has been proven also in lateral farside (right-hand) and nearside (left-hand) collisions[10-14] and rollovers,[9, 15, 16] whereby *the principal reason for the protecting effect is the prevention of ejection.* The injury severity of ejected occupants is three times higher than of those contained.[12,16] According to a NCSS (National Crash Severity Study, U.S.A.) data analysis by Huelke,[17] out of 62,026 car occupants, 1 in 433 of those not ejected suffered from a severe (3 to 6 on the AIS[18]) cervical injury while 1 in 14 of those ejected exhibited such a lesion; this fact indicates the hazard of ejection and, due to the prevention of ejection by the seat belt, the benefit of belt wearing.

After the enactment of a mandatory seat belt law, *the number of severely and fatally injured belted car occupants must increase as a logical consequence.* Therefore, the number of case reports, both in the news and in the scientific literature, of incorrectly called "seat belt injuries" increases as well; this sometimes leads to a growing, but unjustified skepticism toward the seat belt—a skepticism that originated in 1962 with the publication of the paper "The Seat Belt Syndrome," by Garret and Braunstein.[19] On the one hand, the belt prevents ejection and a dangerous impact with the passenger compartment, but, on the other hand, an intensive contact of the body with the strap results. Injuries due to the contact with the belt prove that high decelerations on the body provided by the belt were effective. Without the restraining effect of a seat belt, there would have been, with a high degree of probability, more severe injuries. Jones,[20] concluded after an investigation of 572 injuries with seat belt wearers in frontal impacts, that 164 (29 percent, mainly chest injuries) were caused by the belt system; other injury-inducing structures were the steering assembly (86 of 420 driver injuries—20 percent) and the windscreen or instrument panel (108 out of 572 injuries—19 percent). Therefore, if doubts about the protecting effect of the seat belt arise, it has to be determined what structure had induced the injuries and what kind of injuries would have been caused without a belt. It has to be emphasized that no judgment is feasible without full medical and, especially, technical documentation of the particular case. A good statement on this issue is outlined in the paper "Seat Belt Injuries: The Need for Accuracy in Reporting the Cases."[21]

If no specific citation is noted in this section, the discussion herein is based on a study of 257 severely and 153 fatally injured seat belt wearers in Switzerland in 1976 by the authors and their colleagues.[22]

II. INJURIES CAUSED DIRECTLY OR INDIRECTLY BY BELT CONTACT

A. Neck Injuries

A.1. FRONTAL COLLISIONS   A direct laceration of the carotid artery occurred in our study only once. A driver's neck came into contact with a two-point sash belt during the course of an ejection such that the head was separated from the body. A similar case has been reported by Sladeen[23] and Bierwag.[24] Three other persons, in our sample of 410 victims, sustained a carotid artery laceration that was not caused by a direct belt contact, but rather by the stretching of the neck during the collision (11 o'clock, 2 o'clock, and 6 o'clock impact directions according to the VDI classification,* no head restraint). Excessive soft tissue lacerations in the neck area were observed in only 1 case and 13 minor bruises of the skin occurred. Even with children using sash belts, the soft tissue of the neck, generally, is not in danger[25] due to the fact that the upper part of the body rotates to some extent out of the oblique sash belt and thus the neck is moved clear of the belt.

A "whiplash motion"[26,27] of the head is defined here in a general sense as such a motion that is executed without any kinematic or dynamic constraint (injury caused indirectly—due to deceleration/inertia). This is not restricted to the classic

---

*The Vehicle Damage Index (VDI) codes the direction of an impact (e.g., 12 o'clock is a pure frontal collision; 3 o'clock, a right lateral collision) and the amount of impact deformation (1–9).

hyperextension–hyperflexion type of whiplash in rear impacts. In the presence of a head contact, external forces loading the head are affecting the neck[28] in addition to those forces originating from the retention by the shoulder strap. Head contact is more frequent with lap belts than with lap–shoulder belts.[29] A neck injury found under such circumstances cannot be differentiated with regard to its cause of occurrence. Of the 38 reported cervical spine injuries of AIS $\geq$ 2 (the Abbreviated Injury Scale[18]), 28 were associated with a head contact. Thus, neck injuries induced by a pure whiplash motion were identified only in 10 of 38 cases of AIS $\geq$ 2 and in only 4 of 22 injuries of the high severity AIS $\geq$ 4. Kallieris[30] found the C-4 to C-7 vertebrae to be fractured more often than the C-1 to C-3 with belted cadavers (59 sled tests with 30 to 50 km/h, no head contact possible). Other cervical spine injuries were described, among many other authors, by Arndt,[31] and Taylor.[32] Sköld,[29] Grattan,[33] Grime,[34] and Rattenbury[35] very rarely registered severe neck injuries without head impact. *This fact suggests that the majority of the cervical spine injuries would have occurred without restraint and at a higher degree of severity.*

Nordentoft[36] found a higher incidence of minor injuries to the cervical spine with belted occupants than with unbelted ones due to the whiplash mechanism in impacts without head contact; however, the severe injuries to the neck were considerably reduced by the belt. Burke[37] found similar results in Australia after the introduction of the mandatory seat belt law. The rebound in the second phase of the impact that causes a hyperextension of the neck (rearward bending) is of little energy. So, even if no head restraint is available, the neck of a belted occupant is not significantly endangered in a frontal impact due to the rearward bending. This can also be proved by the fact that, according to our study, belted occupants without head restraint in frontal collisions did not exhibit more severe neck injuries than those with head restraint.

A.2. LATERAL COLLISIONS   Some concern with regard to the possibility of unfavorable interactions between the belt and the neck in nearside lateral collisions has arisen because field accident studies, as well as corresponding dummy experiments, showed rather large excursions of the unrestrained upper body part through the side window in lateral nearside collisions. It could, therefore, be hypothesized that the neck of a belted occupant contacts the shoulder belt and thereby receives direct or indirect neck injuries. The impact of the shoulder mechanism could even be enhanced if the lap belt is not fastened tightly enough to hold the pelvis on the seat. However, statistical analysis of the 98 pertinent cases contained in the two large samples of Swiss[22,38] and French[8] field studies on accidents involving a total of 810 severely or fatally injured restrained occupants revealed that *with belted car occupants the incidence of "neck" injuries of any kind in nearside lateral collisions was not more frequent than in all other impact configurations and that the number of hazardous effects of three-point belts to the neck region is insignificant.*[39]

In the Walz 1981 study[39] there were 98 impacts of nearside sitting occupants with a VDI direction of 2, 3, 4, 8, 9, or 10 o'clock. In 7 percent ($N = 7$) of those nearside lateral collisions, neck injuries of AIS ≥ 2 were registered, whereby in only two cases it could not be excluded with sufficient probability that the reported neck injuries were induced by an immediate belt contact. The seven neck injuries mentioned ranged from lesions of AIS 2 (moderate skin laceration) to AIS 3 (cervical spine fracture, luxation), up to AIS 5 (cord lesion C-4/5). In five of the seven cases an additional head injury was registered. Under such circumstances, however, the neck injury cannot be attributed to any kind of sideways whiplash mechanism that would include the belt as a major injury-inducing source. The neck injuries, in those five cases exhibiting a concurrent head impact, therefore, need not be caused by a direct or an indirect mechanism involving any belt action; in contrast, these neck injuries occurred with a high degree of probability in spite, and not because, of the belt.

A.3. REAR IMPACTS It has been hypothesized that in a rear impact an attached occupant without head restraint could suffer from a more severe whiplash injury than a nonrestrained occupant because of the hyperflexion (forward bending) of the neck in the second phase of the impact. However, Langwieder[6] has shown that seat belt wearers do not exhibit a higher proportion of such lesions because the forward "rebound" is of little importance. In a further analysis, Langwieder[40] found that *seat belt wearers, in general, suffered only minor neck injuries after rear impacts.* These statements are supported by the results of our investigation.

B. Thoracic Injuries

Injuries to the thoracic region with AIS ≥ 2 were the second most frequent ones (46 percent of the victims with AIS ≥ 2 injuries, 30 percent of those with AIS ≥ 3 injuries, see Figure 6-1 on p. 102). Internal thoracic lacerations (aortic rupture in 14 cases, pulmonary lacerations in 42 cases, heart contusions in 11 cases, and heart ruptures in 12 cases) were usually combined with multiple rib fractures. Injuries to the internal thoracic organs of belt wearers, therefore, are not necessarily caused by deceleration effects; they also may be caused by a direct mechanical impact trauma. *Persons older than 50 years of age sustained significantly more often severe thoracic injuries* (p $\leq$ *0.05*) *due to their greater bone fragility.*

The investigation of 54 frontal crashes with no or minimal passenger compartment intrusions identified the following injury aggravating mechanisms (in some of the cases the causes occurred in combination):

occupants $\geq$ 50 years of age: 23
excessive belt slack ascertained: 19
overloading due to backseat passenger: 13
system failure (rupture, submarining):   10

Mechanical incompatibility between the restraint system and the thorax due to old age is seen to be a primary cause. The effect of belt slack was investigated for the whole sample of accidents and was thereby found to be statistically significant. The following figures show the Injury Severity Score (ISS)[18, 41]:

	average ISS
excessive belt slack ascertained:	29.6 ± 4.3
minimal slack (mostly retractable systems):	15.0 ± 1.1

In 23 percent of the whole sample of frontal collisions a backseat passenger was sitting behind the severely injured restrained occupant; in general traffic this is the case in only about 13 percent of the collisions.[3] This shows that in a sample of severely injured seat belt wearers backseat passengers projected against the latter are overrepresented due to the injury-aggravating effect of rear loading. Bohlin,[5] Rattenbury,[35] and Holt[42] consider this mechanism to be the most hazardous one for the belted occupant.

Based on a study on 103 sled tests with fresh human cadavers in frontal collisions, Schmidt[43] set the level of rib fracture tolerance for those 12 to 30 years of age at 50 km/h, for those 30 to 50 years of age at 40 km/h, and at 30 km/h for those over 50 years of age. These values have to be judged in view of the findings of Fayon,[44] who found a considerable scattering within the results of cadaver tests, and Foret-Bruno,[45] who registered in a comparative study of belted cadavers and real-world accidents with similar severity three to five rib fractures more with cadavers than with accident victims. The important influence of age on the occurrence of thoracic injuries is also documented by Thomas.[46] Other bio-mechanically relevant data come from Rattenbury[35]: at Equiv-alent Test Speeds (the same impact severity as a frontal crash against a rigid barrier with that speed) of 50 km/h, only 7 percent of the belted drivers exhibited severe injuries, 35 percent moderate, and 58 percent no or minor lesions. This shows that *even at high effective collision speeds severe injuries to belted occupants are rare.*

Fractures of the upper and middle thoracic spine (6 cases) were seen in rollover accidents, whereas the lower part of the thoracic spine and the lumbar spine were involved in frontal impacts (18 cases). In contrast to the lumbar spine injuries with lap belt users, where the lap belt riding up into the abdomen acts as a fulcrum at the anterior part of the lumbar spine,[42] in our sample of occupants using three-point or shoulder belts injuries consisted mainly of ventral compression frac-tures with anterior wedging.[38] Huelke,[47] Dehner,[48] Rogers,[49,50] and Smith[51] described the indirectly lap-belt-induced lesions as distraction fractures of L1–L4 with no evidence of either compression or anterior wedging. Huelke[52] found that occu-pants using lap belts compared to those who were not sus-tained significantly less severe injuries to the lower torso, except to the lumbar spine.

Patients with heart pacemakers sometimes report experi-encing pain and skin irritation from the friction of the belt during normal driving. Accident situations in which a belt had caused a failure of the pacemaker or the electrodes are not contained in our sample. Krueger[53] published similar findings in 1980; he recommended a padded protection shield to be mounted between the area of the pacemaker and the strap. Since obviously no hazardous interaction between the belt and the pacemaker is known, in countries with a manda-tory seat belt law no exemption certificates are granted (Switzerland, the Federal Republic of Germany, and Aus-tralia).

C. Abdominal Injuries

In 23 percent of the cases with AIS ≥ 2 injuries and in 22 percent of those with AIS ≥ 3 injuries, an abdominal injury was reported (liver in 45 cases, spleen in 34, kidney in 12, small bowel and colon in 20). With drivers it is usually difficult to decide whether an abdominal injury was caused by the lap belt or by the lower part of the steering wheel rim. Abdominal injuries have been described frequently in the literature, but most of the papers are case reports on one or just a few cases.[48, 54-60] *A very important cause of abdominal injuries for belt wearers is the so-called "submarining."*

Submarining may be ascertained in a frontal crash with a high degree of probability if:

- Bruises are detected over one or both pelvic crests caused by an "upward traveling" belt.
- Bowel lacerations are present and no possibility of a steering wheel contact existed.
- Severe knee, thigh, and pelvic injuries are identified, but no head injuries and no passenger compartment intrusion are found.

The application of these restrictive criteria to the 410 cases yielded the result that only in 13 cases was submarining highly probable (3 percent of all cases and 9 percent of the frontal impacts). *The percentage of submarining depends upon the proportion of cars with soft seat cushions.* Rattenbury[35] had no evidence of submarining in a study conducted in England, where cars very rarely are equipped with soft seats, while in France, where there are soft car seats, this phenomenon is seen more often.

III. ALL INJURIES TO SEAT BELT WEARERS

Figure 6-1 shows the location and frequency of all injuries in our sample (due to the belt or despite the belt). In both categories, AIS ≥ 2 and AIS ≥ 3, head injuries were prominent, occurring in 63 percent and 32 percent of all injuries, respectively. In crashes with a 12 o'clock impact direction, drivers sustained significantly more head injuries than did passengers, due to a steering wheel contact ($p \leq 0.001$). In underrun accidents, both facial bone fractures and severe brain contusions occurred more frequently than in the other collision types ($p \leq 0.001$). The *large percentage of head injuries among*

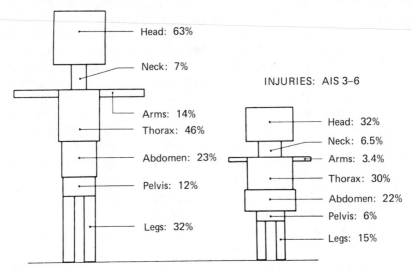

INJURIES: AIS 2–6

Head: 63%

Neck: 7%

INJURIES: AIS 3–6

Arms: 14%

Thorax: 46%

Head: 32%

Neck: 6.5%

Abdomen: 23%

Arms: 3.4%

Thorax: 30%

Pelvis: 12%

Abdomen: 22%

Pelvis: 6%

Legs: 32%

Legs: 15%

Figure 6-1 Location of injuries to 410 severely injured seat belt wearers in Switzerland.

all injuries for wearers of three-point belts has previously been reported in the literature.[7, 61-63] This does not contradict, however, those numerous reports that conclude that *three-point belts offer substantial head protection in the range of 50 to 75 percent.*[5, 6, 9, 63] Due to the highly exposed location and high sensitivity of the head even to moderate impacts, injuries to this body region are frequent and hazardous in any trauma circumstance. Table 6-1 summarizes the location and frequency of injuries to seat belt wearers from four different studies located in three different countries.

A. Pregnancy and Seat Belts

Some pregnant women feel uneasy wearing lap belts and are afraid of a seat-belt-induced injury to their unborn child. *However, specific accident investigations and experiments with pregnant baboons have proved that virtually in every possible accident circumstance the mother and the unborn child are better off with seat belts.*[64-68] Steenman[68] described seven cases of severe injuries to women pregnant in the twenty-second to the thirtieth week. Five had a uterine rupture, with one placentar avulsion occurring. In each case except one these lesions were followed by the immediate death of the fetus. In two additional cases the placentar avulsion was not accompanied by a severe injury of the mother [OAIS (Overall Abbreviated Injury Scale)* equal to 1]; nevertheless, the fetuses were killed. Our sample contains three cases of severely injured pregnant women (in the twenty-second to thirty-second week); twice the fetus survived without injury despite rib fractures and leg fracture of the mother in one case and multiple pelvic and thigh/leg fractures in the other. The third accident—an extremely violent right-frontal impact with massive compartment intrusion at a ΔV of 60 to 80 km/h—led to the death of both the mother and the fetus.

It has to be emphasized that correctly worn seat belts (across the pelvic girdle and not the abdominal wall) protect the mother effectively and do not increase the hazard to the unborn child. Furthermore, the chance of survival for the fetus is much better if the mother is not severely injured.

IV. ADVERSE EFFECTS OF SEAT BELTS

Most of the doubts mentioned about the protecting effect of seat belts are due to reports of single or just a few unrepresentative cases that were not carefully investigated with regard to their dynamic circumstances. Consequently, severe injuries of belt-attached car occupants reported by physicians were often taken for "severe injuries caused by seat belts." This fact can also be seen in connection with the fear of being trapped in a car after an accident due to releasing difficulties of the buckle or to being strangled by the strap. According to Berger[69] *a mandatory seat belt law is the most adequate measure to overcome these unjustified reservations concerning seat belts.*

Adopting a procedure proposed by Beier,[70] the accidents with severe or fatal injuries to seat belt wearers in our study were classified according to five effectiveness groups.[22,71,72] Classification was done independently by different members of the team, as well as by interdisciplinary assessment. However, the qualitative scaling leaves a margin of subjective judgment.

---

*OAIS, Overall AIS, is a measure of the clinical judgment of the effect of all single AIS-coded injuries (1–6). Since 1980, the MAIS, Maximum AIS, has been used; it is identical to the highest AIS code of a victim.

Table 6-1 Injuries to Seat Belt Wearers According to Four Different Injury Data Sets (1977) from Three Countries

INJURY LOCATION[a]	WALZ STUDY[b] 12 O'CLOCK DRIVER	OCCUPANT	LATERAL NEAR	FAR	ALL	DANNER STUDY[c] LATERAL NEAR	FAR	SWISS FEDERAL BUREAU OF STATISTICS[d]	CAMERON STUDY[e]
Eye lac	10	2			21	1	1		51
Face fx	37	7	6	4	95	10	9	51	94
Skull fx	12	4	4	2	49	} 9	} 5	} 104	34
Base fx	9	2	8	1	54				25
Brain									
contusion	21	7	6	4	85	} 54	} 38	} 689	45
concussion	34	11	7	5	128				72
Other head								517	8
Aotra lac	1	3	1		14				49
Lung lac	7	1	7	2	42				26
Heart lac	5	1	2	1	23				
Rib fx > 2	21	5	12	3	102	20	8	} 296	} 241
Rib fx = 2	10	11	8	4	47	30	10		
Sternum fx					31	1			
Intern. thorax trauma									
Abdominal trauma	9	8	3	2	47				
Kidney lac	3	3	3	2	26	13	4	} 271	20
Bowel lac	4	5	2		20				9
Spleen lac	5	2	5	2	34				34
Liver lac	11	2	4	2	45				30

Injury									Total
Lumb. spine	4	1			13				
Thor. spine	1	1			19	32	21	41	16
Cerv. spine	3	1	2		38	23	3	19	29
Carotid artery					4				
Hand fx	4	1	2	2					
Arm fx	8	5	12	2	69	41	22	177	96
Clavicle fx	7	3	5	2	29	23	3	78	
Leg fx	7	4							36
Knee	28	10	5	2	156	30	24	330	
Thigh fx	21	7	15	2	53				49
Pelvic fx	5	2				29	5	85	48
Occupants:									
OAIS ≥ 2	86	55	33	16	410	257	129	2603	?
OAIS ≥ 1									2276

[a] Abbreviations used: (lac) laceration, (fx) fracture.

[b] F. Walz, U. Zollinger, A. Renfer, R. Wegmann, M. Meier, B. Niederer, and H. Rudin, "Unfalluntersuchung Sicherheitsgurten, Einjahresstudie (1976) über schwere und tödliche Verletzungen bei angegurteten Autoinsassen" (Bern: EJPD, 1977); and F. Walz, "Verletzungen der Brust- und Lendenwirbelsäule bei Gurtenträgern." Unfallheilk. 129:278–284 (1977).

[c] Data from J. Danner, "Accident and Injury Characteristics in Side Collisions and Protection Criteria in Respect to Belted Occupants." Proceedings of the 21st Stapp Car Crash Conference (New Orleans, 1977), pp. 151–212.

[d] Data from Bundesamt für Statistik, Strassenverkehrsunfälle der Schweiz 1976. Heft 600. (Bern, 1977).

[e] Data from M. H. Cameron and P. G. Nelson, "Injury Patterns with and Without Seat Belts." Proceedings 6th IAAIM Conference (Melbourne, Australia, 1977), pp. 423–479.

Group I (185 cases):
The occupant under consideration sustained less severe injuries than would have to be expected with a high degree of probability in a similar crash without a restraint.

Group II (183 cases):
The occupant under consideration sustained, "in spite" of the restraint system, injuries of a severity comparable to that which would have to be expected with a high degree of probability in a similar crash without a restraint because of:

1. Excessive slack or other improper belt usage
2. System defects
3. Collision environment under which the restraint system cannot deploy its full efficiency (e.g., compartment destruction)
4. Rare or unknown causes

Group III (27 cases):
The occupant under consideration sustained, "because of the restraint system," injuries of a severity comparable to that which would have to be expected with a high degree of probability in a similar crash without a restraint.

Group IV (5 cases):
The occupant under consideration sustained, "because of the restraint system," more severe injuries than would have to be expected with a high degree of probability in a similar crash without a restraint.

Group V (10 cases):
Cases without sufficient documentation concerning this issue.

Since the study was restricted to severe and fatal injuries, the amount of cases in group I must be relatively small (185). As a rule, fatalities were not added to this first group. The large portion of group II cases among the fatal cases (135 of 153 fatal cases—88 percent) points out that the severity of the impacts in our sample was such that the passenger compartment was very often demolished; consequently, there was only a limited chance of survival.

The injuries in group III ("because of the restraint system")—direct lesions caused by the strap itself and indirect lesions due to the restraining effect—have to be differentiated. *If directly belt-induced abdominal injuries were seen, most often an unfavorable seat construction (soft cushion), badly placed anchor points, or other shortcomings concerning the belt geometry enhanced the tendency of submarining.*

The injury aggravating mechanisms of seat belts in the critical group IV were found to be:

- Burns due to *belt-releasing difficulty* (OAIS = 3, two occupants in the same accident).
- Decapitation caused by a *two-point shoulder belt* during an ejection in a rollover accident (one fatal case).
- Fatal thorax injuries resulting from the *rearward displacement of the B-pillar* in a side-swipe accident with a truck (one fatal case).
- Fatal internal bleeding with a driver under medication hindering the clotting of blood (anticoagulation) caused by a *belt-buckle-induced kidney injury* without external signs in a minor crash with a 3 o'clock impact direction (one fatal case).

In order to obtain an upper limit for the probability of the occurrence of adverse belt effects in general, a statistical confidence interval has to be established and the number of the identified cases has to be extrapolated to the estimated total number of severely injured persons in a given period. First, a rank test[73] reveals that the number of the adverse belt cases is not statistically dependent on the OAIS distribution. Under the assumption that cases exhibiting adverse belt effects are Poisson-distributed, a one-sided upper confidence limit of 2.6 percent is obtained at the 95 percent level. Among the estimated total number of 1700 injured belt wearers in 1976 with an OAIS $\geq$ 2, there are, therefore, with a probability of 95 percent *less than 44 cases in which seat belts had an adverse effect.* It is now meaningful to relate this figure to the total number of belt-wearing persons who sustained injuries of OAIS $\geq$ 1 ($N = 6700$). So, injuries of a higher severity because of the belt are less frequent than 0.65 percent at the 95 percent level in relation to the total number of accidents in which injuries occur at all (OAIS $\geq$ 1). The sample contained 17 percent diagonal belts; it can be expected that in a sample with only three-point belts this percentage would be even lower. Other studies of injured car occupants with smaller samples show a corresponding percentage of 1 percent,[74] less than 1 percent,[70] and 1.3 percent and 0.2 percent, depending on the sample taken as basis.[4] *Altogether, no serious accident analysis has proved, to date, that the three-point belt represents more than a negligible "hazard" to the wearer.*

V. HAS A SEAT BELT BEEN WORN OR NOT?

A. Medical Indications

In a particular case, *virtually any injury can be caused either by a belt contact or another structure in the car interior.* If an occupant is ejected—a situation not impossible with seat belt wearers[75,76]—the relation of an injury to the structure of traumatization is nearly impossible. Only the injury pattern with regard to the car damage gives good evidence. Even a perfect injury documentation is usually not sufficient, except where an evident contusion along the strap is visible; however, such erroneously called "typical belt contusions" are sometimes also seen with unbelted occupants—or even with pedestrians and motorcyclists.

It should be kept in mind that *only in about 50 percent of all car accidents a significant force is conveyed from the belt to the occupant,* namely, in frontal collisions. In all other impacts—side or rear end or rollovers—no considerable energy transfer takes place between the belt and the body. Thus, in the latter cases no contusion marks on the body and, of course, no marks on the belt webbing or the anchor points are to be expected. Moreover, *in very severe head-on collisions, the rapid compartment intrusion in front of the occupant does not permit any forward movement of the body.* As such, no loading of the belt occurs and, therefore, neither on the body nor on the belt system are any signs of force transfer to be seen.

Nevertheless, *there exist some accident–injury configurations where the injury pattern can give good indication that a three-point belt has been worn.* These statements hold only for cases with a high loading in the frontal direction and no major compartment destruction:

- Contusion marks, abrasions, or burn signs (friction between the belt and the skin during the stretching of the webbing) along the strap across the chest or the abdominal wall, especially abrasions on the lateral pelvic protuberances (spina iliaca anterior superior, iliac crest) caused by the upward traveling lap belt.

- Fractures of the ribs or the clavicle corresponding to the geometry of the strap (driver/passenger).
- Abdominal injuries (liver, spleen, bowel lacerations) mainly to the passenger (no steering wheel rim as injury-causing structure in this body area). The submarining usually prevents a head impact.
- Injuries to the distal part of the extremities that are projected forward while the rest of the body is restrained and protected.

If the external lesions listed above are absent, it cannot necessarily be concluded that no belt has been worn; *thick clothing can prevent external injuries* (but increase the severity of the corresponding internal lesions due to increased slack). The existence of head injuries in frontal collisions should not lead to the conclusion that no belts have been worn; *even if the shoulder belt is fastened tightly, a head contact with the steering wheel may occur in severe impacts. This mechanism is, of course, enhanced with greater belt slack.* Similar findings were reported by Gloyns,[77] Herbert,[78] Kaplan,[79] and Mackay.[7] If submarining of a belted occupant takes place, knee injuries are very likely to occur.

B. Technical Indications

Usually, evidence that the belt system was loaded during a frontal crash is more reliable than medical indications. These technical indications are as follows:

- Webbing partly or completely torn apart.
- Broken anchors or fittings.
- Webbing cut apart by rescuing team and corresponding testimonies.
- Abrasions on the webbing in the area of the fittings (D-ring, buckle) or vice versa (rough surface) or mutual material transfer (melted fibers, plastic fittings).
- Material transfer between webbing and clothing or webbing and contacted car interior, e.g., seat back, seat cushion, head restraint.

- Permanent deformation of the underlying seat structure due to the compression of the seat cushion during the submarining mechanism (submarining does not occur with unbelted occupants).

Most of these indications are seen mainly with automatic retractor belts; the so-called *film-reel effect* and the considerable *stretching* (temporarily up to 40 percent of the initial length) causes the webbing to slide under load through the fittings for about 10 cm (4 inches). It has to be emphasized, however, that the stretching only remains for hours or days and that the capability of energy dissipation of *the webbing is restored completely.* Martin[80] found that a belt that had undergone 10 dynamic dummy tests (50 km/h or 30 mph against a rigid barrier) did not show any alteration in the force-deformation characteristics. Due to the fact that the geometry of the fibers is restored soon after the loading, no changes can be seen by means of microscopic inspection of the webbing.

As to the abrasions on the webbing, it has to be pointed out that friction between the webbing and adjacent structures can take place either under high loading during a few milliseconds (accident) or under little loading over a long period of time (buckling up for every trip over the years). The latter circumstance causes very smooth and even friction areas; no signs of heat transfer is seen microscopically, i.e., no melted end points of the fibers.

If no such alterations are visible macroscopically, it can be assumed that a seat belt keeps its performance up to a limit of 10 years even in cases of increased exposure to sunlight.[81]

VI. SUMMARY

The effectiveness of seat belts in reducing number and severity of injuries to car occupants is well proven to date. However, it cannot be expected that in a very severe crash, especially with compartment intrusion, belts can prevent every injury. It is important to bear in mind that the existence of severe injuries with a seat belt wearer does not, necessarily, indicate a malfunction of the restraint system. Such injuries can occur either despite or due to the belt. In cases of lesions clearly attributable to a belt contact (e.g., fracture of the clavicle), it has to be determined whether or not the kind and severity of the injuries would have been different without seat belts. No statement is possible before all the lesions have been assigned to their origin. *Medical data alone, without full technical documentation, is insufficient as to a judgment of seat belt performance.*

Severe lesions of the cervical spine of belt wearers are usually caused by a head contact (as with unbelted occupants) and, therefore, are not due to the restraint system but to the fact that the (frontal) impact was either too violent or the impact point was located at an *unfavorable area of the car* (door, A- or B-pillar). "Whiplash" is a description of an injury mechanism and can result in any kind of injury severity. *Minor traumatization of the cervical spine is more frequent with belt users than with unbelted occupants. However, the severe injuries of the upper spine are reduced by the belt* due to the prevention of head impact in crashes not exceeding a certain energy level. *Soft tissue lesions of the neck (carotid artery, throat) caused by direct belt contact are extremely rare because, in most critical impacts, the neck is moved clear of the belt due to the slight rotation of the thorax out of the sash belt.*

In severe crashes, head and thorax injuries are frequent but, of course, are reduced by the belt. Most of the thoracic injuries to belt wearers are caused directly by the webbing, especially with passengers where no steering assembly can create a hazard to the thorax (or the head or the abdomen). In fact, thoracic lesions prove that high deceleration levels were acting during the crash and that without belts more severe injuries would have occurred with a high degree of probability. Belt slack, old age of the occupant, and overloading by non-attached backseat passengers increase the severity of thoracic injuries. Depending on the age of the accident victim, the tolerance limit of rib fractures is between 30 to 50 km/h Equivalent Test Speed (same impact severity as a frontal crash against a rigid barrier with that speed). Patients with heart pacemakers and pregnant women are not specifically endangered by belts. On the contrary, the latter and the unborn child are well protected if the lap belt is located across the strong pelvic girdle and not the abdomen.

Abdominal lesions rank third among belt wearers. These injuries could be avoided to a great deal if no submarining occurred. Submarining causes the lap belt to slide upward into the abdomen. *Excessive slack, poor lap belt geometry (flat angle of the belt to the horizontal plane), and a soft seat cushion increase the probability of submarining.*

Adverse effects of seat belts do exist. However, the number is much smaller than could be assumed from the numerous papers reporting single cases of alleged "seat-belt-induced injuries." The statistical risk of being injured more severely by the belt action than could be expected in a similar crash without a belt is well below 1 percent (in our study below 0.65 percent).

Medical data alone only very seldom give enough indication as to the question whether or not a seat belt has been worn; full technical documentation of the crash is needed.

CITATIONS

Note the following special abbreviations used in the citations:

AAAM:	American Association for Automotive Medicine, No. 40, 2nd Ave, Arlington Heights, IL 60005, U.S.A.
AMA:	American Medical Association
BASt:	Bundesanstalt für Strassenwesen, Cologne (FRG)
EJPD:	Swiss Federal Department of Justice
IAATM:	International Association of Accident and Traffic Medicine
IRCOBI:	International Research Committee on the Biokinetics of Impacts, 109, Ave Salvador Allende, 69500 Bron, France
SAE:	Society of Automotive Engineers, 400 Commonwealth Drive, Warrendale, PA 15096, U.S.A.
Stapp:	Colonel J. P. Stapp, M.D., Conference Proceedings by SAE

[1]L. S. Robertson, "Estimates of Motor Vehicle Seat Belt Effectiveness and Use: Implications for Occupant Crash Protection." *Am. J. Pub. Health*, 66(9):859–864 (1976).

[2]B. Friedel et al., *Sicherheitsgurte in Personenkraftwagen. Unfall und Sicherheitsforschung Strassenverkehr*. BASt, 1978.

[3]HUK-Verband, *Innere Sicherheit im Auto: Untersuchungen über 29'000 PKW-Unfälle mit Insassenverletzung*. Hamburg, 1975.

[4]G. Beier et al., "Risk and Effectiveness of Seat Belts in Munich Area Automobile Accidents." *Proceedings 25th Stapp Car Crash Conference*, San Francisco, 1981, pp. 765–790.

[5]N. Bohlin, "Fifteen Years with the Three Point Safety Belt." *Proceedings 6th IAATM Conference*, Melbourne, 1977, pp. 142–159.

[6]K. Langwieder, *Reduzierung von Verletzungen und Aenderung des Verletzungsbildes durch Anlegen der Sicherheitsgurte. Unfall- und Sicherheitsforschung Strassenverkehr 10*. BASt, 1977, pp. 105–119.

[7]G. M. Mackay, "Belted Occupants in Frontal Crashes." *Proceedings 6th IAATM Conference*, Melbourne, 1977, pp. 351–358.

[8]C. Thomas et al., "Comparative Study of 1624 Belted and 3242 Non-Belted Occupants: Results on the Effectiveness of Seat Belts." *Proceedings 24th AAAM Conference*, Rochester, N.Y., pp. 422–436.

[9]F. Walz, "Sitzgurten und Kopfstützen bei Autoinsassen." *Unfallheilk.*, 114:242–252 (1973).

[10]H. Appel et al., "Accident Analysis of Vehicle Side Collisions." *IRCOBI Proceedings*, Berlin, 1977, pp. 251–269.

[11]J. Danner, "Accident and Injury Characteristics in Side Collisions and Protection Criteria in Respect to Belted Occupants." *Proceedings 21st Stapp Car Crash Conference*, New Orleans, 1977, pp. 151–212.

[12]F. Hartemann et al., "Occupant Protection in Lateral Impacts." *Proceedings 20th Stapp Car Crash Conference*, Dearborn, MI., 1976, pp. 189–219.

[13]F. Hartemann et al., "Belted or Not Belted: The Only Difference Between Two Matched Samples of 200 Car Occupants." *Proceedings 21st Stapp Car Crash Conference*, New Orleans, 1977, pp. 95–150.

[14]I. S. Jones, "Benefits of Restraint Use with Particular Reference to Accidents Involving Compartment Intrusion." Buffalo, N.Y.: Calspan Corp., 1975.

[15]D. F. Huelke, T. E. Lawson, and J. C. Marsh, "Injuries, Restraints and Vehicle Factors in Rollover Crashes." *Accid. Anal. Prev.*, 9:93–107 (1977).

[16]C. Tarrière, "Efficacité des Ceinture '3 Points' en Accidents Réels." *Proceedings 4th ESV Conference*, Kyoto, 1973.

[17]D. F. Huelke et al., "Cervical Injuries Suffered in Automobile Crashes." *J. Neurosurg.*, 54(3):316–322 (1981).

[18]*The Abbreviated Injury Scale (AIS 80)*. Arlington Heights, IL.: American Association for Automotive Medicine, 1980.

[19]J. W. Garret and P. W. Braunstein, "The Seat Belt Syndrome." *J. Trauma*, 2:220–238 (1962).

[20]I. S. Jones, "Injury Severity Versus Crash Severity for Front Seat Car Occupants Involved in Front and Side Impacts." *Proceedings 26th AAAM Conference*, Ottawa, 1982.

[21]D. F. Huelke and R. G. Snyder, "Seat Belt Injuries: The Need for Accuracy in Reporting of Cases." *J. Trauma*, 15(1):20–23 (1975).

[22]F. Walz, U. Zollinger, A. Renfer, R. Wegmann, M. Meier, P. Niederer, and H. Rudin, *Unfalluntersuchung Sicherheitsgurten, Einjahresstudie (1976) über schwere und tödliche Verletzungen bei angegurteten Autoinsassen*. Bern: EJPD, 1977.

[23]T. Sladeen, "Fatal Neck Injuries by the Use of Diagonal Safety Belts." *J. Trauma*, 7(6):856–862 (1967).

[24]K. Bierwag, "Dekapitation durch unzweckmässigen Sicherheitsgurt." *Unfallheilk.*, 73:421–424 (1970).

[25]H. Norin and B. Andersson, "The Adult Belt—A Hazard to the

Child?" *Proceedings 6th IAATM Conference.* Melbourne, 1977, pp. 329–344.

[26]J. R. Gay and K. W. Abbott, "Common Whiplash Injuries of the Neck." *JAMA*, 152:1698–1704 (1953).

[27]J. D. States et al., "The Enigma of Whiplash Injuries." *N.Y. State J. Med.*, 70:2971–2978 (1970).

[28]P. Hinz, *Die Verletzung der Halswirbelsäle durch Schleuderung und durch Abknickung. Die Wirbelsäule in Forschung und Praxis 47*, Hippokrates. Stuttgart, 1970.

[29]G. Sköld and G. E. Voigt, "Spinal Injuries in Belt Wearing Car Occupants Killed by Head-on Collisions." *Injury*, 9(2):151–161 (1977).

[30]D. Kallieris, "Reactions of the Cervical Spine During Frontal Impacts of Belt Protected Cadavers." *IRCOBI Proceedings*, 1975, pp. 126–142.

[31]R. D. Arndt, "Cervical-thoracic Transverse Process Fracture: Further Observations on the Seat Belt Syndrome." *J. Trauma*, 15(7): 600–602 (1975).

[32]T. K. Taylor et al., "Seat Belt Fractures of the Cervical Spine." *J. Bone Joint Surg.*, 58-B(3):328 (1976).

[33]E. Grattan, N. G. Clegg, and J. G. Wall, "Intracranial or Neck Injuries in Belted Car Occupants." *IRCOBI Proceedings*, 1975, pp. 114–120.

[34]G. Grime, "Head and Neck Injuries to Car Occupants Wearing Safety Belts in Frontal Collisions." *IRCOBI Proceedings*, 1975, pp. 30–34.

[35]S. J. Rattenbury et al., "The Biomechanical Limits of Seat Belt Protection." *Proceedings 23rd AAAM Conference*, Louisville, KY., 1979, pp. 163–176.

[36]E. L. Nordentoft, H. V. Nielsen, E. Eriksen, and E. Weeth, "Effect of Mandatory Seat Belt Legislation in Denmark, with Special Regard to Minor and Moderate Injury." *Proceedings 6th IAATM Conference*, Melbourne, 1977, pp. 72–79.

[37]D. C. Burke, "Spinal Cord Injuries and Seat Belts." *Med. J. Aust.*, 2:801 (1973).

[38]F. Walz, "Verletzungen der Brust- und Lendenwirbelsäule bei Gurtenträgern." *Unfallheilk.*, 129:278–284 (1977).

[39]F. Walz, P. Niederer, C. Thomas, and F. Hartemann, "Frequency and Significance of Seat Belt Induced Neck Injuries in Lateral Collisions." *Proceedings 25th Stapp Car Crash Conference*, San Francisco, 1981, pp. 131–146.

[40]K. Langwieder, S. H. Backaitis, W. Fan, S. Partyka, and A. Ommaya, "Comparative Studies of Neck Injuries of Car Occupants in Frontal Collisions in the U.S. and in the Federal Republic of Germany." *Proceedings 25th Stapp Car Crash Conference*, San Francisco, 1981, pp. 71–129.

[41]S. P. Baker et al., "The Injury Severity Score. A Method of

Describing Patients with Multiple Injuries and Evaluating Emergency Care." *J. Trauma,* 14:187–196 (1974).

[42]B. W. Holt, "Spines and Seat Belts." *Med. J. Aust.,* 2:411–413 (1976).

[43]G. Schmidt et al., "Neck and Thorax Tolerance Levels of Belt Protection Occupants in Head-on Collisions." *Proceedings 19th Stapp Car Crash Conference,* San Diego, 1975, pp. 225–257.

[44]A. Fayon et al., "Thorax of Three Point Belt Wearers During a Crash (Experiments with Cadavers)." *Proceedings 19th Stapp Car Crash Conference,* San Diego, 1975, pp. 195–223.

[45]J. Y. Foret-Bruno, F. Hartemann, C. Thomas, A. Fayon, C. Tarrière, C. Got, and A. Patel, "Correlation Between Thoracic Lesions and Force Values Measured at the Shoulder of 92 Belted Occupants Involved in Real Accidents." *Proceedings 22nd Stapp Car Crash Conference,* Ann Arbor, MI., 1978, pp. 269–292.

[46]C. Thomas et al., "Influence of Age and Restraint Force Value on the Seriousness of Thoracic Injuries Sustained by Belted Occupants in Real Accidents." *IRCOBI Proceedings,* 1979, pp. 49–62.

[47]D. F. Huelke and H. Kaufer, "Vertebral Column Injuries and Seat Belts." *J. Trauma,* 17(4):304–318 (1977).

[48]J. R. Dehner, "Seat Belt Injuries of the Spine and Abdomen." *Am. J. Roentgenol.,* 4:833–843 (1971).

[49]L. F. Rogers, "The Roentgenographic Appearance of Transverse or Chance Fractures of the Spine: The Seat Belt Fracture." *Am. J. Roentgenol.,* 4:844–849 (1971).

[50]L. F. Rogers, "Injuries Peculiar to Traffic Accidents: Seat Belt Syndrome, Laryngeal Fracture, Hangman's Fracture." *Tex. Med.,* 70:77–83 (1974).

[51]W. S. Smith and H. Kaufer, "Patterns and Mechanisms of Lumbar Spine Injuries Associated with Lap Seat Belts." *J. Bone Joint Surg.,* 51-A:239–254 (1969).

[52]D. F. Huelke and T. E. Lawson, "Lower Torso Injuries an Automobile Seat Belts." SAE paper 760370. Warrendale, PA.: Society of Automotive Engineers, 1976.

[53]P. Krueger et al., "Pace Makers and Seat Belts—Risks, Necessities —Resolutions." *Proceedings 24th AAAM Conference,* Rochester, N.Y., 1980, pp. 410–414.

[54]K. Benz, "Isolierte Dünndarmverletzung infolge Sicherheitsgurt." *Unfallheilk.,* 10:604–607 (1981).

[55]R. Hartung and B. Egger, "Schwere isolierte Neierenruptur durch Sitzgurttrauma." *Unfallheilk.,* 79:117–119 (1976).

[56]E. J. Lubbers, "Injury of the Duodenum Caused by Fixed Three Point Seat Belt." *J. Trauma,* 17(12):960 (1977).

[57]R. Margreiter, "Ueber ein schweres Nierentrauma durch den Sicherheitsgurt." *Z. Chir.,* 16:998–1000 (1976).

[58]J. Stevenson, "Severe Thoracic, Intra-abdominal and Vertebral Injury Occurring in Combination in a Patient Wearing a Seat Belt." *Injury,* 5:321–323 (1976).

[59]I. D. Vellar, "Rupture of the Bowel due to Road Trauma: The Emergence of the Seat Belt Syndrome," *Med. J. Aust.*, 1:694–696 (1976).

[60]J. E. Wright, "Gallbladder Rupture, an Isolated Seat Belt Injury." *Med. J. Aust.*, 1:785–786 (1976).

[61]M. H. Cameron and P. G. Nelson, "Injury Patterns with and Without Seat Belts." *Proceedings 6th IAATM Conference*, Melbourne, 1977, pp. 423–479.

[62]M. S. Christian, "Non-Fatal Injuries Sustained by Seat Belt Wearers: A Comparative Study." *Br. Med. J.*, 2:1310 (1976).

[63]P. G. Petty, "The Influence of Seat Belt Wearing on the Incidence of Severe Head Injury." *Proceedings 6th IAATM Conference*, Melbourne, 1977, pp. 489–493.

[64]W. M. Crosby et al., "Impact Injuries in Pregnancy. Experimental Studies." *Am. J. Obstet. Gynecol.*, 101:100–110 (1968).

[65]W. M. Crosby and J. P. Costillos, "Safety of Lap Belt Restraint for Pregnant Victims of Automobile Collisions." *N. Engl. J. Med.*, 284:632 (1971).

[66]C. D. Matthews, "Incorrectly Used Seat Belt Associated with Uterine Rupture Following Vehicular Collision." *Am. J. Obstet. Gynecol.*, p. 1015 (1975).

[67]K. Schumann, "Sicherheitsgurt und Schwangerschaft." *Fortschr. Med.*, 94:27 (1976).

[68]G. Steenman, "Le port de la ceinture de sécurité par la femme enceinte." Dissertation, University of Bordeaux II, France, Medical Department, 1980.

[69]H. J. Berger and G. Bliersbach, *Psychologische Forschung zum Sicherheitsgurt und Umsetzung ihrer Ergebnisse. Unfall- und Sicherheitsforschung Strassenverkehr*. BASt, 1974.

[70]G. Beier et al., *Häufigkeit von Unfällen, bei denen der Sicherheitsgurt nicht zur Verminderung der Folgen beigetragen hat*. München: Inst. f. Rechtsmed, 1975.

[71]P. Niederer, F. Walz, and U. Zollinger, "Adverse Effects of Seat Belts and Causes of Belt Failures in Severe Car Accidents in Switzerland During 1976." *Proceedings 21st Stapp Car Crash Conference*, New Orleans, 1977, pp. 53–94.

[72]U. Zollinger, "Häufigkeit und Umstände nachteiliger Auswirkungen von Sicherheitsgurten." *der verkehrsunfall*, 4:67–76 (1978).

[73]E. L. Lehmann, *Nonparametrics: Statistical Methods Based on Ranks*. New York: McGraw-Hill, 1975.

[74]K. Luff and U. F. Lutz, *Zur Frage nachteiliger Wirkungen des Sicherheitsgurtes. Abt. II, Rechtsmed*. Frankfurt/M, 1975.

[75]B. A. Vazey and B. W. Holt, *In-Depth Analysis of Fatalities to Wearers of Seat Belts*. Report 2. New South Wales, Aust.: Department of Motor Transport, 1976.

[76]F. Walz, U. Zollinger, and P. Niederer, "Ejection and Safety Belts." *Accid. Anal. Prev.*, 11:19–22 (1979).

[77]P. F. Gloyns et al., "Steering Wheel Induced Head and Facial Injuries Amongst Drivers Restrained by Seat Belts." *IRCOBI Proceedings*, 1981, pp. 30–48.

[78]D. C. Herbert et al., "Head Space Requirements for Seat Belt Wearers." *Proceedings 19th Stapp Car Crash Conference*, San Diego, 1975, pp. 675–704.

[79]R. Kaplan and J. O'Day, "Fatal Injuries to Restrained Passenger Car Occupants." *Proceedings 22nd AAAM Conference*, Ann Arbor, MI., 1978, pp. 221–228.

[80]E. Martin, P. Balmer, and P. Remund, "Performance Tests on Used Safety Belts." *Accid. Anal. Prev.*, 12(3):205–215 (1980).

[81]D. C. Herbert, "The Service Life of Seat Belts." *Accid. Anal. Prev.*, 14(3):193–194 (1982).

7

Carbon Monoxide Poisoning, Toxic Products, and Fire Spread
(Motor Homes, Trailers, Construction Vehicles, and Passenger Vehicles)

ALEXANDER J. PATTON, Ph.D., P.E.
Consulting Engineer
Warwick, Rhode Island

Dr. Alexander J. Patton received graduate degrees in Mechanical Engineering from the University of Michigan and the University of Rhode Island. He has over 10 years of experience in investigating accidents involving personal injury due to carbon monoxide poisoning, toxic fire products, as well as the effects of rapid fire growth and spread. His work has included field investigations, laboratory testing, accident reconstruction, pretrial discovery, and expert testimony in a number of states. These cases have involved natural gas, LP gas, defective heating units, flammable liquids, flammable fabrics, building design, and flammable consumer products. He has worked on cases of national interest, including the Beverly Hills Nightclub fire and the Stouffer's Conference Center fire (White Plains, New York). Dr. Patton is the author of numerous technical articles and is an Adjunct Associate Professor at the University of Rhode Island. He is a member of a number of professional organizations, including the National Fire Protection Association, Society of Fire Protection Engineers (N.E.), the American Society of Safety Engineers, the American Society of Mechanical Engineers, and the National Society of Professional Engineers. He may be reached at 151 Lavan Street, Warwick, Rhode Island 02888 (401-781-8230).

I. INTRODUCTION

Carbon monoxide is a killer. Vehicle engines and other fuel-consuming devices that may be used in vehicles generate carbon monoxide. These simple, basic facts immediately put vehicle designers, manufacturers, distributors, dealers, and mechanics on notice that the product with which they work *requires an extreme level of care*—if care is not taken, death and/or serious injury may result. Carbon monoxide, a product of incomplete combustion, is a gas at normal atmospheric temperatures and pressures; as such, it is easily inhaled. The effects of this gas on beings was known by the ancient Greeks and Romans,[1] who used it for the execution of criminals. The use of the internal combustion engine was identified as a major contributor to carbon monoxide inhalation by the First International Congress of Labor.[2] Shortly thereafter, in 1921, in response to the concern with carbon monoxide exposure of the general public in New York City tunnels, Henderson and his colleagues[3] conducted a study of the physiological effects of automotive exhaust gas to provide a data base for the design of tunnel ventilation. It is interesting to note that this 1921 study recognized the variability in the effects of this gas on persons of different age, activity level, and state of health.

This section will examine carbon monoxide hazards associated with vehicles. Three major areas will be developed: (1) carbon monoxide generated directly from the vehicle engine, (2) carbon monoxide generated by heating, lighting, and cooking devices used within vehicles, and (3) carbon monoxide generated as a result of fire within the vehicle. The physical properties of the gas, the physiological reactions to the gas, as well as ambient levels that may be encountered will also be examined. The last portion of the section will outline other design areas related to the fire safety of vehicles.

II. SOURCES OF CARBON MONOXIDE

Carbon monoxide (CO) is generated within nature by the oxidation of methane within the atmosphere, by forest fires, and by the oceans. It has been estimated that in the Northern Hemisphere, man's production of CO approximates the production by natural sources. On a global scale man contributes only about 10 percent of the total worldwide production. Within the United States, estimates published for 1975 give a value of 85×10^6 metric tons of CO produced by technological sources, with the combustion of fossil fuel in vehicles contributing 67×10^6 metric tons. Although these figures are large, for the most part the carbon monoxide is diluted with ambient air to levels that are harmless. Eventually, within several months after its discharge into the atmosphere, the CO is assimilated by natural conversion processes—by its absorption in the soil and oceans and its take-up by plants—with the resultant by-product carbon dioxide (CO_2). It is estimated that the average concentration of CO in the atmosphere is about 0.1 parts per million (ppm).[2]

Specifically, concerning carbon monoxide as it relates to vehicles, the ever present exhaust gases do discharge CO into the atmosphere and in certain instances into the passenger area. Mayron[4] reported levels of CO for a number of automobile makes (1963 to 1975 models). Exhaust values ranged from a low of 2000 ppm to a high of 75,000 ppm (0.2 to 7.5 percent). It was also reported that within the passenger compartments of these vehicles CO concentrations ranged from 1.5 ppm to over 100 ppm (see Subsection IV, Physiological Effects). Current federal regulations (CFR-40, Part 86) set emission limits of 15 grams of carbon monoxide per vehicle mile for light-duty vehicles, 40 grams per passenger mile for gasoline-fueled heavy-duty vehicles, and 40 grams per brake horsepower mile for diesel heavy-duty engines. Individual states also maintain specific emission levels for their vehicle safety inspection programs, which are usually on a decreasing scale relative to the year of manufacture. Table 7-1 gives an example of such state requirements.

It must be recognized that, in addition to the vehicle engine, other sources of carbon monoxide may be present. Any device that involves the combustion of a fossil fuel should be looked upon as a potential generator of carbon monoxide. An increasing sector of the population are enthusiasts of camping and/or using recreational vehicles. Camping lanterns, portable stoves, built-in ranges and heating units, gas-fired refrigerators, as well as auxiliary generators for the production of electricity, can generate lethal levels of carbon monoxide if the combustion products of these devices accumulate in the living or passenger area. An important concept relative to these devices is that of proper venting. In the same way that the automotive exhaust system is designed to vent the products of combustion to the outside, away from the vehicle, the appliance units listed above for use within vehicles are designed to be of the *direct-vent* type. Heating units and refrigerators of

Table 7-1 Rhode Island Vehicle Emission Standards

YEAR OF MANUFACTURE OF VEHICLE	CARBON MONOXIDE EMISSION LEVEL (% CO)
1967 or earlier	10
1968–1969	8
1970–1974	6
1975–after	3

this type utilize air from outside the vehicle for combustion and vent the resultant products of this combustion back outside. No air within the vehicle is used for the combustion process, and the combustion chamber is sealed from the inside air.

On the other hand, *gas-fired cooking ranges are not vented, and, as such, the products of combustion are discharged directly into the vehicle.* Ordinarily, the stoves are used only for a short time, and there is enough ambient air infiltration within the vehicle to keep the CO level below that which is harmful. *Other portable units, such as lanterns and catalytic heaters, should never be used within vehicles.* Unfortunately, when they are, the CO generated is also directly discharged into the interior of the vehicle and can rapidly reach lethal concentrations.

Finally, it is widely acknowledged that smoking is a source of CO. Wallace and Rutledge[5] report one case of an inhaling cigar smoker with chronic carbon monoxide intoxication. In contrast to the often lethal carbon monoxide levels produced by the previously mentioned sources, smoking produces CO levels that are generally regarded as a health hazard in that they can cause long-term respiratory problems and coronary heart disease.

Thus, there are numerous sources of carbon monoxide present in and around vehicles. In the pursuit of any litigation, *each and every source must be identified,* and ultimately, with proper investigative techniques, the most probable source or sources will be determined.

III. CHEMICAL AND PHYSICAL PROPERTIES OF CARBON MONOXIDE

Carbon monoxide is a product of *incomplete combustion.* In the *complete* combustion of methane (CH_4—natural gas), the exhaust gases (products of combustion) carbon dioxide, water vapor, and nitrogen are given off:

$$CH_4 + 2O_2 + 7.5N_2 \xrightarrow{\text{combustion}} CO_2 + 2H_2O + 7.5N_2$$

$$(air: 21\% \ O_2 + 79\% \ N_2)$$

If, however, this combustion process is inefficient and incomplete, the resultant products will also include carbon monoxide (CO) and unburned hydrogen (H_2), with the relative quantities of these products depending on the degree to which the combustion process is efficient.

The resulting gaseous carbon monoxide will rapidly cool when discharged. It has approximately the *same density as air* and *will readily mix with the air*. The gas is *colorless*, and *cannot be seen*. It has *no odor*, but occasionally a potentially hazardous situation is prevented by persons detecting other odorous products of combustion. Unfortunately, *many CO poisonings occur when people are sleeping or about to go to sleep, and it is well documented that the olfactory sense is readily fatigued and ineffective when one is sleeping.* Table 7-2 summarizes the physical properties of carbon monoxide.

IV. PHYSIOLOGICAL EFFECTS

The effects of carbon monoxide on humans must be viewed not only in terms of exposure to a level of carbon monoxide, but also in terms of the length of time of exposure. Generally, the level of carbon monoxide is expressed in parts per million (ppm). This is a volume measure—i.e., 1000 ppm is a concentration of 0.1 percent CO by volume in air. Inhaled carbon monoxide is reflected in physiological changes measured by the amount of CO taken up by the blood. Under normal conditions, the oxygen inhaled combines with a substance in the blood known as hemoglobin, forming oxyhemoglobin, which is then circulated throughout the body. Oxidation of carbon substances within the body forms carbon dioxide, which subsequently is exhaled. *Hemoglobin, however, has an affinity for carbon monoxide that is more than 200 times greater than its affinity for oxygen.* It is this property of hemoglobin that contributes to the great toxicity of carbon monoxide—given a choice of oxygen or carbon monoxide, the blood's hemoglobin will take the CO. The resulting combination of CO and hemoglobin is known as carboxyhemoglobin (COHb).

Table 7-2 Physical Properties of Carbon Monoxide[a]

Molecular weight:	28.01
Melting point:	$-199°C$
Boiling point:	$-191.5°C$
Density:	1.145 g/l (at 25°C, 1 atm)
Explosive limits:	12.5–74.2%
Solubility in water:	2.32 ml/100 ml (at 20°C)

[a]Data from R. Weast (ed.), *Handbook of Chemistry and Physics*, 56th ed. (Boca Raton, Fl.: CRC Press, 1975).

It is the level of carboxyhemoglobin that is usually determined by the pathologist when there is a possibility of death caused by CO. Figure 7-1 shows the data recorded by Henderson[3] for the long-term exposure to various levels of carbon monoxide. Figure 7-2 illustrates the relationship between level of carbon monoxide being inhaled, time of inhalation, and percent of carboxyhemoglobin in the blood.

Kahn and his colleagues[6] conducted an extensive study of COHb levels for the St. Louis region with regard to smoking habits, occupation, effect of travel, urban–rural differences, sex and age differences, and racial and socioeconomic class differences. The typical ambient levels found in urbanized areas were approximately 4 ppm, with resulting COHb levels between 4 and 5 percent for smokers and approximately 1 percent for the population of nonsmokers. It was also reported that COHb level increases slightly with travel in motor vehicles, but that this increase was small when compared to the levels produced by industrial exposure and smoking (the author of this paper assumes that there were no defective conditions in these vehicles relative to carbon monoxide as described in later portions of this section). Godin[7] gave estimates of the average carbon monoxide exposure for a typical city dweller that ranged from 2 ppm to as high as 160 ppm for brief periods. Levels of blood COHb have been reported as high as 18 percent for inhaling cigar smokers.

It is obvious that it is possible to have an entire spectrum of exposure to carbon monoxide ranging from long-term, low-level exposure to very short-term, high-concentration exposure. Malorny[8] indicates that after an 80-ppm exposure for 1 hour the first apparent disturbances of physiological functions and reactions become apparent. Generally when the level of COHb reaches 15 percent (the equilibrium level at approximately 100 ppm CO in air), headache and some breathing difficulty may occur. As the COHb level increases, fatigue,

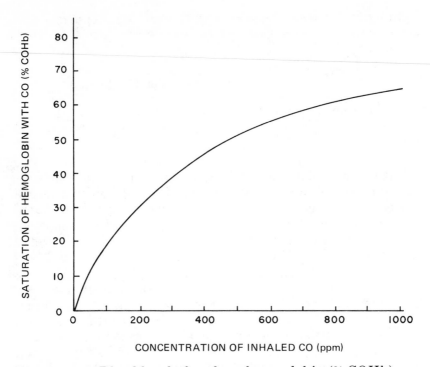

Figure 7-1 Blood level of carboxyhemoglobin (% COHb) as a function of concentration of inhaled carbon monoxide (ppm). (From Y. Henderson et al., "Physiological Effects of Automobile Exhaust Gas and Standards of Ventilation for Brief Exposure." *Journal of Industrial Hygiene*, Vol. 3, No. 3, July 1921.)

nausea, weakness, and decreased response ability become evident. At levels of COHb over 50 percent, coma and death may result. Again, it is important to point out that these responses are measured by COHb levels that must be correlated with actual CO time of exposure information. Table 7-3 summarizes the symptoms of carbon monoxide poisoning at various levels of carboxyhemoglobin.

V. CARBON MONOXIDE AND VEHICLES

As previously mentioned, vehicle exhausts, both gasoline and diesel, are capable of producing a lethal concentration of carbon monoxide. This is evidenced by the well-known suicide technique of using a flexible hose to duct the exhaust gases directly into the passenger compartment. In the evaluation of the vehicle relative to litigation, there are a number of areas to be examined.

The design of the exhaust system must be tight to insure that all exhaust gases are vented out the end of the pipe and away from the vehicle. The connections must be tight, and remain tight, during expected vehicle use. The system must not become worn or damaged by contact with other vehicle parts. The vehicle owner must be supplied maintenance and inspection information relative to the exhaust system—i.e., the designer must determine the time interval for such inspection and replacement. A review of new car owner's manuals reveals that *inspection of the exhaust system is recommended at each oil*

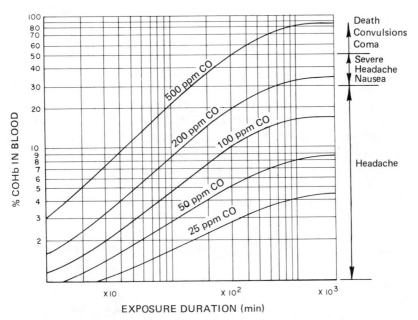

Figure 7-2 Blood level of carboxyhemoglobin (% COHb) as a function of both concentration of inhaled carbon monoxide (ppm) and exposure time (minutes). Note the predicted range of physiological effects. (From J. E. Peterson et al., "Absorption and Elimination of Carbon Monoxide by Inactive Young Men." *Archives of Environmental Health*, Vol. 21, August 1970, p. 168. Reprinted with permission of the American Medical Association, Copyright 1970, American Medical Association.)

Table 7-3 Signs and Symptoms at Various Concentrations of Carboxyhemoglobin[a]

% COHb	SIGNS AND SYMPTOMS
0-10	No signs or symptoms
10-20	Tightness across forehead, possible slight headache dilation of the cutaneous blood vessels
20-30	Headache and throbbing in the temples
30-40	Severe headache, weakness, dizziness, dimness of vision, nausea, vomiting, and collapse
40-50	Same as above, greater possibility of collapse, syncope, and increased pulse and respiratory rates
50-60	Syncope, increased respiratory and pulse rates, coma, intermittent convulsions, and Cheyne-Stokes respiration
60-70	Coma, intermittent convulsions, depressed heart action and respiratory rate, and possible death
70-80	Weak pulse, slow respiration leading to death within hours
80-90	Death in less than an hour
90+	Death in a few minutes

[a]From J. H. Schulte, "Effects of Mild Carbon Monoxide Intoxication." *Archives of Environmental Health*, Vol. 7, 1963, p. 524. (Reprinted with permission of the American Medical Association, Copyright 1963, American Medical Association.)

change, whenever a change in the sound of the exhaust system is noticed, and if the exhaust system or body is damaged or corrosion is noticed. One example of somewhat conflicting and confusing consumer instructions found within a recent owner's manual was a warning to the driver to *open* all windows if it is thought that the exhaust gases are entering the vehicle but to *close* all windows if driving with the trunk open. It would seem that interesting questions might develop if the driver were overcome by CO while driving with the trunk open and all windows closed. The mechanic who performs any work on the vehicle has an obligation to report needed exhaust system repairs to the owner. Proper exhaust system inspection is important; if it is neglected, potential lethal conditions may go unnoticed. The degree of care and warning must be on that level.

Particular care must be taken with recreational vehicles that may be used in rough, off-the-road terrain. The design and consumer warnings given must be such to prevent the buildup of carbon monoxide beneath the vehicle—for instance, when the vehicle is parked in high grass or bush areas.

Even with an exhaust system that is tight, *the design of the vehicle must incorporate a careful consideration of the movement of the exhaust gases after discharge from the tail pipe.* The often cited older model station wagon tailgate window that "sucked" exhaust fumes into the vehicle is one example. The designer must carefully evaluate the aerodynamic fluid mechanic properties of this vehicle relative to potential exhaust gas movement into the passenger area for various speeds and such vehicle conditions as the number of windows open/closed, heating–air conditioning on/off, etc.

We have discussed the exhaust system as the *source* for carbon monoxide. Once emitted, whether through a rusted tail-pipe hole, loose connection, or out the end of the pipe, the gas must find its way into the passenger compartment to do harm. Safe design requires that *penetrations through the so-called "firewall" be gas tight* to prevent exhaust gases from the engine area from entering the passenger compartment. These penetration seals are installed at the factory and should last for the *life* of the vehicle. Similarly, all penetrations and holes on the bottom of the body and in the trunk area must also be sealed. Inspection personnel have a responsibility to report such holes, *including body rust areas.* Holes through recreational vehicles for plumbing and other utilities have provided easy paths for CO entry from below the vehicle, and appropriate care must be exercised when sealing these openings. The importance of such holes through the firewall and body was illustrated in an Alaska case that involved a new station wagon. The owner was overcome by carbon monoxide fumes and suffered brain damage. It was found that *plugs normally installed in holes in the body were missing,* allowing the entry of exhaust gases into the vehicle; the manufacturer consequently was held liable.[9]

We previously noted that the use of lanterns, portable stoves, and heating units inside recreational vehicles has caused CO deaths. As it is foreseeable that such devices might be used within these vehicles, it therefore is the duty of the manufacturers of both the vehicle and the fuel-consuming device to warn the owner of the hazards associated with this situation.

Charcoal briquets produce high levels of CO when burned and are also expected to be used by owners of recreational-camper-type and off-the-road-type vehicles. Keep in mind that the interior volume of these vehicles is small: for every 100 cubic feet of volume only 0.05 cubic feet of carbon monoxide is required to reach the 500 ppm fatal level. The manufacturers of these vehicles have an obligation to warn the consumer of the hazards associated with using these articles within the vehicle.

In summary, the following items must be determined after any vehicle-related carbon monoxide accident:

1. *Identify all sources* of CO—the exhaust system and other sources, such as stoves, lanterns, heating units, etc.
2. Identify the *most probable source*—testing with conditions as close to those existing at the time of the accident will usually reveal the source involved.
3. Determine the *flow path* of CO from the source to the interior of the vehicle.
4. Obtain the *level of carboxyhemoglobin* in the blood of the victim from the hospital records or pathologist's autopsy report. Relate this level of COHb with the CO concentration and duration of exposure.
5. *Evaluate the warnings and instructions* given or not given to the consumer relative to the hazards of CO. If appropriate, obtain the *inspection, repair, and maintenance history* of the vehicle and of the device and related systems that were the source of CO.

VI. CARBON MONOXIDE AND OTHER TOXIC PRODUCTS FROM VEHICLE FIRE—PLASTICS

It has often been stated that we live in a plastic world, and the construction of vehicles is no exception. The passenger compartments of current vehicles are filled with polypropylene, polyvinyl chloride, polyurethane, polyester, and other flammable polymers. Additionally, an increasing amount of plastics is being used within the engine compartment. Here we will take a brief look at the properties of these plastics, including flammability and toxic products produced, as well as some available flame retardants. A 1979 study[10] estimated that there are approximately 500 fatalities per year attributed to passenger car fires, as well as $135 million in property loss.

There are basically eight elements that form today's plastics, as listed below:

- Hydrogen (H)
- Carbon (C)
- Nitrogen (N)

- Oxygen (O)
- Fluorine (F)
- Silicon (Si)
- Sulfur (S)
- Chlorine (Cl)

It has been estimated that approximately 200 pounds of plastic is used per passenger vehicle, with the major types being urethane (40 pounds), polypropylene (35 pounds), polyester (35 pounds), and polyvinyl chloride (20 pounds), and with lesser amounts of ABS (acrylonitrile, butadiene, and styrene), acrylics, nylon, polyethylene, phenolic, and acetal. Typical polymer units are illustrated below:

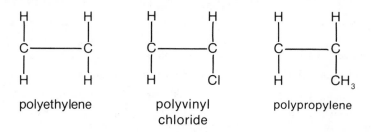

When the polymers undergo pyrolysis (chemical decomposition by heat) and then actual flaming, a number of different toxic products of combustion are produced (the relative amounts and numbers of these products being dependent on the chemical composition of the plastic). Table 7–4 lists the most widely recognized toxic products of combustion and their effects. The values given in Table 7–4 are reference values; higher concentrations could exist in any given fire, producing injury and death after shorter exposures.

VII. FIRE SPREAD AND HEAT RELEASE IN VEHICLE FIRES

In addition to the toxic and lethal products of combustion, the rate of flame spread and heat released during a vehicle fire must certainly be considered relative to fire hazards. Currently, the only federal regulation that governs the rate of flame spread for materials used in occupant compartments of motor vehicles is CFR Title 49, Standard Number 302, "Flam-

Table 7-4 Toxic Products of the Combustion of Plastic and Their Effects[a]

PRODUCT OF COMBUSTION	EXPOSURE EFFECT
Carbon monoxide (CO)	10,000 ppm exposure fatal within 1 minute
Carbon dioxide (CO_2)	70% concentration fatal within several minutes
Hydrogen cyanide (HCN)	450 ppm causes death in 9 to 13 minutes (animal test results)
Hydrogen sulfide (H_2S)	400–700 ppm dangerous in 30 minutes
Sulfur Dioxide (SO_2)	500 ppm exposure fatal in 10 minutes
Ammonia (NH_3)	1000 ppm exposure fatal in 10 minutes
Hydrogen chloride (HCl)	1500 ppm exposure fatal within several minutes
Phosgene ($COCl_2$)	25 ppm fatal within 30 minutes
Acrolein (CH_2CHCHO)	30–100 ppm fatal within 10 minutes
Oxides of nitrogen (NO_x)	200 ppm fatal within 10 minutes

[a]Data compiled from *Fire Protection Handbook*, 15th ed. Boston: National Fire Protection Association, 1981; *Fire Research on Cellular Plastics: The Final Report of the Products Research Committee*, 1980; and P. W. Smith et al., "Effects of Exposure to Carbon Monoxide and Hydrogen Cyanide." Physiological and Toxicological Aspects of Combustion Products: International Symposium. Washington, D.C.: National Academy of Sciences, 1976.

mability of Interior Materials—Passenger Cars, Multipurpose Passenger Vehicles, Trucks and Buses." The test employed is a laboratory-type "bench test" using material specimens, 4 inches wide by 14 inches long, supported horizontally in a metal frame. The sample is ignited at one edge, and the rate of flame travel is then measured. It must not exceed 4 inches per minute.

However, it is widely recognized that *such small-scale tests do not represent the burning characteristics of materials involved in actual fire situations,* as described by Patton[11] for fabric used in clothing. The horizontal position of the test sample allows the hot products of combustion to flow upward, away from the fabric, whereas if tested in a vertical position, these hot products would rise up in contact with the remaining sample piece, preheating the sample and thus helping to raise its temperature. The vertical configuration will produce an accelerating-type flame, more closely related to actual fires than the constant burn rate of the horizontal sample. It must be noted that before this standard became effective, the Center for Auto Safety, the Textile Fibers and By-Products Association, and the National Cotton Batting Institute suggested a zero burn rate, or self-extinguishment requirement, for passing the test with the sample in a vertical direction. At the same time some automobile manufacturers suggested that burn rates as high as 15 inches per minute be acceptable.[12]

The standard *does not recognize the need to evaluate the heat release of the materials,* which can be more than double the heat release of natural fibers such as cotton. The standard *does not evaluate the burning characteristics relative to the actual masses present in the vehicle,* but only evaluates test samples of a maximum ½ inch thickness. The test does not address the well-known *melt–drip hazards* of synthetics, nor does it evaluate the *intensity of the flame* (volume of flame and temperature). Additionally, the design of each material in its final configuration (seat cover, door panel covering, etc.) is not examined relative to fire safety. No measurement or criterion for toxic–lethal products of combustion is required.

A review of the available literature on fire research related to vehicles seems to indicate that automotive manufacturers are not supporting such efforts to the extent that the aircraft and building industries are and, as such, can expect continued and increased litigation in this regard. For the most part, vehicles are small enough so that there is no reason why full-scale fire testing of the vehicle cannot be conducted to evaluate properly the fire safety aspects of the vehicle.

VIII. OTHER DESIGN FEATURES RELATIVE TO FIRE SAFETY

A fire-related accident and resulting burn injury points out other areas of design defect relating to the fire safety of automobiles. A late-model passenger vehicle slid off the road and came to rest against a tree with the driver trapped within the vehicle. Shortly thereafter, a passerby stopped to investigate. He noticed a small fire beneath the hood, which had popped up slightly. Within a matter of minutes, the fire became intense, spreading rapidly through the firewall, igniting the wiring and interior materials of the passenger compartment. The flames coming from within the engine compartment caused the windshield to break and set the interior roofing material on fire. This plastic roofing material burned rapidly, with flaming pieces melting and dripping down on the upholstery and driver. During the early stages of the fire the electrical system shorted out, causing the engine to turn over, resulting in the activation of the fuel pump. By the time the fire department arrived, the interior of the vehicle was an inferno. The driver, who remained conscious throughout the ordeal, did survive, but he suffered severe burn injuries.

Examination of the vehicle later revealed a number of defects that contributed to the rapid spread of the fire and its intensity. This is of particular significance in light of the fact that it is foreseeable that passenger vehicles will have such an accident, causing a fire to start within the engine compartment.

The fuel delivery system was found, for the most part, to have flexible, synthetic hoses, which were consumed by the fire. The hazards of gasoline, even in small quantities is well known, and leakage of this fuel in a fire situation must be prevented. Current Federal Motor Vehicle Safety Standard No. 301, Fuel System Integrity basically addresses the ability of the fuel system to maintain its integrity in crash and rollover situations, but it does *not* address the failure of the system when exposed to fire. The orientation of the vehicle was such that the engine compartment was lower than the rear of the vehicle where the gasoline tank was located. Once fire burned through the flexible fuel line, gasoline flowed by gravity to feed the fire. The intensity and spread of this fire would have been significantly reduced by a fuel system entirely constructed from fireproof components, as presently required for aircraft. There are flexible metallic fuel lines available, and they are designed to be fireproof as well as to give good performance relative to vibration problems. Recommendations for such fire-safe fuel systems, as well as improved electrical systems, were made in 1971 in a comprehensive report sponsored by the National Highway Traffic Administration.[13]

The chronological sequence of events in the accident described were such that the fire developed rapidly after the ignition system shorted out and the engine turned over. When this occurred, the fuel pump was activated, supplying the fire with additional gasoline. *The ignition system should not be designed to allow fuel pump activation during a fire,* particularly with an engine that has flexible gas lines that can be consumed by fire. Another aspect of having the engine turn over during the fire is the rotation of the radiator fan, which will supply additional air to the fire.

The rapid spread of the fire through the firewall into the passenger compartment was due to *multiple, inadequately sealed penetrations through the firewall.* The grommets and seals in the 13 or so penetrations were consumed by the fire; a cluster of these penetrations were located directly in front of the driver. Proper fire-safe design requires that the number of penetrations be kept to a minimum, that they be sealed, and that they remain sealed during a fire. Such sealants are commercially available and are used in aircraft, which require firewalls that are fireproof and impermeable to air, fluid, and flame.

Additionally, in this accident the flames leaving the hood area impinged on the windshield, causing its failure. These flames should, and could, have been confined to beneath the hood with a proper fire-safe design of the hood-to-body seam.

The interior plastic materials that ignited and burned rapidly should have been flame-retardant-treated. Such materials are commercially available, as evidenced by typical aircraft requirements for self-extinguishing material in compartment interiors and as outlined by Miller[14] and Hoke.[15]

The wiring insulation behind the dashboard that burned, melted, and dripped contributed to the driver's injuries and gave off toxic products of combustion. *This wiring insulation should have been the commercially available self-extinguishing type.* A simple fireproof guard across the bottom of the dashboard would have prevented the burning–melting pieces from falling onto the trapped driver.

Considerable research has been conducted for fixed, *automatically activated fire extinguishing systems* by the U.S. Coast Guard and the Federal Aviation Administration. Several government studies have recognized that fire is often the result of an impact and involves the entire vehicle before passengers can escape. These studies have recommended that automatic/manual extinguishing systems be provided for engine compartments. Such a system would have prevented the described tragedy.

Severy[16] stated in 1974 that "measures for reduction in collision-induced fires and associated burn injuries has not kept pace with collision safety innovations serving to reduce impact trauma." Unfortunately, as this paper has demonstrated, the situation has not changed since then. Of some 60 or more Motor Vehicle Safety Standards in effect today, only 2—MVSS 301 and 302—directly address fire hazards, and they do so in a minimal, inadequate manner. Manufacturers will realize through continued litigation that a great amount of design improvement is necessary to increase the fire safety level of vehicles, and, as such, conformance to these minimal safety standards is not an appropriate defense for the injury and suffering now being experienced.

IX. SUMMARY

The current design of vehicles can expose the consumer to a number of death- and injury-producing hazards, including carbon monoxide, other toxic products of combustion, and fire.

In regard to carbon monoxide, the probable source, either from the engine or other fuel-burning device, must be determined as well as the path of entry into the vehicle. Evaluation of design features, operator instructions and warnings, maintenance, and use of the vehicle at the time is required to properly evaluate liability.

The widespread use of plastics in current vehicle design requires evaluation of the flammability characteristics of these materials, including the levels of toxic products produced. For the most part, current vehicle designs are not fire safe in relation to preventing postimpact burn injury. Improvement is needed in the fuel delivery system, ignition system, firewall design, wiring, and flammability of materials, particularly those used within the passenger compartment.

CITATIONS

[1]J. N. Norman and I. M. Ledingham, "Carbon Monoxide Poisoning: Investigation and Treatment," in H. Bour and I. M. Ledingham (eds.), *Carbon Monoxide Poisoning*. Amsterdam: Elsevier Publishing Company, 1967.

[2]*Carbon Monoxide*. Washington, D.C.: National Academy of Sciences, 1977.

[3]Y. Henderson et al., "Physiological Effects of Automobile Exhaust Gas and Standards of Ventilation for Brief Exposures." *Journal of Industrial Hygiene*, Vol. 3, No. 3, July 1921.

[4]L. W. Mayron and J. J. Winterhalter, "Carbon Monoxide: A Danger to the Driver?" *Journal of the Air Pollution Control Association,* Vol. 26, No. 11, November 1976.

[5]N. Wallace and R. Rutledge, "Smoking and Carboxylemoglobin." *Archives of Environmental Health,* Vol. 29, September 1974.

[6]A. Kahn et al., "Carboxyhemoglobin Source in the Metropolitan St. Louis Population." *Archives of Environmental Health,* Vol. 29, September 1974.

[7]G. Godin et al., "Urban Exposure to Carbon Monoxide." *Archives of Environmental Health,* Vol. 25, November 1972.

[8]G. Malorny, "Survey of the Effects of Carbon Monoxide on Man," in *Carbon Monoxide Origin, Measurement, and Air Quality Criteria.* Dusseldorf: VDI-Verlag, 1972.

[9]*Time,* May 23, 1969, p. 66.

[10]*Fire Aspects of Polymeric Materials, Vol. 8: Land Transportation Vehicles.* Washington, D.C.: National Academy of Sciences, 1979.

[11]A. J. Patton, "Flammable Fabrics—A Hazard Evaluation." *Trial,* Vol. 18, No. 4, April 1982.

[12]*Motor Vehicle Safety Standard 302,* Docket No. 3-3, Notice 4, Part 571; 5302, PRE 3-4, January 8, 1971.

[13]N. B. Johnson, *An Assessment of Automotive Fuel System Fire Hazards* (Contract No. DOT FH 11 7579, Report No. DOT/HS-800 624). Washington, D.C.: Department of Transportation, December 1971.

[14]D. P. Miller, "Report on Reactive Flame Retardants." *Plastics Engineering,* February 1980.

[15]C. E. Hoke, "Compounding Flame Retardance into Plastics." *SPE Journal,* Vol. 29, May 1973.

[16]D. M. Severy, D. M. Blaisdell, and J. F. Kerkhoff, "Automotive Collision Fires." *SAE Journal,* Vol. 83, 1974.

8

Crane Design Hazard Analysis

DAVID V. MacCOLLUM, P.E., C.S.P.
President, David V. MacCollum, Ltd.
Sierra Vista, Arizona

*David V. MacCollum is a Consulting Engineer, registered
in the states of Arizona and California, who has specialized
in the field of safety for 33 years. His professional
experience as a safety engineer includes positions with the
state of Oregon, Corps of Engineers, Sixth Army, Army
Test and Evaluation Command, Army Strategic Communications Command, insurance companies, trade
associations, and manufacturers. In the 1950s the author
developed rollover protection standards and other construction equipment safeguards for the Corps of Engineers;
in the 1960s he developed product safety test and evaluation methodology. He was a member of the U.S. Secretary
of Labor's Construction Safety Adivsory Committee,
1969–1972, and President of the American Society of
Safety Engineers, 1975–1976. His professional affiliations, among others, include the National Society of
Professional Engineers, American Society of Safety
Engineers, Human Factors Society, British Tunelling
Society, National Safety Council, and World Safety
Organization. The author is President of David V.
MacCollum, Ltd., a safety research and industrial video
firm, 1515 Hummingbird Lane, Sierra Vista, Arizona
85635 (602-458-4100).*

I. INTRODUCTION

Cranes are the workhorses that have increased productivity and economic growth not only in our country, but also in many other countries all over the globe. It is not unusual in large metropolitan areas to see many crane booms outlined against the skyline within a few blocks of each other; in rural areas cranes are often seen doing a great variety of jobs.

Statistics show, however, that in the performance of its functions, because of inherent hazards that activate during normal work circumstances, cranes are very dangerous pieces of equipment whose economic and productive achievements have been scarred by repetitive types of accidents that have left a trail of injury, death, and destruction wherever used. Crane accidents throughout the world continue to increase in number and severity as these machines grow in size and in number. Court records are viable sources of data for manufacturers, designers, and safety engineers in identifying problem areas and contain a wealth of information as to specific hazards that have caused injury, death, and destruction. The outcome of a trial does not necessarily increase or decrease the importance of eliminating hazards inherent in design—such court records, regardless of the outcome, contain much information as to the primary cause of such accidents.

Serious accidents that occur repeatedly from similar circumstances should be considered as epidemic. They should be examined so that safeguards to eliminate the hazards can be developed in the same diligent manner that the medical profession examines a disease or infection to develop a vaccine or antibiotic for its prevention or control. Unfortunately, at operating level, a crane accident is often labeled as a "freak" accident since personnel at the job site are often totally unaware of similar repetitive occurrences when these occurrences are so widely dispersed worldwide.[1]

For over a decade it has been recommended that system safety analysis, developed in the late fifties and early sixties to assure a reliable quantitative safety factor in aerospace and military equipment, be applied more vigorously by all industries at the time of design of equipment or facilities to overcome critical hazards that have not been effectively controlled by work-practice rules.[2-4]

The worn phrase "operator error" is hastily applied as the cause of most accidents, and no further examination is made to identify "other" as to other cause-factors. "Defective design" is usually completely overlooked as an accident cause.

We know that humans can never be 100 percent perfect 100 percent of the time. Humans do err, and paramount in accident avoidance, along with training (and as an additional aid in accident avoidance), is incorporation of safeguards at the time of design so that training is not the only avoidance method used. Operators need the safest machines possible to enhance whatever training is necessary for safe operation of the machine. If the toll of injury and death from accidents is ever to be reduced substantially, total reliance upon constant perfect human performance through training is not the answer. Safeguards must be incorporated at time of design so that training to avoid inherent hazards is eliminated and the focus of training can be aimed at safer utilization of the machine. Training is still a very necessary component in accident prevention, but its scope can be widened if the operator has the safest machine possible with which to work. In order to provide a safe piece of equipment, designers and manufacturers must understand why people react as they do under given circumstances. People accommodate (put up with; work with or around) hazards for seven basic reasons:

1. They are unaware of the hazard.
2. They are unable to evaluate the possibility of accident risk.
3. They work under competitive peer or production circumstances.

4. They work with machines that have incompatible controls, conflicting instructions, no guards or warnings.
5. They work with machines that exceed human capabilities.
6. They work with machines that create distractions (such as noise) or have visual obstructions.
7. They work under stressful environmental conditions. This cause is often overlooked in accident investigation.

Reduction of crane accidents will only occur when priority is given to include safety in design to compensate for and forgive foreseeable human errors. Safe design includes analyzing the interaction of machine failure, man failure, and a mismatch of the machine and the man, all within the many variables of environment, which can create hazardous circumstances that result in accidents.

In order to understand the importance of addressing hazards and incorporating safeguards at time of design, the following 20 crane failure modes, in which the likelihood and severity of injury and damage has been found to be high, will be discussed:

1. Overloading
2. Outrigger failure
3. Side pull
4. Hoist limitations
5. Two-blocking
6. Killer hooks
7. Boom buckling
8. Upset
9. Pick and carry
10. Unintentional turntable turning
11. Oversteer/crabbing
12. Control confusion
13. Access
14. Guarding
15. Transportation problems
16. Falling objects
17. Boom disassembly
18. Vision compromise
19. Cable compromise
20. Unintentional power-line contact

II. OVERLOADING

It has been recognized for many years that the margin between tipping load and rated capacity for a given boom length and angle provides an exceedingly narrow margin of safety.

In 1954 this problem was addressed by the Portland District Corps of Engineers.[5] At that time, according to the *American Standard Safety Code for Cranes, Derricks and Hoists*, ASA B30.2-1943, paragraph 1311a, truck cranes required only a 17.5 percent margin of stability above rated capacity for a tipping load. Thus, for a 30-ton rated capacity at a given boom length and angle, the safety factor was 5.25 tons, or a tipping capacity of 35.25 tons. This rated capacity was 85 percent of tipping load, or a 15 percent safety factor. This safety factor was found to be too narrow. After study, the Portland District Corps of Engineers (Portland, Oregon) raised the safety factor to 25 percent, requiring rated capacity to be 75 percent of tipping load. This was adopted by the Corps of Engineers and included in its *General Safety Requirements, 1958*.[6] No increase in the margin of safety required under USAS B30.5-1958, *Crawler, Locomotive and Truck Cranes*, and American National Standards Institute (ANSI) standards was made at this time. ANSI B30.5-1973, *Mobile Hydraulic Cranes*, still does not reflect any higher margin of safety. The Society of Automotive Engineers (SAE) in two papers—SAE J987, "Crane Structures, Method of Test," and SAE J1063, "Cantilevered Boom Crane Structures, Method of Test"—addresses the method of conducting the test and the data to be recorded, but SAE fails to define limits between tipping load and recommended safe operating capacity.

The operator of a crane should have the benefit of a 25 percent safety factor rather than the narrow 15 percent requirement. Operators should also have the benefits provided by load-measuring devices or systems that are designed to prevent overloads from occurring. Several well-known manufacturers have developed and marketed such devices. These should be included on cranes as standard equipment. Appendix A contains a list of some of the available products that provide load-measuring capabilities.

The state of California requires load-measuring systems for cranes with booms of 200 feet or 50-ton capacity.

Another method of reducing crane accidents from overloads is by requiring installation of load-measuring and load-moment warning devices. Table 8-1 lists the U.S. Army, Air Force, and Navy military specifications requiring these devices on mobile cranes. These requirements have minimized the number of crane upsets due to overload in military crane operations.

III. OUTRIGGER FAILURE

The majority of crane upsets occur when outriggers are not in place. Because use of outriggers is voluntary and left to the discretion of the operator (who might not perceive a potential hazard), outriggers are not always extended, and many very serious injuries and deaths have resulted because of this oversight. This is a foreseeable human failure.

An analysis of some 300 crane accidents has shown that half of these incidents occurred when the crane operator was either swinging the cab or extending or lowering the telescoping boom (Table 8-2). All of these actions rapidly increase the lifting radius and can cause upset. It can be predicted that once in every 10,000 days of crane usage an operator will make a human error and upset will occur. A mechanical failure rate of this proportion would be considered unacceptable and design changes immediately implemented to eliminate the problem. When human failure is as predictable as this, the surest way to avoid an accident is to make the machine inoperable until the operator activates the necessary safeguards.

Table 8-1 U.S. Military Specifications for Load-Measuring and Load-Moment Warning Devices on Mobile Cranes

DATE	NUMBER	TITLE
11/6/64	MIL-C-27840B(USAF) para. 3.5.3.4	Crane, Truck-Mounted A/S32H-11
8/27/65	MIL-C-27718B(USAF) para. 3.5.3.4	Crane, Truck-Mounted A/S32A-16
4/12/66	MIL-C-27840C(USAF) para. 3.5.3.4	Crane, Truck-Mounted A/S32H-11, 4,000 Crane Capacity, 4 × 4
3/26/68	MIL-T-62089(AT) para. 3.6.4.5	Truck, Maintenance; with Rotating Hydraulic Derrick, Air Transportable, 34,500 Pounds GVW, 6 × 4

(Continued)

Table 8-1 (*Continued*)

DATE	NUMBER	TITLE
12/30/69	MIL-C-28564(YD) para. 3.5.4	Cranes, Hydraulic, Truck-Mounted, 8 × 4, 25-, 40-, and 55-Ton Capacities
9/8/70	MIL-C-27718C (USAF) para. 3.5.5.4	Crane, Hydraulic, Truck-Mounted, A/S32A-16, 16,500-Pound Crane Capacity, 6 × 4, GED
4/8/71	MIL-C-28614(YD) para. 3.6.7	Crane, Hydraulic, Rough Terrain, 25-Ton Capacity, Full Revolving, Wheel-Mounted, 4 × 4, DED
9/30/71	MIL-C-28622(YD) para. 3.6.7	Crane, Hydraulic, Wheel-Mounted, 4 × 4, Full Revolving, 45-Ton Capacity, DED
2/29/72	MIL-C-28629(YD) para. 3.6.7	Crane, Hydraulic, Wheel-Mounted, 4 × 4, Full Revolving (Shipboard Aircraft Crash-Salvage)
10/24/72	MIL-C-52341E(ME) para. 3.12.13.7	Crane, Wheel-Mounted, Diesel-Engine-Driven, 20-Ton, Rough Terrain
12/18/73	MIL-T-62089A(AT) para. 3.6.2.5	Truck, Maintenance; with Rotating Hydraulic Derrick, Air Transportable, 34,500 Pounds GVW, 6 × 4
4/4/74	MIL-C-52326B para. 3.15.1.4	Crane, Crawler Mounted: 60 Ton at 25-Foot Radius, Diesel-Engine-Driven
7/17/74	MIL-C-29352(MC) para. 3.3.2.9	Crane, Wheel-Mounted: Hydraulic, Rough Terrain, 30-Ton Capacity, Full Revolving, 4 × 4, DED
6/12/75	MIL-C-28614A(YD) para. 3.10.7	Cranes, Hydraulic, Full Revolving, Wheel-Mounted, 4 × 4, DED
9/16/75	MIL-C-62253(AT) para. 3.5	Crane: Material Handling (Rebuild)
5/21/76	MIL-C-62135A(AT) para. 3.5	Crane: Material Handling
9/27/76	MIL-C-529911(ME) para. 3.4.10	Crane, Truck-Mounted, Hydraulic, 25-Ton, Commercial Construction Equipment (CCE)
6/9/80	MIL-T-62089B(AT) para. 3.6.2.5	Truck, Maintenance; with Rotating Hydraulic Derrick, Air Transportable, 34,500 Pounds GVW, 6 × 4

Table 8-2 Crane-upset Accident Analysis

ACCIDENTS RESULTING FROM	1972–1976		1977		1978	
	NO.	TOTAL	NO.	TOTAL	NO.	TOTAL
Travel						
Fatality	0		1		2	
Hospitalized	0		3		2	
Treated & released	0		4		3	
Property damage	0		2		3	
No reported death, injury, or damage	0	0	12	22	10	20
Making Swing, Outriggers Not Extended						
Fatality	2		2		0	
Hospitalized	1		7		4	
Treated & released	1		3		5	
Property damage	2		4		11	
No reported death, injury, or damage	5	11	24	40	23	43
Picking Load, Outriggers Not Extended						
Fatality	0		0		0	
Hospitalized	1		1		0	
Treated & released	0		3		4	
Property damage	1		7		6	
No reported death, injury, or damage	5	7	13	24	17	27
Overload with Outriggers Extended						
Fatality	0		2		1	
Hospitalized	1		3		2	
Treated & released	1		1		3	
Property damage	2		10		9	
No reported death, injury, or damage	1	5	7	23	6	21

Use of Outriggers Unknown in Overload

Fatality	1	1	0
Hospitalized	0	1	0
Treated & released	0	0	0
Property damage	0	0	1
No reported death, injury, or damage	1	5	11
	2	7	12

Outriggers Used, Soil/Crib Failure

Fatality	0	0	0
Hospitalized	0	1	1
Treated & released	0	0	1
Property damage	0	5	1
No reported death, injury, or damage	0	8	8
	0	14	11

Outrigger Box Structure Failure

Fatality	0	0	0
Hospitalized	0	0	0
Treated & released	0	0	0
Property damage	0	0	0
No reported death, injury, or damage	5	1	2
	5	1	2

Other Miscellaneous

Fatality	0	0	0
Hospitalized	0	0	0
Treated & released	0	0	0
Property damage	0	0	0
No reported death, injury, or damage	0	7	5
	0	7	5

Total of All Categories	30	138	141 = 309

In this case, installation of a limit switch to prevent boom movement until outriggers are extended and in place would avert upset. A few aerial basket trucks have hydraulic systems with interlocks that preclude boom operation until outriggers are fully extended and fully supporting the crane, with wheels completely off the ground. Interlocks are required in Military Specification MIL-T-62089(AT)—"Truck, Maintenance; with Rotating Hydraulic Derrick, Air Transportable, 34,500 Pounds, GVW, 6×4"—dated March 26, 1968, and its updates, MIL-T-62089(A), December 18, 1973, and MIL-T-62089(B), June 9, 1980.

A mobile hydraulic rough-terrain crane on "rubber" with the outriggers retracted is completely unstable on a side lift, and even a small load over-the-side can cause overload. Whether these cranes are on rubber or truck-mounted, if outriggers are not extended, the lifting capacity at side angles dramatically drops, in many cases to less than the weight of the boom itself. As the crane boom rotates on the turntable, the overload occurs so quickly that the operator cannot perceive the loss of stability until too late.

On mobile hydraulic cranes on rubber with telescoping booms, operators can increase the radius by lowering, extending, or rotating the boom (sluing), and these functions can be performed either singly or simultaneously. If the crane is wheel-mounted, besides performing all of these functions, the crane operator can also move the crane forward or backward in a travel mode. In addition to all of these activities, the operator can also raise or lower the hoist line and must at all times have several visual targets in mind: the tip of the boom to avoid obstructions, the signalman, and the load. With so many multiple functions to perform almost simultaneously, an operator can easily become overtasked. Machine design that overextends the operator's span of control will ultimately result in predictable and foreseeable operator error. This creates a need for devices that will assist the operator and intercede before the danger point of no-return occurs. Load-measuring systems are a must on cranes. Modern load-measuring systems utilize chip computer technology to avoid overload, either on rubber or with outriggers extended, at any boom angle, boom length, or rotating position.

A number of lawsuits for defective design for lack of load-sensing systems have been filed and settled for injuries and damages resulting from crane upset due to overload over-the-side on the basis that the accident would not have occurred had load-sensing equipment been provided on the crane.

There have been a few cases of outrigger collapse when the outriggers themselves have not been sufficiently substantial. To correct this hazardous defect, design improvement is needed.

Some cranes allow the rear outrigger to disengage from the pad when the load is first lifted. When the crane cab/boom is swung around 180°, the outrigger can slip from such an unfixed pad connection and cause the crane to upset or the boom to buckle.

IV. SIDE PULL

Side pull or lateral loading can easily buckle a boom.[7] Many crane operations involve two cranes on a lift, and lateral loading can be unknowingly applied when the load must be turned. Usually operators are completely unaware of the hazard potential that is undetectably created within a "normal" lifting process. A detection system is needed to warn operators of side pull. A bubble level within the crane cab aids the operator in establishing "level" while adjusting his outriggers.

V. HOIST LIMITATIONS

On cranes, the hoist drum is outside the view of the operator. If the "headache" block is replaced with a lighter one, or if for any reason the line is not taut, the line can coil or hang up and not reel in safely. A guide or spooling device is needed since the operator cannot see what is happening. Such a hang-up can cause the hoist line to be unintentionally parted.

VI. TWO-BLOCKING

Two-blocking is a hazard that occurs on both latticework-boom and telescoping-boom cranes. It occurs more frequently on hydraulic telescoping booms because the hoist line is operated by one control and the boom extension by another. Generally, on latticework booms the hoist line has a mechanical linkage to the power source, which tends to provide the safety factor of lugging the engine prior to a parting of the line. This warning feedback to the operator generally gives an opportunity to avoid two-blocking before it causes the hoist line to break. Unfortunately, this does not preclude other hazards from becoming active, such as displacement of the load from the hook or damage to the sheave at the boom tip. Two-blocking can easily occur while extending the boom on a hydraulic crane because the hydraulic pump works quietly and surreptitiously and gives no warning of stress as does a lugging engine. An anti-two-blocking device as standard equipment is essential. ANSI standard B30.15-1973, Mobile Hydraulic Cranes, paragraph 15-1.3.2d, "Two-Blocking Damage Preventive Feature," reads as follows:

> On a telescoping boom crane, with less than 60 feet of extended boom, a two-blocking damage preventive feature shall be provided capable of preventing damage to the hoist rope, and/or other machine components, when hoisting the load, extending the boom, or lowering a boom on a machine having a stationary winch mounted to the rear of the boom hinge.

Human factors logic tells us that when an operator must use two controls, one for the hoist and one for the hydraulic boom extension, the chance of error is increased. An operator can forget to release (payout) the load line when extending the boom. When this occurs, the line can be "accidentally" broken. If the load line, when it breaks, happens to be supporting a worker on a bosum's chair or several workers on a floating scaffold, a catastrophe can result.

Present standards basing use of a two-blocking damage preventive feature upon the length of the boom are ridiculous. From a human factor's standpoint, the device should also be standard for longer booms, since the longer the boom, the harder it is to see if it is in a two-blocking mode. I have been told by those opposed to use of such devices on larger cranes that because they cost more money, larger cranes have more competent operators. This position is not logical. Some 30 lawsuits have highlighted the inadequacy of these safety standards, which fail to require an anti-two-blocking device for mobile hydraulic and long latticework boom cranes. Table 8–3 gives the military regulations governing such devices.

The incidence of accidents resulting from this cause is remarkably lower on cranes used by the military that are equipped with anti-two-blocking devices. Jibs on mobile hydraulic cranes also require the anti-two-blocking device. Where the jib tip has only a light metal guard that can be torn off in two-blocking, the entire hoist line can become displaced

Table 8-3 Military Specifications Requiring Anti-Two-Blocking Devices

DATE	NUMBER	TITLE
11/27/65	MIL-C-27718B (USAF) Para. 3.7.8	Crane, Truck-Mounted, A/S32A-16
4/12/66	MIL-C-27840C (USAF) Para. 3.7.6	Crane, Truck-Mounted, A/S32H11, 4,000-Pound Capacity, 4 × 4
9/8/70	MIL-C-27718C (USAF) Para. 3.7.8	Crane, Hydraulic, Truck-Mounted, AS32A-16, 16,500-Pound Capacity, 6 × 4, GED
4/30/71	MIL-C-28616(YD) Para 3.9.1	Crane, Shovel, Convertible, Crawler-Mounted, Commerical DED
9/30/71	MIL-C-28622(YD) Para. 3.6.2	Crane, Hydraulic, Wheel-Mounted, 4 × 4, Full Revolving (Shipboard Aircraft Crash Salvage)
5/1/72	MIL-C-23877B(YD) Para 3.6.4	Cranes, Hydraulic, Wheel-Mounted, 5- & 12½-Ton Capacities
6/12/75	MIL-C-28614A(YD) Para. 3.10.2	Crane, Hydraulic, Full Revolving, Wheel-Mounted, 4 × 4, DED

and cause the load to fall on a mobile hydraulic crane. Grove mobile hydraulic cranes have made anti-two-blocking as standard equipment since January 1981. The state of California requires anti-two-blocking devices in its crane certification requirements.

Anti-two-blocking devices should also be standard equipment on latticework fixed booms. When walking a crawler crane with a long boom, a great deal of whip is created. The headache ball and empty chokers can drift up to the boom tip when walking a crane without a load. While the crane operator is busy watching the pathway of travel to avoid rough ground that violently jerks the crane, he is not watching the boom tip. When the hoist line two-blocks, it assumes the weight of the boom and relieves the pin-up guys of the load. Then, if the crane crawler breaks over a rock or bump, the flypole action of a long boom is sufficient to break the hoist line. There have been several defective design cases on the lack of two-blocking devices on latticework-boom cranes.

Anti-two-blocking devices are generally electrically initiated. However, a mechanical device has been developed by the Ederer Company of Seattle, Washington. Another method of anti-two-blocking is to have a hydraulic cutout so the hoist line automatically pays out while the boom is being extended. This design is incorporated into the Galion crane.

VII. KILLER HOOKS

The lifting hook is a critical link in lifting a load. One load hoist block found on some cranes fits flat to the boom. When the boom is in a lowered position, the hook can swing into any position and the straps rest safely, deep in the throat of the hook; but when the boom is raised in a nearly vertical position, the hook can rotate, allowing the straps to slide easily out of the hook. As a hook is subjected to wear, normal stresses gradually enlarge the throat, and this further increases the possibility of the straps slipping from the hook. The common sheet metal safety latch becomes critical. There is a long list of over 100 patented, positive-type safety latches that prevent the hook from opening and require depression of the latch pin or lever before the hook opens. Another method is the use of a leveling swivel on the block that allows the block to remain always perpendicular, thus preventing a killer-hook syndrome that can drop a load unexpectedly. The anti-two-blocking device mentioned in the discussion on two-blocking would also preclude holding the lifting block flush to the boom tip.

Another problem area arises when a lifting hook is placed on the back of the bucket of a backhoe so that slings can be attached to use the machine as a lifting device. When the bucket is moved downward underneath the boom, the throat of the hook is turned downward and the straps can easily slip out of the hook. To avoid this hazard, a ring instead of a hook should be used. This requires the use of a shackle to connect the lifting straps.

VIII. BOOM BUCKLING

In the early 1950s boom stops were recognized as being essential to avoid boom buckling. Since then many cranes have been equipped with these devices as standard equipment. Simple, mechanical stops are not always the most efficient. In 1950 the Portland District Corps of Engineers also analyzed the concept of hydraulic snubs to absorb the shock and found "Boom Snub" to be a most efficient safeguard.

Use of boom stops avoids inadvertent pulling over (winching) of a nearly vertical boom by the winch line (two-blocking) and does not allow the boom to be raised beyond a safe angle. Boom stops also help avoid the forces created by a sudden release of the load as well as any forces created by wind. There are two types of boom stops. One is the mechanical type that provides opposing or energy-absorbing force, such as the Boom Snub mentioned above. Most mechanical stops are only spring-loaded devices and offer nominal protection. The other type of boom stop is the electrical interlock system, which is a sensor-type device that intercedes and stops further boom movement. Many cranes today are equipped with both mechanical and electrical systems for controlling this dangerous hazard.

The Portland Corps of Engineers boom-stop requirement of nearly 30 years ago calls for the effectiveness of boom stops to be tested with a load that is equal to almost tipping capacity for a nearly vertical boom, whereas SAE J220 and ANSI B30.5-1968, paragraph 5-1.9.1, have no test requirements.

IX. UPSET

There are several types of crane upset accidents. The first has been thoroughly considered in the discussions on overload.

The second occurs when the crane is in a travel mode on uneven surfaces. Its severe top-heaviness can cause it to upset very easily and roll onto its side. The "tin" weather cab offers little protection from crushing between the ground and the boom in the travel mode.

The third occurs when mobile, hydraulic, rough-terrain cranes are used in the "pick-and-carry" mode. The load can bounce and swing, causing imbalance. A quick release capability to drop the load immediately is needed to avoid upset.

The fourth type of crane upset occurs when moving large latticework-boom crawler cranes. These cranes have very heavy counterweights for balance when the latticework boom is in place. When the latticework-boom sections are removed during the moving of this type of crane, the heavy counterweight imbalances the crane and can cause it to upset backward.

The problem of simple imbalance also occurs when a long boom is in a vertical position and has a heavy counterweight. If outriggers are not in place when the cab is swung, the counterweight is enough to tip over the crane.

Upset is a hazard that results in death or very serious injury and damage. These types of cranes should have rollover protection (ROPS) as standard equipment.

X. PICK AND CARRY

While a load is being moved in a "pick-and-carry" mode, a crane can easily develop dynamics that can unexpectedly pitch the crane forward in an upset and can violently pitch the operator out of the cab. A "quick release" of the hoist line to increase the safety of the machine should be required. The inclusion of this feature is recommended in some operating engineers' handbooks, but it is absent from ANSI standards.

XI. UNINTENTIONAL TURNTABLE TURNING

Many times as a mobile, rough-terrain crane is being moved from one location to another, it becomes imbalanced because the cab unexpectedly starts to rotate on its axis, becomes uncontrollable, and overturns. This occurs because the operator has forgotten to insert the pin that locks the cab in place during travel.

Pilots of planes with retractable landing gears have more protection than do crane operators. If a pilot starts into a landing sequence and the landing gear is not down, an alarm gives warning that this critical function has been overlooked. The crane operator in a mobile, rough-terrain crane does not have this same type of safeguard to warn when the pin is not in place, locking the cab in position.

To overcome this hazard, a simple interlock needs to be installed as standard equipment on all mobile cranes to prevent forward or backward movement until this pin is put in place.

XII. OVERSTEER/CRABBING

In some four-wheel, rough-terrain cranes, rear-wheel drive is actuated by a knob extending out from the dash, one-half inch from the right of the steering wheel. This knob can be accidentally displaced by the right hand on the steering wheel while turning to the left, causing the machine to move crabwise sharply to the left. The knob can be brushed downward when turning to the right, causing the machine to turn sharply to the right with half the normal turning radius.

XIII. CONTROL CONFUSION

The arrangement of controls on the floorboard of cranes needs to be standardized.

There should be adequate space between the pedals to avoid overlapping from one pedal to the next when the operator wears large boots.

Hinge and lever pedals require different movements and can give an operator warning if the wrong pedal has been selected. This gives the operator a "sense of touch" in knowing that his foot is on the proper control. Think of the chaos that would result if foot controls varied from one make of car to another. Crane operators who must use several different types and makes of cranes must cope with such a situation when moving from job to job.

XIV. ACCESS

Footholds used by operators to gain access in and out of equipment are often covered with oil from leaking hydraulics. This is an open invitation for serious falls.

Safe access is outlined in SAE J185, "Access Systems for Construction and Industrial Equipment," first published in 1970. Many manufacturers of equipment ignore these standards under the assumption they do not apply because these requirements are not directed to specific pieces of equipment. This assumption is incorrect. Providing safe access for operators of equipment is necessary to eliminate another source of serious injury.

XV. GUARDING

Workers must sometimes approach the hoist drums when reeling off some line or guiding the cables so they do not overlap or bind. The hoist drum offers an attractive footing. If the flanges are recessed or dangerous footing is eliminated, the worker cannot be caught in the cable as it is reeled in or out.

Hatch covers in crane cabs in some makes and models are defectively designed, for they allow rain water to fall on the brake lining, making cable slippage unavoidable for an operator and the dropping of the boom or load, or both, possible. Watertight cabs are essential to protect the hoist brakes from water.

In confined work spaces, the rotating cab and counterweight of a crane can create dangerous pinch or shear points. In some crane models a very dangerous shear point exists between the cab and the truck bed, and a wider clearance is needed between these two points to reduce this risk. Also, conspicuous warning signs should be posted marking this space as a danger zone and instructing workers to keep out of this area.

XVI. TRANSPORTATION PROBLEMS

Small cranes are often transported long distances on flatbed trucks or low-boy trailers. Unless the crane axles are supported on blocks and the boom is anchored down with chains or straps, the boom can drift or oscillate upward, reducing the amount of clearance between the boom and any bridges or overpasses along the route. In one such accident the crane boom destroyed the girders on an overpass, wrecking the bridge. The crane itself was dumped from the carrying flatbed truck onto a vehicle following behind the truck, resulting in the crippling injuries to the driver of the car and destruction of the crane.

XVII. FALLING OBJECTS

Because of unstable footing or a faulty hook arrangement, loads have been known to fall back on the crane cab, placing the operator in a very vulnerable position, especially on those cranes in which the cab is placed in front of the boom hinge. A substantial cab (a falling objects protective system—FOPS) is needed to protect the operator from such an occurrence. A man was sheared in half when a large steel sheet was dropped lengthwise onto the cab—a typical illustration of what can, and does, happen with falling objects.

XVIII. VISION COMPROMISE

Many cranes and backhoes have very limited vision of the area in front of the right front wheel or track because the boom blocks the view. To overcome this hazard, an automatic travel alarm is needed to warn workers and others as to the movement of the crane or backhoe. Such an alarm should be two-directional since operator visibility to the rear of these machines is also limited. Installation of rearview mirrors is also a must, so the crane operator can be aware of what is going on behind.

XIX. BOOM DISASSEMBLY

Death or serious injury can result from another hazard known to occur many times during dismantling of latticework-boom cranes. Some 18 deaths or paraplegia have been identified from this one hazard. There are at least three foreseeable error-provocative circumstances that lead to accidents when dismantling is being done:

1. Workers are unfamiliar with the equipment.
2. Nonideal dismantling location (narrow, confined roadway requiring reduced boom length to turn).
3. Time limit set in which to complete the function to meet task deadline. This may be while loading a crane for shipment or in moving a crane through a confined area to do a specific job, etc.

An example of a typical accident that could occur when a latticework boom of a truck or a crawler-mounted crane is lowered for dismantling can be described as follows:

A member of the crane crew knocks out the lower connecting bolts between sections of the mast while the pin-up lines support the boom tip with no support from the boom. To remove these pins, a worker usually must place himself under the boom. As soon as the lower bolts are removed, the boom can collapse downward and cause fatal or very serious injuries to the workers below.

There are several types of pins that would substantially reduce the risk if used properly:

1. *Double-ended pin* (can be driven out when standing beside boom).

2. *Step pin* (can only be inserted from outside facing in).
3. *Welded lug* (prevents pin from being entered the wrong way—must be entered outside facing in).
4. *Screw pin* (a thread arrangement that inserts or retracts the pin).

Warnings should be posted at pin connections, and comprehensive text material warning of this hazard and telling how to avoid it should be contained in operators' manuals.

XX. CABLE COMPROMISE

The use of wrong-sized steel cable not only diminishes the life of the line but creates a number of hazards. If the diameter of the rope is too large for the sheave, under tension it will cause the line to pinch and subject both the rope and sheave to severe abrasive wear. If the cable is too small, it tends to flatten a line under tension.

The fastest way to destroy a hoist line is to run it over a sheave that is too small in diameter. Load hoist sheaves should have a diameter of at least 18 times that of the wire rope to be used. Many cranes have a sheave at the boom tip that is minimum or substandard in diameter; this creates adverse wear and shortens the life of the hoist line.

Wire rope is an expendable product that is consumed like a tank of gas. Its life is dependent upon use. When there are six randomly distributed broken wires in one rope lay (a rope lay being the length along a rope in which one strand makes a complete revolution around the rope) or three in one strand in one rope lay, the cable should be replaced and destroyed so it cannot be reused. A rope that has been kinked also needs to be replaced.

XXI. UNINTENTIONAL POWER-LINE CONTACT

A. Introduction

A thorough review of existing statistics shows that safe work practices at the job site have been the only method of preventing injury from unintentional contact with a power line. Reliance upon such work practices has been proven ineffective, as death and injury from this source continue. Therefore, crane safety devices and utility participation are needed.

In the past there have been a number of accident sources available to show that unintentional power-line contact by boom equipment is a common occurrence, which yearly results in approximately four hundred (400) deaths or permanently maiming injuries as detailed in Table 8-4. These "casualties" have risen since 1976, and currently, it is estimated that 500 workers a year are either killed or permanently maimed when a crane boom or hoist line inadvertently contacts bare, uninsulated, high-voltage power lines.

In electrical accidents, the difference between life with seriously maiming injuries (loss of one or more limbs) and death is precariously slim. For this reason a better grasp of the enormity of the problem is gained by grouping fatal and serious injuries into the same category.

The data in Table 8-4 on boom/power-line contact was compiled from the following sources:

1. *A Survey of Non-Employee Electrical Contacts.* This survey of participating utilities was conducted by the National Safety Council over a five-year period from 1964 to 1969 and revealed the following statistics relating to various types of boom equipment:

Fatal accidents involving cranes	185
Sign installation	10
Well drilling	25
Total	220

   This means an average of 44 deaths per year occurred. Serious but nonfatal accidents for the same group was 986, or an average of 197 per year. Only about one-third of all electric utilities are National Safety Council members, so this reporting is understandably incomplete. However, if considered as one-third of actual exposure, the national estimated average would be 132 fatalities and 591 nonfatal injuries per year.

2. The California Public Utilities Commission (which does not include municipal electric systems) published figures on electric line accidents for the years 1965 through 1975 (11 years). Nonemployee fatalities numbered 375 for the period, or an average of 35 per year, and nonfatal injuries totaled 923, or 84 per year. California represents about one-tenth of the nation's

Table 8-4 Annual Estimated Deaths per Year from Power-Line Contact by Boom Equipment

YEAR	CALIFORNIA UTILITY STUDY (1/3 NATL. POPULATION ADJUSTED)	PUBLIC UTILITIES (10% NATL. POPULATION ADJUSTED)	CALIFORNIA H.E.W. VITAL STATISTICS	NATIONAL INDUSTRIAL DIVISION (10% NATL. POPULATION ADJUSTED)	NATIONAL SAFETY COUNCIL ACCIDENT FACTS	AVERAGE[a]
1960			125			125
1961						
1962				170		170
1963				100		100
1964	132	123	135	150		146
1965	132	77	140	200		148
1966	132	90	139	170		129
1967	132	97	133	150		136
1968	132			150		126
1969		183	117	120	162	145
1970		123	125	200	152	150
1971		133	96	90	180	125
1972		110	104	80	155	112
1973		67	113		142	107
1974		120	119		181	140
1975		147	108	110	163	132
1976				120	158	139

[a]Average: 133 deaths per year
266 serious injuries per year
399 deaths/serious injuries per year

population. About one-third of the cases listed related to boom equipment. Using national population figures, an adjusted national average of 120 fatalities per year and 280 serious injuries can be estimated.

3. In the November 1978 issue of *Professional Safety*, a chart showing "Deaths Caused by Electric Shock within the U.S.," prepared by Vital Statistics of the U.S., Accident Mortality, U.S. Department of Health, Education, and Welfare, was reproduced covering the period from 1960 through 1975. This chart shows a total of 490 deaths per year from electric shock occurring on farms (206), on streets and highways (102), and in industry (182), one-third of which fall into the boom/power-line contact category.

4. California's Division of Industrial Safety compiled figures from 1963 through 1972 that show 141 deaths from "contact with overhead high-voltage lines through equipment," or an average of 15 fatalities per year. This division's later records show 11 deaths in 1975 and 12 deaths in 1976 resulting from overhead power-line contact through a tool or other piece of equipment, which again relates to cranes.

National Safety Council's publication *Accident Facts* tabulates the number of deaths attributed to "Industrial Wiring and Appliances," "Other Electric Current," and "Unspecified Electric Current." Its source was the *International List of Causes of Death*, but it fails to pinpoint the hazard of power-line contact with boom equipment. However, the following death figures are given under the category of "Industrial Wiring and Appliances," into which boom/power-line contacts would fall:

1968: 162
1969: 152
1970: 180
1971: 155
1972: 142
1973: 181
1974: 163
1975: 158

or an average of 162 deaths per year.

As a result of power-line contact by boom equipment, a substantial amount of litigation has arisen from this one hazard. In many of these court actions, the electric utility, crane manufacturer, equipment dealer, general contractor, or landowner have been held negligent, either individually or collectively.

A substantial number of articles and references have been published concerning the hazard created by bare uninsulated high-voltage power lines and citing safeguards available to diminish the risk of occurrence. See Appendix B summarizing these references.

Human factors psychologists have discovered that in many circumstances accurate visual judgments of clearance from power lines cannot be made and that people usually observe only one specific thing at a time. In other words, people are unable visually to determine safe boom/power-line clearances and are also single channeled, just as a TV set can only show one station at a time. With these two human traits in mind, it is easy to see why the possibility for error is very great for workers who must work with cranes near power lines and why so many accidents occur resulting from unintentional boom/power-line contact.

The Occupational Safety and Health Act (OSHA) has required for almost a decade that a 10-foot clearance from power lines be maintained, but since workers are humanly unable to judge this distance correctly, serious accidents continue to occur. Because the population of cranes is increasing each year and is projected to double in the next decade, this accident occurrence will continue to rise, unless further preventive measures are taken in addition to the 10-foot rule.

B. Preventive Measures to Reduce Risk of Contact

The hazard of power-line contact needs to be examined in depth to determine what actions could minimize the risk. There are several methods through which this risk could be reduced. Because the danger associated with this hazard is so great, each method should be adopted. One single safeguard is not sufficient when a person's life is at stake. In addition to the 10-foot clearance requirement, the following preventive measures should be taken to reduce the risk of accidental power-line contact.

B.1. MAPPING Map on the ground the "Danger Zone" created by bare, uninsulated, high-voltage power lines so that this zone can be isolated and marked around its perimeter with

Banner Guard ribbon warning tape in blaze-orange labeled **DANGER ZONE—HIGH-VOLTAGE POWER LINES ABOVE.**

Figure 8-1 shows how the danger zone can be identified on the ground. Power lines generally extend from 3 to 5 feet on each side of a pole, depending upon the voltages being transmitted. To be on the safe side, to mark this danger zone, measure out from the power pole 15 feet on each side and sight to the next pole at the same distance out from each side.

This danger zone is also unsuited for storing of materials. Activities should be avoided that involve use of crane booms, hoist lines, forklift extended masts, drill rig masts, pipe, steel, or other conductive material that might inadvertently be raised into this area and cause a power-line contact.

B.2. INSULATED LINK About 80 percent to 90 percent of boom/power-line contacts result from a hoist line's striking a bare, uninsulated power line. It is exceedingly difficult for

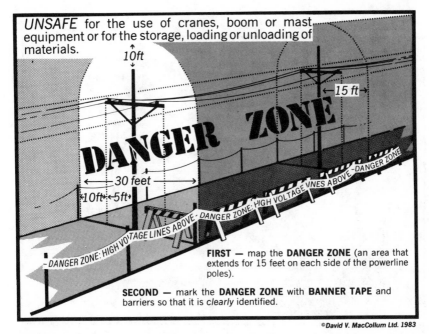

©David V. MacCollum Ltd. 1983

Figure 8-1 Preventive measures to reduce the risk of accidental power-line contact include mapping and clearly marking danger zones.

workers to gauge the clearance between a small power line and a hoist line some 20 feet or more away, especially against the sky's bright background.

Over the years thousands of lives could have been saved if insulated links would have been used. Riggers, signalmen, and crane operators have all made too many disastrous clearance misjudgments in the past. Placing of the blame on a worker for being careless does not avoid reoccurrence of this same type of accident by the same crew or another crew in the future. Figure 8-2 shows how the insulated link serves to insulate the worker from the power line. The insulated link does not, however, provide protection to anyone touching the crane cab; it only protects the worker guiding the suspended load.

About 8 out of 10 power-line contacts are made by hoist lines. When used, insulated links can prevent such death or serious injury. Unfortunately, many safety devices are discounted because they are not 100 percent effective 100 percent of the time; but the medical profession does not ask that an

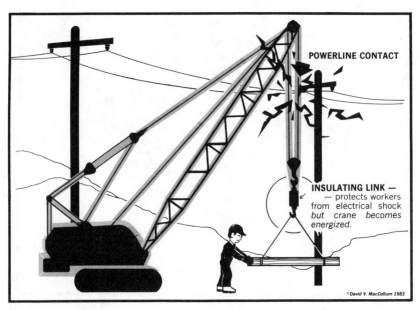

POWERLINE CONTACT

INSULATING LINK —
— protects workers from electrical shock but crane becomes energized.

©David V. MacCollum 1983

Figure 8-2 Crane equipped with an insulated link insulates the worker from the power line and protects against possible electric shock.

antibiotic be discarded simply because it cannot combat all viruses or because some people have an allergic reaction to it.

Links are manufactured by the following companies:

H. J. Hirtzer & Associates
1308 Martino Road
Lafayette, CA 95049
(415) 283-6627

Miller Swivels
SSP Construction Equipment Inc.
P.O. Box 2038
Pomona, CA 91766
(714) 623-6184

By covering the power line with a sheath of non-conductive plastic, the risk of death or injury from accidental boom/power-line contact is further reduced because such dieletric insulation does not allow electricity to pass through to the boom to the worker on the ground. Figure 8–3 shows a power line covered with rubber gutting. Installation of a totally

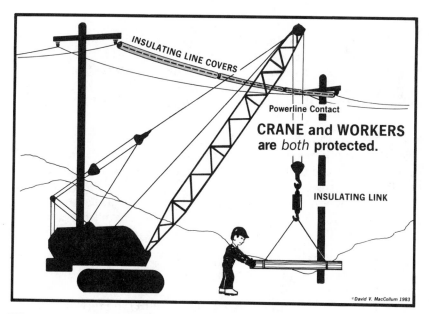

Figure 8–3 Power lines insulated with nonconductive plastic or rubber gutting protect both worker and crane.

nonconductive boom would also protect the worker from electrocution if a boom/power-line contact were inadvertently made.

B.3. PROXIMITY WARNING DEVICES Installation of proximity warning devices on cranes gives the crane operator and the rigging crew a warning before the boom has intruded into the 10-foot danger zone that surrounds a power line. An audible alarm is sounded before the danger zone is compromised so the crane can be stopped and the crew warned of the danger.

The electronic proximity device detects the invisible 60-cycle force field surrounding an energized power line. (This force field causes the hum that interrupts car radio reception when driving under large electric transmission lines.) The proximity alarm device is designed to respond with an audible signal whenever a boom enters the danger zone. This patented device is manufactured and sold by:

SIGALARM, Inc.
P.O. Box 1883
Irvine, CA 92713
(714) 551-2294

The device is an operator aid that extends the crane and rigging crews' ability to perceive danger. The use of this device in accordance with manufacturer's instructions, develops a "safety" regima that identifies unsafe work areas. The device is not a substitute for other safety devices or practices.

B.4. NOTIFICATION OF UTILITY Always notify the electric utility as to when and where a crane is to be used *near* power lines. Ask for the utility's assistance in determining additional safety measures to be taken. Utilities know how dangerous it is to work close to power lines and know the safety measures that assure for a safer environment when working around power lines. These measures include:

- De-energizing the power lines
- Relocating the power lines (construct a shoe-fly around the work area)
- Insulating (temporary or permanent) the power lines
- Burying the power lines

It is the duty of every contractor to notify the utility whenever work with cranes is being done near power lines. However, this important function is often overlooked or not completed because the proper utility contact number is not known. Every contractor should check with the local utility and obtain the correct notification number so that the utility can do its part in avoiding death and injury. The contact number should be posted *conspicuously* in the crane as follows, with the appropriate information filled in:

Before working with this crane in proximity of power lines, contact the following power company representative:

_____

Individual responsible for handling hazard   *Position*

_____

Utility

_____

Address   *Phone*

Then when circumstances change, the proper authority can be quickly contacted for assistance.

B.5. POWER-LINE COMPANIES Power-line companies control power in the distribution system. Philip Wessels has written several articles concerning gigantic ground fault systems that could de-energize the power line in the event of an accidental contact.[8-10]

C. Warning Notices

Posting of warning notices will not keep a worker from making a human error, but a design that includes safeguards to prevent operation until proper steps are taken will prevent the worker from making a fatal mistake. There are, however, times when all safeguards are in place and a warning might be needed to clarify a particular circumstance relating to safe operation. Warnings must never be used as a substitute for safe design. If a warning is deemed necessary, in order to be effective, it should achieve the following objectives:

1. A warning needs to be at a point of operation clearly visible to the operator/user.
2. A warning needs to follow existing patterns that utilize a stereotype format (e.g., danger in white letters on red field with black border). ANSI Standard Z35.1-1972 describes the format to be used that will let the reader know of the danger and how to avoid it.
3. A warning needs to be permanent (stickers won't do). The sign should be made of metal.
4. A warning needs to be comprehensive. This can be achieved by referring to the operator's manual, which should be placed in a cabinet in the cab of the crane with a label stating that important safety information is in the manual and that if the manual is misplaced, it can be replaced by calling a number at the factory.

In one instance, a metric crane load-limit chart was torn off when the crane was returned from Canada to the United States. An operator must have a chart for safe operation. Under this important chart a warning sign should have been posted, separate and apart from the load-limit chart, giving the serial number and model of the crane and advising the user to call an 800 telephone number for a replacement chart for United States use (see Figure 8-4).

D. Judging Clearances

Robert Jenkins, now retired as Safety Director for the U.S. Army Corps of Engineers, investigated the reasons for this high incidence of severe injury in 1950. At that time he conducted a number of tests at Fort Belvoir, Virginia, to ascertain the ability of crane operators to estimate visually safe clearances from power lines. He found that dangerous misjudgments could be made in estimating clearance from a small wire against a bright background. Unfortunately, these important findings were not recorded.

In order to examine the ability to judge clearance distances from power lines from a human factors standpoint, the author and Dr. Lorna Middendorf conducted a field study as a laboratory exercise for students at a Green Shield Professional Development Conference sponsored by the National

Figure 8-4 A warning sign should be posted below a crane's load-limit chart.

Farmers Union Casualty Companies. The results of this field study were published in two papers presented at the 22nd Annual Meeting of the Human Factors Society.[11,12]

E. Litigation

Robert Jenkins presented his findings on clearances in 1973 testimony in the Cook County Circuit Court (Illinois) in the case of *Burke* v. *Illinois Power*, which is presumed to be the first litigation that addressed the need for insulated links and proximity alarms. His testimony was the basis for the decision that crane manufacturers may be strictly liable for failing to equip cranes with known safety devices, such as insulated hooks, boom cages, and proximity alarms. The plaintiff's verdict of $2.5 million was upheld on January 18, 1978, upon appeal.

Since that time numerous cases have been heard concerning the need for safety devices on cranes (insulated links, proximity alarms, dielectric—nonconductive—booms, warning instructions on how to "map" on the job site the danger zone created by the overhead, bare, uninsulated power lines).

A system safety approach in accident prevention is being recognized as essential in containment of hazards because the safety responsibilities of all parties come into focus and proper safeguards can then be implemented in each party's particular area of involvement. Courts are recognizing that everyone has a responsibility in this type of very serious accident—crane operators, riggers, utilities, contractors, and crane manufacturers. It appears that the courts are no longer allowing crane manufacturers to transfer the entire responsibility for safety to the operator when there are well-recognized design features that will make the crane safer.

Such litigation has surfaced the fact that a broad range of safeguards (such as crane safety devices and specific operating procedures) could have been used that would have precluded these accidents. In many instances, the courts have found individual specific safety roles for equipment manufacturers, equipment distributors or leasors, general contractors, subcontractors, owner-contractors, utilities, and landowners. The courts have felt that these parties could have individually initiated accident prevention measures, but they unfortunately assumed someone else had responsibility, did not act themselves, and were, therefore, negligent. Generally, it has been found in such cases that a number of redundant safeguards, including both physical and managerial systems, were lacking; had any or all been implemented prior to the accident, the accident would not have occurred. Often juries have little sympathy for a manufacturer of a crane who has transferred all of the risk to workers, who must use the equipment without safeguards, because they know they will lose their jobs if they object to the danger. Inadvertent assumption of risk by an employee is an invalid defense argument in many states, and liability is becoming increasingly difficult to transfer to the employee, as the courts often view the injured as being unable to be absolutely perfect all the time and in need of backup safeguards when the danger is so great.

Accident litigation proceedings also substantiate the fact that death and serious injury from power-line contact with boom or mast-type equipment occur all too often, that these are not isolated occurrences, and that additional safeguards are essential to reduce the occurrence. Review of depositions given in this type of accident litigation gives the same insight into accident causation and available accident prevention measures as is achieved by formal boards of inquiry.

XXII. CONCLUSIONS

Analysis of accident litigation provides a positive insight into the need for applied system safety approaches in design and manufacture. System safety is often used as an analysis method for the benefit of the court. When referencing various safety standards, it has been found that they are incomplete or state only that certain hazards must be considered. For instance, the National Electrical Safety Code requirements for safe clearance around bare electrical conductors should also warn designers of cranes that these lines also create a hazard for cranes.

System safety analysis can be a viable design review in industrial and manufacturing applications. It is unfortunate that use of the system safety approach has not been adopted to any great extent to provide a higher degree of safety in exceedingly high risk operations. Unfortunately, it has been consistently found that the function of safety engineering has been delegated by crane manufacturers to engineers with experience only in conventional design responsibilities. When such engineers are given the duties involving safety they should be afforded the following:

1. Technical assistance from experienced safety engineers who have developed safety test and evaluation programs.
2. Training in system safety and related subdisciplines in human factors so that they can systematically evaluate the crane on a hazard-by-hazard basis.
3. An extensive reference library on safety engineering.
4. An opportunity to develop a voluntary user/owner accident reporting system so that accident data bank can be developed. Far too often, record management systems or advice of corporate legal (defense) counsel create unrealistic incentives to destroy valuable information. In this day of computers, accident data can be efficiently stored in a manner that clearly identifies critical hazards and foreseeable human errors that warrant design improvements.

Hopefully, system safety expertise will be applied in industry during the next decade to provide the insight that will substantially reduce the high incident of severe injury and death that is occurring with increased use of production equipment.

A great benefit could be achieved if costly governmental programs, such as OSHA, would create incentives for providing safer work environments through design innovations that forgive known variables in human behavior.

CITATIONS

[1]D. V. MacCollum, "Freak Accidents." *Hazard Prevention*, September/October 1978.

[2]D. V. MacCollum, "A Systems Approach for Design Safety." *Professional Engineer*, November 1968.

[3]D. V. MacCollum, "Reliability—A Quantitative Safety Factor." *Professional Safety*, May 1969.

[4]D. V. MacCollum, "Testing for Safety." *National Safety News*, February 1969.

[5]D. V. MacCollum, "How Crane Load Tests Prevent Accidents." *Pacific Builder & Engineer*, March 1957.

[6]*General Safety Requirements*, EM 385-1-1, March 13, 1958, para. 18-4.

[7]C. A. Brolin, "Destructive Testing of Crane Booms." *National Safety Council Proceedings*, October 1977.

[8]P. S. Wessels, "The Overhead Electric Distribution Line Hazard." *Hazard Prevention*, March/April 1978.

[9]P. S. Wessels, "Ground Fault Interruption for Personal Protection of the 12 KV Distribution Line." Institute of Electrical and Electronic Engineers Convention, 1979.

[10]*The Interruption of Downed Conductors on Low-Voltage Distribution Systems*, The Parameters of Distribution Ground Fault Protection Working Groups of the Institute of Electrical and Electronic Engineers Power System Relaying Committee, October 1976.

[11]L. Middendorf, "Judging Clearance Distances Near Overhead Powerlines." *Proceedings of the 22nd Annual Meeting of the Human Factors Society*, Detroit, October 1978.

[12]D. V. MacCollum, "How Safe the Lift?" *Proceedings of the 22nd Annual Meeting of the Human Factors Society*, Detroit, October 1978.

Appendix: Manufacturers of Load-Measuring Systems

1. DILLON Craneguard, Van Nuys, CA, U.S.A.
2. DOLE Electronic Crane Operational Warning Device, Eaton Control Products, Carol Stream, IL, U.S.A.
3. EKCO Load Guard Indicator Systems, EKCO Inst., Ltd., Essex, England.
4. KOEHRING Lorrain Overload Indicator (MC-8150), Alliance, OH, U.S.A.
5. KRUGER Load Moment Indicator, Frielingsdorfweg, Germany.
6. MARTIN DECKER Crane Load Moment Indicator Systems, Santa Ana, CA, U.S.A.
7. P&H Lode-Safe-T Computer, Milwaukee, WI, U.S.A.
8. STANCO Tilt Alarm, Chicago, IL, U.S.A.
9. TRANS-CAL Maxi-Miser Crane Operational Systems, Van Nuys, CA, U.S.A.
10. WARNER & SWASEY Load Monitor, Solon, OH, U.S.A.
11. WEIGHLOAD Automatic Safe Load Indicator, Alliance, OH, U.S.A.
12. WYLIE Safe Load Indicator, London, England.

Appendix: Notable References Relating to the Hazard of Boom/Power-Line Contact and Available Safeguards

1951   *Accident Prevention Manual (APM)*, 2nd ed. Chicago: National Safety Council (NSC), page 12–26.

1954   *Data Sheet #287*, NSC, page 2, para. 5.

1955   *APM*, 3rd ed., NSC, page 14–12.

1958   "Crane Contacts Can Kill," Paul Sheppard, *National Safety News* (NSC), October, page 130.

1959   "Crane Booms v. Powerlines," Sam Elkins, *National Safety News* (NSC), October, page 121.

1959   *APM*, 4th ed., NSC, page 19–2.

1962   *Technical Orders 36C-1-4*, U.S. Air Force, para. 9.1.11C.

1964   *Circular 385-1 Safety*, U.S. Department of Army, February.

1964   *APM*, 5th ed., NSC, page 18–24.

1964   *Handbook of Rigging for Construction & Industrial Operations*, 3rd ed. New York: McGraw-Hill, page 288.

1967   *Technical Bulletin TB-385-101 Safety*, U.S. Department of Army.

1967   *Safety Handbook for Mobile Cranes*. London: Royal Society for the Prevention of Accidents & Institute of Material Handling, page 16.

1967   *General Safety Requirements, EM 385-1-1*, Corps of Engineers, U.S. Department of Army, para. 15.E.09.

1968   *Code for Crawler, Locomotive & Truck Cranes.* New York: American National Standards Institute (ANSI), para. 5.3.4.5b.

1968   *Contacting Overhead Electric Powerlines–Mobile Cranes*, Technical Bulletin #1, Liberty Mutual, Boston, MA, May 20.

1969   *A Survey of Non-Employee Electrical Contacts*, NSC pamphlet.

1969   *Derricks*, B30.6, ANSI, para. 6.3.5.3b.

1969   *APM*, 6th ed., NSC, page 560.

1972   *Safety & Health Regulations*, U.S. Department of Labor (OSHA), Construction Standards, Subpart N, "Cranes, Derricks, Hoists, Elevators & Conveyors," 1926.550.

1973   *Mobile Hydraulic Cranes*, B30.15, ANSI, para. 15.3.4.2b.

1974   *APM*, 7th ed., NSC, page 691.

1976   *MESA Informational Report*, U.S. Department of Interior, page 5.

1979   *Data Sheet 10287*, NSC.

1980   *APM*, 8th ed., NSC, page 166.

9

Recreational Vehicles

LAURIE N. SOLOMON
Baltimore, Maryland

Laurie N. Solomon will receive a law degree from the University of Baltimore School of Law in 1985. From 1977 to 1982 she was a writer/researcher of the Center for Auto Safety in Washington, D.C. She is the co-author of Recreational Vehicles Hazardous to Your Health and Pocketbook, *published by the Center in 1982, and the author of* "Highway Homes—Hazardous to Your Health" *in* Trial *magazine in 1981. She may be contacted at 103 South Beechfield Avenue, Baltimore, Maryland 21229.*

I. INTRODUCTION

Defective recreational vehicles (RVs) threaten both consumers' lives and pocketbooks. The impact of these defects on consumers is increased by an ineffective warranty system that keeps the consumer going back to the chassis and frame manufacturers for repeated repairs that often do not correct the defect.

Recreational vehicles range from a pickup truck with an inexpensive removable cover to a $75,000 motor home that is integrally constructed on a heavy-duty chassis. Other RVs include camping trailers (trailers with collapsible walls for towing), mini–motor homes (homes constructed on the rear section of a van or small truck), travel and fifth-wheel trailers, and van conversions.

Every major RV accident study has found that RVs are leaders in highway deaths and injuries. In a 1978 report to Congress on light truck safety, the Government Accounting Office (GAO) reported that "light trucks and vans have become increasingly popular in recent years, and the trend is expected to continue in the future. Likewise, the number of occupants killed in these vehicles has also increased. . . . During the period 1975 and 1976, light truck fatalities increased 13 percent while passenger car fatalities increased 1 percent."[1]

In 1974, the National Highway Traffic Safety Administration (NHTSA) had received enough evidence of RV hazards to warrant contracting with the University of Kentucky for research that would document RV safety problems. The basic finding of the detailed 275-page report: *the overall risk of accidents on interstates for RVs was more than twice that of other vehicles.*[2]

Other reports are similarly critical of RV safety. A 1972 National Transportation Safety Board (NTSB) special study on the safety of RVs found that "most recreational vehicles have inherent problems related to their design, performance, or operation which differ considerably from those of the ordinary car or truck, and thus require independent treatment" and pointed out that "recreational vehicle passengers are exposed to risks that are not present in ordinary passenger cars."[3]

RVs have had major safety, quality control, and warranty service problems since they were first sold in the 1930s. The RV manufacturers' freedom and willingness to abuse consumers in the absence of any significant state or federal regulation worsens the problem. Although NHTSA has jurisdiction over the safety of the vehicle or chassis part of RVs, the living portion is totally *unregulated*. Even where NHTSA has jurisdiction, crucial passenger car standards, such as head restraints, roof-crush resistance, and side-door strength, do not apply to RVs.

Although NHTSA stated in 1978 that it planned to extend major passenger car standards to RVs, GAO cautioned that this was unlikely to be anything more than just good intentions: "The agency, however, has previously developed plans and promised to extend many of the same standards to light trucks. . . . Even though many were incorporated into notices of proposed rulemaking, light trucks still remain exempt from safety features which have been on passenger cars for more than 10 years. Although the administration has informed the Congress that improving the safety of these vehicles is one of the agency's top priorities, we see little actual movement in that direction."[4]

The Federal Trade Commission (FTC), which has authority to regulate warranty abuses, has taken no steps in a general manner to protect RV purchasers from unscrupulous manufacturers.

The lack of federal protection is not compensated for by industry self-policing. The RVIA, the major industry trade association, has moved only to adopt weak standards in an attempt to ward off federal regulation. The standards, written under the auspices of the American National Standards Institute (ANSI), do not even mention basic construction or crashworthiness.[5]

II. LACK OF CRASHWORTHINESS

While several serious safety problems exist, one of the worst is lack of crashworthiness. The structure of many RVs offer little protection in the event of rollover or a crash. Many RV bodies are made of thin metal or plastic laminate skins fastened to a sandwich of styrofoam (actually a styrofoamlike substance) pressed or glued between two pieces of wood.

The 1972 NTSB special study of RV safety led the researchers to conclude that the wood–plastic–metal frame construction that typifies RV bodies "sometimes cannot withstand the forces involved in crashes, and can either collapse or come apart at the joints, thus increasing the hazards to passengers."[6]

Vehicles with such poor structural integrity exist because federal safety standards are inadequate. There is no dynamic frontal crash testing for occupant safety. In the 1978 GAO report, the GAO urged NHTSA to extend a stiffened Federal Motor Vehicle Safety Standard (FMVSS) 214 (Side-Door Strength) and FMVSS 216 (Roof-Crush Resistance) to light trucks.

Although NHTSA announced in a 1979 Advanced Notice of Proposed Rulemaking that it would extend FMVSS 214 to light trucks, vans, and multipurpose passenger vehicles, this proposal has since joined the graveyard of dead proposals that GAO warned had been the history of NHTSA's light truck rulemaking.

NHTSA has not issued any proposed rule to extend other crashworthiness standards to RVs. NHTSA has no plans to adopt standards such as roof strength (216), which is vital in a rollover, and has merely indicated it might propose standards such as 209 (frontal crash occupant protection) at some future date.

The RV industry has not responded to the continuing warnings and studies over time that crashworthiness should be upgraded substantially. In 1974, a Department of Transportation (DOT) investigatory team pointed out that the poor crashworthiness of RVs was due to the rapid growth of a new industry:

> The camper structure is not well designed, and any lateral or rollover impact literally destroys the body integrity. The amazing lack of foresight of designers of these structures can only be explained by the rapid growth of the recreational vehicle industry and the lack of controls attended to this type of growth.[7]

Three years later the University of Kentucky repeated the findings of the earlier studies; the team strongly recommended that considerable effort be directed "toward improving the crashworthiness of RVs to reduce the probability of occupant ejection, particularly in rollover accidents."[8]

Unsafe motor home construction is so common that it is the subject of advertisement in industry magazines. Superior ran an ad for its motor home in trade magazines that read:

> Would you buy a car with a wooden frame? Would you even want to RIDE in it, at highway speeds? Of course not—that kind of automobile construction went out shortly after the horse and buggy. But there are a number of MOTOR HOMES being built today with wooden frames, or next-to-no frames.

With the push to improve fuel economy in the late 1970s, RV manufacturers have moved to lighter materials that may even be less crush resistant than earlier materials. For example, a company that specializes in the manufacture of "foam core panels" made of "polystyrene bead board and wood wafer board" advertised its popular product in *RV Dealer* (January 1978) as "lightweight and easily worked, . . . ideal for RVs."

While the material may be "ideal" for the RV manufacturer who saves money, it is much too flimsy to add any structural integrity to the construction of RVs. If the RV industry had been prodded by either federal or voluntary crashworthiness standards, they could have taken the opportunity to build safety into the new generation of more fuel-efficient RVs at low cost rather than waste the opportunity and people's lives.

III. FIRE HAZARDS IN RVs

After conducting its three-year study for the DOT, the University of Kentucky reported that *"the incidence rate of RV fires is about eight times the reported rate for all vehicle types."*[9] This abnormally high rate is due to a variety of factors: the highly flammable construction of RVs including the wood paneling, furniture, and high use of plastic materials; the unprotected position of the main and auxiliary gas tanks; and the auxiliary electrical systems in many RVs. In combination, these factors pose a serious fire hazard.

The fire hazard reported by the University of Kentucky is just a fraction of the real risk, for many RV fires occur on campsites and in other nonhighway situations that go unreported. While there are national compilations of data on highway accidents collected by the Highway Loss Data Institute, the DOT's National Accident Sampling System, and the Fatal Accident Reporting System, there is no such comprehensive system for nonhighway accidents involving RVs.

A. Fire Flashover from Polyurethane

Interiors of motor homes are so flammable that any delay in getting out of the vehicle often results in death even if there is no crash, as in the following case. Donald and Minnie Neil were driving along in their $20,000 motor home when the rear of the vehicle caught fire from a fuel leak. According to a June 24, 1978, *Washington Star* report:

> County fire officials said Neil was driving about 3 p.m. yesterday when he was alerted by his wife that a fire had started in the rear of the vehicle.
>
> Neil pulled the motorhome onto the shoulder of the road and tried to open the door, but it was stuck. He then managed to escape through an open window and told his wife to jump.
>
> But fire officials said Mrs. Neil was trapped inside and died in the fire. Firemen said the intensity of the blaze totally destroyed the motorhome. Its aluminum sides were entirely melted, leaving only the frames.

The interior of a motor home or RV is so flammable that many people like Mrs. Neil never get out in time. The RVIA voluntary flammability standard for RV interiors is so weak that it virtually *permits the use of materials that burn faster than people can run.* Until December 1976, there were no restrictions whatsoever on the use of highly flammable foamed plastics. Even today, these foams are banned only for interior finishes and can be used for insulation, in furniture, and for cushions.

Cellular foam or foamed plastic materials refer to polyurethane, usually called urethane, a lightweight, inexpensive product of the plastics revolution. Urethane is inherently flammable. It frequently burns hotter and faster than more traditional materials in home furnishings, such as wood, glass, or cotton, and generates dense smoke and toxic gases.

In 1976, the FTC began a five-year investigation into the plastic industry after hearing of the deaths of two children in a fire attributed to a spray urethane foam. After reviewing files, test results, and company advertisements, the FTC forced the industry officials to agree to a consent order in November 1974. Although the industry admitted to no guilt, it agreed to stop advertising urethane as nonburning or self-extinguishing, to notify past customers of the product's hazards, and to finance a five-year, $5 million research program to develop realistic tests and fire safety guidelines.

Until 1974, urethane manufacturers advertised rigid urethane, the type used for insulation, as being nonburning or self-extinguishing. They based this claim on the results of a test adopted in 1951 by the American Society for Testing and Materials, an 80-year-old nonprofit organization whose tests and standards are almost universally accepted by industry. In the D1692 test, a sample of material 6 inches long, 2 inches wide, and 1/2 inch thick was placed on a horizontal wide mesh screen. A Bunsen burner was applied below one end of the material. If an inch or less of the sample burned after one minute, the material was classified as "nonburning." If more than 1 inch, but less than 5, was destroyed, the material could be rated as "self-extinguishing."

In real fires, however, urethane often behaves far differently. In many cases, urethane is the material primarily responsible for a phenomenon called flashover, a situation in which such a high temperature is reached that the fire audibly and visibly "flashes over" the affected areas. "At this time, the fire is out of control and is acting as a great pump to force smoke and toxic gases through the building," Irving A. Benjamin, Chief of the Fire Safety Engineering Division of the National Bureau of Standards (NBS) explained. "The sooner it reaches flashover, the less the escape time. After flashover, there is a quantum jump in the probability of major loss of life and property."[10]

The National Academy of Sciences (NAS) recently released a report on the hazards of polyurethane in motor vehicles. It stated:

Polymeric materials are major contributors to the high frequency of passenger car fires.

As the diversity and amount of polymeric materials used in vehicles increase, the problems presented by the generation of smoke and toxic gases in a fire also increase.

In many instances death is a result of the toxic combustion products and not a result of the heat and flames from the fire.

In 1977, the Urban Mass Transportation Administration (UMTA) set engineering design specifications that, without mentioning it, effectively ban urethane from seating in new public transit buses that are purchased with federal funds. The agency also has made available what it calls "voluntary guidelines" for subway and other rapid rail transit systems. Washington, Baltimore, and Miami have adopted these voluntary guidelines in purchasing new cars. The UMTA decision, as to the best way of implementing material fire safety standards, is in review and a decision is expected in the near future.[11] The conditions of the standards would effectively ban urethane cushioning until a safe way of having such cushioning is feasible.

Despite the fact that the urethane fire hazard in RVs was reduced somewhat with the interior finish standard mentioned above, *the urethane insulation currently used is a significant fire hazard* about which prospective buyers of RVs are not informed. Instead, manufacturers' brochures extol the virtues of foamed-in-place insulation. One 1978 mini-motor home brochure reads: "Sprayed on all sidewalls, roof and under frame, this superior foam also helps seal and unify the entire body thus providing better soundproofing."

The Center for Auto Safety has received many requests from attorneys whose clients have died or almost died as a result of polyurethane insulation. An attorney from Salinas, California, wrote:

> I was particularly surprised to discover only the one exit door and the fact that the insulation on these motor homes is of polyurethane, a highly flammable substance. When my client's motor home caught fire, it became an intense ball of fire within a matter of seconds, forcing them to leap from the motor home. One of them almost was unable to push the door open against the wind and nearly didn't escape.

Urethane insulation presents serious fire risks because of the way RVs are constructed. Most are built with interior wood paneling over foam plastic insulation and an outer metal skin. Potentially serious fires are due to the flammability of the interior paneling itself and to the interior paneling not providing enough fire protection to the foam insulation.

One well-known fire engineer, James Winger, commented:

> If you're going to use foam insulation then the interior finish should have a low flame spread rating and also protect the foam insulation from an interior fire. One-quarter-inch-thick wood paneling as is used in most RVs is not satisfactory.

Alternatives to urethane or to using urethane alone do exist. Many experts recommend a foam interliner called Vonar, introduced by Dupont in 1976. Vonar is wrapped around the urethane cushioning and in a fire gives off fire retardants and moisture. "We've done a lot of work with it, and it does extremely well in both flaming and smoldering combustion," said Gordon Damant, Chief of California's Home Furnishings Bureau.[12]

Another alternative is solimide. One expert who tested this foam said, "It never did participate in the experimental fire. There was also little or no toxic gases coming off of it."[13]

Another fire safety improvement is flame retarding the urethane. According to one fire engineer, flame retardants are much easier to use on rigid urethane than on flexible urethane. It will delay ignition and/or prevent ignition from small sources, if it is used in the sufficient amount and used properly. However, flame retardants would not protect the urethane in the case of a large enveloping RV fire. But the simplest alternative would be to substitute fire resistant gypsum board in place of flammable foam panels containing urethane.

B. Inadequate Egress

Another serious fire hazard is inadequate egress. Almost all RVs have just one door. Although the RVIA standard has a requirement covering exits, the requirement is so full of loopholes that it is meaningless. Indeed, this standard is a perfect example of why voluntary industry standards do not protect the public's health and safety. The standard calls for "a minimum of two means of egress located remote from each other and so arranged as to provide a means of unobstructed travel to the outside of the vehicle."[14] The alternate exit is a window "located on a wall other than the wall in which the main vehicle exit door is located, or shall be located in the roof."[15]

The standard goes on to say, "the bottom of the alternate means of exit should not be more than 4 feet above the vehicle floor or above a readily accessible horizontal surface capable of supporting a weight of 300 pounds."[16] In the close quarters of the average RV it would be difficult not to find something a person could climb on to reach the window.

In the event of fire, having only one door poses a serious threat to escape. That door could be stuck or obstructed by flames. A window is not a sufficient second exit. Persons panicked by flames, smoke, and hot gases would find the task of scrambling onto a ledge or other object extremely difficult, if not impossible. For small children and elderly persons, this route of escape is out of the question. Numerous consumers have written to the Center for Auto Safety about the deaths of relatives caused by entrapment inside a flaming RV and about accidents they have witnessed where jammed doors prevented escape. In September 1979, Henry Sacra was driving a motor home from Delaware to Maryland. Seated with him in the passenger cabin was his wife Hazel. Seated in the rear living quarters were the Sacra's grandson, Norman, age 13, and his cousin, John Sacra, age 11. Upon entering an intersection, the motor home was hit broadside by a jeep. The impact of the collision caused the motor home to turn at right angles, knock down an electric pole, and roll over onto its roof. Within minutes after the rollover, components of the RV's fuel system exploded and set the motor home ablaze. Henry and Hazel Sacra were rescued with only minor injuries from the burning motor home by passersby. But the two young boys perished in the blaze. The passersby, who had rescued the adults could only watch helplessly as the two young boys burned to death. The motor home with its crushed roof and a single blocked door to the living area had entombed the youths in a fiery incinerator fueled by a flammable structure of the vehicle itself.

C. Ineffective Government Flammability Standard

The problems of fire safety in RVs are compounded by a federal standard that is not only inadequate, but also does not cover all types of RVs. Although FMVSS 302 governs the flammability of interior materials supplied by the chassis manufacturer, it does not cover the living quarters, and travel trailers, fifth-wheel trailers, and van conversions are excluded. FMVSS 302 is only applicable to cars, multipurpose passenger vehicles (MPVs*), trucks, and buses.

The NBS criticized FMVSS 302 as being an ineffective standard. In a 1974 letter to NHTSA, James Winger, Head of Product Flammability Research in the Center for Fire Research at the NBS, wrote:

> Our data shows that the major fire hazard of upholstered furniture and bedding in homes is smoldering ignition from

---

*MPV is a term used by NHTSA to describe motor vehicles with motor power, except a trailer designed to carry 10 persons or less that is constructed either on a truck chassis or with special features for occasional off-road operation.

cigarettes and the resultant smoke and lack of oxygen. Since campers and trailers are used as dwellings while camping, we would expect the fire hazard to be similar to that found in homes. If this supposition is correct, an appropriate standard must measure the resistance to smoldering rather than an open flame burn rate.

In 1984 this statement is still true.

D. Inadequate Voluntary Industry Fire Standard

Voluntary industry fire standards for RVs are safety standards in name only. The maximum flame spread classification of 100 set by the RVIA standard for the allowable flame spread for RV interiors is much too lax. According to one fire engineer at the NBS, "Material with a 200 flame spread will readily propagate fires."[17] Harry Hickey, a fire-research professor at the University of Maryland, explained the meaning of the 200 rating: "A flame spread of between 150 and 200 burns about as quickly as the average adult can run. Anything over 200 will reach the end of a hallway before a running person does."[18]

The industry basis for this inadequate standard is a similarly inadequate standard applied to mobile homes, which are not only similar to some large RVs, but also are built by the same manufacturers.[19] RVs share many fire hazards with mobile homes since both are covered by similar standards and often are built by the same manufacturer. The National Fire Prevention and Control Administration (NFPCA) of the Department of Commerce, which conducted a two-year study of mobile home fires for the Department of Housing and Urban Development (HUD) in 1976, attributed its findings that "mobile homes are the fastest-burning of all homes" to the same characteristics of RVs today:

> . . . their small size, close proximity of heaters and kitchens to sleeping area, the concentration of combustible materials, lack of adequate egress in many cases, and a higher combustibility of interior finishes than in most site-built homes.[20]

Fire standards for both RVs and mobile homes have hazardous exceptions: the flame spread limitation for mobile homes does not apply to windows, doors, or series of doors not exceeding 4 feet in width and permanently attached decorative items such as pictures or accent panels. The RV flame spread limitation does not apply to the interior finish in bath and toilet rooms, to moldings, trim, and splash panels, to doors and cabinets, or to furnishings. Many of these items in both mobile homes and RVs are made out of highly burning plastics.

In 1979, NBS criticized the 200 flame spread in its report *Mobile Home Fire Studies: Summary and Recommendations.*[21] The report proposed three fire safety options to limit the occurrence of flashover from low- and moderate-intensity source fires in the living area, sleeping area, and hallway corridor area. (Flashover is a fire phenomenon in which thermal radiation from the upper walls and ceiling and from the hot gases and smoke layer in the upper part of the room is sufficient to cause ignition and rapid complete fire involvement of all combustible materials in the room.) A HUD contract confirmed that any of these NBS alternatives would be economically feasible.[22]

IV. FORMALDEHYDE: THE HIDDEN TOXIN

No hazard is so overlooked by RV manufacturers and the government as the highly toxic formaldehyde used in the gluing of wood framing, as a binder in particle board, and as insulation. Over time, chemical reactions occur that allow formaldehyde in the insulation and glue to release into the atmosphere. The breakdown is speeded by hot, humid conditions. RVs are more susceptible to formaldehyde build-ups than conventional housing because they are built so tightly.

Health problems that result are breathing difficulties, serious eye and skin irritations, headaches and dizziness, nausea, vomiting, and severe nosebleeds. Dr. Peter Breysse, a University of Washington environmental health professor, believes that foam insulation made of urea-formaldehyde (U.F. foam insulation) is a "possible source of sudden infant death." Deaths such as that of the 6-month-old daughter of Mark Hirsch of Lamberton, Minnesota, after a six-day trip in a motor home support this position.

Inaction relative to formaldehyde in RVs is all the more indefensible in view of research showing that it causes cancer. The Chemical Institute for Toxicology (CIT) found formaldehyde to be carcinogenic to rats in laboratory studies.[23] A Federal Interagency Regulatory Liaison Group composed of scientists from the Consumer Product Safety Commission, the Department of Energy, the Environmental Protection Agency, the National Cancer Institute, and the National Institute of Environmental Health Sciences confirmed CIT's findings and concluded:

> The levels of formaldehyde causing cancer in animals are not greatly different from those to which consumers are exposed; nor do there appear to be significant qualitative metabolic differences between rats and humans with regard to formaldehyde.
>
> Formaldehyde should be presumed to pose a carcinogenic risk to humans.[24]

The panel also found that formaldehyde was mutagenic to a number of different test systems and caused chromosomal aberrations.

While much attention is being given to the use of formaldehyde in conventional and mobile homes by various government agencies, the use of formaldehyde in RVs is being dangerously ignored. In August 1981, HUD began preliminary rulemaking on the formaldehyde problem in mobile homes. Because of the health dangers involved in increased use of formaldehyde foam insulation, HUD has issued a "Use of Materials Bulletin" (UMB 74) to explain the conditions under which HUD will accept U.F. foam insulation for use in new home construction. In April 1982, the Consumer Product Safety Commission (CPSC) banned formaldehyde for insulation in homes but refused to ban its use in RVs.

A. Protection of Consumers by States

Due to the slow pace of the federal government and the refusal of industry to do anything on formaldehyde, various states have taken action to eliminate formaldehyde's health hazards:

- Massachusetts has declared U.F. foam insulation to be a banned hazardous substance and has required its removal from commerce in that state. The Massachusetts ban became effective November 14, 1979.
- Connecticut requires manufacturers to provide pro-

spective purchasers with a notice in all U.F. foam insulation contracts from all manufacturers.

- Denver County (Colorado) has adopted a prohibition against the use of U.F. foam insulation in new or existing construction.
- On September 17, 1980, based on the acute health hazards to consumers, the Colorado Department of Health banned the future installation of U.F. foam insulation in facilities where persons may be exposed for a protracted length of time without knowledge of the presence of the product. The department also requires a disclosure statement in contracts for installation of the product in private dwellings or other buildings not covered by the ban.
- New York and Rhode Island have adopted health- and safety-related disclosure requirements for the product concerning the acute risk of injury.
- On June 23, 1980, a temporary rule was proposed in Minnesota to establish a maximum limit of 0.5 ppm for the air inside newly constructed dwelling units.
- On December 18, 1979, the Virginia Department of Health issued a Health Hazard Alert Sheet on the problems of acute toxicity presented by formaldehyde and U.F. foam insulation.
- In several state legislatures, bills have been introduced to ban or to impose a moratorium on the sale of U.F. foam insulation (Arizona, West Virginia, New Hampshire, and Ohio), or to require safety-related disclosures (Maryland).[25]

B. Consumers Misled by RV Dealers and Manufacturers

RV manufacturers, dealers, and trade magazines laud formaldehyde use in RVs, but they do not tell consumers of its use even when they are informed of formaldehyde-produced symptoms and they give misinformation about how to get rid of formaldehyde fumes and its dangerous consequences. In a review of a fifth-wheel trailer, *Trailer Life* magazine (June 1979) wrote:

> The . . . construction features are impressive. . . . Insulation is . . . urea-formaldehyde foam in the walls, with an insulation factor about twice that of fiberglass, or an equivalent of about four inches of fiberglass.

In April 1980, when two Center for Auto Safety staffers got in a motor home on a visit to a dealership, their eyes started stinging and tearing so badly they could not remain in the RV. When they asked the salesperson what caused the stinging, he did not mention the use of formaldehyde:

Staffer: What made our eyes water like that?

Dealer: Oh, some homes do that when they are new.

Staffer: Why?

Dealer: I don't know. Just something in them, maybe in the materials. If you left the windows open for half an hour, all that would be gone.

Consumers are similarly led away from formaldehyde as the culprit when they complain about formaldehyde symptoms such as stinging eyes. Shortly after buying an $18,000 RV in April 1978, the Francis Masons of Longview, Washington, complained to the salesperson:

Couldn't have friends in, eyes and nose burned so badly couldn't stand it. I asked about formaldehyde and he said it was not used.

When Mr. Mason complained to the manufacturer, the manufacturer did admit the odor was formaldehyde but falsely stated it was required by fire law.

A California transporter of RVs confirmed the prevalence of such fumes and the extent to which manufacturers go to keep it from their own dealers when he wrote the Center for Auto Safety in August 1981 as follows:

The chemicals as well as the adhesives used in the interior of the coach caused temporary sickness and possibly permanent injury to the health of the occupants.

Fumes from gasoline, adhesives, chemicals and components of the coach permeated the interior of the vehicle and may have led to respiratory problems with the drivers.

I have cited a few of the problems I, as well as others, experienced while transporting motorhomes for a period of five years. Perhaps the most significant part of the problems that existed were the orders not to write them on the Bill of Lading or tell the dealer about them.

V. LIQUID PROPANE GAS: TOXIC, FLAMMABLE, AND EXPLOSIVE

In addition to lethal gasoline tanks, many RVs carry liquid propane gas (LP gas) to provide all the convenience of cooking meals, heating water, refrigerating foods, and even air conditioning. Stored as a liquid under pressure and used as a gas, LP gas supplies five to six times as much heat as manufactured gas and two and one-half to three times as much heat as natural gas. These are the pluses that RV dealers and manufacturers are quick to point out. RV dealers and manufacturers fail to relate with equal rigor the hazards of LP gas— asphyxiation, fire, and explosion.

A. Carbon Monoxide Poisoning

Although consumers may be generally aware of the fire and explosion hazards of RVs, they are all too unaware of carbon monoxide (CO) asphyxiation, which is caused by incomplete combustion of LP gas. Any heating device that burns a carbon or hydrocarbon fuel (such as LP gas, wood, coal, charcoal, kerosene, propane, or gasoline) will give off carbon monoxide (CO).

CO is a colorless, odorless, and lethal gas. Asphyxiation occurs because the blood absorbs carbon monoxide from the lungs in preference to oxygen at a ratio of 200 to 1. Lack of oxygen, essential for the body to function, causes asphyxiation. Carbon monoxide poisoning works quickly: it will give a person a headache in an hour or two, cause him to go under in above five hours, and probably kill him during a night's sleep.

In November 1980, Mary Meyer of Jackson, Wyoming, wrote to the Center for Auto Safety about a defective gas-powered generator. Four people were on an outing in their motor home. Before turning in for the night, the RVers turned on the gas-powered generator to keep them warm. They never woke up. A leak in the exhaust pipe of the generator built up fatal levels of CO in the motor home. All four occupants died of asphyxiation.

A similar defect claimed the lives of Anthony J. Lombardino and Marcia J. Greisen of Madison, Wisconsin, on April 2, 1979. They were asphyxiated in a 1979 26-foot motor home when lethal carbon monoxide levels built up after a defectively vented LP gas furnace was turned on. They died because an employee at the manufacturer's plant covered a blemished outside panel without recutting vents for the furnace.

Although the RVIA is well aware of the many fatal causes of CO poisoning, it has not taken any positive action to reduce the hazard. Instead, RVIA has merely issued ANSI standard A119.2 requiring that a warning label be attached adjacent to fuel burning ranges which reads: "It is not safe to use cooking appliances for comfort heating."

An extensive body of behavioral research[26] in the area of public health problems has found that warnings, such as the RVIA advisory sticker, are generally ineffective in altering consumer behavior. The warning label seeks to change the behavior of those RVers who routinely or occasionally leave their LP gas stoves on to heat the RV. Of course, this warning ignores the equally hazardous LP gas refrigerator and the water heater, which stay on all the time. To be effective, then, the precautions on the label must be followed every time the vehicle is operated. *As extensive research in the public health field has demonstrated, strategies that attempt to change the behavior of every individual to be protected, called active strategies, are not as successful as strategies that protect people regardless of their behavior, called passive strategies.* For example, water purification at its source is more likely to reduce disease than attempts to persuade each individual to boil his or her own water before drinking it. In the case of CO poisoning, the proper strategy would be to use a CO warning detector that sounds off as CO levels rise, just as a smoke detector sounds off as smoke rises.

B. LP Gas Leaks and Other Defects

LP gas systems in RVs are more prone to manufacturing defects leading to death and injury than any other system in RVs. The consequences of an LP gas leak are nothing short of disasterous. The LP gas builds up in the RV until it reaches an explosive mixture. If there is a nearby ignition source such as a pilot light, the entire RV could explode.

National Highway Traffic Safety Administration recalls confirm the defective nature of the LP gas system. In 1979, there were 10 safety recalls of 30,917 RV units involving LP gas systems.

B.1. REGULATOR DEFECTS LP gas tanks and systems contain gas-flow regulators that are essential for their safe operation.

Gas leaks can occur if the regulator vent opening becomes frozen—an all too common occurrence. Should this happen, full pressure is delivered to the RV. After the furnace shuts off, pressure build-up in the LP gas lines blows out all pilot lights and the weakest point in the LP system gives way. Any ignition source will then start an explosion. Although ANSI standard A119.2 has a requirement stating that "regulators shall be installed so the regulator vent opening will not be affected by the elements such as sleet, snow, freezing rain, ice, mud or by wheel spray," *this is not followed.*

On November 13, 1977, Judith and Kenneth Henry stopped in St. Clair, Michigan, and parked their 1977 motor home. Unknown to them, the plastic cover of the LP gas regulator trapped water or ice thrown up by the plastic cover of the wheels and had caused the LP pressure regulator valve to malfunction. During the night, hazardous concentrations of LP gas built up in the motor home. Some time during the night, the LP gas reached an ignition source. A violent explosion and fire racked the motor home, leaving Judith Henry with severe burns that permanently disfigured her.

B.2. EXCESS FLOW LIMITERS Before 1976, there was no standard regulating the amount of propane that could escape into the RV in the event of a leak. In 1976, the RVIA acted on a National Transportation Safety Board (NTSB) recommendation to adopt a new standard to prevent gas leaks from becoming larger once they have started. The NTSB based its recommendation on the collision of a motor home in which two 40-pound propane tanks became detached from the vehicle and seriously added to the original gasoline fire.[27] The standard calls for an excess flow valve that cuts off the propane supply if the tank valves, regulators, or service lines become damaged. The valve does nothing about small leaks that allow explosive levels of LP gas to build up in an RV.

Even the RVIA admits that the excess flow valve is not that effective. In April 1981, the RVIA Standards Director Bruce Hopkins said, "It's basically a useless device. If it worked at low outage pressure, then the systems wouldn't function. It's basic function is to keep the full force of the bottle from flowing out if the regulator snaps off." In response to the question of how common that occurrence was, Hopkins said that he "didn't know of any case where the regulator has snapped off." He added that the excess flow valve has been an issue for many years.[28]

C. LP Gas Detectors and Warnings

In order to alert persons to undetected leaks, the National Fire Protection Association (NFPA) has a standard requiring that a warning odorizer be added to the gas.

Mercaptan, the gas usually used as the warning agent, is not always effective. The NFPA itself acknowledges odorizer inadequacies and includes a footnote to the above standard. "It is recognized that no odorant will be completely effective as a warning agent in every circumstance."[29]

Many studies and accident reports stress mercaptan's inability to effectively notify persons of LP gas leaks. Various factors such as unfamiliar out-of-doors settings, falling asleep, age, confusion with other odors, and inability to detect mercaptan's odor due to becoming used to the smell can affect an individual's ability to identify the gas. As far back as 1969, the Department of Health, Education and Welfare (HEW) cited the difficulty of individuals detecting mercaptan's odor in the LP gas fires it investigated.[30]

Many experts point out the particular problem of the elderly, who may lose some of their ability to smell. In an article in the *Journal of Chronic Diseases*, a researcher of accidents among the elderly pointed out that an elderly person may have a difficult time detecting a gas odor that may be easily recognized by a younger person. The alleviation of the gas leak problem should not depend solely on the individual's ability to detect a gas odor.[31]

Even if mercaptan were an adequate odorizer, adding it to LP gas does not ensure that it will get out into an RV for the occupant to smell. Mercaptan is heavier than LP gas. When the vehicle is not in use, there is a risk of mercaptan settling to the bottom of the LP gas and not getting out in sufficient quantities to produce a detectable odor.

The failure of mercaptan to alert RV owners has resulted in lawsuits against suppliers of LP gas. In her lawsuit concerning the LP gas fire in her motor home, Judith Henry was awarded $95,444 against Suburban Propane Gas Corporation for Suburban's failure to add sufficient quantities of mercaptan gas or other odorous chemicals to the LP gas.[32]

Experts familiar with RV accidents, as well as John Ebeling, the former Public Relations Director for Winnebago and investigator for the Second International Congress in Automotive Safety, recommended that *automatic devices that alert persons to LP gas leaks should be mandatory equipment.* Such automatic detectors that use lights and a horn to alert persons of dangerous concentrations of fumes presently come as standard equipment only on some RVs and are offered as an option on others.

VI. UNSOUND CONSTRUCTION

Using glowing terms, cutaway diagrams, and stylish but homey photos to entice the would be purchaser, RV sales brochures offer construction of exceptional strength and integrity, rugged dependability, furnishings like home, and assurance that your RV is built to last. Too few RV owners find these promises to be true. For all too many consumers, the major question is whether their new RV will collapse in a crash or at a piece at a time on the road. In view of the manufacturers' sales claims, and for vehicles that can cost up to $75,000, such poor construction seems inexcusable.

RV quality control problems are rampant and serious. Complaints range from sprung doors and wood rot to entire RVs falling apart. Because the RVIA standard does not cover construction, RV manufacturers are totally free to choose how to construct their units and with what materials. In an effort to cut costs, manufacturers forgo adequate engineering, use inferior materials, and push units out of the factory before they are properly and safely assembled. Even though the *average* motor home costs $32,000 (they go up as high as $150,000), quality commensurate with the price is not included.

Poor construction is not limited to a few inexpensive RVs; it strikes all classes of RVs in epidemic numbers. The analysis by the Center for Auto Safety of its complaints show rampant construction defects in the $3,000 slide-in camper unit as well as the $100,000 motor home. Fully 50 percent of the RV owners who write the Center complain of construction defects in their RVs. While the examples below are dramatic, they are not atypical.

A. Defects in Material and Workmanship

Many consumer problems can be traced directly to use of inferior materials to cut costs. For example, interior doors are made of a very thin wood. As a result, supports crack, edges wiggle, and eventually entire doors fall off. Cabinets often fall apart because glue or staples are used to support them rather than strong wood backing or screws. Plastic is often used instead of metal. Closet and bathroom doors use plastic hinges that do not withstand normal wear.

Inferior materials used in the construction and interior of RVs cannot withstand normal use and in severe cases render units uninhabitable. Roland Bigwood from Merrimack, New Hampshire, owner of a mini-motor home, described the consequences of inferior materials and workmanship:

> [W]e left for [our] shakedown cruise and the bathroom door fell off. It was fastened only through the very thin plywood wall with no inner bracing or support. . . . The oven door fell off and we were unable to use the oven for the duration of our 1200 mile trip. The overhead cabinets pulled way from the plywood wall because there was nothing to fasten them to safely. It is quite an eerie feeling to drive along and see your cabinets vibrating loose.

The owner angrily added:

> The roof sags so that the closet door will not open fully without hitting the floor mounted air conditioner.

Another RV owner who complained about manufacturer defects was W. Day from Hayward, California. His *one-month-old* 1979 motor home had the following:

> The bathroom door is sprung . . . very poorly designed.

> The leg brace for the dinette table fell apart—the screws will not hold in a composition wood surface.

> The screws in the door "catch" to the large outside storage compartment were never installed.

> All of the wooden drawers have fallen apart.

Lloyd Jones, owner of a motor home from Salinas, California, tells of one defect that would be humorous if it were not so frustrating:

> My bathtub (plastic) must sit on an uneven base. There is a hump in the middle which prevents normal drainage, and must be drained by hand.

B. Design Defects

Some RVs suffer from design defects that are built into them from the outset due to poor engineering or even lack of engineering. Many manufacturers do not even have a comprehensive engineering staff. One manufacturer even confirmed this to a customer, when Gustaf W. Holmelin of Crosby, Texas, complained about his 1978 fifth-wheel trailer. The construction of the trailer was so bad that after only five months the frame sagged to such an extent that the back door of the trailer could not be opened and the side and roof exterior aluminum stretched. When Holmelin asked the Customer Relations Director of the manufacturer if he had discussed the sagging condition with his engineer, he replied that the company does not have any engineers or technical staff in its plant. Frames are purchased from a separate manufacturing company. Holmelin was understandably amazed to find that a company that constructs trailers that are sold to the public does not have any technical staff whatsoever.

Consumers suffer financially and physically because of manufacturers' design errors. Marian Sasser of Savannah, Georgia, found that the heater in her travel trailer could not be serviced without dismantling the entire cabinet section of the trailer, at the cost of $150. A service repairperson told her, "The camper was literally built around the heater." Yet, instructions for the trailer read "Clean and oil once a year."

James A. Strine of Oil City, Pennsylvania, counted 29 design defects in his motor home, including the bathroom sink faucet placed so close to the rim that water ran down the counter and onto the floor, a side table too small to fold down, the bathroom cabinet and the lower portions of the bunk side walls placed so low that heads easily bang on them, and limited storage space. "No place for: trash and garbage, shoes, dirty laundry."

Lack of storage space is such a notorious RV problem that manufacturers advertise adequacy of storage space as a selling feature. A recent trade journal ad for travel trailers reads:

> Unlike most travel trailer manufacturers who hide the plumbing pipes, water tanks and heat ducts in closets, in cabinets, under beds, and just generally in the way, [manufacturer] stores them in a trim, heated "Basement."
>
> We put our plumbing in the "basement" so your customers can hang their clothes in the closet.[33]

C. Water Leaks

Water leaks are one of the most serious and frequent complaints. Not only are leaks annoying, but if not repaired, can cause complete deterioration of an RV floor and possibly the side walls. Delamination, or skin popping out from the frame, is a common design problem. It is a result of moisture seepage. Many manufacturers fail to seal properly the RV bottoms, around the holding tank areas, water lines, generator compartments, and electrical wiring. If the generator compartment area is not sealed from the underneath, the insulation may cause water damage and wood rot. One consumer, C. Morrocco of Johnston, Rhode Island, wrote the Center for Auto Safety in February 1983 about continuing battles with water leakage:

> We purchased a [recreational vehicle] in November 1982. The first week it rained, the windshield and doors were badly damaged from leaking. Also the floor was all iced up and one side of the wall was all wet.

> We had it sealed six times with no results.

The leakage problem is due to several factors. The first cause is the lack of and inadequacy of exterior sealants around the roof, bottom, holding tank area, water lines, generator compartment, and electrical wiring. Road vibration, temperature change, and age cause voids even if sealants are initially present. Manufacturers are aware of the problem and advise consumers to check periodically for such voids. The second reason for water leakage is improper thermal bonding in the process used to produce laminated panel in RVs.

The leak problem is so prevalent that a special aftermarket industry has sprung up to sell leak preventative products to dealers and consumers. Parr, a manufacturer of sealants and caulks, advertises that its crack filler "seals fine hairline cracks and gaps up to 1/8 inch. . . . Gives and takes under roughest road vibrations and severest weathering for lasting, leak-tight service."[34]

VII. WARRANTY ABUSES

Difficulty in obtaining satisfactory warranty work is a major and frequent complaint of RV owners. RVs have multiple warrantors, and this is a main cause of warranty problems. There is one warranty for the chassis, another for the tires, and several for the appliances. The result for the owner is runaround. It is not unusual for consumers to spend six months without their RVs while they go back and forth between the dealer and the chassis and vehicle manufacturers' plants, which are often hundreds of miles apart. Nina Hughes of Livermore, California complained to the Center for Auto Safety about her 1978 mini–motor home:

> The unit was built on a Chevy chassis. They overloaded it on the front right side. This caused the unit to lean so badly to the right it was very hard to keep it on the road. Chevrolet disclaims any responsibility for the trouble as they say [the motor home manufacturer] overloaded the side. The president of [the motor home manufacturer] . . . just ignores my letters.

One cause of runaround is the fact that RV manufacturers disclaim responsibility for the chassis. A good example of this can be seen in a letter from the president of a manufacturer to Charles P. Selleck, owner of a 1978 motor home, from Carpinteria, California:

> If you will notice in our warranty we disclaim responsibility for the chassis, [the manufacturer] and Chrysler both warranty the respective parts with 12,000 miles or one year.

When Selleck experienced three transmission failures, Chrysler also disclaimed responsibility. Although it paid for the first replacement, it refused to pay for the next two, with the excuse that the warranty period had expired. Each of the three transmission service center mechanics who worked on the motor home told Selleck that the transmissions were too light for the unit and that they were the heaviest available to them for installation.

RV manufacturers are equally quick to disclaim responsibility for all the separate items in the RV, as well as the chassis. H. T. Overton of Galveston, Texas, summed up the situation in a 1978 letter to the Center about his motor home.

> The rig manufacturer is responsible for very little if anything. If you have problems with the fridge, you see the "authorized" fridge dealer. The same goes for the toilet,

stove, hot water heater, furnace, and most everything else including the engine. If you take it to the dealer he will usually refuse to do anything saying it's up to the manufacturer. Likewise, the manufacturer will say it's up to the dealer. All the while, the poor consumer is caught in the middle.

A. Refusal to Do Warranty Work

Sometimes RV manufacturers and dealers simply refuse to do warranty repair work. Like the warranty runaround, where each warrantor points the finger at another warrantor, the outright refusal to do warranty work is closely related to the number of companies involved in making and selling the RV, with uncertainty as to who is responsible for correcting a particular defect.

Where the dealer refuses to do the repair, the most common reasons given for the refusal are lack of space or necessary equipment, busy schedules, that the RV had not been brought back to the selling dealer for repair, and the lower repair rate authorized by the manufacturer as compared to that for non-warranty work.

Diane Heston from Del Mar, California, owner of a 1977 motor home, was told by five dealers within a 50-mile radius of her home that they were booked for several months. Several other dealers told her that they would not work on her motor home at all. The excuse that the RV has not been brought to the selling dealer is completely contrary to written warranties, which usually state:

> If the selling dealer has ceased to do business . . . or the owner of the motor home is traveling or has moved to a different locality and cannot return to the selling dealer, the owner may obtain warranty repairs or replacement of such items at any authorized . . . dealership.

A mailgram from William Chapman, an angry motor home owner, from Saratoga, California, typifies denial of warranty work by an RV manufacturer:

> [The manufacturer] has ignored and continues to ignore all correspondence. . . . [After one year] I have not received a single written acknowledgment of my attempts to resolve the current situation.

L. E. Reid of Van Nuys, California, a frustrated 1979 motor home owner, wrote that after experiencing several major problems including an electrical failure, a jammed door, plumbing leakage, and front-end misalignment so severe that she could not drink a cup of coffee, she found in the sales contract that the dealer/manufacturer "disclaimed any and all warranties and the contract does not provide for service and repair facilities."

Sometimes the RV dealer blamed its refusal to do warranty work on the manufacturer failing to pay the dealer. Thus, when the toilet failed on a motor home owned by Florence Nelson of Davis, California, the selling dealer refused to repair it under the warranty because the manufacturer had not reimbursed the dealer for other warranty jobs.

Although the FTC reports that 39 states require vehicle manufacturers to reimburse their dealers at the same rate for warranty repairs as the dealer charges the public, dealers frequently complain that warranty work does not pay for itself. Even where manufacturers pay the standard labor rate for repairs, they may not pay for defect diagnostic time or the same price for the parts. RV industry publications have frequently pointed out this problem as the following excerpt from "Service with a Smile" in the October 1980 issue of *RV Dealer* indicates:

> Some manufacturers, dealers say, have somewhat archaic warranty plans, paying the dealer less for labor hours than the amount actually expended. Other manufacturers are gradually becoming more progressive. Sometimes, however, dealers find it's impossible to negotiate reimbursements with manufacturers.

B. Poor Service and Repairs

When the RV owner gets the manufacturer or dealer to take responsibility for warranty repairs, all too often the repairs are poorly done. Common, however, is the recount of angry individuals who are forced repeatedly to take back their RVs to the dealer and even to the manufacturer because of unsolved problems. And these problems are of a serious nature: they concern the plumbing, the construction, or the electrical wiring. Imagine sleeping in your RV and being awakened by water dripping on your face. Impossible? No, sadly, and angrily, say RV owners, not at all.

Two months after purchase of a pickup camper, the Robert Companero's of Mahopac, New York, went to tour the country. Their first problem was a leaking window, followed by a leaking shower area, which caused a severely damaged floor. They returned the RV to the dealer who kept it two months for repair. When the vehicle was finally returned, the repairs were not made. Indeed, a more serious problem resulted—the floor pulled up and the wood separated. Just after getting the RV back, the Companeros tried a short trip. The front window leaked worse than ever and Mr. Companero was awakened by dripping water.

Inadequate warranty repair is a frequent and financially burdensome problem for RV owners. Consumers are forced repeatedly to take their RVs back to the dealers, with no final success. In a period of only six months, Burl Free's (from Fresno, California) 1978 travel trailer had to have four major overhauls, each time being out of his possession from two weeks to several months.

Sometimes even successive attempts at repair cannot solve problems caused by (1) poor design such as failure to prevent water leakage, which results in wood rot and skin delamination and/or (2) lack of proper parts for RVs. Many of the persistent failures are on appliances that are poorly designed for an RV. For example, the Vernon D. Todds from Winthrop Harbor, Illinois, were plagued with poor repair work made on their mini–motor home's refrigerator. Food was spoiled five times in a five-month period. After one such occasion, a dealership employee told the Todds that *they* should take the refrigerator out and put insulation on both sides.

One reason for incompetent work is lack of expertise or training of the repairmen. In a questionnaire sent to RV manufacturers by the Center for Auto Safety in February 1981, manufacturers were asked, "Do you offer training sessions for mechanics who service your RVs? May any such training session be attended by non-franchised dealer mechanics and how do they find out about training if open to them?" Of the companies responding to the Center questionnaire, none indicated that they had a comprehensive training that all mechanics took. Many companies have no training programs. For example, one manufacturer responded:

> [We do] not have a special training school or class. Any dealer or customer is welcome to come to the factory for information on how units are built.

C. Part and Repair Delays

A major factor adding to the repair fiasco is repair delay and delay in getting parts. Complaints of delayed service abound. As William Chapman of Saratoga, California, reported to the Center for Auto Safety, year-long delays can even occur.

> To date the motorhome has been out of my custody and in repair on two occasions for the incredible time period of almost one full year.

Often people are told their RV is ready to be picked up only to find after driving to the dealer or factory hundreds of miles away that their RV is, in fact, not ready. Even if the vehicle is ready, the distance to the RV factory is a major consumer burden. As Roland Bigwood of Merrimack, New Hampshire, wrote the Center in June 1978 about his motor home:

> I have made two trips to . . . the manufacturer, to have major repairs done. This is a journey of 2,000 miles round trip, not an inexpensive journey nor a short one.

Delayed repair service frequently results from unavailable parts. An FTC staff member told the Center, "Apparently, most manufacturers don't keep parts in stock—in some cases, not even for the current model year." As J. C. Moyle of Charlotte, North Carolina, wrote the Center in September 1982 about his motor home when his rear axle failed:

> No parts could be found—an entire new unit was found in Florida, could be trucked to Hanover in a week and repairs would take 2-3 days at a cost of $1700 to $2000.

> The brakes failed. Again no parts could be found. To salvage our vacation, we rented a car and continued on our trip since we had to wait a week to 10 days for repairs. This added expense ballooned our vacation costs from the expected $1200 to $4000 because of hotels, meals, and stretched absence from two weeks to three weeks.

So common is the unavailable parts problem that some members of the industry attempt to use this as a selling point as did Parkway Distributors, a division of Holiday Rambler, when it took out the following ad in the September 1979 issue of *RV Dealer*:

> You wait and wait for your parts and accessories order . . .
> only to find out that 30% of your order was "out of stock." If
> that's your problem, try "The Parkway Hustle."

Parts availability is so bad that some companies exclude liability for delay in meeting their warranty obligations where
parts are unavailable. For example, one 1978 warranty reads:

> . . . will complete any corrective work within 30 calendar
> days (excluding extra time required for [us] to obtain any
> parts which are not then in stock) after its written reply to
> Purchaser.

D. Warranty Lawsuits Can Be Successfully Won

For those RV owners who decide to take legal action against
the dealer and/or manufacturer, warranty lawsuits can be
successfully won. For example, Jack and Peggy Dunlop, of
Tucson, Arizona, are motor-home owners who sued and won.
They had purchased a defective $57,167, 1978 Arctic Sun
Motor Home from Jimmy Recreational Center, manufactured
by Neonex Leisure Products, Inc.

The motor home was sold as a year-round home with a
"full one-year warranty." However, soon after purchase, the
vehicle displayed numerous problems with the heating and
air conditioning systems. Leaks were discovered in the sky-
light, gas lines, and windows. Although the dealer was given
at least a half-dozen chances to correct the defects, they were
unable to repair the Arctic Sun properly. The motor home
was then returned to Neonex of America, the manufacturer.
When the plague of problems continued, the Dunlops refused
further payments. The vehicle was soon repossessed, where-
upon owners filed suit against the dealer and manufacturer
for breach of express and implied warranty as well as for
violations of the Arizona Consumer Fraud Act and the
Magnuson–Moss Warranty Act.

The jury awarded $35,000 in compensatory damages
against Neonex, $45,000 compensatory damages against
Jimmy, $300,000 punitive damages against Neonex, and
$250,000 punitive damages against Jimmy. The court later
awarded $22,000 in attorney's fees.

The Dunlop's attorney, James Fein of Tucson commented,
"The case is a trend setter. The time has finally come when
consumers have decided that they are not going to sit back

and idly accept defective products from companies that are making large profits." He hopes the award will put RV manufacturers and dealers on notice that "conduct of this nature will not be tolerated in the future."

VIII. RECOMMENDATIONS

The eradication of RV safety, quality control, and warranty problems is urgently needed. Changes are needed by the manufacturer, and by state and national governments.

A. For the Industry

RV manufacturers should:

1. Institute better, more consistent, and more comprehensive quality control over RV construction.
2. Establish and carefully define the division of responsibility between RV and chassis factories and dealers for warranty service. This arrangement should be in writing and should be supplied both to dealers and to new RV owners along with their warranty. Manufacturers should terminate dealers unable to meet service responsibilities.
3. Initiate at least minimal training programs for new workers at RV factories.
4. Support the adoption of stronger federal safety standards for RVs to replace the ANSI program.
5. Work to find potential health and safety hazards such as formaldehyde in advance and prevent their use in RVs rather than later trying to correct it at higher expenses.

B. For Government: Overseeing Safety and Quality

Center for Auto Safety research shows that the marketplace fails to protect recreational vehicle buyers adequately and that manufacturers' attempts to set and enforce standards are inadequate. It is also apparent that consumer pressure alone will not be sufficient to affect major upgrading in construction quality and safety. Therefore, it is crucial that state and federal governments step in to protect consumers.

C. Safety Reform

In order to improve substantially the safety of recreational vehicles, the following steps must be taken by the federal government:

1. *Crashworthiness.* The National Highway Traffic Safety Administration should amend its crashworthiness standards to apply Safety Standards 202 (Head Restraints), 208 (Occupant Crash Protection), 214 (Side-Impact Protection), 215 (Bumpers), and 216 (Roof-Crush Resistance and Rollover) to recreational vehicles without further delay.

2. *Flammability.* The National Highway Traffic Safety Administration should immediately amend Safety Standard 302 to apply to the entire interior of the RV and should reduce the allowable flame spread rate to 25 instead of the present 200. Audible LP gas leak sensors should be required for all RVs. NHTSA should require RV manufacturers to test RVs with all auxiliary fuel tanks to the specifications of Safety Standard 301. In addition, Standard 301 should be amended to require a side impact at 40 mph for RVs because of the hazardous location of fuel tanks on the side of all RVs. Finally, all RVs should be required to have an emergency fire exit other than the primary door or window.

3. *Foamed Plastics.* The National Highway Traffic Safety Administration should ban the use of all flammable foamed plastics in RVs due to the toxic gases they produce as well as their incendiary nature.

4. *Formaldehyde.* The Consumer Product Safety Commission should ban the use of formaldehyde in RVs, whether in insulating foam, composite foam board, or particle board.

5. *Handling and Stability.* The National Highway Traffic Safety Administration should set handling and stability standards for large RVs.

Such requirements would compel manufacturers to add to their present interest in volume, cost, and profits a greater concern for safety, quality, and prompt warranty work. RV purchasers could finally be assured of enjoyable traveling and living in safe, well-built, durable RVs.

ACKNOWLEDGMENTS

This section was based upon information previously published in the report *Recreational Vehicles Hazardous to Your Health and Pocketbook*, by the author and Clarence M. Ditlow of the Center for Auto Safety, published by the Center for Auto Safety in June 1982, and "Highway Homes—Hazardous to Your Health," by the author in *Trial* magazine, January 1981.

While many of the examples of abuses referred to in this section are from the late 1970s, the complaints are representative of problems found by RV owners today. Readers may contact the Center for Auto Safety (1223 Dupont Circle Building, Washington, D.C. 20036, 202-659-1126) for further specific information on the topics, incidents, and products mentioned in this section.

CITATIONS

[1]General Accounting Office, *Unwarranted Delays by the Department of Transportation to Improve Light Truck Safety*. Rep. No. CED-78-119. Washington, D.C.: General Accounting Office, 1978, front cover, p. ii.

[2]University of Kentucky, *Recreational Vehicle Accident Investigation Study*. Rep. No. DOT-HS-201-3-766. Springfield, VA.: National Technical Information Service, 1977, p. 63.

[3]National Transportation Safety Board, *Safety Aspects of Recreational Vehicles*, Rep. No. NTSB-HSS-72-2. Washington, D.C.: National Transportation Safety Board, 1972, pp. 17–18.

[4]*Supra* note 1, p. 58.

[5]Standard for Recreational Vehicles, ANSI/NFPA 501 C, sponsored by the National Fire Protection Association and the Recreation Vehicle Industry Association, Boston, 1977. (It covers all types of RVs except van conversions.)

[6]*Supra* note 3, p. 19.

[7]Multi-Disciplinary Accident Investigation Final Report, *Summary of In-Depth Investigations in Bexar County, Texas*. Rep. No. DOT-HS-801 180. Washington, D.C.: Department of Transportation, 1974, p. 29.

[8]*Supra* note 2, p. 75.

[9]*Supra* note 2, p. 85.

[10]R. Gillette and G. Shaw, "Cry for Help Dramatizes Fire Perils." *Los Angeles Times*, January 22, 1979, p. 18.

[11]46 Fed. Reg. 20106 (1981).

[12]R. Gillette, "Smoke Alarms, Caution Called Essential Until Technology Reduces Urethane Perils." *Los Angeles Times*, January 22, 1979, p. 25.

[13]Letter and interview with Edward J. Horkey of Horkey and Associates, Tempe, Arizona, by the author, February 1981.

[14]*Supra* note 5, p. 101.

[15]*Supra* note 5, p. 101.

[16]*Supra* note 5, pp. 101–102.

[17]Telephone conversation with Harold Nelson, fire research engineer, summer 1979.

[18]Center for Auto Safety, *Mobile Homes: The Low Cost Housing Hoax.* Washington, D.C.: Center for Auto Safety, 1975, p. 138.

[19]National Manufactured Housing Construction and Safety Standard, June 15, 1976. (The equivalent of ANSI A119.2 for RVs.)

[20]The National Fire Prevention and Control Administration, *America Burning.* Washington, D.C.: U.S. Government Printing Office, 1976.

[21]E. K. Budnick and D. P. Klein, *Mobile Home Fire Studies: Summary and Recommendations*, Report No. NBSIR 79-1720. Gaithersburg, MD.: National Bureau of Standards, March 1979.

[22]Technology & Economics, Inc., Contract No. H-2514, "Economic Cost-Benefit and Risk Analysis of Results of Mobile Home Safety Research: Fire Safety," April 1980.

[23]Statement on Formaldehyde Concerning Research Findings, Chemical Industry Institute of Toxicology, "Formaldehyde," September 1979.

[24]46 Fed. Reg. 11190 (1981).

[25]46 Fed. Reg. 11207 (1981).

[26]L. A. Robertson, "Behavioral Research and Strategies in Public Health: A. Deumur." *Soc. Sci. Med.*, 9:165–170 (March 1975). (*See also* sources cited therein.)

[27]"Collision of Winnebago Motor Home With Bridge Column." NTSB Rep. No. HAR-76-2. Washington, D.C.: National Transportation Safety Board, 1976.

[28]Interview with Bruce Hopkins by the author, April 14, 1981.

[29]Standard for the Storage and Handling of Liquefied Petroleum Gases, National Fire Protection Association 58, Boston, MA., 1979, p. 14.

[30]"The Carbon Monoxide, Fire, and Explosion Problem in Travel Trailers and Pickup Campers." Washington, D.C.: Department of Health, Education and Welfare, 1969, p. 4.

[31]"Accidents Among the Aged: Incidence, Causes and Prevention. *J. Chronic Dis.*, 17:515–525 (June 1964).

[32]*Henry* v. *Suburban Propane Gas Corp.*, Case No. 15541-M, Cir. Ct. of the City of Chesapeake. (Judgment entered July 16, 1980.)

[33]*RV Dealer*, December 1980, p. 13.

[34]*RV Dealer*, February 1980, p. 65.

III

ACCIDENT ANALYSIS

Automotive design has often been the result of a series of progressive steps that might include concept and theory, design analysis and the application of past experience, developmental engineering and research, testing and models or prototypes, failures or malfunctions and redesign, track or on-road driving performance and design modifications, and tailoring or accommodating to customer preferences. Regardless of the exact sequence of events, it has rarely involved accident analysis in terms of rigorous or systematic accident investigation by and for the design engineer.

The lack of appropriate accident analyses may have been a consequence of the fact that so few engineers have known how to perform a sophisticated accident analysis and fewer still have actually performed a significant number of personal accident investigations and analyses. This may account for some of the continuing problems, conflicts, and misunderstandings relating to automotive vehicle safety that often seem manifest among some groups of automotive engineers. If better information had been available as a result of a more systematic approach to accident analysis and if this derived information had been properly utilized within the automotive industry, would the results have forestalled the advent of heightened governmental safety regulation and vastly increased product liability lawsuits?

Sophisticated accident analyses tend to reveal the very kind of information needed to identify, resolve, and remedy the operative causes of accidents that actually occur during vehicle operation, servicing, maintenance, modification, repair, and disposal. The techniques of accident analysis have been refined and elaborated by many groups, but those who investigate, analyze, and testify in lawsuits have made the major contributions. There are several reasons why lawsuits have forced the development of more valid and meaningful accident investigations and analyses. First, the typical company, police, or research report of an accident generally does not subject the preparer to the kind of critical onslaught of questioning and cross-examination that is expected from lawyers, representing all those having an interest in the accident and who are trained and motivated to uncover and disclose any flaws, shortcomings, biases, errors, and inconsistencies in the accident investigation, analysis, and conclusions. Second, the accident analysis prepared for possible litigation is not the only report of the accident. There may be several other accident investigations and analyses; so comparisons and challenges are expected. Third, various engineers and lawyers, some quite unfriendly, may have years to study and restudy the accident report, gather additional facts, take witness statements and testimony, and perform relevant research on critical issues. Fourth, the accident investigator and analyst are placed under oath and risk the penalty of perjury when they testify as to the facts of the case. Fifth, someone eventually makes an ultimate decision as to the merits of the analysis, whether it is the lawyers settling the case, the judge in determining admissibility of the proferred testimony and reports, or the jury in determining credibility and rendering a verdict. In other words, the accident analyst in a vigorously contested lawsuit soon learns and benefits from a rather intensive and prolonged critical appraisal of his techniques, methods, inferences, and conclusions. Among the seasoned accident analysts, there exists a wealth of knowledge both as to techniques and in terms of unique knowledge concerning automotive vehicles and the causative factors in accidents.

Section 10, Multiple Causation, reflects the fact that accidents generally do have multiple causation (no one fault), a fact that is now reflected in the legal doctrine of pure comparative negligence in which a jury apportions proportional fault and liability (in percentages) among all those who may have contributed in some way to the cause of the accident and the ultimate injury or property damage. Some believe that it is the mark of an unsophisticated accident analysis if the investigative purpose is simply to determine a single cause or to categorize in terms of preexisting generalizations and predetermined superficial accident factors. If a jury can apportion fault among all the causes, why cannot this be done by an accident reconstruction specialist?

Section 11, Metallurgical Failures, illustrates the kind of knowledge and procedures that can illuminate some of the objective factors that should be considered in an accident reconstruction. Sometimes, a great deal of significant information about an accident remains hidden to the untrained eye that does not perceive what might be immediately apparent to a specialist who knows what to look for at the accident site or on the objects involved in the accident. In many respects, the highly developed techniques, objective procedures, and rigorous logic used in failure analysis have served as a model for other areas of accident investigation and analysis. The emphasis on objective evidence and testing has greatly influenced those from other disciplines who have become involved in accident investigation, analysis, and reconstruction.

The analysis of vehicle collisions often results in estimates of initial vehicle speeds and trajectories, determinations of vehicle impact speeds and postimpact trajectories, and descriptions of the dynamics of vehicle rollover and reactions. Skid marks, material deformation, and other objective signs of energy transfer or transformation become highly important in applying the basic laws of physics. A lawyer might want to know if a vehicle was exceeding the speed limit when the brakes were applied, if a vehicle could have stopped or changed direction in time to have avoided an accident, whether the vehicle crossed the center or stop line, what the impact speed was when critical deformation or collapse of a structure occurred, which vehicle was hit first and with what force, and many other fault determinative questions. In order to assure some objectivity and reduce possible errors in interpretation, quantification of vehicle speed and skid-mark distance gradually extended to other conditions common to vehicle collision reconstruction. Abbreviated equations, generalized nomographs, and simplified mathematical models have gradually grown in precision and complexity. Computer-based programs are now available to "plug in" known information on basic variables in order to yield derivative answers and moment-by-moment graphics of vehicle dynamics.

Section 12, Accident Reconstruction Models, presents an interesting review and example of the analytical use of mathematical models to determine vehicle–vehicle collision dynamics. Section 13, Computer-assisted Accident Analysis, illustrates the complexity of the computational process and why computer-assisted accident reconstruction is necessary to provide a clear understanding of what transpired in the brief moments of an automobile accident. As these sections suggest, the methods used in accident analysis are being refined as better data and knowledge become available, they are being used with increasing frequency to provide more answers quickly and economically, and they serve to identify variables where further research and testing should be performed. Appropriate and reliable data, rapidly transformed by computers programmed with generally accepted models of real-world phenomena, can produce descriptive information of great value to lawyers, engineers, and scientists dealing with critical automotive engineering and legal issues.

10

Multiple Causation

SHELDON C. PLOTKIN, Ph.D., P.E.
Sheldon C. Plotkin, PhD., & Associates
Systems Engineering Consultants
Los Angeles, California

*Sheldon C. Plotkin received a Bachelor of Science in
Electrical Engineering in 1946 and a Bachelor of Science
in Aeronautical Engineering in 1949 from the University
of Colorado and a Doctor of Philosophy in Electrical
Engineering in 1956 from the University of California. He
has had more than 30 years experience in analysis and
design of electronic, electromechemical, chemical, and
computer systems and analysis of human factors. His
automotive expertise includes accident and safety analyses,
accident reconstruction, product and safety design, human
factors analysis, and specialized case-oriented experimentation, modeling, and demonstrations. In addition to
his book* Accident and Product Failure Analysis, *he has
published many papers and reports. Dr. Plotkin's
professional affiliations include S.S.S., I.E.E.E., and the
Southern California Federation of Scientists. He is a
Professional Engineer (Safety) in California. At present the
author is a private consultant. He may be reached at
Sheldon C. Plotkin, PhD., & Associates, Systems
Engineering Consultants, 3425 McLaughlin Avenue,
Suite 209, Los Angeles, California 90066 (213-390-0306).*

I. INTRODUCTION

The term causation as used in this section has a much stronger meaning than simply a contributing factor. Something is a causative factor if, and only if, its *elimination* either prevents the accident entirely or, in the least, substantially eliminates the serious injury. While there might be a multitude of factors and facets to consider when evaluating a particular accident, those aspects having to do with causation must fit into this definition.

There is no doubt that simply dealing with a single causative factor in any accident is easier on the psyche. The "facts of life" are such that an easy-to-comprehend situation generally is handled in a straightforward manner. However, the types of accidents that would prompt an attorney or engineer to read this text would generally be of the more complex variety. Such "complexity" is generally due to *multiple factors* with respect to *causation*.

Thus, the purpose of this section is to attempt a general overall approach to accident reconstruction analysis that accounts for multiple causation.[1] A number of specifics will be included in order to illustrate exactly what kinds of things might be involved.

One of the best defenses for an accident in which the plaintiff was noncontributory is to show that one or more *other factors* actually contributed to that accident. A plaintiff attorney must show for his/her side of the case how all factors fit together. While it may be easier to consider only single-factor causation, there is no substitute for technical accuracy. If there were more than one cause, as is the situation a significant fraction of the time, such contributing factors must be included.

Most of the time (perhaps as much as 90 percent) accidents have simple causes, or only one failure-mode (to use engineering language). There will be a smaller percentage of the time that there will be two causes, a still smaller percentage for three causes, and even less for four causes. It must be emphasized that two and three separate and independent, but simultaneous, causes are prevalent enough that all accident analysts should be conscious of their possibility. Four causative factors are relatively rare; the author has never experienced more than four in any accident.

Because the definition of a causative factor is one that when removed from the analysis, the accident is prevented, it is most important to separate out a causative factor from failures as a result of the accident. Application of the criteria in the above definition should easily facilitate the determination of a "cause" factor rather than a "result" factor.

II. ANALYTIC APPROACH

The fundamental technique required is sometimes referred to as systems engineering, i.e., the consideration of all failure-mode aspects as being interrelated. Note that human factors are considered, from a technical standpoint, to be no different than physical mechanism factors. In the man-machine interface there can be failure on either side of such an interaction "surface." All accident analysis should be approached as being one involving multiple causes. This means that the analyst must be very careful not to force an analysis into a particular discipline that is comfortable to that reconstructionist, but to make certain all factors are included in the reconstruction analysis.

A person with a structures background might overemphasize the structural aspects of a reconstruction or possibly ignore all other aspects if any part is structural. The human factors specialist often looks for driver or human error, either induced or spontaneous with complete disregard of other aspects. The tire expert looks for a tire failure to be a single cause. On the other hand, in a systems engineering approach, one looks for all possible causes and separates the cause from the effect without regard to which technical discipline the pertinent factors fit.

Accident reconstruction is like a jigsaw puzzle. All the known facts have to fit the reconstruction, one place or another. If any fact does not fit the reconstruction or puzzle, then something is incorrect, more or less, with that reconstruction. Additionally, a missing part or unknown section of the reconstruction is all right from a reconstruction standpoint, and analytical revisions are not necessary for the sake of eliminating unknown factors. Many times the simple delineation of what is unknown facilitates discovery of precisely that factor.

Only when multiple causes have been considered and all but one eliminated can a reconstruction confidently be considered as of single causation. As emphasized at the outset of this section, both plaintiff and defense can win or lose a case by not accounting for a pertinent multiple causation factor.

III. TYPES OF CAUSATIVE FACTORS

The categorizing of factors can be done in either of two basic ways, operational or functional. This may sound as though the situation is deliberately being made excessively complex; however, there is a point involved in these two types of categories that is quite important and somewhat subtle. The operational category comes from an operational analysis of an accident (or system), while the functional category results from a systems engineering analysis. It will be shown that the systems approach is preferred because new failure modes, not recognized previously, can result—as opposed to the analyst being restricted to only presently recognized failure modes.

A. Operational Factors

Let us consider some of the components to be considered in the operational category. A partial list of some of the more prevalent factors might prove useful. This list is not to be considered as exhaustive. It is only intended to assist the reader in looking in the proper directions for the particular factors involved in his/her accident being reconstructed.

Speed:	excessive, direct or induced
	insufficient for higher speed roadway
Highway:	incorrect recommended speed
	too abrupt speed changes
	construction hazard
	design error
	obstructed view
Tires:	steel belt through tread
	soft spot
	sidewall failure
	inadequate vulvanizing
Steering:	oversteer instability
	metallurgical failure in linkage
	engine failure effect on power steering operation
Suspension:	metallurgical failure
	inadequate torque on critical nuts and bolts
	damper or other component disconnection
Body:	metallurgical failure or weakness at critical points
	design error

Wheels: alloy fracture
                   weld failure
                   rivet leaks

This partial list should orient the analyst's approach. Besides some of the obvious and usually recognized causes listed in this operational category, there are a number of more subtle ones. It is these that many times require a very experienced, or at least a very versatile, analyst rather than the more usual or more mundane aspects. Emphasis should be on the accident specifics to dictate or lead the analyst to an accurate reconstruction, recognizing that accident reconstruction is an inexact science.

In this regard, the functional categories into which the type of causative factors are grouped is a more useful technique. These categories might be roughly considered as being inherent vehicle structure, structural appendages, internal human factors, external human factors, and external or roadway factors. While some of these factor categories will overlap in specific instances, they, hopefully, will not be confusing because of the lack of categorial delineation. The phenomena involved are easily understood and devoid of confusion.

B. Functional Factors

Specific functional causes can be spelled out in greater detail in order to provide the reader with something definitive.

B.1. INHERENT VEHICLE STRUCTURE

1. Structural rigidity of suspension members. This includes torquing of attachment bolts as well as metallurgical integrity of components.
2. Steering tie rods, pitman arm, and steering gear or equivalent.
3. Crashworthiness strength of passenger compartment structure. This will generally be a moot point, for plaintiffs will claim insufficient strength and defense will claim adequate strength for general use. In general, additional money can always be spent to provide a more "passenger protective structure" than that which was actually used. What is "adequate" is dependent upon definition.

B.2. STRUCTURAL APPENDAGES

1. Tires are generally in a category by themselves. Much accident analysis work is spent determining whether or not failed tires were a cause or result of an accident. Obviously, a disintegrated steel-belted tire that failed in the characteristic manner, i.e., the upper belt poking through the tread, would generally be a cause. And the flat intact tire whose wheel is severely dented would generally be a result of the accident and not a cause. Breaks in the sidewall, leaking tires from nails, faulty valves, or faulty rivet seals are more difficult to evaluate.

2. Window strength adequacy can have a bearing on injuries.

3. Proper seat belt function can be critical (as well as having no influence). Recent DOT frontal crash testing into a rigid barrier at 35 mph has revealed some basic seat belt problems. Small modifications can make very large differences vis-à-vis reduced injury effectiveness. Such factors as belt material, accelerometer latching, and belt mounting points are in this "small modification" category.

4. Impact bumper effectiveness, while not much of a problem consideration today, can be expected to play a major role in future vehicle designs. Withstanding frontal impacts at 50 mph must include more substantial energy-absorbing bumpers than present vehicle designs.

5. Windshield wiper effectiveness is certainly a safety aspect that has been ignored by manufacturers of some of the more expensive automobiles. A small number of accidents are bound to be effected in at least a small way by such a design deficiency.

6. Visibility has always been a safety problem and can easily be a major accident factor. Differences between the variety of vehicles on the market is quite large. Note that passenger vehicles traditionally have a blind spot at the right rear, whereas large diesel trucks have a blind spot at the right front.

B.3. INTERNAL HUMAN FACTORS

1. Alcohol, drugs, and drowsiness are all major problems in automotive accidents that cannot be dealt with here in an adequate manner. Needless to say, the use

of any mechanism that requires the driver to pass some sort of test before the engine can be started would be unacceptable because of its inability to be bypassed on special occasions.

2. Misinterpretation of roadway instructions that are relatively well conceived can be a factor. Some of the drivers who drive onto "on" or "off" ramps in the wrong direction fall into this category. Not seeing a well-displayed sign, e.g., speed limit or recommended speed, can be the fault of driver inattention, the reason being internal to the driver.

B.4. EXTERNAL HUMAN FACTORS

1. Visibility deficiency problems having to do with insufficient effort to overcome the design deficiency can be a factor. Windshield wiper effectiveness was mentioned above in the vehicle category, but in most cases a driver can see through an unwiped windshield if sufficient effort is exerted in doing so. Thus, the human driver, if aware, can compensate for vehicle design deficiencies on occasion. The right rear blind spot passenger car problem is alleviated, if not eliminated, by proper adjustment of the right side mirror.

2. Erroneous visibility problems are an entirely different matter. Roadway and street lighting design can provide a driver with information that is actually incorrect. A road might be coming to a T-type end that is not indicated because of street lights on another street beyond which makes the pertinent roadway section appear to continue.

3. Insufficient visibility for the speed limit involved is a common left-turn problem from a stop street into a major roadway.

4. Driver inability to determine that a vehicle ahead is actually stopped is another common problem. A limit of human perception of 25 to 30 milliradians per second has been determined as a practical value for dynamic conditions.[2] Expressed as a formula:

$$V \geq 0.0275s^2/w$$

where
$$V = \text{velocity (feet per second)}$$
$$0.0275 = \text{perception limit (radians per second)}$$
$$s = \text{distance between vehicles (feet)}$$
$$w = \text{width of the stopped vehicle (feet)}$$

B.5. EXTERNAL ROADWAY FACTORS

1. The curved roadway precluding sufficient left-turn visibility for a vehicle at a stop sign has been mentioned above.
2. Side roadways with varying widths can obscure the center line. This can be enhanced by the parked car pattern as well.
3. Actual roadway surface deficiencies are perhaps relatively obvious in most instances, e.g., a vertical 6-inch drop-off at the road edge without warning. However, sometimes such deficiencies are relatively difficult to ascertain, e.g., an increase in downslope just prior to a sharp highway curve in the downward direction or a decrease in curve radius from previous curves without warning.

IV. EXAMPLES OF DUAL CAUSATION

The usual two-party automobile collision in which it is obvious that both parties were more or less at fault is well known. However, two somewhat unusual examples may be interesting.

Example 1

A very inebriated pedestrian was walking very late on a dark night in the middle of a roadway with no illumination. He was warned by police officers to get out of the street and did so at the time, only to wander back into the middle of the roadway some time later. Finally, he was struck by a passing motorist and severely injured. The driver of the vehicle was seemingly blameless in this situation because of the darkness. Speed before impact was about 25 mph.

Considering the fact that properly adjusted headlamps will illuminate a person in the roadway 100 feet away (the criteria for proper adjustment) and the distance required for stopping at 25 mph is about 70 feet, assuming 0.75 second reaction time and 0.5 G braking deceleration for a panic stop (skid distance $= 0.0668\, V^2_{mph}$), the motorist could have actually stopped before impact had he/she been sufficiently alert.

Example 2

Given the characteristic steel-belted tire, failure coupled with excessive speed is perhaps not too difficult to discern. However, when steel-belted tires were first introduced into the United States market, the normal tire specialists were not familiar with the difference between steel-belted tire failures and older, fabric-designed tire failures. (There appears to be no basic failure mode differences between fabric radials and fabric bias-ply tires.)

The specific failure being considered in this case is the upper steel belt forcing its way sideways through the tread. This failure coupled with excessive speed causes the tire literally to disintegrate as the tread and steel belts peel off. Because this causes the driver to lose control, serious accidents result.

No specific accident details were given here because this type of failure mode happens many times. It might be pointed out that the original steel-belted tire design did not possess this failure mode. Only when steel-belted radials were introduced into the United States market did the foreign manufacturers change their designs to follow the United States companies.

V. EXAMPLES OF THREE CAUSATIVE FACTORS

Example 1

This example involves highway design, potential vehicle oversteer, and either gravel on the roadway or a rear tire with low air pressure. A number of highway designs are very winding; in fact, the more winding they are, the less the cost of construction, in general. The windingness, in and of itself, is not unsafe. The hazardous aspect is when one curve has a slightly smaller radius of curvature than the majority of other curves and does not have a curve warning sign to that effect.

Vehicle oversteer is caused primarily by the center of gravity of a vehicle being toward the rear, as in a loaded truck or station wagon, or a rear-engined vehicle. The weight toward the rear causes the rear wheels to skid more than those in the front. Thus when such a vehicle is driven around a curve rather fast, the rear wheels skidding out more than the front makes the vehicle turn in an even tighter turn than the driver intended, which makes for more skidding, etc. Another problem is that this process of stable control to instability can occur in about 0.1 seconds, much too fast for a human driver to react. Consequently, the vehicle, under severe conditions, can spin out of control, rolling over if the center of gravity is high enough.

Rear-wheel skidding, which results in oversteer instability, can also be caused by insufficient vertical travel of the rear wheels. The inside rear wheel can actually lift off the ground with such short travel suspension design and the outside rear wheel may not have sufficient traction. Thus, the rear skids out, just as though the vehicle were rear heavy.

Consideration in this example is the condition that has only a potentially oversteer failure mode. Then when another factor is added that produces somewhat more rear-wheel skidding than normal, the vehicle spins completely out of control very abruptly. Such an added factor could be something on the roadway surface, such as gravel, or a low rear tire caused by a slow leak—nail, tube-type mounted as a tubeless, or wheel rivet leak.

Thus the three causes are one curve of slightly smaller radius without a curve warning, a vehicle capable of oversteer, and a tire or road problem that enhances the inherent oversteer characteristic.

Example 2

Another three-causation example is a new motorcycle whose rear tire has a soft spot that quickly wears significantly and causes excessive vibration. Because the motorcycle was brand new, the tire defect was not detected at the outset. After riding several hundred miles, the motorcycle was traversing a curve; the driver lost control and suffered serious injury. Investigation analysis revealed the loss of control occurred considerably after the curve apex. Further investigation revealed equally spaced road bumps.

Calculations of the speed (which was within safe values normally), road bump spacing, and inherent resonant frequency of the motorcycle based upon suspension spring constant and weight showed that the speed and road bump spacing along with wheel vibration from the tire soft spot put the motorcycle into an uncontrolled oscillation.

Thus the three causes were a tire defect, road bumps–vehicle speed combination, and the inherent resonant frequency of the motorcycle suspension system. The tire soft spot can be caused by the tire sitting in a softening chemical or because of insufficient batch mixing, i.e., the fundamental tire rubber ingredients were not mixed well enough before tire manufacture.

VI. EXAMPLES OF FOUR CAUSATIVE FACTORS

Although the occurrence of four simultaneous dynamic deficiencies is very rare, there are so many chances among the multitude of vehicles and conditions throughout the country for such an occurrence that it is bound to arise occasionally.

Accidents having four causes is the most the author has personally experienced, therefore, examples will cease with the two that follow.

Example 1

Consider a fully loaded gasoline truck[2] that consisted of a conventional diesel tractor manufactured prior to 1973 and a circular cross-section tank rather than the usual elliptic cross-section. Just as the truck passed the crest of a hill to begin a long and gradual downhill stretch, the trailer brakes failed for an unknown reason. When the driver attempted to stop the rig, the tractor brakes faded (because of excessive heat) and the brake drums expanded to the point where the brake lining could not reach the brake drum surface. As the truck proceeded down the curved road at approximately the speed limit, it slowly rolled over on the smallest radius curve. Crash photos showed a structural failure in a suspension support member of the trailer.

Obviously, the failure of the trailer brakes initiated the sequence of events. The question is whether it should have been possible to stop the truck with half braking. What difference did the circular cross-section tank make? And, finally, was the speed sufficient to have caused the truck to roll over or did the tank suspension failure have something to do with it, i.e., did the tank suspension fail as a result of the rollover or was it one of the causes, having occurred before rollover?

In this example the original brake failure was never determined; however, it is not unusual for automobiles and particularly large trucks to lose part of their braking capacity on occasion. Without any brake failures, it is known that the large diesel trucks before 1973 possessed braking capacity only half as effective as the average passenger cars. This was caused by *not* using front brakes, "finned" brake drums (to prevent fading by dissipating heat quickly), oversized lining, which was available, and/or an engine braking system applicable to only diesel engines that automatically provides full engine power for braking.

As for the circular versus elliptic tank, it was calculated that the center of gravity was increased 11 percent for a fully loaded circular tank. A rollover analysis was then required to determine whether this was sufficient to roll the truck over, even at a speed somewhat greater than the speed limit. When this analysis proved negative, it was then concluded that the structure failure had to have occurred before the accident. Thus there were four separate causes for the accident including the initial trailer brake failure.

Example 2

Our second example involves a long curve of constant, but relatively small, radius that contained a drainage depression at the apex of the curve for a divided roadway. The vehicle involved had a rear "shock absorber" (oscillation damper) loose at one end as well as aluminum alloy wheels. Accident dynamics consisted of a vehicle speed about 20 percent greater than the recommended curve speed. Skidding generally begins at about 150 percent recommended speed. The drainage trough induced wheel oscillations that the loose rear damper ("shock absorber") could not dampen. The rear end lost traction and slipped out, causing a momentary oversteer condition. Such momentary loss of control caused the vehicle to jump the road divider curb. Wheel impact with the curb induced a brittle aluminum alloy rear wheel to begin fracturing. The tire involved lost air pressure very abruptly, and the vehicle then spun about the disintegrating wheel. Rollover finally resulted from the sequence, accompanied by severe injury to the vehicle occupants.

In accord with the original definition of causative factors in this section, elimination of the excess speed, roadway drainage trough, loose rear damper, or aluminum alloy wheels would have prevented the accident.

VII. CONCLUSIONS

A one-sentence synopsis of the major theme of this section is that the basic requirement for an accident with multiple causes is that at the outset, as soon as possible after the accident has occurred, *an all-encompassing "systems" engi-*

neering analysis should be performed. Such analyses need not be complete at the beginning as far as the compiling of all necessary data to support whatever claims are made, nor must any of the demonstration material even be itemized or planned. The all-encompassing aspect has to do with performing an overall analysis taking into account all pertinent factors and evaluating their significance relative to each other. At that point applicable realistic decisions can be made as to what generally has to be done and when.

The designation "systems engineering approach" is used because a systems engineer[3] deals with interacting elements and considers their interaction or interrelation. In these matters it is important to determine the interacting aspects of *all* accident facets. Many attorneys, without realizing the exact technical nature of what they are doing, perform the systems engineering function themselves by relating the different analytical aspects. As accident and personal injury litigation has progressed, the engineering analyses required have become more complex and the interconnection of various aspects required are becoming more important. It is one thing to determine and present to the court the major cause of an accident, but it is perhaps more important to provide a complete picture of *all* related causes and facets, particularly how they all fit together. The latter—the complete picture—makes for court confidence regarding whatever decisions are made and perchance more favorable judgments thereby.

Many times it is not obvious that an accident has multiple causes; so then what does an attorney do? Perhaps it is obvious that nothing is lost if each case is treated as though it actually had more than one cause. A complete, all-encompassing analysis including human factors and basic design, as well as construction and special circumstances, should result in relatively precise knowledge of accident causation. It is possible to tackle these complex-type accidents in a systematic manner. There are essentially two options open to the trial attorney: (1) perform the systems engineering function oneself or (2) make use of a systems engineer to coordinate the analysis and specify the precise work required of each engineer or analyst. The approach used depends upon the attorney's understanding of the specific engineering matters involved and the complexity of the accident scene. Note that it is a generalized understanding of the engineering concepts involved in the case that is required of the attorney for this coordinating function and not specific engineering training.

CITATIONS

[1]S. C. Plotkin, "Accidents With Multiple Causes." *Advocate*, 5(9): 12-14 (1977). Los Angeles Trial Lawyers Association.

[2]S. C. Plotkin, *Accident and Product Failure Analyses*. California Syllabus, Oakland, CA., 1976.

[3]S. C. Plotkin, "Systems Engineer, A New Type of Expert Witness." *California Trial Lawyers Journal*, 13(3):91-94 (1974).

11

Metallurgical Failures:
Analysis of Structural Fractures
Relative to Accident Causation

DAVID K. FELBECK, Sc.D., P.E.
Professor of Mechanical Engineering
University of Michigan
Ann Arbor, Michigan

*The author received his undergraduate engineering
education at Cornell University and did his graduate
research studies in the field of metallurgical fracture at
Massachusetts Institute of Technology, receiving his
doctorate in 1952. He served two years on the M.I.T.
faculty and has been at the University of Michigan since
1961. His professional experience includes several hundred
product liability cases involving analyses of the causes for
service fracture of metals. He has published extensively in
technical journals, is the author of two textbooks on the
mechanical behavior of solids, and is a registered professional engineer. Professor Felbeck may be contacted at
2060 Scottwood, Ann Arbor, Michigan 48104
(313-994-6662)*

I. INTRODUCTION

Careful examination of a broken metal part can often reveal much information about how it broke. One may then draw some conclusions about why it broke, which may in turn also establish some limits on *when* it broke. Because answers to these questions usually have some bearing on precisely establishing the causes of an accident, such a study can be important to the designer of a product, so he can avoid such failures in the future, and also to those parties involved in a lawsuit that might result from a failure.

This section is intended to describe the possible extent of the conclusions that are available through the examination of broken metal parts. Therefore, we must first discuss the kinds of fracture that occur in metals, then describe the techniques that are used for examining fractures, examine the tests that may be helpful, and finally consider any additional support that other analyses may provide.

In order to describe adequately the various procedures that are used, some technical presentation is essential. However, we will limit its depth so that an informed nontechnical person should be able to follow the argument. The references cited provide sufficient additional detail for the reader who wishes to delve more deeply into any particular subject. The most comprehensive reference currently available describes many of these approaches and provides numerous examples.[1]

II. CHARACTERISTICS OF DIFFERENT KINDS OF FRACTURE

A. Ductile Overload or Underdesign

When a part breaks, it has obviously been subjected to some forces that are greater than it can withstand. (Force or load is usually considered by the designer in the form of *stress*, which is force per unit of area over which it acts.) If the part has the dimensions and other characteristics that have been specified by the designer (that is, it has no flaws or manufacturing defects), and if the part then breaks in service, either it must have been inadequately designed (this is *underdesign*), or it has been subjected to stresses greater than the designer expected would occur under normal service conditions (this is *overload*). The appearance of the part in the vicinity of the fracture under these circumstances depends upon the kind of loads to which it is subjected.[2] These are discussed in the following paragraphs.

A.1. TENSION Fracture from a large pulling force, called *tension*, is usually associated in metals with stretching and thinning prior to fracture of the part. Such metals are termed *ductile* because the stretching that precedes fracture requires a relatively large amount of energy. (A metal is *brittle* when a relatively small amount of energy is required for fracture, which will be discussed subsequently.) Fracture from ductile overload tension is usually quite easy to diagnose, owing to the permanent elongation (which is called *plastic deformation*) and thinning in the region of the fracture; the only kind of fracture that might be confused with this is the result of high-temperature *creep*, which will be considered later. Since creep can occur only at temperatures that are above about half the absolute melting temperature, fractures that are not at such elevated temperatures cannot be the result of creep. Figure 11-1 shows a tensile fracture that resulted from under-design.

A.2. SHEAR When scissors are used to cut paper, the fracture is by *shear*. But since shear stresses almost always coexist with tensile stresses, the two kinds of fracture cannot be simply separated. For instance, most of the fracture surfaces visible in Figure 11-1 are the result of local shear stresses that originated from tensile forces in the barrel. Thus, it is usually not necessary to discriminate between the two kinds of fracture; they have essentially the same characteristics.

A.3. BENDING The stresses throughout a section of a part being bent will usually range from tension on one side to compression on the other side, so the resultant fracture is more complex than in the case of simple tension or shear. However, a ductile part that fails by overload bending still exhibits the characteristic permanent deformation already described for tensile fracture, but in this case the deformation is by bending. Furthermore, the terminal portion of the fracture usually has a slight characteristic curvature as a result of the locally changing stresses that occur as the fracture progresses across the section.

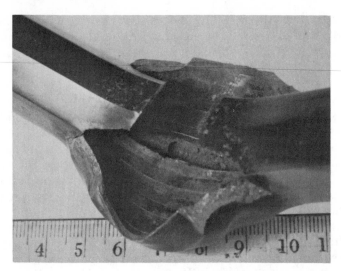

Figure 11-1 Fracture of the steel barrel of an 0.50-caliber muzzle loader as a result of excessive tensile stresses from under-design. Note the extensive deformation in the fractured area. A transverse slot had been milled in the barrel which left an insufficient wall thickness.

A.4. TORSION A twisting load, called a *torque*, can lead to overload torsion fracture in ductile metals, but only after some permanent deformation by twisting has occurred. This fracture type is therefore relatively easy to identify by the presence of the prior twisting.

B. Brittle Fracture

A part that fractures with very little permanent deformation and consequently low energy is said to be *brittle*. Glass and most ceramics are usually brittle, for example. But many metals can be brittle under certain circumstances. Thus, in contrast to the ductile overload fracture discussed above, brittle parts can fracture with very little deformation and sometimes at a much lower load than if they behaved in a ductile manner. This may occur because of the presence of inhomogeneities in the metal, since all solids have some imperfections to their structure if viewed on a sufficiently fine scale. *Fracture toughness* is the ability of a metal to resist fracture when a flaw exists in the structure.[3] Ductile metals, such as the kind of steel that most automobile fenders are made of, are very insensitive to flaws. That is, they will be almost as strong in the presence of a flaw as without it.

Brittle fracture becomes an important problem when it is unexpected. If the designer expects that his material will be able to resist flaws, or if he expects that any flaws present will be smaller than some anticipated value (the smaller the flaw, the higher the stress required for brittle fracture), but his part instead behaves in a brittle fashion contrary to his expectations, then fracture may occur at stresses lower than the service stresses in a sudden and catastrophic manner. Figure 11-2 shows the appearance of a brittle fracture in steel that involved very little plastic deformation.

Brittle fracture is not the only type of fracture that can occur with very little plastic deformation. Both fatigue and stress corrosion cracking, which are discussed in the next two subsections, may also occur with very little plastic deforma-

Figure 11-2 Brittle fracture of a large low-carbon steel bolt in bending. The fracture initiated at the right edge, with very little associated plastic deformation. Note also how the fracture has curved at the left (terminal) side out of the plane in which it initiated; this is characteristic of bending fractures.

tion. The techniques used for discriminating among these three kinds of fracture will be described there and in the subsection on examination techniques.

C. Fatigue

If a steel paper clip is plastically bent back and forth by hand 10 or 20 times, it will fracture by *fatigue* (more specifically, *low-cycle fatigue*). Fatigue occurs because a crack grows by a small amount with each cycle of reversed bending, until the crack has progressed far enough across the paper clip to allow it to fracture completely on the last bending. If we examine this fracture surface with a low-power microscope, it is possible to see, and count, the small increments of crack growth that occurred with each cycle. They are visible because the initiating and terminating characteristics of each crack increment in the paper clip are different and involve different amounts of local plastic deformation as well as small changes in direction. If the crack increments are clearly visible, in an ideal case (which seldom occurs), we can conclude that the paper clip fractured by low-cycle fatigue, and we can estimate approximately how many cycles were required for fracture.

If the paper clip is subjected to a very large number of cycles of bending stresses that are so small that there is no permanent (plastic) deformation, fatigue fracture (this time *high-cycle fatigue*) may occur. Stresses that are too low to cause plastic deformation are called *elastic stresses*, and the level of stress at which plastic deformation first occurs is called the *yield stress*. Thus, fatigue can occur at stresses lower than the yield stress, often at values as small as half the yield stress. If a designer expects that the only kind of failure to worry about is the plastic deformation that occurs when the yield stress is reached, and he designs the part so as to stay below the yield stress, he may still have an unexpected fracture if the part is subjected to a large number of reversed or alternating stresses. Fatigue can therefore be an unexpected kind of fracture unless the designer anticipates it and designs so as to avoid it.

Identification of fatigue fracture (we will drop the phrase "high-cycle" from now on) is based on the characteristics of its gradual stepwise growth, on both the *macro* (visible to the naked eye) and *micro* (visible only in a microscope) scales.

Figure 11-3 exhibits the *progression marks* (also called *beach marks* or *clamshell marks*) that occur during fatigue that results from stress that is variable and/or intermittent.

D. Stress Corrosion Cracking and Hydrogen Embrittlement

Under sustained tensile stress below the yield stress, in some metals a crack will grow gradually over a period of time when the part is exposed to certain gaseous or liquid environments; this is *stress corrosion cracking*. It differs from fatigue in that the stress can be constant instead of varying, and it requires a particular environment, while fatigue can occur in a vacuum or in a completely inert environment. The environment actually reduces the strength of the metal at its surface so that in regions of high tensile stress a short crack can form. Then, after the damaging elements in the environment diffuse with time to the bottom of the crack, the crack grows by an

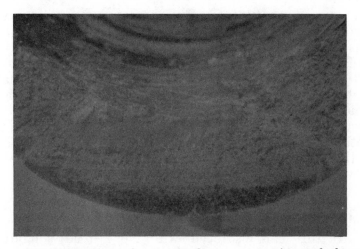

Figure 11-3 Fatigue fracture of an automotive axle housing made of medium carbon steel. The fracture initiated at the bottom of the photograph and progressed until it was sufficiently large so that the rest of the housing fractured completely under the last cycle of load application. The progression marks are visible in the initiation region. The much rougher fracture surface is the terminal region.

additional short increment. Thus stress corrosion cracking causes gradually growing cracks.

Hydrogen embrittlement is similar in some ways, in that gradual crack growth can occur in the presence of hydrogen and tensile stresses as a result of weakening of the surface layer of metal exposed to hydrogen. But a part can also be subject to *hydrogen damage* even in the absence of tensile stresses, when the hydrogen collects at a single location in the form of hydrogen gas and exerts a pressure sufficiently large to cause local cracking. This cracking, which is irreversible, then causes the whole part to be brittle.

Both kinds of environmentally assisted cracking can have an appearance similar to the progression marks visible to the naked eye in the case of fatigue, and there is usually relatively little plastic deformation in the fracture region. The key differences in fracture appearance occur at the micro scale and will be discussed in the section below on microscopic examination.

E. Creep

When exposed to sustained tensile stress at temperatures of the order of half the absolute melting temperature or higher, metals and alloys can exhibit a very slow elongation and eventual fracture that occur with time. This mode of failure is called *creep*. A part will then fail either by (1) eventually exceeding its allowable length as specified in its design or (2) fracturing suddenly after it has elongated for some time. The rate of extension depends on the alloy composition, the operating temperature compared with its melting temperature, the magnitude of the stress applied, and a number of other variables relating to its micro-scale structure.

The appearance of creep fracture is usually somewhat similar to the overload fracture of ductile metals, with considerable permanent elongation preceding fracture. However, creep fracture can also occur after very little elongation. Because creep failure occurs only at relatively high temperatures, its diagnosis is generally straightforward. For example, a pure iron with a melting temperature of 1538°C (which is $1538 + 273 = 1811$ K) would be expected to show some creep behavior at $1811/2 = 906$ K, which is 632°C or 1170°F. (Here the symbol K stands for degrees Kelvin, which is the scale of absolute temperature; absolute zero Kelvin is minus 273 degrees Celsius.) When a designer is operating at such a high temperature as 632°C, half the melting temperature of iron, he is usually aware of the problem of creep. However, some alloys have much lower melting temperatures. For example, a 60% lead–40% tin solder has a melting temperature of 183°C; half its absolute melting temperature works out to be −45°C or −49°F. Thus this alloy creeps very nicely at room temperature, say 20°C, and is not very useful as a structural material in this temperature range.

III. EXAMINATION TECHNIQUES

A. Macro: Naked Eye and Magnifying Glass

The hand-held magnifying glass is probably the most useful tool for analysis of fractures. In conjunction with a general examination of the part, and especially in the region of the fracture, the characteristics described above for each of the several kinds of fracture can be observed. In many cases a reasonably accurate preliminary diagnosis can be made, subject only to later confirmation by examination in a microscope.

At the macro level, some features of a fracture surface not already mentioned may be visible.

A.1. VOIDS AND INCLUSIONS As all metal parts are melted at some stage in their fabrication, voids may form during the solidification process. These may be in the form of a large single hole or a series of smaller holes or pores. Also, inclusions that are not metallic may result from the melting and solidification procedures and be visible with a low-power magnifying glass. An example of a solidification void is shown in Figure 11-4.

A.2. POSTFRACTURE DAMAGE Most fractures cannot be examined by an expert immediately after they occur. Mechanical damage can occur to a fracture surface as a direct consequence of the failure by contact with other parts and later during disassembly, handling, and shipping of the broken part. Because a fracture surface usually consists of irregular contours (like hills and valleys on a very fine scale), it is very fragile and thus easily altered by almost any mechanical contact. Examination of the surface with a magnifying glass will usually permit identification of such *postfracture damage*, for in the form of dents, gouges, and scratches such

Figure 11-4 Large casting void in a malleable iron part. The lower two-thirds of the central region of the fracture, which is darker, consists not of a fracture surface but a *dendritic* surface, which forms when the metal solidifies. A higher magnification view of the surface of this void is shown in Figure 11–12.

damage is usually quite distinct from the original fracture surface. A special case of postfracture damage can occur after a fracture has propagated part way across a part, and the matching surfaces of the fracture can rub against each other before the two halves of the part separate completely. Such behavior often occurs during fatigue fracture and accounts for the shiny burnished surface that is often evident on fatigue fracture surfaces.

B. Optical Microscopy

Optical microscopy can be used effectively in the study of fracture surfaces at relatively low power, no more than about 60× magnification. (Magnification at 60× means that an image appears to be 60 times as wide in the microscope as it actually is.) Most optical magnification is at no more than 20× or 30×, for at higher powers the limitation of the *depth of focus* causes most of the image to be out of focus, with only a small region at one particular depth from the microscope lens being in focus. Even with changing the position of the lens, at higher magnifications it becomes increasingly difficult to obtain an accurate idea of the contour of the surface, and to take a single photograph is usually useless, for almost all of it will be out of focus. Nevertheless, the optical microscope at 10× to 30× is simple to use for a preliminary examination and provides information on the *color* of a fracture surface that cannot be obtained from the electron microscope (see below).

C. Metallography

A small piece can be cut from a fractured specimen, mounted in plastic to permit ease of handling, then polished until the surface is very smooth. Then this surface is usually etched to bring out the differences in the fine-scale structure, called *microstructure*. Etching is an accelerated corrosion of the surface, such as is caused by acid, that corrodes some regions faster than others and therefore results in slight elevation differences in the surface. These surface contours are visible when the surface is examined in an optical metallurgical microscope at magnifications to about 1000×; this procedure is called *metallography*.[4] Such high magnifications can be used because the surface being examined is very flat, avoiding the problem with the depth of focus that occurs on examination of a rough fracture surface.

Metallographic examination is usually made of specimens cut from regions remote from the fracture surface, so as to allow the fracture to remain intact. From this examination it is often possible to infer the approximate composition of the alloy and its heat treatment and mechanical processing (e.g., rolling, forging). Fine-scale defects, such as fine porosity and nonmetallic inclusions of various types are visible by this technique.

A special application of metallography is in the study of stress corrosion cracking, for which one of the characteristics is branching of the growing crack. A section of the metal cut perpendicular to the plane of the crack and parallel to the crack growth direction may then reveal a pattern of branching cracks. Such an examination must, of necessity, destroy that portion of the fracture surface; so it is often not done.

D. Electron Microscopy

An electron beam has a vastly smaller wavelength than a light wave. This makes possible much higher magnifications, since magnification is limited by the wavelength of the radiation (wave) being used. Furthermore, using short wavelength radiation provides much greater depth of focus in the microscope. The principal disadvantage of microscopes using electron beams is that, since an electron will not travel very far in air, it must be used in a vacuum; this results in relatively high cost and limits the size of specimen that can be put in the microscope.

D.1. TRANSMISSION ELECTRON MICROSCOPE (TEM) Fracture surface contours can be examined at very high magnification in the TEM through the following procedure. A plastic replica, or casting, is made of a region of interest, without any damage or change to the fracture surface except for the possible removal of contamination or rust. The replica is mounted on a fine wire grid of about 2-mm external diameter and is then shadowed with chromium, a metal relatively opaque to electrons, at an angle of about 45 degrees, to bring out the contours of the surface as described below. The entire replica is coated with carbon to provide it with mechanical strength for handling, and the plastic is then dissolved away so it will not contaminate the TEM chamber; this leaves only the carbon supporting the chromium. The replica is placed inside the TEM, and a focused electron beam is passed through it. The beam is magnified to provide a view of the appearance of the fracture surface. Where the surface has been shadowed with chromium, the electrons do not pass through and therefore do not impinge on the photographic film that is placed underneath the replica. Such regions are "dark" in the final print, and regions where the electrons pass through the replica are "light" in the final print. In this way we have formed an image of the surface contours. Practical use of the TEM in ordinary fractography is limited to about 30,000× magnification.

Since the TEM can be used only with replicas, the surfaces to be examined must be at least moderately flat if accurate replicas are to be made. Surfaces with deep holes, cracks, or very rough surfaces cannot be accurately replicated and therefore are not suitable for TEM examination.

Because the shadowing of the surface brings out fairly subtle contours, the TEM is especially powerful in the detection of the fine *striations* that are the unique characteristic of fatigue fracture. The small growth of the (high-cycle) fatigue crack that occurs with each cycle (if the stress is high enough, of course) leaves slight variations in the surface contour that are similar to those already described for low-cycle fatigue. The position of the crack after each cycle is completed is thus a straight or curved line, when viewed from above the fracture surface. When the crack grows by a very small amount with the next stress cycle, the tip of the crack reaches a new position and leaves a new line, slightly displaced from the former line. The more-or-less parallel lines formed by the successive positions of the crack after a series of alternating stress cycles are what are called *fatigue striations*, as shown for example in Figure 11-5.

An emerging, potentially powerful tool for failure analysis is in estimating the number of stress cycles that a failed part experienced prior to final fracture. A lower limit to the number of cycles could be obtained from a direct or indirect count of the striations, but this and similar approaches do not yet provide useful estimates, for the following reasons:

1. It is usually not possible to see all the striations, because of mechanical damage or corrosion.
2. Making the TEM replicas and actually counting the striations would be a monumental task that would take thousands of hours to complete. (If one could count 1000 striations an hour, it would take 1000 hours

Figure 11-5 TEM micrograph (at 8100× magnification) of fatigue striations from the fracture surface in the fatigue region near the bottom of Figure 11-3, in approximately the same orientation. Note that the striations are not quite straight, more or less parallel, and of varying widths; these characteristics are common in service fatigue.

to count 1 million striations; fatigue may run to 10 or 100 million cycles.)

3. An intermediate method that avoids actually counting all the striations consists of estimating the probable stress history and conducting a numerical analysis involving the varying circumstances as the crack grows, for as the crack becomes larger, the width of each resultant striation becomes greater for the same alternating forces on the part. Such a procedure, however, is only as accurate as the assumptions in the analysis regarding such factors as initial crack size, the history of load magnitude and direction, the rate of crack growth for given loads, and the crack shape at every stage of crack growth. These factors usually are largely unknown.

4. Lastly, and probably most significantly, a large (and generally unknown) number of fatigue cycles are required for the initiation of the fatigue crack, before any striations are formed. So at the present state of knowledge on fatigue, accurate estimation of the actual number of cycles is still not possible; consequently, the procedure remains of limited use in failure analysis.

Electron microscopy can also effectively reveal fine-scale fracture features, as follows:

1. Overload tension of ductile metals leads to *microvoids*. These are very fine voids that form and grow so as eventually to connect with each other and lead to complete fracture. The fracture surface thus reveals microvoids in the form of pits on the surface. Figure 11-6 shows the appearance of typical microvoids. Since microvoids often initiate where fine particles exist in the microstructure, particles can often be seen inside some of the microvoids (see Figure 11-11 on page 247). If the part is exposed to sliding forces that distort the microvoids prior to complete fracture, then *elongated* or *parabolic* microvoids may be observed, as shown in Figure 11-7.

2. The brittle fracture of some metals, notably iron (and steel), can lead to *cleavage fracture*. This occurs from fracture across particular crystallographic planes and produces an almost flat surface, with fine *river*

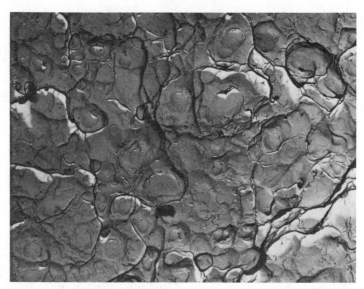

Figure 11-6 TEM micrograph (at 4800× magnification) of microvoid fracture in a very high-carbon steel.

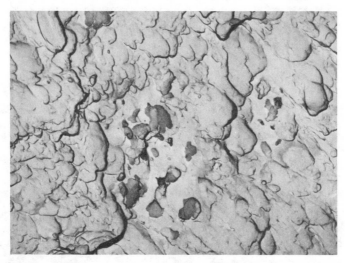

Figure 11-7 TEM micrograph (at 13,300× magnification) of parabolic microvoids in a high-carbon steel.

marks, which occur because imperfections in the crystal can cause the fracture to run on parallel but different planes. When these fractures connect, they leave a small step in the surface, and when the steps connect to form larger and fewer steps, they have the appearance of a river with tributaries. Figure 11-8 shows a typical cleavage surface with river marks (this is an SEM micrograph; see discussion that follows).

3. Stress corrosion cracking often, but not always, leads to a characteristic fracture appearance based on the *intergranular* nature of the fracture. Metals are usually made up of a collection of very fine individual *crystals,* also called *grains,* that are bound together across the grain boundaries by strong atomic-level forces. Fractures commonly occur *through* or *across* the individual grains of a metal, a process called *transgranular fracture.* But when intergranular fracture occurs, the fracture follows the three-dimensional shape of the surface of the grain boundary, as shown in Figure 11-9.

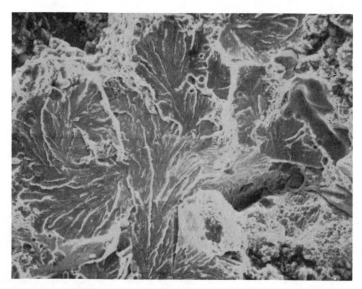

Figure 11-8 SEM micrograph (at 400× magnification) of cleavage fracture, with river marks, in malleable iron.

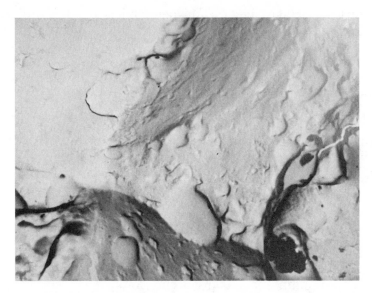

Figure 11-9 TEM micrograph (at 7900× magnification) of intergranular fracture of a medium-carbon steel automobile axle.

D.2. SCANNING ELECTRON MICROSCOPE (SEM) While the TEM detects changes in electrons that *travel through* a replica, the SEM detects changes in electrons that are *reflected from* a fracture surface. The SEM is designed to form an image based on the difference in intensity of the reflected electrons, as influenced by the texture and orientation of each point on the fracture surface. The SEM can be used on specimens that are very thick, but the specimen size is limited by the size of the vacuum chamber of the SEM. Consequently, small specimens for SEM examination must be cut out if a part is too large for the vacuum chamber (which is typically 12 to 75 mm in diameter and length, or 1/2 to 3 inches).

Because the SEM forms an image of the actual fracture surface, there are virtually no limitations to the roughness of the surface that can be examined in the SEM. However, the SEM is not as sensitive as the TEM to subtle contour changes, and the SEM is inherently limited to somewhat lower magnifications because of the electronics involved. Practical use in fractography limits it to about 10,000× magnification. Thus we see that the TEM is more powerful for examination of fairly flat fracture surfaces and does not require any destruction of the surface. The SEM specimen is much simpler to prepare, but it does usually require that a portion of the fracture surface be cut out. Both have excellent depth of focus, and the SEM in particular is much used for fractography that was formerly done with the optical microscope, down to as low as 15× magnification in some instruments.[5]

An example of an SEM micrograph of microvoids is shown in Figure 11-10. A higher magnification micrograph of microvoids and a deep hole is shown in Figure 11-11. Clear evidence of the dendrites that were described earlier can be seen in Figure 11-12.

IV. SUPPLEMENTARY TESTS

Although analysis of fracture surfaces yields much information about the circumstances of fracture, it frequently does not fully explain the basic reasons for the occurrence of a failure. Supplementary testing can often help in this respect. There are several more-or-less routine tests that should be

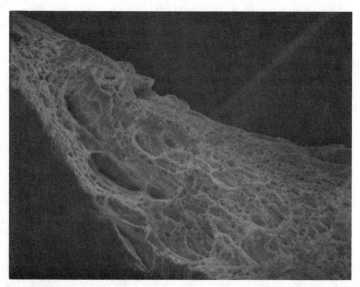

Figure 11-10 SEM micrograph (at 600× magnification) of a cold-worked, low-carbon steel, showing microvoids of a wide range of size.

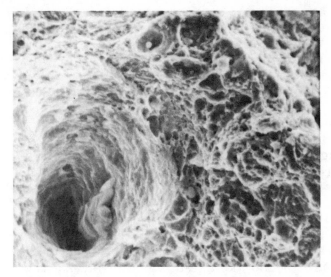

Figure 11-11 SEM micrograph (at 3000× magnification) of ductile overload microvoids in a low-carbon steel. Note the fine particles in several of the smaller microvoids.

Figure 11-12 SEM micrograph (at 40× magnification) of region at lower center of Figure 11-4, showing dendrites that are the result of solidification at the interior wall of a void that occurred when the casting was made.

performed whenever possible, usually with the expectation that the results will be the same as specified for the metal. But failure to meet design specifications occurs just often enough to warrant the tests, and the cause of the failure may then be fully understood.

A. Hardness Tests

One of the simplest and most useful tests is the *hardness test*. Although there are numerous forms of the hardness test, all measure the resistance of the metal to permanent (plastic) indentation.[6] The typical test consists of pressing a small hard ball or conical indenter into the metal and then measuring either the dimensions of the indentation or the depth of indentation. These values are then converted into *hardness numbers*. The two most commonly used tests in the United States are the *Rockwell* test, which involves a range of indentation forces and small indenters, and the *Brinell* test, which always uses a 10-mm diameter ball but uses a range of indentation forces. The Rockwell test uses much smaller forces and produces a much smaller indentation than the Brinell test. In steel the typical Brinell indentation is of the order of 5-mm diameter (0.2 inches), while a Rockwell indentation is perhaps 1-mm diameter (0.04 inches).

A strong correlation exists for most ductile metals between hardness and *strength* (defined below); therefore, a hardness test often eliminates the need for a tensile test. For many of the harder brittle metals, hardness provides a measure of resistance to wear. Thus a simple, virtually nondestructive hardness test can yield extremely useful information. The most direct use of a hardness test is for comparison with the hardness that is specified for the part, for if the hardness is much different from that specified, this may provide a valid cause for the failure. An important additional application of the hardness test is in *indentation hardness analysis* (described below).

B. Tensile Tests

Strength is defined as the maximum stress that a specimen can withstand in a *tensile test*. A standard-sized specimen is pulled in a machine until it breaks, with the load being measured continuously; thus the highest load divided by the initial cross-sectional area of the specimen is the strength.

The designer uses strength and *yield strength* (the stress when plastic deformation begins), as well as *fatigue strength* (the stress above which fatigue will occur in a specific application), in his selection of material and size when he designs a part. Therefore, a tensile test can provide an accurate measure of the strength of a part.

Several practical problems interfere with the routine use of the tensile test in failure analysis. Most important is the inherently destructive nature of the test: a specimen must be machined from metal taken from the part, and this specimen is deformed and pulled apart in the test. If the original failed part is small, this may not provide enough metal for a standard-sized tensile test, and substandard-sized tests will not in general give exactly the same strengths as standard-sized tests. Directionality may be important, as cold-worked and forged parts have different strengths in different directions. If a test is designed to measure the strength that existed at the fractured section, the test specimen must therefore be oriented in the same direction. Furthermore, if the part was substantially deformed during the failure, the strength of a specimen tested after deformation may actually be higher than the original strength of the part.

C. Chemical Analysis

Measuring the percentage of each of the chemical elements present in an alloy will identify the actual alloy that was used. In conjunction with metallographic examination (described above), chemical analysis then provides a reasonably accurate indication of the properties of the part. A chemical analysis is a relatively simple procedure for the failure analyst, but it does involve some very expensive and sophisticated equipment in the specialized laboratory that actually performs the analysis. A small piece of metal of the order of 5 grams (about 1/5 ounce) must be cut from the part in question.

Spectrographic analysis involves measuring the optical spectrum that is emitted from an electrical arc applied to the specimen; the intensity and frequency range of the radiation are compared with standard specimens of similar composition to establish the exact percentage of each element. Determination of the carbon content, which is usually of great importance in steels, is carried out in a separate test that involves complete combustion and hence destruction of the specimen.

The resultant chemical analysis can be compared with the specification for the part, which may have been either by a detailed description of the required range of percentage of each element or by specification of a standard alloy for which the range of chemical analysis has been established and published.[7-9] If the part fails to meet the required analysis in some significant way, this may provide an explanation for the failure.

D. Partial Simulation Tests

Tests may be required in order to check on a particular aspect of a failure, but without attempting to duplicate fully the circumstances of the actual failure. For example, the maneuvering behavior of a particular model of automobile can be tested by using an identical production vehicle. Or the behavior of a vehicle with deliberately loosened wheel nuts can be tested. Such tests can provide useful information that can indicate some of the limits of possible and impossible explanations for a failure.

E. Full Simulation Tests

In most instances the circumstances at the time of a failure are so imprecisely known that they would be impossible to duplicate *in every way*. Since a test that purports to duplicate fully an actual failure, but in fact does not, is more useless than no test at all, full simulation tests should be conducted only with great care.

V. SUPPLEMENTARY ANALYSES

A. Stress Analysis

Determination of the stress history of a part can provide information useful in establishing the cause of failure of a part. Seldom is the exact history of loads on a part known, so certain assumptions about the maximum and minimum loads must be made—and the usefulness of the resultant analysis will be restricted accordingly. From the loads, it is usually possible through use of routine analytical procedures to establish the stresses at critical regions in the part and from this to determine whether the part was likely to have failed during normal use as a result. Many cases of fracture in automotive vehicles can be reduced to the essential question of whether the part failed and led to the accident, or the accident occurred from some other cause and the part was fractured as a result of the forces in the accident. Thus, analysis of the stresses from normal service, used in conjunction with fractography, may indicate whether a part broke during normal service or during the accident.

B. Indentation Hardness Analysis

In the course of a vehicle accident, metal parts come in contact with each other and cause local indentations at the contacting points. It is possible through *indentation hardness analysis* to infer the approximate forces that were required to cause a particular indentation,[10] based on the hardness of the impinging surfaces, their shape, and the size of the resultant indentation(s).

This technique, while only approximate, is particularly useful in establishing whether an indentation could have resulted from normal service or was the result of some gross abuse or accident. Since the forces in a typical vehicle accident are usually many times greater than the forces during normal service, even approximate determination of the forces involved can often provide irrefutable discrimination between the two possibilities. Then, by inference, it may be possible to conclude that a critical part was or was not intact at the time of an accident, and this may lead to an explanation for the original failure.

C. Dimensional Variances

Careful measurement of the shape and dimensions of a part can be a useful supplemental tool for the failure analyst, for any changes in shape or dimensions from the original part may reveal the load history. Alternatively, a part may not have been manufactured within the limits of dimensional tolerance as specified by the designer, and *this* may have contributed to the accident. Other factors that can change the dimensions include wear and corrosion; these also must be considered in any inference of the history of a part.

CITATIONS

[1]*Metals Handbook*, 8th Ed., Vol. 10, *Failure Analysis and Prevention*. Metals Park, OH.: American Society for Metals, 1975.

[2]*Metals Handbook*, 8th Ed., Vol. 9, *Fractography and Atlas of Fractographs*. Metals Park, OH.: American Society for Metals, 1974.

[3]R. M. Caddell, *Deformation and Fracture of Solids*. Englewood Cliffs, N.J.: Prentice-Hall, 1980.

[4]*Metals Handbook*, 8th Ed., Vol. 8, *Metallography, Structures and Phase Diagrams*. Metals Park, OH.: American Society for Metals, 1973.

[5]L. Engel and H. Klingele, *An Atlas of Metal Damage*. Englewood Cliffs, N.J.: Prentice-Hall, 1981.

[6]D. K. Felbeck and A. G. Atkins, *Strength and Fracture of Engineering Solids*. Englewood Cliffs, N.J.: Prentice-Hall, 1984.

[7]*Metals Handbook*, 9th Ed., Vol. 1, *Properties and Selection: Irons and Steels*. Metals Park, OH.: American Society for Metals, 1978.

[8]*Metals Handbook*, 9th Ed., Vol. 2, *Properties and Selection: Nonferrous Alloys and Pure Metals*. Metals Park, OH.: American Society for Metals, 1979.

[9]*Metals Handbook*, 9th Ed., Vol. 3, *Properties and Selection: Stainless Steels, Tool Materials and Special-Purpose Metals*. Metals Park, OH.: American Society for Metals, 1980.

[10]A. G. Atkins and D. K. Felbeck, "Applying Mutual Indentation Hardness Phenomena to Service Failures," *Source Book in Failure Analysis*. Metals Park, OH.: American Society for Metals, 1974, p. 364.

12

Accident Reconstruction Models

YAU WU, Ph.D.
President, Dynamic Analysis Corporation
Concord, Massachusetts

and

Research Professor
Boston University
Boston, Massachusetts

*Dr. Wu received a B.S. from the National Taiwan
University, an M.S. from the University of Illinois, an
S.M. from M.I.T., and a Ph.D. from New York University.
He has been a faculty member at Princeton University,
the University of Illinois, Virginia Polytechnic Institute,
M.I.T., and Boston University. In addition, he has served
as a consultant for Boeing, the U.S. Army, Air Force, and
Navy, NASA, and the Department of Transportation. His
research involves automobile collision, vehicular dynamics,
high-speed ground transportation, particle collisions, and
kinetic theory. His membership affiliations include, among
others, the AIAA, APS, Sigma Xi, American Men of
Science, and the New York Academy of Science. The
author may be contacted at the Dynamic Analysis Corporation, 201 Indian Pipe Lane, Concord, Massachusetts
01742 (617-369-8266).*

I. INTRODUCTION

During recent years, McHenry (SMAC model) and Rau (Shell model) have proposed independently a linearized isotropic model for the simulation of automobile collisions with different dynamic approaches. Since 1976, Wu has developed a more general, linear and nonlinear anisotropic model for automobile collisions (IMPACT model) based on his "Equal-Potential method." It has proven to be the most efficient mathematical model to predict the detailed vehicle–vehicle collision motion through an interactive time-sharing computer terminal. A combined program of IMPACT and the initial impact speed estimation (ISE) becomes a complete mathematical model of accident reconstruction in an iterative process.

II. BACKGROUND

In 1924, Bergen was the first to study the basic physical laws of a vehicle collision during collision impact. Bruderlin proposed a momentum theorem approach for vehicle–vehicle collisions in 1941. With a similar approach, both Lossagh and Eherkorst in 1958 attempted to solve the central impact of vehicles as two-point masses without considering any angular motions. For many years, investigators—including Eherhorst (1962), Marguard (1962, 1964, 1966), Silber (1964), Emori (1968), Kamal (1970), McHenry (1971), and Wilson (1973)—used the impact theory for vehicle collision problems based on momentum, angular momentum, and energy conservation principles, with various simplifications and assumptions for both equations and solutions. But the impact theory is formulated on a limited and insufficient number of moment equations. The solution is not unique and becomes inconsistent, due to many subjective simplifications, in most general impact situations.

In 1965, Hofen investigated the applicability of impact principles with collisions of small-model vehicles. Bohn and Horz, in 1968, advanced a simple computer program for the treatment of noncentral impact of vehicles. Two years later Plankensteiner proposed a graphical interactive accident reconstruction method.

Substantial progress has been made through the years to evolve a dynamic model of vehicle collision. It is recognized that a dynamic model based on the equation of motion will

provide a unique solution during the entire course of interaction. With sufficient impact test data available for the
vehicle's deformation behavior and the modern high-speed
computer capability, it is apparent that the vehicle collision
impact should be treated as a complete realistic dynamic
problem.

Since 1971, McHenry has proposed a linear, isotropic
vehicle model for automobile collision as a dynamic system
(SMAC—Simulation Model of Automobile Collision). In 1975,
Rau suggested independently a linear isotropic model (Shell
model) for solving the dynamic equation of motion of two
colliding vehicles. Since 1976, Wu has proposed an Equal-
Potential method that is capable of solving a very general
linear and nonlinear anisotropic dynamic model for vehicle-
vehicle collisions (IMPACT—Improved Mathematical Predi-
cation of Automobile Collision and Trajectory).

III. ACCIDENT SIMULATION MODELS

For many years, accident research has been concentrated on
detailed evidence investigation and the generation of simple
solutions based on momentum and energy equations. The
Simulation Model of Automobile Collision (SMAC—linear
model) and the Improved Mathematical Prediction of Automobile Collision and Trajectory (IMPACT—linear and nonlinear model) will greatly influence future accident simulation
research. Both programs have led to a much broader spectrum
of applications. Because of their eventual widespread use
throughout the world, it is important that the simulation
models be as versatile and as accurate as possible. The limitations due to simplified structure assumptions should be identified and quantified precisely through an extensive validation
program. It is also important to improve the precision and utility of the present simulation models and extend validation to
cover as wide a range of operating conditions as possible.

The IMPACT model is designed to simulate the dynamic
motion between two colliding vehicles with nonlinear anisotropic structure characteristics. Since the general equations
of motion of two interacting elastic–plastic bodies cannot be
formulated explicitly, it is not possible to describe the interactive surface and force as a mathematical function in terms
of the positions, directions, and velocities of the two interactive deformable bodies. It is also required that the inter-

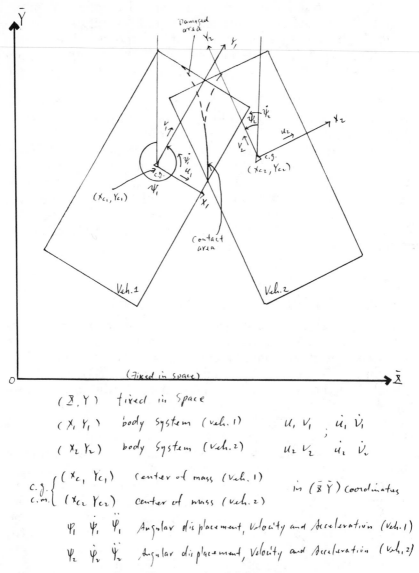

$(\bar{X}, \bar{Y})$ fixed in Space

$(X_1 Y_1)$ body System (veh. 1) u_1, V_1 ; $\dot{u}_1, \dot{V}_1$

$(X_2 Y_2)$ body System (veh. 2) $u_2 V_2$ $\dot{u}_2, \dot{V}_2$

c.g. $\begin{cases} (X_{c_1}, Y_{c_1}) & \text{center of mass (Veh. 1)} \\ (X_{c_2} Y_{c_2}) & \text{center of mass (veh. 2)} \end{cases}$ in $(\bar{X} \bar{Y})$ Coordinates

c.m.

$\Psi_1 \quad \dot{\Psi}_1 \quad \ddot{\Psi}_1$ Angular displacement, Velocity and Acceleration (Veh. 1)

$\Psi_2 \quad \dot{\Psi}_2 \quad \ddot{\Psi}_2$ Angular displacement, Velocity and Acceleration (Veh. 2)

Figure 12-1 Coordinates of vehicles—IMPACT model.

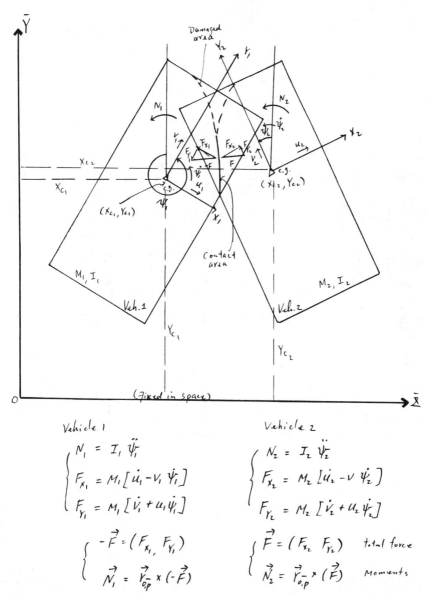

Figure 12-2 Interacting forces and moments, and equation of motions—IMPACT model.

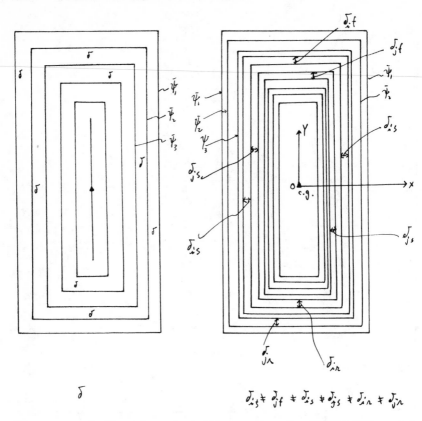

Figure 12-3 Equal potential lines using the IMPACT model. Linear model (*left*); nonlinear model (*right*).

acting contact surface between two vehicles be determined in a closed form solution. A mathematical model must also inherently describe the physical properties of a realistic deformable body. It has to bring together a mixed geometric problem and a dynamic problem into a mathematically explicit form.

An Equal-Potential theory has been proposed to serve as a very efficient tool for this complex system or any other impact system with large deformations (see Figures 12-1

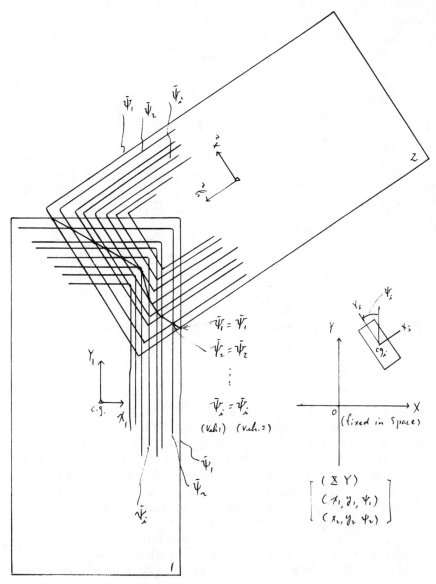

Figure 12-4 The IMPACT Equal-Potential method for inter-acting vehicles.

```
VEHICLE --- 1     FULL SIZE

   MASS                    12.    DISTANCE TO FRONT WHEEL    60.5
   MOMENT OF INERTIA   44563.     DISTANCE TO REAR WHEEL     63.0
                                  AXLE LENGTH                63.1

POTENTIAL    RIGHT FRONT          LEFT FRONT           LEFT REAR            RIGHT REAR
    50.    (  39.6, 100.5)    ( -39.6, 100.5)    ( -39.6,-119.6)    (   39.6,-119.6)
   150.    (  37.6,  98.5)    ( -37.6,  98.5)    ( -37.6,-117.6)    (   37.6,-117.6)
   250.    (  35.6,  96.5)    ( -35.6,  96.5)    ( -35.6,-115.6)    (   35.6,-115.6)
   350.    (  33.6,  94.5)    ( -33.6,  94.5)    ( -33.6,-113.6)    (   33.6,-113.6)
   450.    (  31.6,  92.5)    ( -31.6,  92.5)    ( -31.6,-111.6)    (   31.6,-111.6)
   550.    (  29.6,  90.5)    ( -29.6,  90.5)    ( -29.6,-109.6)    (   29.6,-109.6)
   650.    (  27.6,  88.5)    ( -27.6,  88.5)    ( -27.6,-107.6)    (   27.6,-107.6)
   750.    (  25.6,  86.5)    ( -25.6,  86.5)    ( -25.6,-105.6)    (   25.6,-105.6)
   850.    (  23.6,  84.5)    ( -23.6,  84.5)    ( -23.6,-103.6)    (   23.6,-103.6)
   950.    (  21.6,  82.5)    ( -21.6,  82.5)    ( -21.6,-101.6)    (   21.6,-101.6)
  1050.    (  19.6,  80.5)    ( -19.6,  80.5)    ( -19.6, -99.6)    (   19.6, -99.6)
  1150.    (  17.6,  78.5)    ( -17.6,  78.5)    ( -17.6, -97.6)    (   17.6, -97.6)
  1250.    (  15.6,  76.5)    ( -15.6,  76.5)    ( -15.6, -95.6)    (   15.6, -95.6)
  1350.    (  13.6,  74.5)    ( -13.6,  74.5)    ( -13.6, -93.6)    (   13.6, -93.6)
  1450.    (  11.6,  72.5)    ( -11.6,  72.5)    ( -11.6, -91.6)    (   11.6, -91.6)
  1550.    (   9.6,  70.5)    (  -9.6,  70.5)    (  -9.6, -89.6)    (    9.6, -89.6)
  1650.    (   7.6,  68.5)    (  -7.6,  68.5)    (  -7.6, -87.6)    (    7.6, -87.6)
  1750.    (   5.6,  66.5)    (  -5.6,  66.5)    (  -5.6, -85.6)    (    5.6, -85.6)
  1850.    (   3.6,  64.5)    (  -3.6,  64.5)    (  -3.6, -83.6)    (    3.6, -83.6)
  1950.    (   1.6,  62.5)    (  -1.6,  62.5)    (  -1.6, -81.6)    (    1.6, -81.6)

CORNERING STIFFNESS
   RIGHT FRONT              -11572.0
   LEFT FRONT               -11572.0
   LEFT REAR                -11113.0
   RIGHT REAR               -11113.0
```

Figure 12-5 The standard IMPACT linear model (potential lines).

through 12-8). The interacting surface between two colliding bodies can be determined in a closed form solution. By eliminating the damaged portion of the contact surface, the real interacting boundary can be defined. The deformable body is formulated as a two-dimensional elastic–plastic system, and the force-deformation function can be described as a set of discrete equal-pressure contours, so called Equal-Potential lines. These intrusion pressure functions are, in general, nonlinear and anisotropic characteristics, which are determined based on various crush test data. Questions might be raised that the crushing automobile structure is a highly complex impedance involving masses and that the nonlinear springs and dampers and the force-deformation properties involved in one test will not be the same in another of a different velocity. Although this question is valid in principle, its effect has been proved to be small (Kamal's BASHSIM model) in a dynamic response impact test at any speed. It is apparently because the spring elements are very stiff relative to the mass impedances so that the system's resonant period is long rela-

```
MIDGET       L          40  80   1
MIDGET       R          40  80   2
MIDGET       H          40  80   3
MINI         L          40  80   4
MINI         R          40  80   5
MINI         H          40  80   6
MIDI         L          40  80   7
MIDI         R          40  80   8
MIDI         H          40  80   9
COMPACT      L          40  80  10
COMPACT      R          40  80  11
COMPACT      H          40  80  12
INTERM       L          40  80  13
INTERM       R          40  80  14
INTERM       H          40  80  15
STANDARD     L          40  80  16
STANDARD     R          40  80  17
STANDARD     H          40  80  18
FULL         L          40  80  19
FULL         R          40  80  20
FULL         H          40  80  21
LARGE        L          40  80  22
LARGE        R          40  80  23
LARGE        H          40  80  24
LUXURY       L          40  80  25
LUXURY       R          40  80  26
LUXURY       H          40  80  27
LIMO         L          40  80  28
LIMO         R          40  80  29
LIMO         H          40  80  30
MINICAR      STD        40  80  31
SUBCOMPACTSTD           40  80  32
COMPACTCARSTD           40  80  33
INTRMEDIATSTD           40  80  34
FULLSIZE     STD        40  80  35
LARGECAR     STD        40  80  36
MINICAR      HR         40  80  37
SUBCOMPACTHR            40  80  38
COMPACTCARHR            40  80  39
INTRMEDIATHR            40  80  40
FULLSIZE     HR         40  80  41
LARGECAR     HR         40  80  42
MINICAR      S          40  80  43
SUBCOMPACTS             40  80  44
COMPACTCARS             40  80  45
INTRMEDIATS             40  80  46
FULLSIZE     S          40  80  47
LARGECAR     S          40  80  48
MINICAR      C          40  80  49
SUBCOMPACTC             40  80  50
COMPACTCARC             40  80  51
INTRMEDIATC             40  80  52
FULLSIZE     C          40  80  53
LARGECAR     C          40  80  54
MINICAR      W          40  80  55
SUBCOMPACTW             40  80  56
COMPACTCARW             40  80  57
INTRMEDIATW             40  80  58
FULLSIZE     W          40  80  59
LARGECAR     W          40  80  60
SMALL        ST         40  80  61
MEDIAN       ST         40  80  62
REGULAR      ST         40  80  63
LARGESIZE    ST         40  80  64
BARRIER      MOVING     40  80  65
BARRIER      FIXED      40  80  66
```

Figure 12-6 The standard IMPACT model (random file).

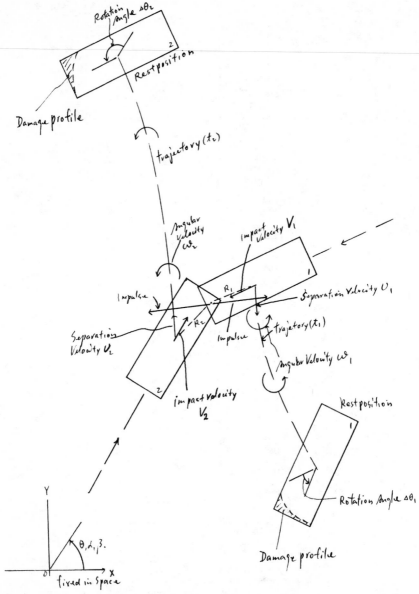

Figure 12-7 Coordinates of vehicles, velocities, impact positions, and trajectories—ISE model.

$$\sum_i m_i \bar{V}_i = \sum_i m_i \bar{U}_i \qquad \text{momentum}$$

$$(\bar{R}_i \times \bar{F}_i) \cdot \hat{K} = I_i \omega_i \qquad \text{Angular momentum}$$

$$\bar{F}_i = m_i \bar{U}_i - m_i \bar{V}_i$$
$$\left.\begin{array}{c}\end{array}\right\} \quad \text{Impulse - momentum}$$
$$\bar{F}_i = -\bar{F}_j \qquad i \neq j$$

$$\sum_i \tfrac{1}{2} m_i \bar{V}_i^2 = \sum_i \tfrac{1}{2} m_i \bar{U}_i^2 + \sum_i \tfrac{1}{2} I_i \omega_i^2 + W_{D_i}$$

$$W_{D_i} = A_i \, a_i + B_i \, b_i + \frac{A_i^2 L_i}{2 B_i}$$

$$W_{f_i} = 0.85 \, m_i \, g \, \mu_i \, S_i + \mu_i \, m_i \, g \left(\frac{WB_i}{2}\right) \Delta \beta_i$$

$$W = \sum_i (W_{D_i} + W_{f_i})$$

$$\left.\begin{array}{c}\\[4ex]\\[4ex]\\[4ex]\end{array}\right\} \text{Energy}$$

Figure 12-8 Basic equations of the ISE model for momentum, angular momentum, and energy (during and after collisions).

tive to the rise time in an impact. There may also be a compensatory effect as a result of the dynamic rate factor. By using a simple phenomenological vehicle model and the Equal-Potential theory, a step-by-step numerical integration of calculating the time-history solution of a dynamic system can be made in a simulated collision environment. Due to the efficient approach to the evaluation of the contact forces between the colliding vehicles, the computer time required for this linear and nonlinear anisotropic model (IMPACT) is one order of magnitude lower than the linear isotropic model (SMAC).

The CDC Cybernet (NOS) digital computer is used for the IMPACT program. It is a time-sharing system with an inter-

active terminal in a worldwide network. The computer programming is the most time-consuming process in this project.
There are many numerical criteria that have to be proposed
and implemented at each stage of the development. The three
basic stages of the computer program are (1) precollision,
(2) collision, and (3) postcollision. The collision period is the
most complex portion of the program. The interface of the
colliding vehicles is evaluated according to the Equal-Potential
theory. The equations of motion will be integrated by the
Runge-Kutta method or Predictor–Corrector method. The
tire–ground friction is defined by the typical "circle principle." Both linear and nonlinear models of the vehicle will be
treated and programmed in complete forms. The interactive
terminal will receive all the input data and tire, steering, and
braking information from the investigator. It will also provide all the dynamic solutions and damage profiles before,
during, and after collision.

A large portion of the data about the vehicle can be stored
in the random file. The classification of the vehicle can be
made according to its weight and wheel base. The information
about the various obstacles can also be stored in the random
file, which can be retrieved directly from the terminal. Therefore, all the available information about both vehicle and the
obstacle should be categorized in a systematic manner so that
it can easily be identified and recalled from the terminal.

IV. EXHIBITS

Exhibit 12-1 (pages 265–276) details accident reconstruction
from initial report to final solutions and diagrams, according
to the ISE model, based on the evidence, vehicle properties,
and physical laws. Exhibits 12-2 and 12-3 (pages 277–284,
285–287) present computer simulations of automobile collision
and trajectory based on the IMPACT mathematical model.

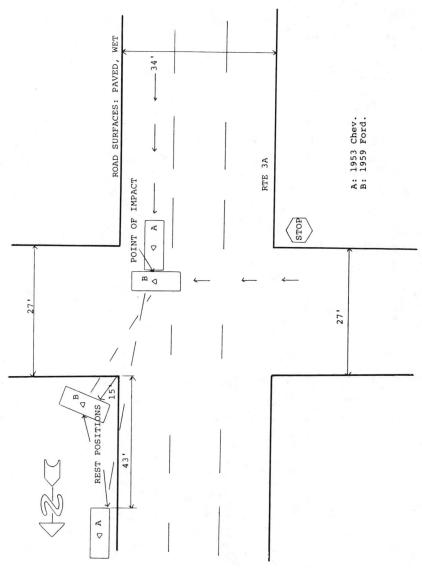

Exhibit 12-1 Accident reconstruction based on the Impact Speed Estimation (ISE) program, from police diagram to final accident diagrams.

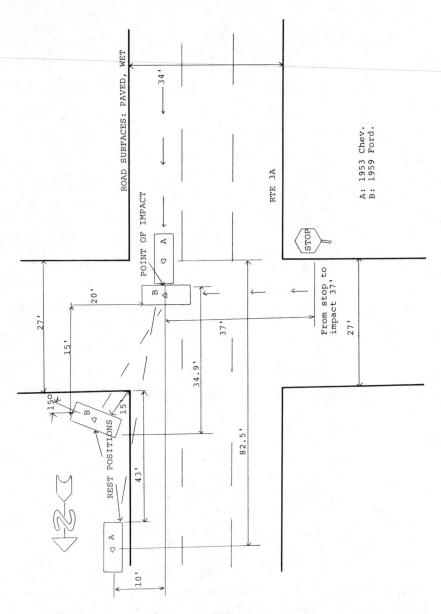

Exhibit 12-1 (*Continued*)

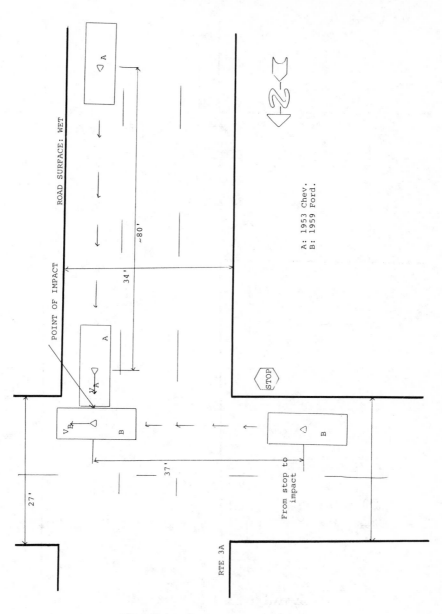

Exhibit 12-1 (*Continued*)

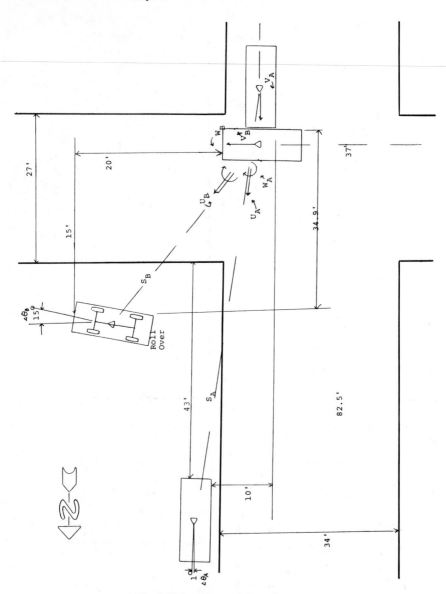

Exhibit 12-1 (*Continued*)

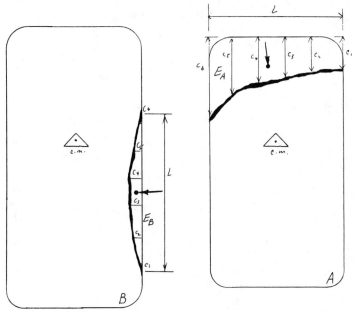

Exhibit 12-1 (*Continued*)

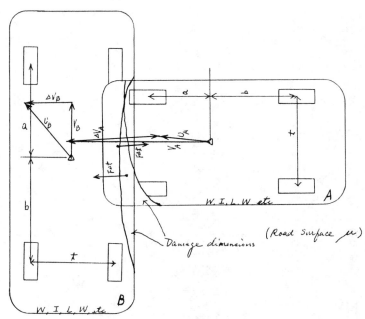

Exhibit 12-1 (*Continued*)

```
ENTER: MU1,MU2,MU3,MU4,MU5
? .2 .23 .25 .28 .3

ENTER: GAMA1,GAMA4
? 279 282

ENTER: W,I,A,B FOR VEHICLE 1
? 3500 34000 54.5 60.5
ENTER: ALFA,BETA,R,PHI,S,DBETA FOR VEHICLE 1
? 90 78 85 101 1080 1
ENTER: L,C(II-1),C(II-2),C(II-3),C(II-4),AA,BB FOR VEHICLE 1
? 75 24 22 20 18 0 50

ENTER: W,I,A,B FOR VEHICLE 2
? 4000 42000 56 62
ENTER: ALFA,BETA,R,PHI,S,DBETA FOR VEHICLE 2
? 0 55 225 680 -15
ENTER: L,C(II-1),C(II-2),C(II-3),C(II-4),AA,BB FOR VEHICLE 2
? 82 10 14 14 10 0 50

MU= .20
```

GAMA/DEG	V(1)/MPH	V(2)/MPH	U(1)/MPH	U(2)/MPH	OMEGA1/DG	OMEGA2/DG	F/LB-SEC	DV1/MPH	DV2/MPH	DE/RATIO	AMU(1)	AMU(2)
	XI(1)	YI(1)	XI(2)	YI(2)	XF(1)	YF(1)	XF(2)	YF(2)	XT	YT	E1/FT-LB	E2/FT-LB
279.00	36.65	15.78	16.00	-22.43	16.94	-168.33	3389.46	21.26	18.60	-.20	.11	.42
	.0	5842.2	2874.3	0.0	530.2	2494.5	2344.1	3347.7	2874.3	5842.2	69375.0	27713.0
280.00	36.81	15.43	17.06	21.49	8.14	-163.80	3257.29	20.43	17.88	-.17	.13	.38
	.0	5868.8	2811.7	0.0	565.6	2661.0	2246.1	3207.8	2811.7	5868.8	69375.0	27713.0
281.00	36.96	15.11	18.05	20.62	.00	-159.58	3135.68	19.67	17.21	-.16	.14	.36
	.0	5892.9	2753.6	0.0	598.3	2814.8	2155.3	3078.1	2753.6	5892.9	69375.0	27713.0

Exhibit 12-1 (*Continued*)

MU= .23

| GAMA/DEG | V(1)/MPH | V(2)/MPH | U(1)/MPH | U(2)/MPH | OMEGA1/DG | OMEGA2/DG | F/LB-SEC | DV1/MPH | DV2/MPH | DE/RATIO | AMU(1) | AMU(2) |
XI(1)	YI(1)	XI(2)	YI(2)	XF(1)	YF(1)	XF(2)	YF(2)	XT	YT		E1/FT-LB	E2/FT-LB
279.00	37.97	16.35	16.57	23.24	17.56	-174.41	3511.74	22.03	19.27	-.14	.12	.45
.0	6053.0	2978.0		0.0	549.4	2584.5	3468.5		2978.0		69375.0	27713.0
280.00	38.14	15.99	17.68	22.27	8.44	-169.71	3374.80	21.17	18.52	-.11	.14	.41
.0	6080.6	2913.2		0.0	586.0	2757.0	3323.5		2913.2		69375.0	27713.0
281.00	38.30	15.66	18.70	21.37	.00	-165.34	3248.80	20.38	17.83	-.10	.15	.38
.0	6105.5	2852.9		0.0	619.9	2916.4	3189.1		2852.9		69375.0	27713.0

MU= .25

| GAMA/DEG | V(1)/MPH | V(2)/MPH | U(1)/MPH | U(2)/MPH | OMEGA1/DG | OMEGA2/DG | F/LB-SEC | DV1/MPH | DV2/MPH | DE/RATIO | AMU(1) | AMU(2) |
XI(1)	YI(1)	XI(2)	YI(2)	XF(1)	YF(1)	XF(2)	YF(2)	XT	YT		E1/FT-LB	E2/FT-LB
279.00	38.83	16.71	16.95	23.76	17.95	-178.34	3590.95	22.53	19.71	-.10	.13	.47
.0	6189.5	3045.2		0.0	561.7	2642.8	3546.7		3045.2		69375.0	27713.0
280.00	39.00	16.35	18.08	22.77	8.63	-173.53	3450.92	21.65	18.94	-.07	.14	.43
.0	6217.7	2978.9		0.0	599.2	2819.2	3398.5		2978.9		69375.0	27713.0
281.00	39.16	16.01	19.12	21.85	.00	-169.07	3322.08	20.84	18.23	-.05	.16	.40
.0	6243.2	2917.3		0.0	633.9	2982.2	3261.0		2917.3		69375.0	27713.0

Exhibit 12-1 (*Continued*)

MU= .28

| GAMA/DEG | V(1)/MPH | V(2)/MPH | U(1)/MPH | U(2)/MPH | OMEGA1/DG | OMEGA2/DG | F/LB-SEC | DV1/MPH | DV2/MPH | DE/RATIO | AMU(1) | AMU(2) |
XI(1)	YI(1)	XI(2)	YI(2)	XF(1)	YF(1)	XF(2)	YF(2)	XT	YT	E1/FT-LB	E2/FT-LB	
279.00	40.08	17.25	17.49	24.53	18.53	-184.08	3706.59	23.25	20.34	-.04	.13	.50
.0	6388.9	3143.3		0.0	579.8	2727.9	2563.4	3661.0	3143.3	69375.0	27713.0	
280.00	40.26	16.88	18.66	23.50	8.91	-179.12	3562.05	22.34	19.55	-.01	.15	.46
.0	6417.9	3074.8		0.0	618.5	2910.0	2456.3	3507.9	3074.8	69375.0	27713.0	
281.00	40.42	16.53	19.74	22.55	.00	-174.52	3429.06	21.51	18.82	.01	.17	.43
.0	6444.3	3011.2		0.0	654.3	3078.2	2356.9	3366.1	3011.2	69375.0	27713.0	

MU= .30

| GAMA/DEG | V(1)/MPH | V(2)/MPH | U(1)/MPH | U(2)/MPH | OMEGA1/DG | OMEGA2/DG | F/LB-SEC | DV1/MPH | DV2/MPH | DE/RATIO | AMU(1) | AMU(2) |
XI(1)	YI(1)	XI(2)	YI(2)	XF(1)	YF(1)	XF(2)	YF(2)	XT	YT	E1/FT-LB	E2/FT-LB	
279.00	40.89	17.60	17.85	25.03	18.91	-187.82	3781.72	23.72	20.76	-.00	.14	.52
.0	6518.4	3207.0		0.0	591.6	2783.2	2615.4	3735.2	3207.0	69375.0	27713.0	
280.00	41.07	17.22	19.04	23.98	9.09	-182.75	3634.25	22.80	19.95	.03	.16	.48
.0	6548.0	3137.1		0.0	631.1	2969.0	2506.1	3579.0	3137.2	69375.0	27713.0	
281.00	41.24	16.86	20.14	23.01	.00	-178.05	3498.57	21.95	19.20	.05	.18	.44
.0	6574.9	3072.3		0.0	667.6	3140.6	2404.7	3434.3	3072.3	69375.0	27713.0	

Exhibit 12-1 (*Continued*)

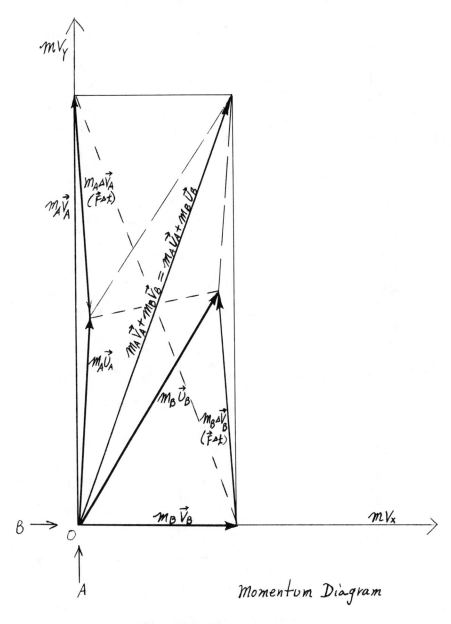

Momentum Diagram

Exhibit 12-1 (*Continued*)

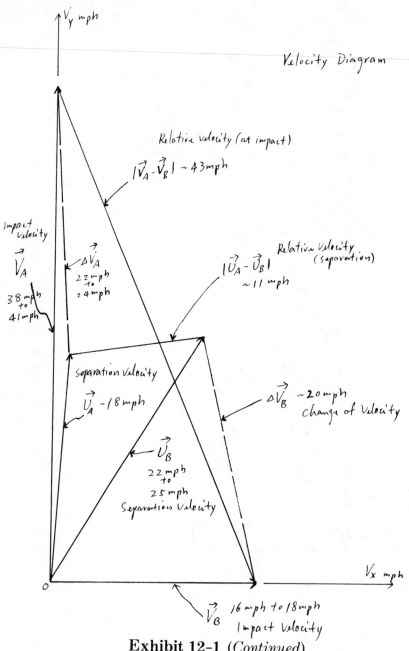

Exhibit 12-1 (Continued)

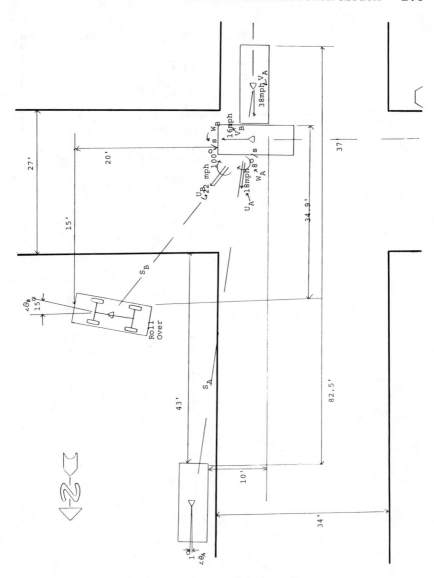

Exhibit 12-1 (*Continued*)

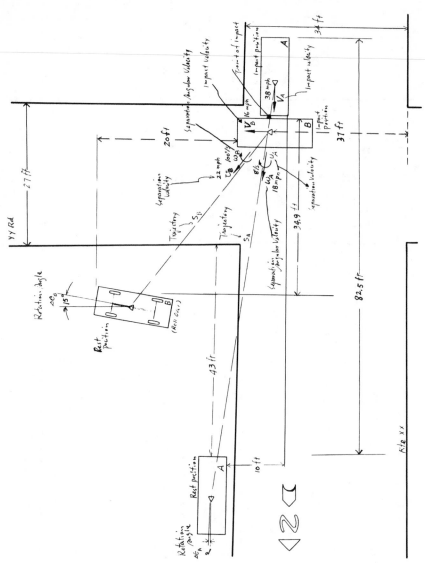

Exhibit 12-1 (*Continued*)

```
EASTERN CYBERNET CENTER SN147 NOS      1.0/411.433.0-0
PASSWORD
████████
TERMINAL:    114,TTY
RECOVER/ CHARGE: CHAR,S84727L,*DWU*
READY.
BATCH
$RFL,20000.
/GET,TAPE30=VDATA10
/GET,IMPAC8
/SETTL(15)
$SETTL(15)
/IMPAC8
 ENTER MODEL YEAR FOR VEHICLE 1
? 70
 ENTER MAKE OF VEHICLE 1
? FORD
 ENTER MODEL FOR VEHICLE 1
? LTD
 DO YOU WANT FULL INFLATION FOR ALL TIRES?
? Y
 ENTER MODEL YEAR FOR VEHICLE 2
? 70
 ENTER MAKE OF VEHICLE 2
? DODGE
 ENTER MODEL FOR VEHICLE 2
? DART
 DO YOU WANT FULL INFLATION FOR ALL TIRES?
? Y
 DO YOU WANT TO USE A FORCE INCREMENT OF   100. OR   200.
? 100
 ENTER TIME STEP (SECONDS) DURING COLLISION
? .01
 ENTER TIME STEP (SECONDS) AFTER COLLISION
? .02
 DO YOU WANT THE FULL TERMINAL LISTING?
? Y
 ENTER XC,YC,PSI,PSID,U,V FOR VEHICLE 1
? 90 -128.4 30 0 0 29.6
 ENTER XC,YC,PSI,PSID,U,V FOR VEHICLE 2
? 2.4 0 270 0 0 29.6

 CORNER 1 OF VEHICLE 1 STRIKES EDGE 1 OF VEHICLE 2
 EDGE 1 IS USED TO UPDATE DAMAGES FOR VEHICLE 1

 EDGE 4 USED TO UPDATE DAMAGES FOR VEHICLE 2


 TIME FROM START 0.000 SECONDS    CONTACT
                   XC        YC       PSI      PSID      U         V
 VEHICLE 1        90.0    -128.4     .524     0.000     0.0      521.0
 VEHICLE 2         2.4       0.0    4.712     0.000     0.0      521.0
                   FX        FY       FN        GX        GY       G
 VEHICLE 1     2.111E+03  -9.388E+03  -4.158E+05     .46    -2.04    2.09
 VEHICLE 2    -7.075E+03  -6.522E+03   1.981E+05   -2.28    -2.10    3.10
 CENTER OF MASS AT ( 54.7, -76.7)

 TIME FROM START .010 SECONDS    CONTACT
                   XC        YC       PSI      PSID      U         V
 VEHICLE 1        87.4    -123.9     .523     -.078     1.8      513.1
 VEHICLE 2         7.6       .0     4.713      .075    -8.8      512.8
                   FX        FY       FN        GX        GY       G
 VEHICLE 1     3.183E+03  -1.380E+04  -5.589E+05     .69    -3.00    3.08
 VEHICLE 2    -1.037E+04  -9.649E+03   1.899E+05   -3.34    -3.11    4.57
 CENTER OF MASS AT ( 55.3. -74.0)
```

Exhibit 12-2 Collision simulation based on the Improved Mathematical Prediction of Automobile Collision and Trajectory (IMPACT) program.

```
TIME FROM START  .020 SECONDS    CONTACT
                  XC        YC       PSI      PSID      U          V
     VEHICLE 1   84.9    -119.5     .522    -.182      4.0       501.5
     VEHICLE 2   12.6       .2     4.714     .146    -21.4       500.8
                  FX        FY       FN        GX        GY        G
     VEHICLE 1   4.512E+03  -1.878E+04  -6.971E+05    .98    -4.08    4.20
     VEHICLE 2  -1.405E+04  -1.326E+04   1.223E+05  -4.53    -4.28    6.23
     CENTER OF MASS AT (  55.8, -71.3)

TIME FROM START  .030 SECONDS    CONTACT
                  XC        YC       PSI      PSID      U          V
     VEHICLE 1   82.5    -115.2     .519    -.312      6.9       485.7
     VEHICLE 2   17.6       .5     4.716     .193    -38.1       484.3
                  FX        FY       FN        GX        GY        G
     VEHICLE 1   6.131E+03  -2.416E+04  -8.249E+05   1.33    -5.25    5.42
     VEHICLE 2  -1.798E+04  -1.726E+04  -1.413E+04  -5.80    -5.57    8.04
     CENTER OF MASS AT (  56.4, -68.6)

TIME FROM START  .040 SECONDS    CONTACT
                  XC        YC       PSI      PSID      U          V
     VEHICLE 1   80.2    -111.0     .516    -.467     10.6       465.4
     VEHICLE 2   22.3      1.0     4.717     .187    -59.6       462.9
                  FX        FY       FN        GX        GY        G
     VEHICLE 1   8.073E+03  -2.969E+04  -9.386E+05   1.76    -6.46    6.69
     VEHICLE 2  -2.196E+04  -2.155E+04  -2.223E+05  -7.09    -6.95    9.93
     CENTER OF MASS AT (  56.9, -65.9)

TIME FROM START  .050 SECONDS    CONTACT
                  XC        YC       PSI      PSID      U          V
     VEHICLE 1   78.1    -107.0     .510    -.642     15.2       440.5
     VEHICLE 2   26.8      1.8     4.719     .103    -86.1       436.1
                  FX        FY       FN        GX        GY        G
     VEHICLE 1   8.276E+03  -3.777E+04  -9.110E+05   1.80    -8.21    8.41
     VEHICLE 2  -2.909E+04  -2.547E+04  -3.957E+05  -9.38    -8.22   12.47
     CENTER OF MASS AT (  57.5, -63.2)

TIME FROM START  .060 SECONDS    CONTACT
                  XC        YC       PSI      PSID      U          V
     VEHICLE 1   76.2    -103.2     .503    -.812     19.3       408.9
     VEHICLE 2   31.0      2.8     4.719    -.046    -122.0       404.5
                  FX        FY       FN        GX        GY        G
     VEHICLE 1   1.047E+04  -4.205E+04  -1.015E+06   2.28    -9.14    9.42
     VEHICLE 2  -3.201E+04  -2.922E+04  -6.684E+05 -10.32    -9.42   13.98
     CENTER OF MASS AT (  58.0, -60.5)

TIME FROM START  .070 SECONDS    CONTACT
                  XC        YC       PSI      PSID      U          V
     VEHICLE 1   74.5     -99.7     .494   -1.002     24.8       373.7
     VEHICLE 2   34.8      4.3     4.717    -.298    -162.0       368.0
                  FX        FY       FN        GX        GY        G
     VEHICLE 1   1.272E+04  -4.442E+04  -1.119E+06   2.76    -9.66   10.05
     VEHICLE 2  -3.326E+04  -3.208E+04  -9.197E+05 -10.73   -10.35   14.91
     CENTER OF MASS AT (  58.6, -57.8)

TIME FROM START  .080 SECONDS    CONTACT
                  XC        YC       PSI      PSID      U          V
     VEHICLE 1   73.1     -96.4     .483   -1.211     31.7       336.7
     VEHICLE 2   38.3      6.1     4.713    -.645    -204.6       327.5
                  FX        FY       FN        GX        GY        G
     VEHICLE 1   1.248E+04  -4.856E+04  -1.067E+06   2.71   -10.56   10.90
     VEHICLE 2  -3.723E+04  -3.358E+04  -1.081E+06 -12.01   -10.83   16.17
     CENTER OF MASS AT (  59.1, -55.1)
```

Exhibit 12-2 (*Continued*)

```
TIME FROM START  .090 SECONDS   CONTACT
                 XC        YC        PSI      PSID      U          V
VEHICLE 1       72.0     -93.4      .469   -1.411     38.1      296.3
VEHICLE 2       41.4       8.4     4.704   -1.053   -253.1      284.3.
                FX        FY        FN        GX        GY       G
VEHICLE 1     1.394E+04  -4.972E+04  -1.232E+06    3.03   -10.81   11.23
VEHICLE 2    -3.775E+04  -3.523E+04  -1.160E+06  -12.18   -11.37   16.66
CENTER OF MASS AT (  59.7, -52.4)

TIME FROM START  .100 SECONDS   CONTACT
                 XC        YC        PSI      PSID      U          V
VEHICLE 1       71.1     -90.8      .454   -1.641     45.6      255.0
VEHICLE 2       44.0      11.1     4.692   -1.491   -303.2      237.8
                FX        FY        FN        GX        GY       G
VEHICLE 1     1.377E+04  -3.918E+04  -1.019E+06    2.99    -8.52    9.03
VEHICLE 2    -2.854E+04  -3.017E+04  -1.204E+06   -9.21    -9.73   13.40
CENTER OF MASS AT (  60.2, -49.7)

TIME FROM START  .110 SECONDS   CONTACT
                 XC        YC        PSI      PSID      U          V
VEHICLE 1       70.5     -88.4      .437   -1.831     53.0      222.9
VEHICLE 2       46.3      14.3     4.674   -1.946   -342.3      195.6
                FX        FY        FN        GX        GY       G
VEHICLE 1     1.401E+03  -6.282E+02  -1.135E+05     .30     -.14     .33
VEHICLE 2     8.209E+01  -1.533E+03  -4.478E+04     .03     -.49     .50
CENTER OF MASS AT (  60.8, -47.1)

TIME FROM START  .120 SECONDS   CONTACT
                 XC        YC        PSI      PSID      U          V
VEHICLE 1       70.1     -86.2      .418   -1.853     50.1      223.3
VEHICLE 2       48.4      17.7     4.655   -1.963   -346.0      187.1
                FX        FY        FN        GX        GY       G
VEHICLE 1     1.401E+03  -6.286E+02  -1.146E+05     .30     -.14     .33
VEHICLE 2     8.311E+01  -1.533E+03  -4.463E+04     .03     -.49     .50
CENTER OF MASS AT (  61.3, -44.4)

TIME FROM START  .130 SECONDS   CONTACT
                 XC        YC        PSI      PSID      U          V
VEHICLE 1       69.6     -83.9      .400   -1.874     47.2      223.7
VEHICLE 2       50.4      21.0     4.635   -1.979   -349.5      178.4
                FX        FY        FN        GX        GY       G
VEHICLE 1     1.400E+03  -6.289E+02  -1.158E+05     .30     -.14     .33
VEHICLE 2     8.409E+01  -1.532E+03  -4.449E+04     .03     -.49     .50
CENTER OF MASS AT (  61.9, -41.7)
```

Exhibit 12-2 (*Continued*)

```
SEPARATION AT T =  .140
   VELOCITY CHANGE OF VEHICLE 1 =  314.94
   VELOCITY CHANGE OF VEHICLE 2 =  467.34
DO YOU WANT TO ZERO THE STEERING ANGLES?
? N

TIME FROM START  .140 SECONDS    AFTER
                  XC          YC         PSI       PSID        U             V
   VEHICLE 1      69.2      -81.7       .381    -1.896       44.1        224.1
   VEHICLE 2      52.5       24.3      4.615    -1.996     -353.0        169.5
                  FX          FY          FN         GX         GY         G
   VEHICLE 1  -9.400E+01  -1.750E+02   1.802E+05     -.02       -.04       .04
   VEHICLE 2   1.908E+03   3.260E+01  -3.261E+03      .62        .01       .62
                  PHI
   VEHICLE 1      .11       .11    0.00    0.00
   VEHICLE 2      .03       .03    0.00    0.00
   CENTER OF MASS AT (  62.5,  -39.0)

TIME FROM START  .340 SECONDS    AFTER
                  XC          YC         PSI       PSID        U             V
   VEHICLE 1      60.5      -37.1       .069    -1.224      -29.4        222.7
   VEHICLE 2      92.3       86.9      4.214    -2.017     -348.2         30.7
                  FX          FY          FN         GX         GY         G
   VEHICLE 1  -8.636E+01  -3.787E+02   1.791E+05      .02        .08       .08
   VEHICLE 2   1.901E+03   2.716E+02  -1.787E+03      .61        .09       .62
                  PHI
   VEHICLE 1      .25       .25    0.00    0.00
   VEHICLE 2      .26       .26    0.00    0.00
   CENTER OF MASS AT (  73.3,   12.8)

TIME FROM START  .540 SECONDS    AFTER
                  XC          YC         PSI       PSID        U             V
   VEHICLE 1      51.3        6.3      -.110     -.581      -68.7        208.0
   VEHICLE 2     128.9      141.1      3.809    -2.023     -290.0        -92.7
                  FX          FY          FN         GX         GY         G
   VEHICLE 1   8.130E+02  -1.481E+02   1.285E+05      .18       -.03       .18
   VEHICLE 2   1.884E+03   4.012E+02   4.453E+02      .61        .13       .62
                  PHI
   VEHICLE 1      .23       .23    0.00    0.00
   VEHICLE 2      .39       .39    0.00    0.00
   CENTER OF MASS AT (  82.6,   60.5)

TIME FROM START  .740 SECONDS    AFTER
                  XC          YC         PSI       PSID        U             V
   VEHICLE 1      44.3       48.7      -.189     -.254      -60.1        202.5
   VEHICLE 2     159.6      188.5      3.406    -2.012     -188.1       -181.7
                  FX          FY          FN         GX         GY         G
   VEHICLE 1   1.964E+03   8.975E+01   6.162E+04      .43        .02       .43
   VEHICLE 2   1.880E+03   4.679E+02   2.799E+03      .61        .15       .62
                  PHI
   VEHICLE 1      .17       .17    0.00    0.00
   VEHICLE 2      .46       .46    0.00    0.00
   CENTER OF MASS AT (  90.7,  105.0)

TIME FROM START  .940 SECONDS    AFTER
                  XC          YC         PSI       PSID        U             V
   VEHICLE 1      43.4       90.2      -.217     -.029      -33.1        202.2
   VEHICLE 2     182.0      231.9      3.006    -1.974      -59.0       -222.4
                  FX          FY          FN         GX         GY         G
   VEHICLE 1   1.782E+03   5.171E+01   5.425E+04      .39        .01       .39
   VEHICLE 2   1.946E+03   4.956E+02   8.977E+03      .63        .16       .65
                  PHI
   VEHICLE 1      .11       .11    0.00    0.00
   VEHICLE 2      .49       .49    0.00    0.00
   CENTER OF MASS AT (  99.2,  147.3)
```

Exhibit 12-2 (*Continued*)

```
TIME FROM START 1.140 SECONDS    AFTER
                 XC        YC       PSI     PSID    U         U
   VEHICLE 1     47.9     130.7    -.209    .078   -11.4     202.9
   VEHICLE 2    195.8     274.9    2.638  -1.579    55.6    -220.9
                 FX        FY               FN      GX        GY       G
   VEHICLE 1   5.854E+02  1.449E+01       2.619E+03    .13   .00    .13
   VEHICLE 2   3.668E+02 -3.133E+02       8.882E+04    .12  -.10    .16
                 PHI
   VEHICLE 1     .05      .05   0.00   0.00
   VEHICLE 2     .49      .49   0.00   0.00
   CENTER OF MASS AT ( 107.5, 188.7)

TIME FROM START 1.340 SECONDS    AFTER
                 XC        YC       PSI     PSID    U         U
   VEHICLE 1     54.8     170.7    -.195    .057    -3.1     203.1
   VEHICLE 2    209.0     319.0    2.365  -1.272    91.1    -210.3
                 FX        FY               FN      GX        GY       G
   VEHICLE 1   1.081E+02  2.555E+00      -9.522E+03    .02   .00    .02
   VEHICLE 2  -1.824E+03 -4.590E+02       6.070E+03   -.59  -.15    .61
                 PHI
   VEHICLE 1     .02      .02   0.00   0.00
   VEHICLE 2     .43      .43   0.00   0.00
   CENTER OF MASS AT ( 116.9, 230.4)
*SBU JOB STEP LIMIT*
S,4

TIME FROM START 1.540 SECONDS    AFTER
                 XC        YC       PSI     PSID    U         U
   VEHICLE 1     62.1     210.7    -.186    .026     -.6     203.1
   VEHICLE 2    229.4     358.9    2.112  -1.256    94.3    -197.8
                 FX        FY               FN      GX        GY       G
   VEHICLE 1   1.808E+00  2.932E-01      -6.252E+03    .00   .00    .00
   VEHICLE 2  -2.070E+03 -4.457E+02       2.935E+03   -.67  -.14    .68
                 PHI
   VEHICLE 1     .01      .01   0.00   0.00
   VEHICLE 2     .38      .38   0.00   0.00
   CENTER OF MASS AT ( 129.5, 270.3)

TIME FROM START 1.740 SECONDS    AFTER
                 XC        YC       PSI     PSID    U         U
   VEHICLE 1     69.5     250.6    -.183    .009     -.0     203.1
   VEHICLE 2    256.8     391.3    1.863  -1.230    90.5    -185.4
                 FX        FY               FN      GX        GY       G
   VEHICLE 1  -1.068E+01  1.989E-02      -2.713E+03   -.00   .00    .00
   VEHICLE 2  -2.064E+03 -4.200E+02       4.937E+03   -.67  -.14    .68
                 PHI
   VEHICLE 1     .00      .00   0.00   0.00
   VEHICLE 2     .36      .36   0.00   0.00
   CENTER OF MASS AT ( 144.9, 307.3)

TIME FROM START 1.940 SECONDS    AFTER
                 XC        YC       PSI     PSID    U         U
   VEHICLE 1     76.9     290.6    -.182    .003      .1     203.1
   VEHICLE 2    289.2     414.6    1.622  -1.176    83.4    -174.5
                 FX        FY               FN      GX        GY       G
   VEHICLE 1  -6.552E+00  2.708E-04      -9.247E+02   -.00   .00    .00
   VEHICLE 2  -1.989E+03 -4.015E+02       1.050E+04   -.64  -.13    .65
                 PHI
   VEHICLE 1     .00      .00   0.00   0.00
   VEHICLE 2     .34      .34   0.00   0.00
   CENTER OF MASS AT ( 162.3, 340.5)
```

Exhibit 12-2 (*Continued*)

```
TIME FROM START 2.140 SECONDS    AFTER
              XC        YC        PSI       PSID      U          V
  VEHICLE 1   84.2     330.6     -.182      .000      .0       203.1
  VEHICLE 2  324.0     428.2    1.396    -1.072     73.7     -166.3
              FX        FY        FN        GX        GY         G
  VEHICLE 1  -2.716E+00  -6.153E-05  -2.460E+02   -.00   -.00    .00
  VEHICLE 2  -1.880E+03  -3.806E+02   1.800E+04   -.61   -.12    .62
              PHI
  VEHICLE 1   -.00   -.00   0.00   0.00
  VEHICLE 2    .32    .32   0.00   0.00
  CENTER OF MASS AT ( 180.8, 369.8)

TIME FROM START 2.340 SECONDS    AFTER
              XC        YC        PSI       PSID      U          V
  VEHICLE 1   91.6     370.5     -.182     -.000      .0       203.1
  VEHICLE 2  359.1     432.3    1.198     -.906     61.2     -161.7
              FX        FY        FN        GX        GY         G
  VEHICLE 1  -8.863E-01   8.570E-06  -4.148E+01   -.00    .00    .00
  VEHICLE 2  -1.753E+03  -3.500E+02   2.668E+04   -.57   -.11    .58
              PHI
  VEHICLE 1   -.00   -.00   0.00   0.00
  VEHICLE 2    .29    .29   0.00   0.00
  CENTER OF MASS AT ( 199.3, 395.4)

TIME FROM START 2.540 SECONDS    AFTER
              XC        YC        PSI       PSID      U          V
  VEHICLE 1   98.9     410.5     -.182     -.000      .0       203.1
  VEHICLE 2  392.7     427.7    1.039     -.672     45.0     -161.2
              FX        FY        FN        GX        GY         G
  VEHICLE 1  -2.221E-01   4.586E-06   3.709E+00   -.00    .00    .00
  VEHICLE 2  -1.612E+03  -3.044E+02   3.656E+04   -.52   -.10    .53
              PHI
  VEHICLE 1   -.00   -.00   0.00   0.00
  VEHICLE 2    .25    .25   0.00   0.00
  CENTER OF MASS AT ( 217.2, 417.4)

TIME FROM START 2.740 SECONDS    AFTER
              XC        YC        PSI       PSID      U          V
  VEHICLE 1  106.3     450.4     -.182     -.000      .0       203.1
  VEHICLE 2  423.6     415.6     .933     -.396     26.6     -163.5
              FX        FY        FN        GX        GY         G
  VEHICLE 1  -3.129E-02   8.271E-07   7.222E+00   -.00    .00    .00
  VEHICLE 2  -1.067E+03  -1.602E+02   2.702E+04   -.34   -.05    .35
              PHI
  VEHICLE 1   -.00   -.00   0.00   0.00
  VEHICLE 2    .20    .20   0.00   0.00
  CENTER OF MASS AT ( 234.0, 436.4)
*SBU JOB STEP LIMIT*
S,2

TIME FROM START 2.940 SECONDS    AFTER
              XC        YC        PSI       PSID      U          V
  VEHICLE 1  113.6     490.4     -.182     -.000      .0       203.1
  VEHICLE 2  451.9     398.5     .869     -.257     17.3     -164.6
              FX        FY        FN        GX        GY         G
  VEHICLE 1   7.150E-03   8.795E-08   4.010E+00    .00    .00    .00
  VEHICLE 2  -5.854E+02  -5.974E+01   1.191E+04   -.19   -.02    .19
              PHI
  VEHICLE 1   -.00   -.00   0.00   0.00
  VEHICLE 2    .14    .14   0.00   0.00
  CENTER OF MASS AT ( 249.8, 453.4)
```

Exhibit 12-2 (*Continued*)

```
TIME FROM START 3.140 SECONDS    AFTER
                  XC        YC       PSI      PSID      U         U
  VEHICLE 1     121.0     530.3    -.182    -.000     -.0      203.1
  VEHICLE 2     478.5     378.8     .826    -.183     12.3    -165.0
                  FX        FY                FN       GX        GY        G
  VEHICLE 1    8.134E-03  4.999E-09         1.613E+00   .00      .00      .00
  VEHICLE 2   -4.047E+02 -2.940E+01         7.955E+03  -.13     -.01      .13
                 PHI
  VEHICLE 1     -.00    -.00   0.00   0.00
  VEHICLE 2      .10     .10   0.00   0.00
  CENTER OF MASS AT ( 264.9, 469.3)

TIME FROM START 3.340 SECONDS    AFTER
                  XC        YC       PSI      PSID      U         U
  VEHICLE 1     128.3     570.3    -.182    -.000     -.0      203.1
  VEHICLE 2     503.8     357.5     .795    -.131     8.8     -165.3
                  FX        FY                FN       GX        GY        G
  VEHICLE 1    4.163E-03 -3.316E-11         5.171E-01   .00     -.00      .00
  VEHICLE 2   -2.898E+02 -1.511E+01         5.696E+03  -.09     -.00      .09
                 PHI
  VEHICLE 1      .00     .00   0.00   0.00
  VEHICLE 2      .07     .07   0.00   0.00
  CENTER OF MASS AT ( 279.5, 484.6)

TIME FROM START 3.540 SECONDS    AFTER
                  XC        YC       PSI      PSID      U         U
  VEHICLE 1     135.6     610.3    -.182    -.000     -.0      203.1
  VEHICLE 2     528.2     335.1     .772    -.094     6.3     -165.4
                  FX        FY                FN       GX        GY        G
  VEHICLE 1    1.599E-03 -1.579E-11         1.269E-01   .00     -.00      .00
  VEHICLE 2   -2.077E+02 -7.773E+00         4.086E+03  -.07     -.00      .07
                 PHI
  VEHICLE 1      .00     .00   0.00   0.00
  VEHICLE 2      .05     .05   0.00   0.00
  CENTER OF MASS AT ( 293.7, 499.5)

TIME FROM START 3.740 SECONDS    AFTER
                  XC        YC       PSI      PSID      U         U
  VEHICLE 1     143.0     650.2    -.182     .000     -.0      203.1
  VEHICLE 2     551.9     312.0     .756    -.068     4.5     -165.4
                  FX        FY                FN       GX        GY        G
  VEHICLE 1    4.902E-04  5.325E-12         1.669E-02   .00      .00      .00
  VEHICLE 2   -1.488E+02 -3.997E+00         2.929E+03  -.05     -.00      .05
                 PHI
  VEHICLE 1      .00     .00   0.00   0.00
  VEHICLE 2      .04     .04   0.00   0.00
  CENTER OF MASS AT ( 307.6, 514.0)

TIME FROM START 3.940 SECONDS    AFTER
                  XC        YC       PSI      PSID      U         U
  VEHICLE 1     150.3     690.2    -.182     .000     -.0      203.1
  VEHICLE 2     575.0     288.3     .745    -.048     3.2     -165.5
                  FX        FY                FN       GX        GY        G
  VEHICLE 1    1.120E-04  1.824E-12        -4.806E-03   .00      .00      .00
  VEHICLE 2   -1.066E+02 -2.054E+00         2.100E+03  -.03     -.00      .03
                 PHI
  VEHICLE 1      .00     .00   0.00   0.00
  VEHICLE 2      .03     .03   0.00   0.00
  CENTER OF MASS AT ( 321.3, 528.4)
```

Exhibit 12-2 (*Continued*)

```
TIME FROM START 4.140 SECONDS    AFTER
              XC        YC       PSI      PSID      U          U
  VEHICLE 1   157.7    730.1    -.182    .000      -.0       203.1
  VEHICLE 2   597.7    264.2    .736    -.035      2.3      -165.5
              FX        FY                FN        GX        GY        G
  VEHICLE 1   1.071E-05  2.842E-13  -4.948E-03    .00       .00       .00
  VEHICLE 2  -7.639E+01 -1.056E+00   1.505E+03   -.02      -.00       .02
              PHI
  VEHICLE 1    .00    .00   0.00    0.00
  VEHICLE 2    .02    .02   0.00    0.00
  CENTER OF MASS AT ( 334.8, 542.6)

TIME FROM START 4.160 SECONDS    STOP
              XC        YC       PSI      PSID      U          U
  VEHICLE 1   158.4    734.1    -.182    .000      -.0       203.1
  VEHICLE 2   600.0    261.8    .736    -.034      2.2      -165.5
              FX        FY                FN        GX        GY        G
  VEHICLE 1   1.071E-05  2.842E-13  -4.948E-03    .00       .00       .00
  VEHICLE 2  -7.639E+01 -1.056E+00   1.505E+03   -.02      -.00       .02
              PHI
  VEHICLE 1    .00    .00   0.00    0.00
  VEHICLE 2    .02    .02   0.00    0.00
  CENTER OF MASS AT ( 336.2, 544.0)
*INTERRUPTED*
BYE

X1472DC LOG OFF  10.55.40.
SBU       32.281
TIO =    22726
```

Exhibit 12-2 (*Continued*)

```
ENTER MODEL YEAR FOR VEHICLE 1
? 75
ENTER MAKE OF VEHICLE 1
? FORD
ENTER MODEL FOR VEHICLE 1
? LTD
DO YOU WANT FULL INFLATION FOR ALL TIRES?
? Y
ENTER MODEL YEAR FOR VEHICLE 2
? 75
ENTER MAKE OF VEHICLE 2
? FORD
ENTER MODEL FOR VEHICLE 2
? LTD
DO YOU WANT FULL INFLATION FOR ALL TIRES?
? Y
DO YOU WANT TO USE A FORCE INCREMENT OF   100. OR   200.
? 200
ENTER TIME STEP (SECONDS) DURING COLLISION
? .005
ENTER TIME STEP (SECONDS) AFTER COLLISION
? .02
DO YOU WANT THE FULL TERMINAL LISTING?
? Y
ENTER XC,YC,PSI,PSID,U,V FOR VEHICLE 1
? 0 -140 0 0 0 40
ENTER XC,YC,PSI,PSID,U,V FOR VEHICLE 2
? -55 0 90 0 0 40


CORNER 1 OF VEHICLE 1 STRIKES EDGE 2 OF VEHICLE 2
EDGE 1 IS USED TO UPDATE DAMAGES FOR VEHICLE 1
```

(diagram: FORD-LTD ← 40 MPH ; ↑ 40 MPH ; FORD-LTD)

```
TIME FROM START 0.000 SECONDS    CONTACT
                XC        YC        PSI      PSID      U         V
    VEHICLE 1    0.0    -140.0    0.000    0.000      0.0     704.0
    VEHICLE 2   -55.0      0.0    1.571    0.000      0.0     704.0
                FX        FY        FN       GX        GY        G
    VEHICLE 1  -4.356E+03  -7.920E+03    4.373E+05    -.91    -1.65    1.88
    VEHICLE 2   7.920E+03  -4.356E+03    6.081E+05    1.65     -.91    1.88
CENTER OF MASS AT ( -27.5, -70.0)

TIME FROM START  .005 SECONDS    CONTACT
                XC        YC        PSI      PSID      U         V
    VEHICLE 1    -.0    -136.5    .000     .049     -1.8     700.8
    VEHICLE 2   -58.5      .0    1.571    .068      3.2     702.2
                FX        FY        FN       GX        GY        G
    VEHICLE 1  -4.356E+03  -7.920E+03    4.221E+05    -.91    -1.65    1.88
    VEHICLE 2   7.920E+03  -4.356E+03    6.358E+05    1.65     -.91    1.88
CENTER OF MASS AT ( -29.3, -68.2)

TIME FROM START  .010 SECONDS    CONTACT
                XC        YC        PSI      PSID      U         V
    VEHICLE 1    -.0    -133.0    .000     .096     -3.3     697.6
    VEHICLE 2   -62.0      .0    1.571    .140      6.6     700.5
                FX        FY        FN       GX        GY        G
    VEHICLE 1  -4.354E+03  -7.921E+03    4.070E+05    -.91    -1.65    1.88
    VEHICLE 2   7.920E+03  -4.356E+03    6.630E+05    1.65     -.91    1.88
CENTER OF MASS AT ( -31.0, -66.5)

TIME FROM START  .015 SECONDS    CONTACT
                XC        YC        PSI      PSID      U         V
    VEHICLE 1    -.0    -129.5    .001     .142     -4.8     694.4
    VEHICLE 2   -65.5      .1    1.572    .214     10.3     698.7
                FX        FY        FN       GX        GY        G
    VEHICLE 1  -1.254E+04  -2.217E+04    1.148E+06    -2.61    -4.62    5.31
    VEHICLE 2   2.216E+04  -1.255E+04    1.926E+06    4.62     -2.61    5.31
CENTER OF MASS AT ( -32.8, -64.7)
```

Exhibit 12-3 Staged collision simulation based on the IMPACT program (U.C.L.A. Series II: 90 degree rear-side impact at 40 mph—L0651). (A) Initial input.

```
TIME FROM START  .035 SECONDS    CONTACT
                  XC        YC       PSI      PSID      U          V
VEHICLE 1        -.4     -116.0    .010      .816    -27.1      650.5
VEHICLE 2       -79.3       .6    1.587     1.349     62.1      671.1
                  FX        FY               FN        GX        GY       G
VEHICLE 1    -2.090E+04  -3.279E+04      1.754E+06   -4.35     -6.83    8.10
VEHICLE 2     3.267E+04  -2.109E+04      3.248E+06    6.81     -4.40    8.10
CENTER OF MASS AT ( -39.8, -57.7)

TIME FROM START  .040 SECONDS    CONTACT
                  XC        YC       PSI      PSID      U          V
VEHICLE 1        -.6     -112.8    .014     1.012    -32.9      637.4
VEHICLE 2       -82.6       .9    1.594     1.713     79.8      662.2
                  FX        FY               FN        GX        GY       G
VEHICLE 1    -2.070E+04  -3.884E+04      1.827E+06   -4.31     -8.09    9.17
VEHICLE 2     3.865E+04  -2.105E+04      3.673E+06    8.05     -4.39    9.17
CENTER OF MASS AT ( -41.6, -55.9)

TIME FROM START  .045 SECONDS    CONTACT
                  XC        YC       PSI      PSID      U          V
VEHICLE 1        -.8     -109.7    .020     1.217    -38.0      622.0
VEHICLE 2       -85.9      1.3    1.604     2.125    101.0      653.0
                  FX        FY               FN        GX        GY       G
VEHICLE 1    -1.835E+04  -3.794E+04      1.647E+06   -3.82     -7.91    8.78
VEHICLE 2     3.770E+04  -1.885E+04      3.563E+06    7.86     -3.93    8.78
CENTER OF MASS AT ( -43.4, -54.2)

TIME FROM START  .050 SECONDS    CONTACT
                  XC        YC       PSI      PSID      U          V
VEHICLE 1       -1.1     -106.6    .027     1.402    -41.6      606.9
VEHICLE 2       -89.2      1.7    1.616     2.525    123.2      644.4
                  FX        FY               FN        GX        GY       G
VEHICLE 1    -1.631E+04  -3.703E+04      1.495E+06   -3.40     -7.72    8.43
VEHICLE 2     3.673E+04  -1.698E+04      3.463E+06    7.65     -3.54    8.43
CENTER OF MASS AT ( -45.1, -52.4)

TIME FROM START  .055 SECONDS    CONTACT
                  XC        YC       PSI      PSID      U          V
VEHICLE 1       -1.4     -103.6    .034     1.570    -43.9      592.3
VEHICLE 2       -92.4      2.2    1.629     2.914    146.1      636.0
                  FX        FY               FN        GX        GY       G
VEHICLE 1    -1.457E+04  -3.610E+04      1.370E+06   -3.04     -7.52    8.11
VEHICLE 2     3.573E+04  -1.544E+04      3.369E+06    7.45     -3.22    8.11
CENTER OF MASS AT ( -46.9, -50.7)

TIME FROM START  .060 SECONDS    CONTACT
                  XC        YC       PSI      PSID      U          V
VEHICLE 1       -1.7     -100.7    .042     1.724    -45.1      578.1
VEHICLE 2       -95.6      2.8    1.645     3.292    169.7      627.6
                  FX        FY               FN        GX        GY       G
VEHICLE 1    -1.312E+04  -3.512E+04      1.270E+06   -2.73     -7.32    7.81
VEHICLE 2     3.469E+04  -1.422E+04      3.279E+06    7.23     -2.96    7.81
CENTER OF MASS AT ( -48.7, -48.9)

TIME FROM START  .065 SECONDS    CONTACT
                  XC        YC       PSI      PSID      U          V
VEHICLE 1       -2.1      -97.8    .051     1.866    -45.4      564.4
VEHICLE 2       -98.8      3.5    1.662     3.660    194.0      619.1
                  FX        FY               FN        GX        GY       G
VEHICLE 1    -1.196E+04  -3.410E+04      1.194E+06   -2.49     -7.11    7.53
VEHICLE 2     3.359E+04  -1.331E+04      3.191E+06    7.00     -2.77    7.53
CENTER OF MASS AT ( -50.4, -47.2)

SEPARATION AT T = .070
   VELOCITY CHANGE OF VEHICLE 1 =  174.62
   VELOCITY CHANGE OF VEHICLE 2 =  174.62
```

Exhibit 12-3 (B) Collision phase (DV = inches/second).

```
TIME FROM START  .070 SECONDS    AFTER
              XC        YC       PSI     PSID      U         V
VEHICLE 1    -2.5     -95.1     .061    2.000    -45.0     551.1
VEHICLE 2  -101.9       4.2    1.681    4.018    218.9     610.2
              FX        FY               FN       GX        GY              G
VEHICLE 1  2.149E+02    0.            -1.615E+05  .04      0.00            .04
VEHICLE 2 -8.373E+02    0.            -1.052E+05 -.17      0.00            .17
              PHI
  VEHICLE 1    0.00   0.00   0.00   0.00
  VEHICLE 2    0.00   0.00   0.00   0.00
CENTER OF MASS AT ( -52.2, -45.5)

TIME FROM START  .270 SECONDS    AFTER
              XC        YC       PSI     PSID      U         V
VEHICLE 1   -18.2      14.6     .394    1.432    130.9     538.2
VEHICLE 2  -228.5      31.6    2.473    3.976    570.5     293.9
              FX        FY               FN       GX        GY              G
VEHICLE 1 -2.153E+03    0.            -3.731E+04 -.45      0.00            .45
VEHICLE 2 -2.775E+03    0.             7.955E+03 -.58      0.00            .58
              PHI
  VEHICLE 1    0.00   0.00   0.00   0.00
  VEHICLE 2    0.00   0.00   0.00   0.00
CENTER OF MASS AT (-123.3,  23.1)

TIME FROM START  .470 SECONDS    AFTER
              XC        YC       PSI     PSID      U         V
VEHICLE 1   -38.9     122.3     .674    1.400    233.5     488.0
VEHICLE 2  -352.2      54.8    3.272    4.002    586.3    -193.0
              FX        FY               FN       GX        GY              G
VEHICLE 1 -3.013E+03    0.             1.482E+04 -.63      0.00            .63
VEHICLE 2 -2.892E+03    0.             3.301E+03 -.60      0.00            .60
              PHI
  VEHICLE 1    0.00   0.00   0.00   0.00
  VEHICLE 2    0.00   0.00   0.00   0.00
CENTER OF MASS AT (-195.5,  88.6)

TIME FROM START  .670 SECONDS    AFTER
              XC        YC       PSI     PSID      U         V
VEHICLE 1   -66.8     224.5     .961    1.469    314.9     410.2
VEHICLE 2  -471.1      80.1    4.074    4.001    235.7    -556.7
              FX        FY               FN       GX        GY              G
VEHICLE 1 -3.136E+03    0.             1.016E+04 -.65      0.00            .65
VEHICLE 2 -1.329E+03    0.            -9.980E+04 -.28      0.00            .28
              PHI
  VEHICLE 1    0.00   0.00   0.00   0.00
  VEHICLE 2    0.00   0.00   0.00   0.00
CENTER OF MASS AT (-269.0, 152.3)

TIME FROM START  .870 SECONDS    AFTER
              XC        YC       PSI     PSID      U         V
VEHICLE 1  -100.5     318.8    1.257    1.495    371.4     308.5
VEHICLE 2  -589.9     109.8    4.801    3.246   -203.5    -585.2
              FX        FY               FN       GX        GY              G
VEHICLE 1 -3.276E+03    0.             5.044E+03 -.68      0.00            .68
VEHICLE 2  1.521E+03    0.            -9.434E+04  .32      0.00            .32
              PHI
  VEHICLE 1    0.00   0.00   0.00   0.00
  VEHICLE 2    0.00   0.00   0.00   0.00
CENTER OF MASS AT (-345.2, 214.3)

TIME FROM START 1.070 SECONDS    AFTER
              XC        YC       PSI     PSID      U         V
VEHICLE 1  -137.4     403.5    1.559    1.519    395.7     192.5
VEHICLE 2  -709.8     136.5    5.438    3.195   -478.8    -368.2
              FX        FY               FN       GX        GY              G
VEHICLE 1 -3.326E+03    0.             5.970E+03 -.69      0.00            .69
VEHICLE 2  3.121E+03    0.             1.088E+04  .65      0.00            .65
```

Exhibit 12-3 (C) Trajectory phase.

13

Computer-assisted Accident Analysis (CAAA)

R. D. JABLONSKY, P.E.
Consulting Engineer
Altadena, California

R. D. Jablonsky is a specialist in accident investigation and reconstruction. He has been awarded a B.S.E.E., an M.S.S.E., an M.S. in Computer Systems, and an M.S. in Safety. He is a Registered Professional Engineer in California and Missouri and is a Certified Safety Professional. His society memberships include S.A.E., A.S.S.E., A.I.I.E., H.F.S., I.E.E.E., A.S.T.M., and I.E.S. He has been an accident investigation specialist 18 years, a systems engineering design engineer 10 years, and a management heavy-industry manufacturing engineer 14 years. He may be contacted at his offices— R. D. Jablonsky, Inc., P.O. Box 672, Altadena, California 91001-0672 (213-798-6100 or 213-681-8444).

I. INTRODUCTION

Vehicle accident reconstruction often involves estimates of vehicle speed and descriptions of vehicle dynamics (applying the laws of physics). To permit handling of a more accurate and complex dynamic representation of a collision that cannot be effectively or efficiently handled computationally by manual calculation methods, the digital computer is being widely employed. Computer-assist techniques have additionally served in reducing subjectivity and differences of opinion as the result of method standardization, which is an inherent part of the computer-assist techniques.

The techniques to improve the determination of preimpact performance or vehicle speed from postimpact conditions or physical evidence or occupant behavior during collision have developed and improved significantly during the past two decades. These developments can be attributed to the increased interest in the design-related vehicle performance during collision conditions, the accumulation of data on vehicle and occupant behavior, and the increased availability of computational facilities. Many groups sponsored the necessary research, including the transportation industry, government agencies, automobile manufacturers, individual scientists and forensic engineers, universities, and engineering societies. The references cited list publications by some of the many who have significantly contributed to the evolutionary refinement of the computer-assisted accident analysis techniques.

Predicting vehicle performance, by the use of analytical methods or mathematical modeling of the vehicle, probably stems from analagous techniques used in the design of high-performance aircraft in the years prior to 1940. The desired automobile performance through and even beyond this period was developed, for the most part, by skilled drivers and through the use of empirical "methods."

II. DEVELOPMENT OF MATHEMATICAL ANALYTICAL TECHNIQUES FOR VEHICLE ACCIDENT RECONSTRUCTION

An early effort to represent the vehicle as a dynamic mechanical system and to predict the vehicle motion by use of mathematical representation was reported by Segal[1] in 1956. The mathematical representation of vehicle motion was validated through the use of an instrumented 1953 Buick that was supplied by the General Motors Corporation. A comparison of the theory to the experiment was found to be well within the range of engineering acceptability. There is no direct evidence to indicate that these early studies were the primary motivating basis for the evolution of the currently available analytical methods useful in vehicle accident reconstruction. However, the research organization involved in this early project is among the leaders in the development of the scientific procedures designed for collision analysis and accident reconstruction.

It would seem obvious that basic physics should be applied to vehicle accident reconstruction, but could it be done accurately, reliably, and effectively? The early studies indicated that vehicle motion could be represented accurately by a mathematical model, and this could form the basis for describing vehicle performance during collision. The initial evolutionary step, however, consisted of controlled crash experiments. This experimental work employed the use of standard vehicles colliding at known speeds. Each vehicle was thoroughly instrumented, and through the use of high-speed motion pictures such parameters as collision forces, vehicle damage, and postimpact trajectories were accurately recorded. Significant experimental work was pursued by Severy[2] and others in the series of controlled crash experiments performed at the University of California at Los Angeles. These studies were conducted during the early 1960s.

Concurrent with the controlled crash experiment programs, analytical studies were performed for the purpose of determining whether or not the colliding vehicles and their postimpact trajectories could be accurately mathematically represented. There were numerous studies by many research institutes, each contributing to the development of useful analytical techniques and appropriate data. The work published by Emery[3] demonstrated that the colliding vehicles could be represented mathematically to the extent of predicting crush damage, impact forces, and postimpact trajectories. In 1967, works published by a research group of Cornell Aeronautical Laboratory, Inc.,[4] doing work on computer simulation of single-vehicle accidents had come to the same conclusion as Emery. Other and extensive references to the development of analytical models for representing vehicles under a wide variety of collision conditions can be found in publications of the Society of Automotive Engineers, Inc.

(including the proceedings of the STAPP Car Crash Conferences, beginning with the 11th Conference, held in October 1967).

The investigation of automobile collisions, the desire to understand the cause of a collision, and the determination of vehicle speeds from postimpact information and the use of graphic testimony in automobile accident cases was reported in *Scientific American* in 1922.[5] An early reference to the relationship of the braking distance and air and tire resistance to the coefficient of friction of the roadway surface for the purpose of determining vehicle speed was published in 1917 by the Society of Automotive Engineers.[6] From these early references until the work that demonstrated that the motion of the vehicle could be mathematically represented both for normal and collision conditions, the determination of vehicle speed from postimpact information was, for the most part, determined by relatively simple applications and energy loss and conservation of momentum principles. Energy loss and conservation of momentum principles remain the basis for predicting vehicle speed from postimpact information by even the most sophisticated analytical models. The fundamental changes that have taken place are in the representation of the vehicles. The simplistic application of energy loss and conservation of momentum principles usually considered the vehicle as a point mass and disregarded the dynamic properties of the vehicle and its components. One useful, but simplistic, application of these basic laws of physics is shown in Chapter 9 of the *Transportation and Traffic Engineering Handbook*.[7] The extent of the differences between a simplistic and a fully descriptive mathematical representation of colliding vehicles can be appreciated by examining the force vectors considered for each technique. Figure 13-1 depicts the force vectors during collision considered for the simple conservation of the model. Figure 13-2 shows the force vectors considered by a complex mathematical modeling of the colliding vehicles. Even a slight change in force vectors may be significant in lawsuits, in regulatory compliance, or in evaluating proposed engineering design changes.

In addition to the understanding and formalization of the mathematics of vehicle motion, there were two other developments that resulted in the rapid advancement of sophisticated analytical techniques for the reconstruction of vehicle accidents. While the fundamental laws of motion that apply to vehicle motion are relatively simple, the fact that there are

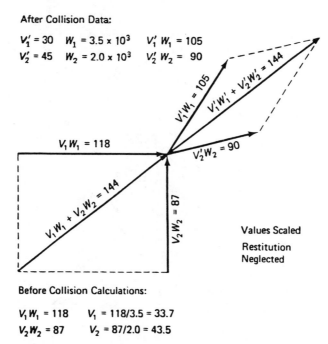

Figure 13-1 Graphical solution to momentum exchange between two vehicles in an angle collision. Combined momentum of vehicles before collision is equal in amount and direction to combined momentum after collision. (From J. E. Baerwald (ed.), *Transportation and Traffic Engineers Handbook*. Institute of Transportation Engineers. Englewood Cliffs, N.J.: Prentice-Hall, 1976. Reprinted with copyright permission of Prentice-Hall, Inc., © 1976.)

many interacting degrees of freedom that affect vehicle motion sometimes causes the mathematical representation to be complex. More significantly, the numerical solution to the mathematical representation requires the handling of numerical computations of such proportions that manual computations are impractical. The rapid development of computers, capacity and usefulness, numerical problem-solving techniques, and the availability of computers at research centers accelerated the development, refinement, and application of the currently available vehicle accident reconstruction methods. It was not until the availability of computational facilities proliferated beyond research institutions that the vastly im-

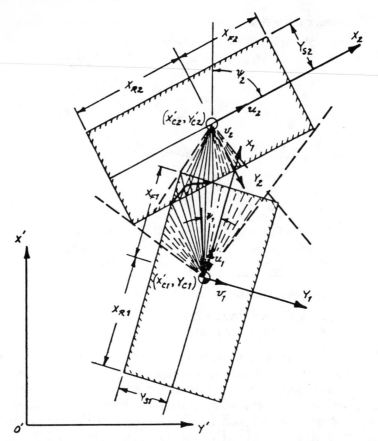

Figure 13-2 Analytical definition of colliding vehicles. (From R. R. McHenry, "Computer Program for Reconstruction of Highway Accidents." SAE paper 73098. Warrendale, PA.: Society of Automotive Engineers, 1973. Reprinted with permission © 1973 Society of Automotive Engineers, Inc.)

proved analytical techniques became available as an engineering tool for the practitioners involved in vehicle accident reconstruction.

III. COMPUTER INTERACTIVE COMPUTATIONAL METHODS

Both government and private agencies have funded research institutes for the purpose of developing computer-assist vehicle accident reconstruction methods. These efforts have resulted in interactive computational methods whereby the user can simply employ and effectively use the complex mathematical models that represent the vehicle motion from a computer terminal keyboard. The computer programs routinely handle the complex mathematical computations and the computer produces the calculated results in an orderly and meaningful manner. The interactive feature that permits the user to respond to queries provided to him by the program are also included on the programs. By this interactive means the data that define the accident to be reconstructed are simply supplied in a meaningful way to the computer by the user.

It is the standardized mathematical representation of the vehicle motion and the interactive feature of the computer program that constitutes the basic useful tool for the accident reconstruction practitioner. To use the tool successfully, however, it is necessary for the user to have a basic and thorough understanding of the simulation or mathematical model. It is not necessary for the user to understand fully the numerical computational methods employed, or even the validity of the computational methods employed, if the model has been validated by comparing computed results to results of controlled experiments. However, the user must understand the mechanics of the simulated representation. Without such understanding the required input data may not be correctly formulated and the effects of input data on computed results cannot be properly evaluated.

The interactive feature involves questions that automatically appear on the computer screen or printout. Each must be responded to properly by the user. Each question that is numbered must be responded to before the next question is asked.

IV. AVAILABLE COMPUTER ACCIDENT RECONSTRUCTION PROGRAMS

There are three interactive type computer-assist vehicle accident reconstruction techniques that are available from numerous sources throughout the United States. The employment of these computer-assist methods does not require an investment in expensive computer equipment. Access to the computer programs is available through numerous commercial[7] and research-oriented computer centers.[8,9] Telephone communication networks[10] permit direct connection to the computer centers that provide access to the computer program. Thus, the programs can be used from remote terminal locations. Computing and telephone communication network cost are reasonably priced such that the cost of using the computer-assist methods is a small element of the total cost of reconstructing an accident. Remote location terminals in the simplest form can be adapted from personal-type computers or word processing systems. The modification necessary is to provide for the communication network connection. As of 1983, the computer-assist methods available to the accident reconstruction practitioner require computational capabilities that exceed the capacity of the low-cost personal computers. Developments of higher speed microprocessors and the expected continuous reduction in the cost of computer components should result in inexpensive personal-type computers capable of handling the currently available interactive accident reconstruction programs within the next several years.

The three most widely available computer-assist accident reconstruction programs are user-oriented. They have been widely publicized and adequately validated. They are listed below:

1. *Calspan Reconstruction of Accident Speeds on the Highway,* identified by the acronym CRASH. It was developed by Calspan under contract with the National Highway Traffic Safety Administration.

2. *Simulation Model of Automobile Collision,* identified by the acronym SMAC. It was developed by Calspan for the National Highway Traffic Safety Administration.

3. *Simplified, Interactive Simulation for Predicting the Braking and Steering Response of Commercial Vehicles,* identified by the acronym TBS. It was developed by the Highway Safety Research Institute of the University of Michigan. The research was sponsored by the Motor Vehicle Manufacturers Association.

Each of these programs is adequately described by individual user guides and technical manuals. The program CRASH has perhaps undergone the greatest amount of ongoing development, all of which has been pursued by Calspan. The initial version of CRASH[11] was superseded by the program CRASH2.[12] CRASH2 has since been superseded by CRASH3.[13] The development work leading to these versions of CRASH span the period from the early 1970s until 1980. The improvements have dealt with computational techniques, updating them to include the configuration of currently produced vehicles and interactive features.

The program SMAC was developed considerably before CRASH. SMAC, as the name implies, fits the definition of a simulation model. CRASH is a computational technique that employs, for the most part, a more basic application of the laws of motion, although it has evolved to include simulation methods employed by SMAC. The program SMAC appears to have been more widely published in the technical journals. [14-17] As originally constituted, SMAC was not interactive and user-oriented. It was the development of CRASH that resulted in SMAC being readily available to users who did not have direct access to large computer facilities. The amount of input data required to operate SMAC is considerably greater than that required by CRASH. This is necessarily so because SMAC is a more complex representation of the vehicles and provides considerably more information to the user. Additionally, however, as originally constructed, the input data to SMAC was furnished through the use of punched cards. The program CRASH, in addition to providing its designed output, sets up the data required by the program SMAC and in the proper format to cause the program to run. Thus, indirectly through the use of CRASH, SMAC becomes a somewhat interactive type of program. The use of CRASH and SMAC jointly permits the results of a CRASH analysis to be checked against the results of a SMAC analysis.

The program TBS evolved in somewhat the same type of scenario as the CRASH–SMAC evolution. As originally formulated, the simulation model for predicting braking and steering response for commercial vehicles was extremely complex and required a very large number of input parameters. These parameters were used to identify the properties of the vehicles. The large number of input variables and probably the difficulty experienced in collecting the basic data resulted in research directed toward a simplification of the original simulation model, which gave rise to the program TBS. The original version of the simulation model was thoroughly validated through the use of tests performed on standard commercially available vehicles. The efforts to develop a simplified model included verifying that its results would be acceptably comparable to the validated results of the original complex model. The *User's Manual for TBS* [18] includes the results of this validation analysis. TBS is a user-oriented interactive program quite similar in format to that of CRASH.

To use either CRASH, SMAC, or TBS effectively, it is necessary for the user to be familiar with the materials provided by the user guide. A review is important to furnish the basis for an understanding of the models and the specific input data required. In each case the input data is derived from a description of the vehicles involved, a description of the accident such as is usually provided by a traffic accident report (or similar statement), plus detail information concerning the accident scene usually not supplied by the traffic accident report and an inspection of the vehicles. The accident reconstructionist is required to convert the accumulation of collected data into the format required by the computer program. This usually necessitates preparation of a sketch drawn to scale and a tabulation of the input parameters in the exact format as required by the program. Such an orderly procedure for summarizing the input data is helpful in assessing the validity of the description of the accident in the traffic accident report.

The user-oriented interactive features of the program facilitate their use. The complexity of the models and the number of variables of the input data demand that more than a single simulation experiment be conducted to arrive at confident results. The criteria for judging the number of experiments that should be performed using the computer-assist techniques should be predicated upon the observed variability of results. A sufficient number should be performed in order to provide the user with a good understanding of the mechanics of the accident under consideration. It is necessary to identify the critical variables of the input data and their effect upon the computed results.

V. SAMPLE COMPUTER PROGRAM SESSIONS

Some insight into the application and usefulness of the programs CRASH, SMAC, and TBS can be derived from an examination of a typical session with each computer program. For CRASH and TBS this is particularly true because these programs are primarily interactive and user-oriented. Thus, the input data as requested by the computer program is in a generally nontechnical and understandable format. For these two programs the listing of the input data in an orderly form provides a basis for identifying the most important features of an accident. For SMAC, while the input data is orderly tabulated in matrix format, each item is not described. Thus, if it is desirous or necessary to identify each of the parameters of input data from the input data matrix, one must consult the user's manual. The computed output of SMAC does, however, provide descriptive titles and the value of each input parameter used.

A. CRASH

The program CRASH is designed to compute the impact speeds of two colliding vehicles. The program is designed for direct impact-type collisions involving two vehicles. It may not as reliably handle sideswipe-type collisions. The CRASH program also deals with collision damage. The energy loss during collision is computed as is the extent of collision damage on a comparative basis to the Society of Automotive Engineers' "Procedure for Collision Deformation Classification" (SAE J224). Should the user so elect, the CRASH program will set up the table of data necessary for the SMAC program.

B. CRASH2

A complete session with CRASH2 through the setting up of the SMAC table of input data is set forth in Figure 13-3. This figure consists of 10 pages, which have been identified sequentially as Figure 13-3A through Figure 13-3J (pages 300-309). All of the printed data above the item:

    1. ENTER A DESCRIPTIVE TITLE? (80 CHAR. MAX.)

which appears in Figure 13-3A, is provided by the computer when the program is called. Each question asked thereafter is designated by a number such as is indicated above. The user must respond to each question. In the case of the question number 1 the user response was

    CALSPAN TEST MRA # 1 —— OFFSET FRONTAL
    AT 30 MPH

CRASH2   (7 JUL 79)

ENTER TYPE OF CRASH RUN?
(COMPLETE,ABBREVIATED,RERUN,PRINT,BATCH,SMAC,OR END)
COMPLETE


```
**********************************************************************
*                                                                    *
*                          C R A S H                                 *
*                                                                    *
*       CALSPAN RECONSTRUCTION OF ACCIDENT SPEEDS ON THE HIGHWAY      *
*                                                                    *
*                                                                    *
*    NOTE: ANSWER ALL QUESTIONS AS DIRECTED.                         *
*          TERMINATE ALL RESPONSES WITH A CARRIAGE RETURN.           *
*          RESPONSES MAY BE PLACED ANYWHERE ON A LINE.               *
*          SEPARATE RESPONSES BY ONE OR MORE BLANKS.                 *
*          ENTER A ? TO GET THE COMPLETE VERSION OF A QUESTION.       *
*          ENTER A $ TO BACKSPACE TO THE PREVIOUS QUESTION.           *
*          ENTER A BLANK LINE TO GET THE PREDEFINED DEFAULT VALUE.    *
*          IF YOU MAKE A MISTAKE: (1) BEFORE HITTING CARRIAGE RETURN, *
*          TYPE SOME GARBAGE THAT YOU KNOW THE COMPUTER WILL REJECT - *
*          THE COMPUTER WILL COMPLAIN AND RESUBMIT THE QUESTION.      *
*          (2) AFTER HITTING CARRIAGE RETURN, YOU'LL HAVE TO USE THE  *
*          BACKSPACE COMMAND ON THE NEXT QUESTION.                    *
*                                                                    *
*          COORDINATE SYSTEM CONVENTIONS: + Y-AXIS RUNS TO THE RIGHT  *
*          OF THE + X-AXIS. POSITIVE HEADING ANGLES ROTATE CLOCKWISE  *
*                                                                    *
**********************************************************************
```

  1. ENTER A DESCRIPTIVE TITLE?   (80 CHAR. MAX.)
CALSPAN TEST MRA # 1 —— OFFSET FRONTAL AT 30 MPH

  2. ENTER SIZE CATEGORIES FOR VEHICLE # 1 AND VEHICLE # 2
     LEGAL CATEGORIES: MINICAR   SUBCOMPACT COMPACT   INTERMEDIATE
                        FULLSIZE   LARGE   RIGID   BARRIER
     SAMPLE: FULLSIZE   MINI   (ABBREVIATIONS ARE OK)
 I I

  3. ENTER A 7 CHARACTER VEHICLE DAMAGE INDEX FOR VEHICLE # 1
     NOTE: REFER TO APPENDIX-1 IN THE CRASH USERS GUIDE
           FORM: 10LZEW2
12FYEW4

Figure 13-3A

The user response to question number 2 was

  I I

indicating that Vehicle 1 and Vehicle 2 were INTERMEDIATE
category vehicles. The balance of the questions are set forth in
Figures 13-3A through 13-3E plus question 52, which is

4. ENTER A 7 CHARACTER VEHICLE DAMAGE INDEX FOR VEHICLE # 2
   NOTE: REFER TO APPENDIX-1 IN THE CRASH USERS GUIDE
         FORM: 06RYEW3
12FYEW5

5. ARE ANY ACTUAL WEIGHTS KNOWN?
   NOTE: A NEGATIVE RESPONSE WILL CAUSE AN AUTOMATIC WEIGHT ENTRY
         BASED UPON THE PREVIOUSLY SELECTED VEHICLE CATEGORY
         OBVIOUSLY, ACCURACY IS ENHANCED BY PROVIDING AN ACTUAL WEIGHT
         (ANSWER YES OR NO)
Y

6. ENTER THE ACTUAL WEIGHT OF VEHICLE # 1
   NOTE: INCLUDE WEIGHT OF OCCUPANTS,CARGO,AND FUEL
         FORM: 3622. (LBS.)
3080

7. ENTER THE ACTUAL WEIGHT OF VEHICLE # 2
   NOTE: INCLUDE WEIGHT OF OCCUPANTS,CARGO,AND FUEL
         FORM: 2497. (LBS.)
3950

8. ARE BOTH REST AND IMPACT POSITIONS KNOWN?
   NOTE: A NEGATIVE RESPONSE LIMITS PROGRAM RESULTS TO
         VELOCITY CHANGE APPROXIMATIONS BASED ON DAMAGE DATA ONLY
         (ANSWER YES OR NO)
Y

9. ENTER REST POSITIONS AND HEADINGS FOR VEHICLE # 1 AND VEHICLE # 2
   FORM: XCR1(FT) YCR1(FT) PSIR1(DEG) XCR2(FT) YCR2(FT) PSIR2(DEG)
-7.3 4.2 -25.0 0.7 -2.5 162.5

10. ENTER IMPACT POSITIONS AND HEADINGS FOR VEHICLE # 1 AND VEHICLE # 2
    FORM: XC10(FT) YC10(FT) PSI10(DEG) XC20(FT) YC20(FT) PSI20(DEG)
-8.4 1.0 0.0 8.4 -1.0 180

11. DID ROTATIONAL AND/OR LATERAL SKIDDING OF VEHICLE # 1 OCCUR?
    NOTE: THIS REFERS TO THAT PORTION OF THE TRAJECTORY DURING WHICH
          THE FRONT AND REAR WHEELS DO NOT RUN IN THE SAME TRACKS
          (ANSWER YES OR NO)
Y

12. DID ROTATIONAL AND/OR LATERAL SKIDDING OF VEHICLE # 1 STOP BEFORE
    REST POSITION WAS REACHED?
    NOTE: IT IS COMMON IN A SKIDDING TRAJECTORY TO HAVE AN ABRUPT
          CHANGE IN MOTION AS THE WHEELS START TRACKING ONE ANOTHER AND
          THE VEHICLE MOVES OUT TO REST IN A NON-SKIDDING FASHION
          OF COURSE,THE NON-SKID SECTION MAY BE A STRAIGHT LINE OR
          A CURVED PATH DEPENDING ON THE STEER CONDITIONS
          (ANSWER YES OR NO)
Y

Figure 13-3B

13. ENTER POSITION AND HEADING OF VEHICLE # 1 AT END OF
    ROTATIONAL AND/OR LATERAL SKIDDING
    NOTE: RESPONSE SHOULD DEFINE THE POSITION AND HEADING OF THE VEHICLE
          AT THE POINT IN THE TRAJECTORY AT WHICH THE FRONT AND
          REAR WHEELS RUN IN THE SAME TRACKS
          FORM: XC11(FT)   YC11(FT)   PSI11(DEG)
-7.3 4.2 -25.0

14. WAS THE SPINOUT PATH OF VEHICLE # 1 BETWEEN SEPARATION
    AND STOP OF ROTATION CURVED?
    NOTE: TRY TO VISUALIZE THE PATH OF THE VEHICLE C.G.
          IF A PROMINENT ARC IS PRESENT, ANSWER AFFIRMATIVELY
          (ANSWER YES OR NO)
N

16. WHICH DIRECTION DID VEHICLE # 1 ROTATE?
    NOTE: CLOCKWISE ROTATION TURNS FROM THE X-AXIS TOWARDS THE Y-AXIS
          FOR THE CASE OF PURELY LATERAL SKIDDING ENTER NONE
          (RESPOND WITH: CW   CCW   NONE)
CCW

17. DID VEHICLE # 1 ROTATE MORE THAN 360 DEGREES BETWEEN SEPARATION
    AND REST?
    NOTE: THIS IS A RARE OCCURANCE AND SHOULD BE VERIFIED
          FROM TIRE MARK DATA
          (ANSWER YES OR NO)
N

18. DID ROTATIONAL AND/OR LATERAL SKIDDING OF VEHICLE # 2 OCCUR?
    NOTE: THIS REFERS TO THAT PORTION OF THE TRAJECTORY DURING WHICH
          THE FRONT AND REAR WHEELS DO NOT RUN IN THE SAME TRACKS
          (ANSWER YES OR NO)
Y

19. DID ROTATIONAL AND/OR LATERAL SKIDDING OF VEHICLE # 2 STOP BEFORE
    REST POSITION WAS REACHED?
    NOTE: IT IS COMMON IN A SKIDDING TRAJECTORY TO HAVE AN ABRUPT
          CHANGE IN MOTION AS THE WHEELS START TRACKING ONE ANOTHER AND
          THE VEHICLE RUNS OUT TO REST IN A NON-SKIDDING FASHION
          OF COURSE, THE NON-SKIDDING SECTION MAY BE A STRAIGHT LINE OR
          A CURVE DEPENDING ON THE STEER CONDITIONS
          (ANSWER YES OR NO)
N

21. WAS THE SPINOUT PATH OF VEHICLE # 2 BETWEEN SEPARATION
    AND REST CURVED?
    NOTE: TRY TO VISUALIZE THE PATH OF THE VEHICLE C.G.
          IF A PROMINENT ARC IS PRESENT, ANSWER AFFIRMATIVELY
          (ANSWER YES OR NO)
N

Figure 13-3C

23. WHICH DIRECTION DID VEHICLE # 2 ROTATE?
    NOTE: CLOCKWISE ROTATION TURNS FROM THE X-AXIS TOWARDS THE Y-AXIS
          FOR THE CASE OF PURELY LATERAL SKIDDING ENTER NONE
          (RESPOND WITH: CW   CCW   NONE)
CCW

24. DID VEHICLE # 2 ROTATE MORE THAN 360 DEGREES BETWEEN SEPARATION
    AND REST?
    NOTE: THIS IS A RARE OCCURANCE AND SHOULD BE VERIFIED
          FROM THE TIRE MARK DATA
          (ANSWER YES OR NO)
N

25. ENTER THE NOMINAL TIRE-GROUND FRICTION COEFFICIENT?
    NOTE: REFER TO TABLE   2 IN THE CRASH USERS GUIDE FOR TYPICAL
          TIRE-GROUND FRICTION VALUES
          FORM: MU
.5

26. ROLLING RESISTANCE MAY BE ENTERED AS:
    1 —— THE DECIMAL PORTION OF FULL ROTATIONAL LOCKUP AT EACH WHEEL
    2 —— THE LEVEL OF LONGITUDINAL DECELERATION, IN G UNITS,
          PRODUCED BY ROTATIONAL RESISTANCE AT THE WHEELS
    (ANSWER 1 OR 2)
1

27. ENTER ROLLING RESISTANCES OF WHEELS OF VEHICLE # 1
    NOTE: CAN BE CAUSED BY BRAKING,DAMAGE,ENGINE BRAKING,ETC.
          ENTER VALUE FOR EACH WHEEL FROM 0.0 TO 1.0
          1.0 = FULL WHEEL LOCKUP
          FORM: RF   LF   RR   LR
0 1 0 0

28. ENTER ROLLING RESISTANCES OF WHEELS OF VEHICLE # 2
    NOTE: CAN BE CAUSED BY BRAKING,DAMAGE,ENGINE BRAKING,ETC.
          ENTER VALUE FOR EACH WHEEL FROM 0.0 TO 1.0
          1.0 = FULL WHEEL LOCKUP
          FORM: RF   LF   RR   LR
0 1 0 0

31. DO YOU WANT THE RESULTS CHECKED BY A TRAJECTORY SIMULATION?
    NOTE: THE SEPARATION VELOCITIES NORMALLY CALCULATED BY CRASH ARE
          USED BY A TRAJECTORY SIMULATION TO DETERMINE IF THE ENTERED
          EVIDENCE MATCHES THE CALCULATED SPEEDS
          IF NOT, APPROPRIATE SPEED ADJUSTMENTS ARE MADE TO OBTAIN
          AGREEMENT WITH THE EVIDENCE.
          (ANSWER YES OR NO)
N

Figure 13-3D

37. ARE ANY ACTUAL DAMAGE DIMENSIONS KNOWN?
    NOTE: A NEGATIVE RESPONSE WILL PRODUCE DAMAGE DATA BASED ON THE
          SUBMITTED VDI
          OBVIOUSLY, PROVIDING DAMAGE MEASUREMENTS WILL ENHANCE RESULTS
          (ANSWER YES OR NO)
Y

41. ENTER WIDTH OF DAMAGED AREA ALONG END OF VEHICLE # 1
    NOTE: USE ONLY THE DIRECT CONTACT DAMAGE RATHER THAN THE INDUCED
          DAMAGE (SHEET METAL BUCKLING INDUCED BY COLLISION)
          FORM: L1 (INCHES)
34

42. ENTER A PROFILE OF THE EXTENT OF DAMAGE FOR VEHICLE # 1
    NOTE: AT TWO,FOUR,OR SIX POINTS ALONG THE WIDTH OF THE DENT
          MEASURE THE DEPTH OF THE DAMAGE FROM THE ORIGINAL END
          DIMENSIONS (ENTRY SEQUENCE IS FROM DRIVER TO PASSENGER SIDE)
          FORM: C1 C2 C3 C4 C5 C6   (INCHES)
46.5 35.8 25.2 14.5 0.0 0.0

43. ENTER DISTANCE ALONG VEHICLE # 1 AXIS BETWEEN THE C.G. AND
    THE MIDDLE OF THE DAMAGED REGION
    NOTE: IF THIS DISTANCE RUNS OFF TOWARDS THE DRIVER SIDE
          ENTER IT AS A NEGATIVE NUMBER
          FORM: D1 (INCHES)
-25.5

47. ENTER WIDTH OF DAMAGED AREA ALONG END OF VEHICLE # 2
    NOTE: USE ONLY THE DIRECT CONTACT DAMAGE RATHER THAN THE INDUCED
          DAMAGE (SHEET METAL BUCKLING INDUCED BY COLLISION)
          FORM: L2 (INCHES)
35

48. ENTER A PROFILE OF THE EXTENT OF DAMAGE FOR VEHICLE # 2
    NOTE: AT TWO,FOUR,OR SIX POINTS ALONG THE WIDTH OF THE DENT
          MEASURE THE DEPTH OF THE DAMAGE FROM THE ORIGINAL END
          DIMENSIONS (ENTRY SEQUENCE IS FROM DRIVER TO PASSENGER SIDE)
          FORM: C1 C2 C3 C4 C5 C6   (INCHES)
57.0 49.8 42.7 35.5 0.0 0.0

49. ENTER DISTANCE ALONG VEHICLE # 2 AXIS BETWEEN THE C.G. AND
    THE MIDDLE OF THE DAMAGED REGION
    NOTE: IF THIS DISTANCE RUNS OFF TOWARDS THE DRIVER SIDE
          ENTER IT AS A NEGATIVE NUMBER
          FORM: D2 (INCHES)
23.

Figure 13-3E

shown at the top of Figure 13-3F. The input data provided
were taken from the *CRASH2 User's Manual*.

The summary of the CRASH results is given in the outlined table of data shown in Figure 13-3F and at the top of
13-3G. The impact speed has been calculated for each vehicle
using both the conservation of momentum principles and the
damage data provided by the Vehicle Damage Index number,

52. ARE THE DIRECTIONS OF THE PRINCIPAL IMPACT FORCES KNOWN MORE
    ACCURATELY THAN THE ENTERED VDI CLOCK DIRECTIONS?
    NOTE: THE CLOCK DIRECTION LIMITS PRINCIPAL FORCE DIRECTIONS
          TO 30 DEGREE INCREMENTS
          IF YOU CAN SPECIFY THESE ANGLES MORE ACCURATELY, ANSWER YES
          (ANSWER YES OR NO)
N

                        THANK YOU VERY MUCH
MENU = 1

                   SUMMARY OF CRASH RESULTS

CALSPAN TEST MRA # 1 ── OFFSET FRONTAL AT 30 MPH

                      VEHICLE # 1
****
*   *   *   *
*   *   SPEED CHANGE   *   *
IMPACT SPEED   MPH   *   *
*   *   *   BASIS   *
*   MPH   *****************************   OF   *
*   *   *   *   *   RESULTS   *
*   * TOTAL * LONG.   * LATERAL *   *
*   *   *   *   *   *
****
*   *   *   *   *   *
*   *   *   *   *SPINOUT TRAJECTORIES*
*   *   *   *   *AND CONSERVATION OF *
*   *   *   *   *LINEAR MOMENTUM   *
*   *   *   *   *   *
****
*   *   *   *   *   *
*   *   *   *   *SPINOUT TRAJECTORIES*
*   28.6*   28.5*   -28.1*   4.7*   AND   *
*   *   *   *   *   DAMAGE   *
*   *   *   *   *   *
****
*   *   *   *   *   *
*   * 28.1* -28.1*   0.0* DAMAGE DATA ONLY *
*   *   *   *   *   *
****

Figure 13-3F

which was given in response to questions 3 and 4. The favorable comparison of the speed change figures demonstrates that the collision damage information as provided by the user is consistent with the damage due to the computed speeds using the conservation of momentum principles. The data at the bottom of Figure 13-3G, in Figure 13-3H, and at the top

```
                          VEHICLE # 2
*************************************************************
*           *                              *                *
*           *      SPEED   CHANGE          *                *
*IMPACT SPEED*          MPH                *                 *
*           *                              *   BASIS        *
*   MPH     ******************************     OF           *
*           *                              *   RESULTS      *
*           *  TOTAL  *  LONG.  * LATERAL  *                *
*           *         *         *          *                *
*************************************************************
*           *         *         *          *                *
*           *         *         *          **SPINOUT TRAJECTORIES*
*           *         *         *          **AND CONSERVATION OF *
*           *         *         *          **LINEAR MOMENTUM     *
*           *         *         *          *                *
*************************************************************
*           *         *         *          *                *
*           *         *         *          **SPINOUT TRAJECTORIES*
*     30.7* 22.0*  -21.9*    2.2*       AND         *
*           *         *         *          *    DAMAGE      *
*           *         *         *          *                *
*************************************************************
*           *         *         *          *                *
*           *   21.9*  -21.9*    0.0*  DAMAGE DATA ONLY  *
*           *         *         *          *                *
*************************************************************
```

```
                        SCENE INFORMATION

                                  VEHICLE # 1      VEHICLE # 2

IMPACT X-POSITION                   -8.40  FT.        8.40  FT.
IMPACT Y-POSITION                    1.00  FT.       -1.00  FT.
IMPACT HEADING ANGLE                 0.00  DEG.     179.98  DEG.

REST X-POSITION                     -7.30  FT.        0.70  FT.
REST Y-POSITION                      4.20  FT.       -2.50  FT.
REST HEADING ANGLE                 -25.00  DEG.     162.48  DEG.

END-OF-ROTATION X-POSITION          -7.30  FT.
END-OF-ROTATION Y-POSITION           4.20  FT.
END-OF-ROTATION HEADING ANGLE      -25.00  DEG.

DIRECTION OF ROTATION                CCW                CCW
AMOUNT OF ROTATION                  <360               <360
```

Figure 13-3G

of Figure 13-3I are a recapitulation of input data used to perform the calculations.

After the run has been completed, the user is again asked the initial question as to the type of run desired. In this case, as is indicated, the type of run selected was SMAC. Because the program will generate the table of data required to run

COLLISION CONDITIONS

VEHICLE # 1			VEHICLE # 2		
XC10'	=	-8.4 FT.	XC20'	=	8.4 FT.
YC10'	=	1.0 FT.	YC20'	=	-1.0 FT.
PSI10	=	0.0 DEGREES	PSI20	=	180.0 DEGREES
PSI1D0	=	0.0 DEG/SEC	PSI2D0	=	0.0 DEG/SEC
U10	=	28.6 MPH	U20	=	30.7 MPH
V10	=	0.0 MPH	V20	=	0.0 MPH

SEPARATION CONDITIONS

XCS1	=	-8.4 FT.	XCS2	=	8.4 FT.
YCS1	=	1.0 FT.	YCS2	=	-1.0 FT.
PSIS1	=	0.0 DEG	PSIS2	=	180.0 DEG
US1	=	0.5 MPH	US2	=	8.8 MPH
VS1	=	4.7 MPH	VS2	=	2.2 MPH
PSISD1	=	-0.9 DEG/SEC	PSISD2	=	-0.4 DEG/SEC

RELATIVE VELOCITY DATA

	VEHICLE # 1	VEHICLE # 2
SPEED CHANGE (TRAJ. + DAMAGE)	28.5 MPH	22.0 MPH
	-9.5 DEG	-5.7 DEG
SPEED CHANGE (DAMAGE ONLY)	28.1 MPH	21.9 MPH
	0.0 DEG	0.0 DEG
IMPACT SPEED	28.6 MPH	30.7 MPH
ENERGY DISSIPATED BY DAMAGE	58684.9 FT-LB	124116.9 FT-LB
SPEED ALONG LINE THRU CGS	28.4 MPH	30.4 MPH
SPEED ORTHOG. TO CG LINE	3.4 MPH	3.6 MPH
CLOSING VELOCITY	58.8 MPH	

Figure 13-3H

SMAC, the required table of data must be stored in a location that can be identified to the program SMAC when SMAC is run. This is accomplished by assigning a file name to the table of SMAC input data. In this case the file was assigned the name CALSPA.CR2. The final question of the run was answered NO. Thus, the SMAC table was not printed out at the terminal. The session with CRASH2 was completed by selecting the END option.

An alternative to RUN could have been COMPLETE, RERUN, ABBREVIATED, PRINT, or BATCH. Initially, if ABBREVIATED was selected, there would have been no descriptive material provided with each question, as in the case of COMPLETE. Selecting RERUN permits the user to make a change to the response given to the previous run. PRINT will cause the output of the previous run to be printed

```
SUMMARY OF DAMAGE DATA                    (* INDICATES DEFAULT VALUE)

      VEHICLE # 1                             VEHICLE # 2

   TYPE--------INTERMEDIATE               TYPE--------INTERMEDIATE
   WEIGHT------    3080.0 LBS.            WEIGHT------    3950.0 LBS.
   VDI---------12FYEW4                    VDI---------12FYEW5
   L-----------      34.0 IN.             L-----------      35.0 IN.
   C1----------      46.5 IN.             C1----------      57.0 IN.
   C2----------      35.8 IN.             C2----------      49.8 IN.
   C3----------      25.2 IN.             C3----------      42.7 IN.
   C4----------      14.5 IN.             C4----------      35.5 IN.
   C5----------       0.0 IN.             C5----------       0.0 IN.
   C6----------       0.0 IN.             C6----------       0.0 IN.
   D-----------     -33.0 IN.             D-----------     -29.7 IN.
   RHO---------       1.00      *         RHO---------       1.00      *
   ANG---------     360.0 DEG.  *         ANG---------     360.0 DEG.  *
```

```
                   DIMENSIONS AND INERTIAL PROPERTIES

   A1     =      54.7 INCHES          A2     =      54.7 INCHES
   B1     =      59.2 INCHES          B2     =      59.2 INCHES
   TR1    =      61.8 INCHES          TR2    =      61.8 INCHES
   I1     = 29819.6 LB-SEC**2-IN      I2     = 38242.6 LB-SEC**2-IN
   M1     =   7.971 LB-SEC**2/IN      M2     =  10.223 LB-SEC**2/IN
   XF1    =      98.8 INCHES          XF2    =      98.8 INCHES
   XR1    =    -114.0 INCHES          XR2    =    -114.0 INCHES
   YS1    =      38.5 INCHES          YS2    =      38.5 INCHES
```

```
                         ROLLING RESISTANCE

      VEHICLE # 1                             VEHICLE # 2

   RF----------      0.00                 RF----------      0.00
   LF----------      1.00                 LF----------      1.00
   RR----------      0.00                 RR----------      0.00
   LR----------      0.00                 LR----------      0.00


   MU----------      0.50
```

Figure 13-3I

by the line printer at the computer. Selecting BATCH permits the user to run the program at a lower computing charge. For all other modes, the user has direct and continuous access to the central processing unit of the computer. In the BATCH mode the input data is queued in a batch. The queuing system will deliver the data to the central processing unit only at a time when the CPU is not in use by a subscriber demanding direct access to the CPU. The BATCH charge rated could be one-half to one-third of the COMPLETE rate.

```
CRASH 2    (7 JUL 79)


ENTER TYPE OF CRASH RUN?
(COMPLETE,ABBREVIATED,RERUN,PRINT,BATCH,SMAC,OR END)
SMAC

SMAC input file name?
CALSPA.CR2

DO YOU WISH SMAC INPUT FILE PRINTED ON YOUR TERMINAL?
(ANSWER YES OR NO)
N



CRASH 2    (7 JUL 79)


ENTER TYPE OF CRASH RUN?
(COMPLETE,ABBREVIATED,RERUN,PRINT,BATCH,SMAC,OR END)
END

                      CRASH PROGRAM COMPLETED.
STOP

END OF EXECUTION
CPU TIME: 16.38 ELAPSED TIME: 22:13.20
EXIT
```

Figure 13-3J

The program SMAC computes the postimpact trajectories for the vehicles based upon the input data generated by the CRASH2 run. The SMAC model simulates the collision phase and postcollision phase based upon the speeds, positions, and orientations of the vehicles as derived from the CRASH2 run. The postimpact trajectories and the points of rest of the vehicles are computed. If the computed trajectories and points of rest are consistent with those provided to the CRASH2 run, then the correctness of the CRASH2 run is verified by the SMAC run.

Detailed information concerning the postimpact trajectories are provided by SMAC. The location of each tire at any desired instant of time relative to the instant of impact is computed. Additionally, the angular, longitudinal, and lateral components of distance, velocity, and acceleration of each vehicle are available on the same scale basis. Whether or not

```
SIMULATION MODEL OF AUTOMOBILE COLLISIONS    (USING CRASH RESULTS)
CALSPAN TEST MRA # 1 —— OFFSET FRONTAL AT 30 MPH
     0.0      4.0    0.025    0.001    0.01    0.001    30.0     5.0     2.0     1
  -100.80    12.00    0.00     0.00   503.11    0.00                             2
   100.80   -12.00  179.97     0.00   539.55    0.00                             3
    54.7     59.2    61.8   29819.6    7.971     0.0    98.8  -114.0    38.5      4
    54.7     59.2    61.8   38242.6   10.223     0.0    98.8  -114.0    38.5      5
-10434.0 -10434.0  -9641.0  -9641.0                                             6
-10434.0 -10434.0  -9641.0  -9641.0                                             7
    0.125    0.185    0.01     0.00                                             8
     0.0      0.0      0.0      0.00     0.00     0.00     0.00
     0.0      0.0      0.0   -200.11  -400.21  -400.21  -400.21
     0.0      0.0      0.0      0.00     0.00     0.00     0.00
     0.0      0.0      0.0      0.00     0.00     0.00     0.00
    0.125    0.185    0.01     0.00                                             9
     0.0      0.0      0.0      0.00     0.00     0.00     0.00
     0.0      0.0      0.0   -256.63  -513.26  -513.26  -513.26
     0.0      0.0      0.0      0.00     0.00     0.00     0.00
     0.0      0.0      0.0      0.00     0.00     0.00     0.00
     0.0      0.3      0.1      1.0                                             10
     0.0      0.3      0.1      1.0                                             11
 -6000.00  6000.00  6000.00  6000.00    0.50     0.70     0.00                  12
     2.0      0.2     15.0      5.0     51.00    51.00     0.55                  13
0.064233.5417-34.7381-5                                                         14
                                                                             9999
```

Figure 13-4

each individual tire is rolling or sliding over the pavement so as to leave tire marks is identified by wheel.

In addition to the detailed information concerning the postimpact trajectories of the vehicles, the collision damage to each vehicle is calculated based upon the stiffness characteristics of the particular vehicle and the area of the collision. The information concerning the location of each vehicle along the postimpact trajectories, vehicle speeds and accelerations and the collision damage description are provided in tabular form. A summary of this information is given in recap form and graphically. A summary of the trajectory information and the Vehicle Damage Index is given in tabular form. A graphic display of the vehicle positions at impact, the post-impact trajectories, and the vehicle locations at their points of rest can be presented using graphic display terminals. Additionally, the extent of collision damage to the vehicles can be displayed graphically.

Figure 13-4 displays the table of data generated as a result of the computer session with CRASH2 covered by Figures 13-3A through 13-3I. Some editing of this table was needed to have it more realistically represent the postimpact conditions.

To permit the editing to be accomplished at the computer terminal, some intermediate steps must be taken. The table (Figure 13-4) was set up in a file in response to the second question after the SMAC option was selected. This response is indicated in Figure 13-3I. By using a text editor the file CALSPA.CR2 was changed. The changed version was identified as file CALSPA.CRN and stored. The file was caused to be printed on the terminal display by entering TYPE CALSPA.CRN and is shown in Figure 13-5.

File CALSPA.CRN was created as set forth in Figure 13-5. Notice that the lines in the printout are numbered at the far right margin. The second line beneath line 8 and the second line beneath line 9 shown in Figure 13-5 differ from those shown on Figure 13-4. The four lines beneath lines 8 and 9 permit the user to specify the braking for each wheel for each vehicle according to a desired braking schedule. The numerical values indicated are the braking force at the tire-road surface interface. Each of the lines represents a wheel. Each column represents a time during the collision elapsed time interval. The braking time schedules are given by lines 8 and 9. The second line in each of the braking tables for the example given represents the braking force attributable to the damaged right front wheels. The damage to these wheels prevented rolling after impact. Thus, these wheels caused a drag force that affected the postimpact trajectories. The drag force provided by Figure 13-4 existed for the time period 0.125 seconds after trajectory to 0.185 seconds after trajectory.

```
SIMULATION MODEL OF AUTOMOBILE COLLISIONS   (USING CRASH RESULTS)
CALSPAN TEST MRA # 1 —— OFFSET FRONTAL AT 30 MPH
  0.000    4.000    0.025    0.001    0.010    0.001   30,000    5.000    2.000        1
-100.80    12.00     0.00     0.00   503.11     0.00                                   2
 100.80   -12.00   179.97     0.00   539.55     0.00                                   3
   54.7     59.2     61.8  29819.6      8.0      0.0     98.8   -114.0     38.5         4
   54.7     59.2     61.8  38242.6     10.2      0.0     98.8   -114.0     38.5         5
-10434.0-10434.0  -9641.0  -9641.0                                                     6
-10434.0-10434.0  -9641.0  -9641.0                                                     7
   0.13     3.13     0.50     0.00                                                     8
   0.00     0.00     0.00     0.00     0.00     0.00     0.00
-200.11  -400.21   400.21  -400.21  -400.21  -400.21  -400.21
   0.00     0.00     0.00     0.00     0.00     0.00     0.00
   0.00     0.00     0.00     0.00     0.00     0.00     0.00
   0.13     3.13     0.50     0.00                                                     9
   0.00     0.00     0.00     0.00     0.00     0.00     0.00
-256.63  -513.26  -513.26  -513.26  -513.26  -513.26  -513.26
   0.00     0.00     0.00     0.00     0.00     0.00     0.00
   0.00     0.00     0.00     0.00     0.00     0.00     0.00
   0.00     0.30     0.10     1.00                                                    10
   0.00     0.30     0.10     1.00                                                    11
-6000.00  6000.00  6000.00  6000.00     0.50     0.70     0.00                        12
   2.00     0.20    15.00     5.00    51.00    51.00     0.55                         13
.642E-01.354E-02.474E-04                                                             14
                                                                                   9999
```

Figure 13-5

In Figure 13-5 the drag force prevailed for the period 0.13 seconds after impact throughout the entire distance of postimpact trajectory.

C. SMAC

Figure 13-6 shows the session with SMAC. Notice that the name of the input file CALSPA.CRN is provided. The tabular form of the output data is called to be delivered to the line

```
        S M A C

Name of input file?CALSPA.CRN

"L" for line printer or "F" for output file?L

Tektronix output file? ( <CR> for none ): CALSPA.CRP

Do you wish a summary of results printed on your terminal? Y

----CPU usage is 0000015021. milliseconds---

----CPU usage is 0000030016. milliseconds---

----CPU usage is 0000045019. milliseconds---

CALSPA.CRP CALSPAN TEST MRA # 1 ---- OFFSET FRONTAL AT 30 MPH

                    Vehicle 1            Vehicle 2
        Initial
        CG(ft)
          X               -7.98                7.95
          Y                1.00               -1.00
        Heading           -0.00              179.97
        Velocity
          FWD(MPH)        28.57               30.64
          LATERAL(MPH)     0.00                0.00
          ANG(d/s)        -0.11               -0.12
        Final Position
        Time=    1.99
          X              -16.44                1.42
          Y                3.19               -1.72
        Heading           -4.78              171.79
        Remarks         in motion          in motion

        Vehicle 1       damage indexes     Delta V(mph)
                        12LFEW3                34.30

        Vehicle 2       damage indexes     Delta V(mph)
                        12LFEW3                26.93
        STOP

END OF EXECUTION
CPU TIME: 52.82 ELAPSED TIME: 2:43.89
EXIT
```

Figure 13-6

printer. The line printer is located at the main computer. An option for a graphic display is available. A graphic-equipped terminal is required to utilize this manner of output presentation. A graphic output file is requested and identified as CALSPA.CRP. A summary of the results will be printed on the terminal after the computations are computed. The next three lines of data indicate the time utilized by the CPU. For this particular run, the CPU time was 45 seconds. The summarized results are set forth in table format beneath the assigned title heading. After the END OF EXECUTION statement the CPU time in seconds and the total elapsed time in minutes are given.

Because the plotted output option was selected, the output of the run was presented graphically. Three pages of graphics are provided. These plotted results produced by a graphic plotter are found in Figures 13-7A, 7B, and 7C. Figure 13-7A contains the same table of data as shown in Figure 13-6. Figure 13-7B is a graphic plot showing the vehicles as oriented at the point of impact, the postimpact trajectories as indicated by tire marks, and the positions of rest of the vehicles. Figure 13-7C shows the computed damage to the left front of each vehicle. These results compare reasonably favorably to those of the input data provided to the CRASH2 run.

```
CALSPA.CRP CALSPAN TEST MRA # 1 --- OFFSET FRONTAL AT 30 MPH
                    Vehicle 1              Vehicle 2
Initial
CG(ft)
    X                 -7.98                 7.95
    Y                  1.00                -1.00
  Heading             -0.00               179.97
  Velocity
    FWD(MPH)          28.57                30.64
    LATERAL(MPH)       0.00                 0.00
    ANG(d/s)          -0.11                -0.12
Final Position
  Time=     1.99
    X                -16.44                 1.42
    Y                  3.19                -1.72
  Heading             -4.78               171.79
Remarks            in motion             in motion

Vehicle 1          damage indexes        Delta V(mph)
                   12LFEW3                  34.30

Vehicle 2          damage indexes        Delta V(mph)
                   12LFEW3                  26.93

please clear screen and depress RETURN key
```

Figure 13-7A

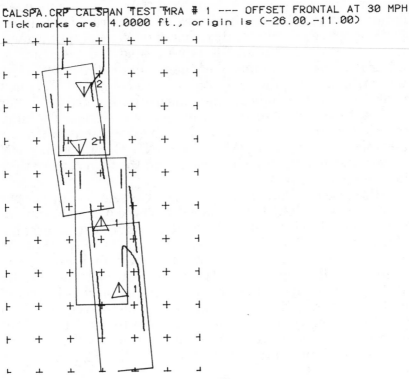

CALSPA.CRP CALSPAN TEST MRA # 1 --- OFFSET FRONTAL AT 30 MPH
Tick marks are 4.0000 ft., origin is (-26.00,-11.00)

Figure 13-7B

D. CRASH3

The latest improvements and developments of the CRASH
program are represented by CRASH3. By early 1982, CRASH2
had been installed by many computer services and was available on a share-time basis. The CRASH3 version is available
through a few share-time services. The improvements incorporated into the CRASH3 version are sufficiently important
to make it more desirable than CRASH2. While the improvements are significant, CRASH3 does not make CRASH2
obsolete. The improved features of CRASH3 can be generalized into four categories: (1) the dynamic modeling techniques
employed, (2) the numerical computational methods, (3) the
physical representations of current model vehicles, and (4) the
interactive features of the program. The general format of
CRASH3 is very similar to that of CRASH2. An additional
feature of CRASH3 is that the user's manual appears to have

been more thoroughly considered than the CRASH2 manual. The CRASH3 manual contains basic information necessary for the correct and proper determination of some of the input data.

The format of the computed results using CRASH3 is essentially the same as CRASH2. CRASH3 is used to set up the table of input data necessary for running SMAC.

A typical session with CRASH3 is shown in Figures 13–8A through 13–8T (pages 316–335). Figures 13–8A through 13–8F include all of the responses that provide the necessary input data. In each case the user's response is that which is indicated after INPUT. Figures 13–8G through 13–8K show the computed results and a listing of the input data upon which the computed results are based. Near the bottom of Figure 13–8K the user is again given the option of the type of run desired. In this case the option selected was that of rerunning the existing input data with a change made in the input data. The change selected was the employment of the trajectory simulation. In the initial run the collision velocities were computed based upon an application of the principles of

CALSPA.CRP CALSPAN TEST MRA # 1 --- OFFSET FRONTAL AT 30 MPH
DAMAGED VEHICLE DISPLAY

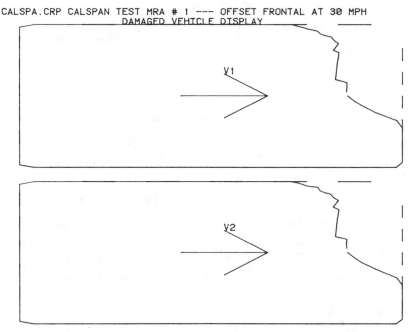

Figure 13-7C

conservation of momentum and collision damage. Both CRASH2 and CRASH3 have an option that may be employed wherein the computed results based upon conservation of momentum principles can be checked by using the trajectory simulation technique employed by SMAC. As a result of the more accurately described postimpact trajectories as represented by the mathematical model of SMAC, the CRASH-computed collision velocities using the conservation of momentum principles will be adjusted to represent more accurately the

CRASH3

Enter type of crash run (Complete, Abbreviated, Rerun, Print, Smac or End)

INPUT>COMPLETE

```
***********************************************************************
*                         C R A S H                                  *
*                                                                    *
*      Calspan Reconstruction of Accident Speeds on the Highway      *
*                                                                    *
*       Messages beginning with "%" are information only             *
*       Messages beginning with "?" are error messages               *
*                                                                    *
*          1. Data is sent with a carriage return.                   *
*             Use carriage return after entering requested data.     *
*                                                                    *
*          2. Separate responses by at least one blank.              *
*                                                                    *
*          3. Type "?" for full text of question with some help.     *
*             Type "$" to back up to the previous question.          *
*                                                                    *
*          4. If a typing error is made BEFORE a carriage return     *
*             is typed, use "DEL" or "DELETE" to remove the most     *
*             recent character. Continue using "DEL" or "DELETE"     *
*             until the error is reached. Type Control-R to view     *
*             the current state of the line. (Hold "CONTROL" or      *
*             "CTRL" while pressing "R".)                            *
*                                                                    *
*          5. If a typing  error is made AFTER the  carriage ret     *
*             urn is typed,  use "$" to  backup to the erroneous     *
*             question.                                              *
*                                                                    *
*          6. Coordinate system conventions: +Y-Axis runs to the     *
*             RIGHT of the +X-Axis.  Positive heading angles ro-     *
*             tate clockwise.                                        *
***********************************************************************
```

1. Enter run name:
INPUT>SAMPLE RUN   RICSAC   CASE # 8   11/26/82

Figure 13-8A

2. Enter classifications and weights for both vehs

Enter classification number	defined as
1	80.0 to 94.8 inch wheelbase
2	94.8 to 101.6
3	101.6 to 110.4
4	110.4 to 117.5
5	117.5 to 123.2
6	123.2 to 150.0
7	109.0 to 130.0 (use for VAN)
10	Movable barrier
11	Immovable barrier

Valid weights are 1000 to 50000 lbs.
FORMAT: Class(V1) Weight(W1)   Class(V2)   Weight(W2)

INPUT>4 4479 4 4710

3. Enter veh damage index and direction of principal force Veh 1
%The CDC is a 7-character code as defined in appendix 2
of the CRASH3 user's guide. The PDOF entry allows the
entry of principal force more accurately than thru the
use of the 12-position CDC clock. This data is not required.
FORMAT: CDC (7 char code)   PDOF (+/- 180 deg max)
Example: INPUT>12RFEW3   17.

INPUT>11FDEW1 -45

4. Enter veh damage index and direction of principal force Veh 2
%The CDC is a 7-character code as defined in appendix 2
of the CRASH3 user's guide. The PDOF entry allows the
entry of principal force more accurately than thru the
use of the 12-position CDC clock. This data is not required.
FORMAT: CDC (7 char code)   PDOF (+/- 180 deg max)
Example: INPUT>12RFEW3   17.

INPUT>02RYEW2 45

5. Enter the stiffness categories for veh 1 and veh 2
%The stiffness category is an integer code for the crush
resistance of each veh. Enter the appropriate value for
the stiffness category from table 8-2 in section 8 of
the CRASH3 user guide. Use 10 & 11 for moving and fixed
barriers, respectively.
INPUT>4 4

Figure 13-8B

6. Are both rest and impact positions known?

>   %A "NO" response will limit program results to velocity
>   change approximations based on damage data only. Answer
>   "YES" if available, "NO" if not.

INPUT>YES

7. Enter rest positions and headings for veh 1 and veh 2
     Format: XCR1(FT) YCR1(FT) PSIR1(DEG) XCR2(FT) YCR2(FT) PSIR2(D
EG)
INPUT>-0.5 12 46 6.5 21 141

8. Enter impact positions and headings for veh 1 & veh 2
     Format: XC10(FT) YC10(FT) PSI10(DEG) XC20(FT) YC20(FT) PSI20(DE
G)
INPUT>-10.9 3.2 0 0 1.9 90

9. Did either or both vehs have a side slip angle prior to impact? (Yes
or No)
     %Side slip is a direction of motion that is not straight ahead
          (answer YES or NO)
INPUT>NO

11. Was veh contact sustained from impact to rest?
     %A yes answer indicates that veh to veh contact was
     maintained from impact to rest. (answer YES or NO)
INPUT>NO

12. Did rotational or lateral skidding occur (veh 1)?
     %This refers to that portion of the trajectory during
     which the front & rear wheels do not run in the same
     tracks   (answer YES or NO)
INPUT>YES

13. Did rotational and/or lateral skidding of veh 1 stop before
    rest position was reached?

>   %In a skidding trajectory, it is common to have an abrupt
>   change in motion as the wheels start tracking one another
>   and the vehicle out to rest in a non-skidding fashion. Of
>   course, the non-skid section may be a straight line or a
>   curved path depending on steer conditons. Answer YES/NO.

INPUT>NO

Figure 13-8C

15. Was the spinout path of veh 1 between separation and rest curved?
    %Try to visualize the path of the veh CG. If a prominent arc is
    present, answer YES. (answer YES or NO)
INPUT>NO

17. Which direction did veh 1 rotate?
    %Clockwise rotation turns from the x-axis towards the y-axis
    For the case of purely lateral skidding enter none
    (Respond with: CW   CCW   NONE)
INPUT>CW

18. Did veh 1 rotate more than 360 deg betweenseparation and rest?
    %This is a rare occurance and should be verified
    from tire mark data   (Answer YES or NO)
INPUT>NO

19. Did rotational and/or lateral skidding of veh 2 occur?
    %This refers to that portion of the trajectory during
    which the front & rear wheels do not run in the same
    tracks   (answer YES or NO)
INPUT>YES

20. Did rotational and/or lateral skidding of veh 2 stop before rest
    position was reached?

       %In a skidding trajectory, it is common to have an abrupt
       change in motion as the wheels start tracking one another
       and the vehicle out to rest in a non-skidding fashion. Of
       course, the non-skid section may be a straight line or a
       curved path depending on steer conditons. Answer YES/NO.

INPUT>NO

22. Was the spinout path of veh # 2 between separation and rest curved?
    %Try to visualize the path of the veh CG. If a prominent arc is
    present, answer YES. (answer YES or NO)
INPUT>NO

24. Which direction did veh 2 rotate?
    %Clockwise rotation turns from the x-axis towards the y-axis
    For the case of purely lateral skidding enter none
    (Respond with: CW   CCW   NONE)
INPUT>CW

25. Did veh 2 rotate more than 360 deg between separation and rest?
    %This is a rare occurance and should be verified
    from tire mark data   (Answer YES or NO)
INPUT>NO

Figure 13-8D

26. Enter the nominal tire-ground friction coefficient?
    %Refer to table 2 in the CRASH users guide for typical
    values   Format: MU
INPUT>.87

27. Enter rolling resistance:
    Rolling resistance may be entered as:
    1 The decimal portion of full rotational lockup at each wheel
    2 The level of longitudinal deceleration, in G Units produced
       by rotational resistance at the wheels. (Answer 1 or 2)
INPUT>1

28. Enter rolling resistances of wheels of veh 1
    %Can be caused by braking, damage, engine braking, etc.
    Enter value for each wheel from .0 to 1.0; 1.0 = Full wheel lockup
         FORM: RF   LF   RR   LR
INPUT>.01 .01 .2 .2

29. Enter rolling resistances of wheels of veh 2
    %Can be caused by braking, damage, engine braking, etc.
    Enter value for each wheel from .0 to 1.0; 1.0 = Full wheel lockup
         FORM: RF   LF   RR   LR
INPUT>.01 .01 .2 .2

32. Do you want the results checked by a trajectory' simulation?

        %The separation velocities normally calculated by CRASH
        are used by a trajectory simulation to determine if the
        evidence entered matches the calculated speeds. If not,
        appropriate speed adjustments are made to force agree-
        ment with the evidence. Answer YES/NO.

INPUT>NO

38. Are any actual damage dimensions known?

        %A NO response will produce damage data based on the sub-
        mitted CDC only. If available, this data should be input
        to enhance results. Answer YES/NO.

INPUT>YES

42. Enter width of damaged area along end of veh 1

        %NASS investigators should ermember the protocol for in-
        cluding induced damage. These rules require the inclu-
        sion of both direct contact and induced damage in the
        width (L) entered into CRASH3.

INPUT>73.0

Figure 13-8E

43. Enter a profile of the extent of damage for veh 1

    %At 2, 4, or 6 points along the width of the dent, measure
    the depth of the damage from the original side. Entry se-
    quence is from rear to front of veh.
    FORMAT: C1 C2 C3 C4 C5 C6 (Inches)

INPUT>2.7 3.6

44. Enter dist along veh 1 axis between the CG and the middle of
the damaged region

    %If this dist runs off towards the drivers side, enter as
    a negative number.

INPUT>0.0

45. Enter width of damaged area along side of veh 2

    %NASS investigators should ermember the protocol for in-
    cluding induced damage. These rules require the inclu-
    sion of both direct contact and induced damage in the
    width (L) entered into CRASH3.

INPUT>84.5

46. Enter a profile of the extent of damage for veh 2

    %At 2, 4, or 6 points along the width of the dent, measure
    the depth of the damage from the original side. Entry se-
    quence is from rear to front of veh.
    FORMAT: C1 C2 C3 C4 C5 C6 (Inches)

INPUT>6.2 8.3 9.2 5.9 4.4 .8

47. Enter dist along veh 2 axis between the' CG and
    the middle of the damaged region

    %If this dist runs off towards the drivers side, enter as
    a negative number.

    Format: D2 (inches)
INPUT>15

Figure 13-8F

%CRASH input completed
Type CR to begin print of results...

S U M M A R Y   O F   C R A S H 3   R E S U L T S

SAMPLE RUN   RICSAC   CASE # 8   11/26/82

Veh 1


```
***********************************************************************
*               *               *               *                    *
*   Impact      *               *               *                    *
*    Speed      *     Speed change              *                    *
*     Mph       *         Mph                   *        Basis        *
*               *               *               *                    *
*****************************************************    Of          *
*       *       *       *       *       *       *                    *
*  Fwd  *  Lat  * Total * Long  * Lateral *            Results        *
*       *       *       *       *       *       *                    *
***********************************************************************
*       *       *       *       *       *       *                    *
*       *       *       *       *       * Spinout trajectories and   *
* 16.7  *  0.0  * 12.6  * -6.9  *    10.5  * Conservation of linear   *
*       *       *       *       *       * momentum                   *
*       *       *       *       *       *       *                    *
***********************************************************************
*       *       *       *       *       *       *                    *
*       *       *       *       *       * Spinout trajectories and   *
*       *       *       *       *       * Damage                     *
*       *       *       *       *       *       *                    *
***********************************************************************
        *       *       *       *       *                            *
        * 11.8  * -8.3  *    8.3  * Damage data only                 *
        *       *       *       *       *                            *
***********************************************************************
```
Figure 13-8G

Veh 2

```
************************************************************************
*                *                        *                           *
*    Impact      *                        *                           *
*    Speed       *   Speed change         *                           *
*    Mph         *       Mph              *          Basis            *
*                *                        *                           *
*******************************************          Of               *
*        *       *       *       *        *                           *
* Fwd  * Lat  * Total * Long * Lateral *        Results              *
*        *       *       *       *        *                           *
************************************************************************
*        *       *       *       *        *                           *
*        *       *       *       *        * Spinout trajectories and  *
* 25.7 * 0.0 * 12.0 * -10.0 *  -6.6  * Conservation of linear     *
*        *       *       *       *        * momentum                  *
*        *       *       *       *        *                           *
************************************************************************
*        *       *       *       *        *                           *
*        *       *       *       *        * Spinout trajectories and  *
*        *       *       *       *        * Damage                    *
*        *       *       *       *        *                           *
************************************************************************
         *       *       *        *        *                          *
         * 11.2 * -7.9 *  -7.9  * Damage data only           *
         *       *       *        *        *                          *
         ***********************************************************
```

Scene information

	Veh 1	Veh 2
Impact X-position	-10.90Ft	0.00Ft
Impact Y-position	3.20Ft	1.90Ft
Impact heading angle	0.00Deg	89.99Deg
Rest X-position	-0.50Ft	6.50Ft
Rest Y-position	12.00Ft	21.00Ft
Rest heading angle	45.99Deg	140.98Deg
Direction of rotation	CW	CW
Amount of rotation	<360	<360

Figure 13-8H

Collision Conditions

--------------Veh 1--------------   --------------Veh 2------

XC10'	=	-10.9Ft	XC20'	=	0.0Ft
YC10'	=	3.2Ft	YC20'	=	1.9Ft
PSI10	=	0.0Deg	PSI20	=	90.0Deg
PSI1D0	=	0.0Deg/Sec	PSI2D0	=	0.0Deg/Sec
BETA1	=	0.0Deg	BETA2	=	0.0Deg

Separation conditions

XCS1'	=	-10.9 Ft	XCS2'	=	0.0 Ft
YCS1'	=	3.2 Ft	YCS2'	=	1.9 Ft
PSIS1	=	0.0 Deg	PSIS2	=	90.0 Deg
US1	=	9.8 Mph	US2	=	15.7 Mph
VS1	=	10.5 Mph	VS2	=	-6.6 Mph
PSISD1	=	58.2 Deg/Sec	PSISD2	=	54.5Deg/Sec

Summary Of Results

Impact speed (trajectory and conservation of linear momentum)

	Forward	Lateral
Veh 1	16.7 Mph	0.0 Mph
Veh 2	25.7 Mph	0.0 Mph

Speed change (damage)

	Total	Long	Lat	Ang
Veh 1	11.8Mph	-8.3Mph	8.3Mph	-45.0Deg
Veh 2	11.2Mph	-7.9Mph	-7.9Mph	45.0Deg

Speed change (linear momentum)

	Total	Long	Lat	Ang
Veh 1	12.6Mph	-6.9Mph	10.5Mph	-56.6Deg
Veh 2	12.0Mph	-10.0Mph	-6.6Mph	33.4Deg

Energy dissipated by damage:

Veh 1:	38479.3Ft-Lb
Veh 2:	31220.8Ft-Lb

Figure 13-8I

Relative Velocity Data

Speed along line thru CGs (linear momentum)
    Veh 1   16.6Mph
    Veh 2   3.0Mph
Speed orthog to CG line (linear momentum)
    Veh 1   2.0Mph
    Veh 2   -25.5Mph
Closing velocity (linear momentum)
          19.7Mph

---------------------Summary Of Damage Data--------------------
                          (*—Indicates default value was used)

          Veh 1   Veh 2

Type——————— Category 4		Type——————— Category 4	
Weight—————— 4479.Lbs.		Weight—————— 4710.Lbs.	
CDC——————————11FDEW1		CDC——————————02RYEW2	
L——————————— 73.0In		L——————————— 84.5In	
C1—————————— 2.7In		C1—————————— 6.2In	
C2—————————— 3.6In		C2—————————— 8.3In	
C3—————————— 0.0In		C3—————————— 9.2In	
C4—————————— 0.0In		C4—————————— 5.9In	
C5—————————— 0.0In		C5—————————— 4.4In	
C6—————————— 0.0In		C6—————————— 0.8In	
D——————————— 0.0		D——————————— 15.0	
RHO————————— 1.00	*	RHO————————— 1.00	*
Ang————————— -45.0Deg		Ang————————— 45.0Deg	
D'—————————— 1.7In		D'—————————— 7.8In	

Figure 13-8J

Dimensions and inertial properties

A1	=	54.7In	A2	=	54.7In
B1	=	59.2In	B2	=	59.2In
TR1	=	61.8In	TR2	=	61.8In
I1	=	43364.2Lb-Sec**2-In	I2	=	45600.7Lb-Sec**2-In
M1	=	11.592Lb-Sec**2/In	M2	=	12.189Lb-Sec**2/In
XF1	=	98.8In	XF2	=	98.8In
XR1	=	-114.0In	XR2	=	-114.0In
YS1	=	38.5In	YS2	=	38.5In

Rolling Resistance

Veh 1

RF----------	0.01
LF----------	0.01
RR----------	0.20
LR----------	0.20

Veh 2

RF----------	0.01
LF----------	0.01
RR----------	0.20
LR----------	0.20

MU---------- 0.87

%End output
Enter type of crash run (Complete, Abbreviated, Rerun, Print, Smac, or E
nd)
INPUT>RERUN

Data elements to change
INPUT>32

32. Trajectory simulation? (Y or N)
INPUT>YES

%CRASH input completed

+++++ RESULTS OF TRAJECTORY SIMULATION +++++

VEHICLE # 1   TRAJECTORY ITERATION # 1
US = 172.9 VS = 184.7 PSISD = 1.02 SSDOT= 253.0 GAMS = 0.82
REST: 448.1   302.9 0.40   END-OF-ROT: -35.3   100.1 0.39
POINT-ON-CURVE: -130.8   38.4
ERRORS: 2.94   0.00   0.50   0.00   0.00   Q = 3.45   T = 5.95

Figure 13-8K

+++++ RESULTS OF TRAJECTORY SIMULATION +++++

VEHICLE # 1   TRAJECTORY ITERATION # 2
US =   91.6 VS = 143.0 PSISD = 1.17 SSDOT= 169.8 GAMS = 1.00
REST: 60.4 141.1 0.40   END-OF-ROT: -82.7   80.6 0.40
POINT-ON-CURVE: -130.8   38.4
ERRORS: 0.41   0.00   0.50   0.00   0.00   Q = 0.91   T = 3.40

+++++ RESULTS OF TRAJECTORY SIMULATION +++++

VEHICLE # 1   TRAJECTORY ITERATION # 3
US =   64.6 VS = 140.7 PSISD = 1.35 SSDOT= 154.9 GAMS = 1.14
REST: -9.6 125.0 0.47   END-OF-ROT: -94.7   82.1 0.46
POINT-ON-CURVE: -130.8   38.4
ERRORS: 0.12   0.00   0.42   0.00   0.00   Q = 0.54   T = 2.77

+++++ RESULTS OF TRAJECTORY SIMULATION +++++

VEHICLE # 1   TRAJECTORY ITERATION # 4
US =   58.6 VS = 148.6 PSISD = 1.52 SSDOT= 159.8 GAMS = 1.20
REST: -10.4 140.9 0.55   END-OF-ROT: -95.9   88.7 0.54
POINT-ON-CURVE: -130.8   38.4
ERRORS: 0.03   0.00   0.32   0.00   0.00   Q = 0.35   T = 2.85

+++++ RESULTS OF TRAJECTORY SIMULATION +++++

VEHICLE # 1   TRAJECTORY ITERATION # 5
US =   59.6 VS = 150.2 PSISD = 1.67 SSDOT= 161.6 GAMS = 1.19
REST: 0.2 156.9 0.59   END-OF-ROT: -93.6   93.4 0.59
POINT-ON-CURVE: -130.8   38.4
ERRORS: 0.09   0.00   0.26   0.00   0.00   Q = 0.35   T = 3.05

Figure 13-8L

```
+++++ RESULTS OF TRAJECTORY SIMULATION +++++


VEHICLE # 2              TRAJECTORY ITERATION #  1
US =  276.9  VS = -115.9  PSISD =  0.95  SSDOT= 300.2  GAMS =  1.17
REST: -367.5   599.9 2.34      END-OF-ROT:  -30.4   252.7 2.34
POINT-ON-CURVE:      0.0     22.8
ERRORS:     2.33    0.00    0.13    0.00    0.00      Q =  2.47    T =  6.27


+++++ RESULTS OF TRAJECTORY SIMULATION +++++


VEHICLE # 2              TRAJECTORY ITERATION #  2
US =  119.7  VS = -183.5  PSISD =  0.99  SSDOT= 219.1  GAMS =  0.58
REST:   49.1    92.8 2.27      END-OF-ROT:   54.0    87.3 2.27
POINT-ON-CURVE:      0.0     22.8
ERRORS:     0.67    0.00    0.21    0.00    0.00      Q =  0.88    T =  1.40


+++++ RESULTS OF TRAJECTORY SIMULATION +++++


VEHICLE # 2              TRAJECTORY ITERATION #  3
US =  221.2  VS = -229.6  PSISD =  1.06  SSDOT= 318.8  GAMS =  0.77
REST:   71.5   186.5 2.73      END-OF-ROT:   80.8   182.6 2.73
POINT-ON-CURVE:      0.0     22.8
ERRORS:     0.27    0.00   -0.30    0.00    0.00      Q =  0.57    T =  1.90


+++++ RESULTS OF TRAJECTORY SIMULATION +++++


VEHICLE # 2              TRAJECTORY ITERATION #  4
US =  259.2  VS = -240.7  PSISD =  0.94  SSDOT= 353.7  GAMS =  0.82
REST:   45.3   249.2 2.74      END-OF-ROT:   78.0   235.3 2.74
POINT-ON-CURVE:      0.0     22.8
ERRORS:     0.14    0.00   -0.32    0.00    0.00      Q =  0.45    T =  2.67


+++++ RESULTS OF TRAJECTORY SIMULATION +++++


VEHICLE # 2              TRAJECTORY ITERATION #  5
US =  241.1  VS = -266.5  PSISD =  0.84  SSDOT= 359.3  GAMS =  0.74
REST:   81.9   234.1 2.60      END-OF-ROT:  105.3   220.1 2.60
POINT-ON-CURVE:      0.0     22.8
ERRORS:     0.08    0.00   -0.15    0.00    0.00      Q =  0.23    T =  2.47
Type CR to begin print of results...
```

Figure 13-8M

S U M M A R Y   O F   C R A S H 3   R E S U L T S

SAMPLE RUN   RICSAC   CASE # 8   11/26/82

    Impact speed (trajectory and conservation of linear momentum)

	Forward	Lateral
Veh 1	19.3 Mph	0.0 Mph
Veh 2	21.8 Mph	0.0 Mph

    Speed change (damage)

	Total	Long	Lat	Ang
Veh 1	11.8Mph	-8.3Mph	8.3Mph	-45.0Deg
Veh 2	11.2Mph	-7.9Mph	-7.9Mph	45.0Deg

    Speed change (linear momentum)

	Total	Long	Lat	Ang
Veh 1	18.1Mph	-15.9Mph	8.5Mph	-28.2Deg
Veh 2	17.2Mph	-8.1Mph	-15.1Mph	61.8Deg

Energy dissipated by damage:
                         Veh 1:   38479.3Ft-Lb
                         Veh 2:   31220.8Ft-Lb
Speed along line thru CGs (linear momentum)
   Veh 1   19.2Mph
   Veh 2   2.6Mph
Speed orthog to CG line (linear momentum)
   Veh 1   2.3Mph
   Veh 2 -21.7Mph
Closing velocity (linear momentum)
           21.7Mph
Enter type of crash run (Complete, Abbreviated, Rerun, Print, Smac, or E
nd)
INPUT>PRINT

Type CR to begin print of results...

Figure 13-8N

S U M M A R Y   O F   C R A S H 3   R E S U L T S

SAMPLE RUN   RICSAC   CASE # 8   11/26/82

Veh 1

```
***********************************************************************
*             *                              *                        *
*   Impact    *                              *                        *
*   Speed     *        Speed change          *                        *
*    Mph      *           Mph                *          Basis          *
*             *                              *                        *
*********************************************************     Of       *
*        *       *        *        *          *                        *
*  Fwd  *  Lat  * Total * Long   * Lateral *         Results          *
*        *       *        *        *          *                        *
***********************************************************************
*        *       *        *        *          *                        *
*        *       *        *        *          * Spinout trajectories and *
* 19.3 *  0.0 * 18.1 * -15.9 *   8.5   * Conservation of linear  *
*        *       *        *        *          * momentum                *
*        *       *        *        *          *                        *
***********************************************************************
*        *       *        *        *          *                        *
*        *       *        *        *          * Spinout trajectories and *
*        *       *        *        *          * Damage                  *
*        *       *        *        *          *                        *
***********************************************************************
         *        *        *          *                                *
         * 11.8 * -8.3 *   8.3   * Damage data only       *
         *        *        *          *                                *
***********************************************************************
```

Figure 13-8O

Veh 2

```
***********************************************************************
*                *             *                *                     *
*    Impact      *             *                *                     *
*    Speed       *    Speed change              *                     *
*     Mph        *       Mph                    *      Basis          *
*                *                              *                     *
********************************************* Of                      *
*         *      *       *       *             *                     *
*  Fwd  * Lat  * Total * Long  * Lateral *      Results              *
*         *      *       *       *             *                     *
***********************************************************************
*         *      *       *       *         *                          *
*         *      *       *       *         * Spinout trajectories and *
* 21.8  * 0.0  * 17.2 * -8.1  * -15.1  * Conservation of linear       *
*         *      *       *       *         * momentum                 *
*         *      *       *       *         *                          *
***********************************************************************
*         *      *       *       *         *                          *
*         *      *       *       *         * Spinout trajectories and *
*         *      *       *       *         * Damage                   *
***********************************************************************
         *       *       *       *         *                          *
         * 11.2 * -7.9  * -7.9  * Damage data only                    *
         *       *       *       *         *                          *
***********************************************************************
```

Scene information

	Veh 1	Veh 2
Impact X-position	-10.90Ft	0.00Ft
Impact Y-position	3.20Ft	1.90Ft
Impact heading angle	0.00Deg	89.99Deg
Rest X-position	-0.50Ft	6.50Ft
Rest Y-position	12.00Ft	21.00Ft
Rest heading angle	45.99Deg	140.98Deg
Direction of rotation	CW	CW
Amount of rotation	<360	<360

Figure 13-8P

Collision Conditions

---------------Veh 1---------------   ---------------Veh 2------
------

XC1O'	=	-10.9Ft	XC2O'	=	0.0Ft
YC1O'	=	3.2Ft	YC2O'	=	1.9Ft
PSI1O	=	0.0Deg	PSI2O	=	90.0Deg
PSI1DO	=	0.0Deg/Sec	PSI2DO	=	0.0Deg/Se
c					
BETA1	=	0.0Deg	BETA2	=	0.0Deg

Separation conditions

XCS1'	=	-10.9 Ft	XCS2'	=	0.0 Ft
YCS1'	=	3.2 Ft	YCS2'	=	1.9 Ft
PSIS1	=	0.0 Deg	PSIS2	=	90.0 Deg
US1	=	3.4 Mph	US2	=	13.7 Mph
VS1	=	8.5 Mph	VS2	=	-15.1 Mph
PSISD1	=	95.6 Deg/Sec	PSISD2	=	47.9Deg
/Sec					

Summary Of Results

Impact speed (trajectory and conservation of linear momentum)

	Forward	Lateral
Veh 1	19.3 Mph	0.0 Mph
Veh 2	21.8 Mph	0.0 Mph

Speed change (damage)

	Total	Long	Lat	Ang
Veh 1	11.8Mph	-8.3Mph	8.3Mph	-45.0Deg
Veh 2	11.2Mph	-7.9Mph	-7.9Mph	45.0Deg

Speed change (linear momentum)

	Total	Long	Lat	Ang
Veh 1	18.1Mph	-15.9Mph	8.5Mph	-28.2Deg
Veh 2	17.2Mph	-8.1Mph	-15.1Mph	61.8Deg

Energy dissipated by damage:
Veh 1:   38479.3Ft-Lb
Veh 2:   31220.8Ft-Lb

Figure 13-8Q

Relative Velocity Data

Speed along line thru CGs (linear momentum)
   Veh 1   19.2Mph
   Veh 2   2.6Mph
Speed orthog to CG line (linear momentum)
   Veh 1   2.3Mph
   Veh 2   -21.7Mph
Closing velocity (linear momentum)
            21.7Mph

Trajectory Simulation Results

Veh 1 did not converge
Veh 2 did not converge

Nruns(1)	=	5		Nruns(2)	=	5
El(1)	=	0.088		E2(1)	=	0.076
El(2)	=	0.000		E2(2)	=	0.000
El(3)	=	0.260		E2(3)	=	-0.155
El(4)	=	0.000		E2(4)	=	0.000
El(5)	=	0.000		E2(5)	=	0.000
Qminl	=	0.348		Qmin2	=	0.231

--------------------Summary Of Damage Data--------------------
                    (*--Indicates default value was used)

	Veh 1			Veh 2	
Type-------	Category 4		Type-------	Category 4	
Weight------	4479.Lbs.		Weight------	4710.Lbs.	
CDC----------11FDEW1			CDC----------02RYEW2		
L-----------	73.0In		L-----------	84.5In	
Cl---------	2.7In		Cl---------	6.2In	
C2---------	3.6In		C2---------	8.3In	
C3---------	0.0In		C3---------	9.2In	
C4---------	0.0In		C4---------	5.9In	
C5---------	0.0In		C5---------	4.4In	
C6---------	0.0In		C6---------	0.8In	
D----------	0.0		D----------	15.0	
RHO--------	1.00	*	RHO--------	1.00	*
Ang---------	-45.0Deg		Ang---------	45.0Deg	
D'----------	1.7In		D'----------	7.8In	

Figure 13-8R

Dimensions and inertial properties

A1	=	54.7In	A2	=	54.7In
B1	=	59.2In	B2	=	59.2In
TR1	=	61.8In	TR2	=	61.8In
I1	=	43364.2Lb-Sec**2-In	I2	=	45600.7Lb-Sec**2-In
M1	=	11.592Lb-Sec**2/In	M2	=	12.189Lb-Sec**2/In
XF1	=	98.8In	XF2	=	98.8In
XR1	=	-114.0In	XR2	=	-114.0In
YS1	=	38.5In	YS2	=	38.5In

Rolling Resistance

Veh 1   Veh 2

RF----------	0.01	RF----------	0.01
LF----------	0.01	LF----------	0.01
RR----------	0.20	RR----------	0.20
LR----------	0.20	LR----------	0.20

MU---------- 0.87

%End output
Enter type of crash run (Complete, Abbreviated, Rerun, Print, Smac, or E
nd)
INPUT>SMAC

Do you want SMAC input file printed on your terminal
in addition to the disk copy? (Answer Yes or No)
INPUT>YES

Enter filename to store SMAC table: RICSAC.CR3

Figure 13-8S

```
Simulation model of automobile collisions   (using results from program CRASH)
SAMPLE RUN    RICSAC    CASE # 8    11/26/82
    0.0      4.0    0.025    0.001     0.01    0.001    30.0      5.0     2.0      1
 -130.80    38.40    0.00     0.00   339.78    0.00                               2
    0.00    22.80   89.98     0.00   383.78    0.00                               3
   54.7     59.2    61.8   43364.2   11.592    0.0     98.8   -114.0    38.5      4
   54.7     59.2    61.8   45600.7   12.189    0.0     98.8   -114.0    38.5      5
-10434.0 -10434.0 -9641.0  -9641.0                                               6
-10434.0 -10434.0 -9641.0  -9641.0                                               7
   0.125    0.185    0.01     0.00                                               8
     0.0      0.0      0.0    -5.06   -10.13   -10.13   -10.13
     0.0      0.0      0.0    -5.06   -10.13   -10.13   -10.13
     0.0      0.0      0.0   -93.57  -187.14  -187.14  -187.14
     0.0      0.0      0.0   -93.57  -187.14  -187.14  -187.14
   0.125    0.185    0.01     0.00                                               9
     0.0      0.0      0.0    -5.32   -10.65   -10.65   -10.65
     0.0      0.0      0.0    -5.32   -10.65   -10.65   -10.65
     0.0      0.0      0.0   -98.40  -196.79  -196.79  -196.79
     0.0      0.0      0.0   -98.40  -196.79  -196.79  -196.79
     0.0      0.3      0.1      1.0                                             10
     0.0      0.3      0.1      1.0                                             11
 -6000.00 6000.00  6000.00  6000.00    0.87     0.70    0.00                    12
    2.0      0.2     15.0      5.0     51.00    51.00    0.55                    13
   0.064233.5417-34.7381-5                                                      14
                                                                             9999
@
```

Figure 13-8T

velocities necessary to cause the vehicles to move from the designated impact locations to the rest locations.

The trajectory simulation process employed generally consists of an adjustment of the CRASH-computed velocities through a series of incremental steps, not to exceed five. These steps are designed to achieve a more accurate match between impact velocities and the trajectories provided to the CRASH program through designating impact, heading, rest, and direction of rotation information. Figures 13-8K through 13-8M show the results of the trajectory simulation calculations. The summary of the results of the trajectory simulation run is depicted in Figure 13-8N. Comparing these results to the tables of data shown in Figures 13-8G and 13-8H, one can see that the speed of Vehicle 1 has been adjusted upward from 16.7 miles per hour to 19.3 miles per hour and Vehicle 2 has been adjusted downward from 25.7 to 21.8 miles per hour. The data shown in Figure 13-8N is only provided in summary form. The last line of Figure 13-8N indicates that a complete printout of the output of the run incorporating the trajectory simulation was requested. The complete output is given in Figures 13-8O through 13-8S. The last response shown by the last line in Figure 13-8S calls for the SMAC table of input data to be set up. Figure 13-8T shows the table of input data necessary to run SMAC. Figure 13-9 is a session with SMAC using the input data represented by the table of data shown in Figure 13-8T. The comments previously made regarding Figures 13-6 and 13-7A, 13-7B, and 13-7C are appropriate for the data represented on Figures 13-9A through 13-9D.

E. TBS

The program TBS is interactive in nature. It deals with tractor-trailer-type vehicles and trucks, and it considers stability during braking and steering maneuvers. It does not deal with collisions. The connection between the tractor and trailer is represented as a typical fifth-wheel mechanism. Thus, the mechanism does not transmit pitch-and-roll motion as in the case of a hitch ball and coupler, such as is used in vehicles towing travel trailers. Due to the nature of the program, however, it appears to provide comparable results to simulation models and validation test runs that include the conventional hitch ball and coupler configuration for some test conditions where pitch-and-roll forces are not significant. There are 82 individual computed outputs dealing with vehicle position, heading, velocity, acceleration, articulation angle, and various load factors. These outputs are available at any selected time interval in a manner somewhat similar to the operation of SMAC. Certain limiting constraints are provided or are included in the program. The user can limit the maximum articulation angle. The program is designed to stop when any wheel load reaches zero. The program does not contain plotting capabilities. Thus, the computed results are only available in tabular form. Because of the nature of the computed results, plotted results could be accomplished without significant additions to the program.

A complete session with TBS is shown in Figures 13-10A through 13-10N (pages 341-354). The interactive format requires that the question be answered immediately after the question mark. The response to the questions set forth in Figures 13-10A through 13-10C, through question 22, defines the configuration of the equipment. In Figure 13-10C, questions 23, 24, and 25 set the speed, simulation time, and maximum articulation angle allowed for the particular run.

```
----CPU usage is 0000000007. milliseconds---
Wait...



      S M A C

Name of input file?RICSAC.CR3

"L" for line printer or "F" for output file?L

Tektronix output file? ( <CR> for none ): RICSAC.PR3

Do you wish a summary of results printed on your terminal? Y

----CPU usage is 0000015009. milliseconds---

----CPU usage is 0000030009. milliseconds---

----CPU usage is 0000045009. milliseconds---

----CPU usage is 0000060012. milliseconds---

RICSAC.PR3 SAMPLE RUN   RICSAC   CASE # 8   11/26/82
                    Vehicle 1              Vehicle 2
Initial
  CG(ft)
    X               -10.90                  0.00
    Y                 3.20                  1.90
  Heading             0.00                 89.98
  Velocity
    FWD(MPH)         19.31                 21.81
    LATERAL(MPH)      0.00                  0.00
    ANG(d/s)          0.00                  0.00
Final Position
  Time=    4.02
    X                12.93                -16.00
    Y                17.80                 41.78
  Heading            31.61                139.45
Remarks           in motion             in motion


Vehicle 1         damage indexes        Delta V(mph)
                  11FDEW2                  14.14


Vehicle 2         damage indexes        Delta V(mph)
                  02RYEW3                  12.12

STOP


END OF EXECUTION
CPU TIME: 1:7.78          ELAPSED TIME: 2:52.29
EXIT
@
```

Figure 13-9A

```
RICSAC.PR3 SAMPLE RUN   RICSAC   CASE # 8   11/26/82
                       Vehicle 1            Vehicle 2
Initial
 CG(ft)
   X                    -10.90                0.00
   Y                      3.20                1.90
 Heading                  0.00               89.98
 Velocity
   FWD(MPH)              19.31               21.81
   LATERAL(MPH)           0.00                0.00
   ANG(d/s)               0.00                0.00
Final Position
 Time=    4.02
   X                     12.93              -16.00
   Y                     17.80               41.78
 Heading                31.61              139.45
Remarks               in motion           in motion

Vehicle 1             damage indexes      Delta V(mph)
                      11FDEW2               14.14

Vehicle 2             damage indexes      Delta V(mph)
                      02RYEW3               12.12

please clear screen and depress RETURN key
```

Figure 13-9B

```
RICSAC.PR3 SAMPLE RUN   RICSAC   CASE # 8   11/26/82
Tick marks are  4.0000 ft., origin is (-25.00, -7.00)
```

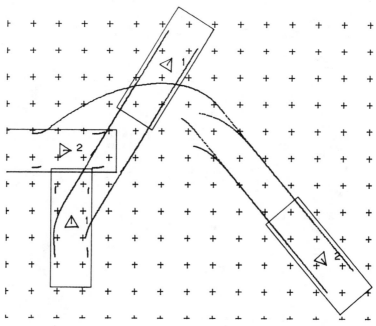

Figure 13-9C

RICSAC.PR3 SAMPLE RUN   RICSAC   CASE # 8   11/26/82
DAMAGED VEHICLE DISPLAY

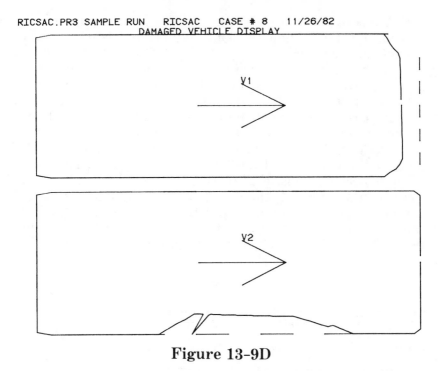

Figure 13-9D

Figures 13-10C and 13-10D deal with the matter of the tire forces. Figure 13-10D covers the data concerning brake forces for the particular experiment. At the top of Figure 13-10E the steer angle for the particular experiment is called for. After the completion of the input of the steer angle information given, Figure 13-10F provides an option to allow changes in the input parameters. This is a built-in editing feature of TBS. The editing feature is demonstrated by requesting a change to the brake force table. In Figure 13-10G a listing of the output variables is an option. The output variables are listed in Figures 13-10G, 13-10H, and 13-10I. The output of the run could be filed if desired. Of the 82 output variables, only 6 can be printed at a time. The output is arranged so that the 6 columns will fit on a sheet of 8½-inch-wide paper. The final question deals with the increment of time for the printed output. In this case a time of 0.15 seconds was requested for the 6-minute run, which was established in response to question 24 in Figure 13-10C.

  Four typical pages of output data are shown in Figures 13-10J through 13-10N. Figure 13-10J provides the X and Y coordinates of the tractor, the heading angle, the articulation angle, and the longitudinal and traverse components of the vehicle velocity. Figure 13-10K, in addition to giving the X and Y coordinates of the tractor center of gravity, provides the angular velocity of the heading angle, the angular velocity of the articulation angle, the turn radius, and the tire slip angle of the tractor. Figure 13-10L, in addition to furnishing the X and Y coordinates of the tractor center of gravity, lists the longitudinal and traverse accelerations of the tractor and the heading and articulation angle angular accelerations. Figure 13-10M provides the X and Y components of force at the fifth wheel. In Figure 13-10N the option of saving the input data was selected. The input data can be assigned a file name. This permits the input information to be recalled and changed if required so as to provide for

```
     T B S

You are about to run the University of Michigan HSRI simulation
program for a tractor-trailer in the horizontal plane.

Program explanations ("Y" for yes or "N" for no) ?Y

     Since the "explanation option" has been requested,
supplementary information is printed the first time through
the execution of the program to aid the user in understand-
ing the program.
     In responding to any question following, a yes-response
will be assumed if the first letter of the response is "Y."
Any other response will be assumed to be no.

List input parameters?
By entering "Y", the value entered for each par-
ameter is preceded by its identifying parameter number, its
abbreviation, and its verbal description.
Enter response: ?Y

Read data from file?N


*** Begin input ***

41.  Antilock code for (1) tractor front, (2) tractor
rear, and (3) trailer (0 = no antilock or 1 = independent
antilock for each of three axles)
Identical antilock systems are assumed for tandem axles.     ?0 0 0


42.  Code for (1) tandem axles tractor rear, (2) dual
tires tractor rear, (3) tandem axles trailer, and (4) dual
tires trailer (0 = no or 1 = yes in four places)     ?1 1 1 1
```

Figure 13-10A

Input parameter table

No.	Symbol	Description	Initial Value
01.	GVW1	wt. of tractor (lbs)	?14970
02.	GVW2	wt. of trailer (lbs)	?11160
03.	IZZ	tractor mom. of inertia (in-lb-sec**2)	?241636
04.	ITZZ	trailer mom. of inertia (in-lb-sec**2)	?736983
05.	AA	dist. between tractor tandem axles (in)	?54.4
06.	AAT	dist. between trailer tanden axles (in)	?49.3
07.	A1	dist. from tractor CG to front axle(in)	?63.9
08.	A2	dist. from tractor CG to rear axle (in)	?78.1
09.	A3	dist. from trailer CG to fifth whl (in)	?261.2
10.	A4	dist. from trailer CG to axle (in)	?104.8
11.	BB	dist. from tractor rear suspension to fifth whl (in). Fifth whl located aft of suspension is negative.	?0.0
12.	TRA1	half lat. dist. between centers of tire contact on trailer front axle (in)	?40.0
13.	TRA2	half lat. dist. between center of tire contact on tractor rear axle/s (in)	?36.0
14.	TRA3	half lat. dist. between centers of tire contact on trailer axle/s (in)	?36.0
15.	Z0	height of fifth whl above ground (in)	?48.0
16.	Z1	height of tractor CG above ground (in)	?39.9
17.	Z2	height of trail CG above ground (in)	?55.5
18.	MU5	fifth wheel friction coefficient	? .05

Figure 13-10B

19.	RAD5	equivalent radius of fifth wheel (in)	?19.0
20.	GAM1	portion of total lat. load transfer on front axel of tractor	?0.16
21.	GAM3	tractor tandem axle load x-fer coef.	?-.38
22.	GAM4	trailer tandem axle load x-fer coef.	?-.38
23.	VEL	initial velocity: U-direction (mi/hr) (ft/s)	?26.8
24.	TIMF	max. simulation time for this run (sec)	?6.0
25.	IQUIT	max. articulation angle allowed (deg)	?30.0

39.31

Tire Parameters and I.D. Numbers:
Numbers in parentheses associated with tire properties CALF, MUP, MUS, and SP refer to a particular tire.
The tires are numbered as follows:
1 and 2: Tractor left front and right front, respectively.
3 and 4: Tractor left rear and right rear, respectively.
If the tractor has tandem axles, 3 and 4 are the left and
right tire, respectively, on the leading tandem.
5 and 6: Tractor left trailing tandem and right trailing
tandem, respectively. 5 and 6 are ignored if single axle
on tractor rear.
7 and 8: Trailer left and right, respectively. If the
trailer has tandem axles, 7 and 8 are the left and right
tires, respectively, on the leading tandem.
9 and 10: Trailer left trailing tandem and right trailing
tandem, respectively. 9 and 10 are ignored if single axle
on trailer.

Values are entered per tire, even if duals are indicated.
Tires 1 and 2 are assumed equivalent; tires 3, 4, 5, and
6 are assumed equivalent; and tires 7, 8, 9, and 10 are
assumed equivalent. If single MU-slip curve is opted,
tires 1 to 10 have the same MU-slip curve. In this
case values for tire 1, only, are entered.

	CALF	cornering stiffness of tires (lbs/deg)	
29.		CALF(1)	?467
30.		CALF(3)	?208
31.		CALF(7)	?200

Figure 13-10C

Do all tires have the same mu-slip curve?N

	MUP	peak tire-road friction coefficient	
32.			MUP(1) ?.942
33.			MUP(3) ?.939
34.			MUP(7) ?.960
35.	MUS	sliding tire-road friction coef.	MUS(1) ?.895
36.			MUS(3) ?.895
37.			MUS(7) ?.895
38.	SP	slip corresponding to peak MU	SP(1) ?.11
39.			SP(3) ?.11
40.			SP(7) ?.11

Brake Force Table:
At least one line must be entered. The initial time
must be at time T=0. Brakes are numbered in the same
manner as are tires. Brakes 3 and 5 are equivalent as are
4 and 6 (though brakes 5 and 6 are ignored if the tractor
has a single rear axle). Therefore, tabular data is
not entered for brakes 5 and 6. The same is true for the
trailer brakes. Tabular data is entered for brakes 7 and
8 only. Brakes 9 and 10 are assumed identical to brakes
7 and 8, respectively, or ignored if the trailer has a
single axle. Line 1 for a step brake input without side
to side imbalance may be: 0.,0.,0.,1000.,1000.,1500.,1500.

Brake Force Table
Number of lines: 7

Time (sec)	FSX(1)	FSX(2)	Desired forces: FSX(3)	FSX(4)	FSX(7)	FSX(8)

```
0.,0.,0.,0.,0.,0.,0.
2.19,0.,0.,0.,0.,0.,0.
2.125,77.4,77.4,0.,0.,0.,0.
2.315,387.,387.,420.,420.,0.,0.
2.41,682.,682.,713.,713.,812.,812.
2.41,682.,713.,713.,812.,812.,812.
2.443,682,682,713.,713.,1094.,1094.
```

Figure 13-10D

Echo table?Y

Time (sec)	FSX(1)	FSX(2)	Desired forces: FSX(3)	FSX(4)	FSX(7)	FSX(8)
0.0000	0.00	0.00	0.00	0.00	0.00	0.00
2.1900	0.00	0.00	0.00	0.00	0.00	0.00
2.1250	77.40	77.40	0.00	0.00	0.00	0.00
2.3150	387.00	387.00	420.00	420.00	0.00	0.00
2.4100	682.00	682.00	713.00	713.00	812.00	812.00
2.4100	682.00	713.00	713.00	812.00	812.00	812.00
2.4430	682.00	682.00	713.00	713.00	1094.00	1094.00

Steer Table:
At least one line must be entered, and the first line
must be at time T=0. Each line contains the time followed
by the average steer angle (in degrees) of the tractor
front wheels.

Steer Table
Number of lines: 2

Time (sec)	Steer Angle (deg)

0.,0
1.0,4.62

Echo table?Y

Time (sec)	Steer Angle (deg)
0.0000	0.00
1.0000	4.62

Change parameters?N

Change tire friction coefficients?

Since the "explanation option" has been requested,
supplementary information is printed the first time through
the execution of the program to aid the user in understanding the program.
In responding to any question following, a yes-response
will be assumed if the first letter of the response is "Y."
Any other response will be assumed to be no.

N

Figure 13-10E

Change brake force table?Y

Add new lines?N

How many lines are to be changed?2

Line number(s) to be changed?5 6

Enter corrections:
2.385,604.,604.,713.,713.,598.,598.
2.41,682.,692.,713.,713.,812.,812.

Time (sec)	FSX(1)	FSX(2)	Desired forces: FSX(3)	FSX(4)	FSX(7)	FSX(8)
0.0000	0.00	0.00	0.00	0.00	0.00	0.00
2.1900	0.00	0.00	0.00	0.00	0.00	0.00
2.1250	77.40	77.40	0.00	0.00	0.00	0.00
2.3150	387.00	387.00	420.00	420.00	0.00	0.00
2.4100	682.00	682.00	713.00	713.00	812.00	812.00
2.4100	682.00	713.00	713.00	812.00	812.00	812.00
2.4430	682.00	682.00	713.00	713.00	1094.00	1094.00

Is table correct now?Y

Change steer table?N

Echo static loads?N

Initial articulation angle?0

Will articulation angle be varied?
A "Y" response will allow you to enter an initial
artic. angle when you change parameters. Otherwise, the
initial artic. angle will be assumed to be 0.0
Enter response: ?Y

Any data changes now?YY\N

*** End of input. ***

Would you like to enter new slip roll-off table?N

Figure 13-10F

Do you want a list of output variables?Y

*** Position Variables ***

1	X0—COORD
2	Y0—COORD
3	PSI
4	GAMMA

*** Velocity Variables ***

5	U—VEL
6	V—VEL
7	PSIDOT
8	GAMMADOT

***

9	TURN RAD
10	SIDESLIP

*** Tire Slip Angles ***

11	ALFA 1+2
12	ALFA 3+4
13	ALFA 5+6
14	ALFA 7+8
15	ALFA9+10

*** Acceleration Variables ***

16	U—DOT
17	V—DOT
18	PSI—DDOT
19	GAM—DDOT
20	LONG ACC
21	LAT. ACC

Figure 13-10G

```
*** Tire—Road Interface Forces ***
*** Brake Forces: FX(I), Side Forces: FY(I) ***

22              FX(1)
23              FX(2)
24              FX(3)
25              FX(4)
26              FX(5)
27              FX(6)
28              FX(7)
29              FX(8)
30              FX(9)
31              FX(10)
32              FY(1)
33              FY(2)
34              FY(3)
35              FY(4)
36              FY(5)
37              FY(6)
38              FY(7)
39              FY(8)
40              FY(9)
41              FY(10)

*** Load Transfers, Long. DFX(I), Lat. DFY(I) ***

42              DFX(1)
43              DFX(2)
44              DFX(3)
45              DFX(4)
46              DFX(5)
47              DFX(6)
48              DFX(7)
49              DFX(8)
50              DFX(9)
51              DFX(10)
52              DFY(1)
53              DFY(2)
54              DFY(3)
55              DFY(4)
56              DFY(5)
57              DFY(6)
58              DFY(7)
59              DFY(8)
60              DFY(9)
61              DFY(10)
```

Figure 13-10H

*** Instantaneous Load Forces ***

62	FZ(1)
63	FZ(2)
64	FZ(3)
65	FZ(4)
66	FZ(5)
67	FZ(6)
68	FZ(7)
69	FZ(8)
70	FZ(9)
71	FZ(10)

*** Programmed Brake Forces ***

72	FSX(1)
73	FSX(2)
74	FSX(3)
75	FSX(4)
76	FSX(5)
77	FSX(6)
78	FSX(7)
79	FSX(8)
80	FSX(9)
81	FSX(10)

*** Hitch Forces ***

82	XH
83	YH

Write output on file?N

Total number of output variables (1 to 6)?6

Number(s) of variables you want (1 to 83)?1 2 3 4 5 6

Time increment to be printed out?.15

Figure 13-10I

TIME	XO-COORD	YO-COORD	PSI	GAMMA	U-VEL	V-VEL
0.00	0.00	0.00	0.00	0.00	39.31	0.00
0.16	6.29	0.01	0.04	-0.04	39.31	0.07
0.30	11.79	0.03	0.21	-0.20	39.30	0.16
0.46	18.08	0.11	0.64	-0.57	39.30	0.24
0.60	23.58	0.23	1.24	-1.07	39.29	0.31
0.76	29.86	0.47	2.19	-1.81	39.28	0.37
0.90	35.35	0.79	3.26	-2.58	39.26	0.41
1.06	41.61	1.29	4.76	-3.58	39.24	0.43
1.20	47.07	1.88	6.25	-4.49	39.22	0.39
1.36	53.29	2.71	8.05	-5.44	39.19	0.33
1.52	59.47	3.74	9.90	-6.26	39.17	0.29
1.66	64.85	4.80	11.54	-6.85	39.15	0.27
1.82	70.95	6.19	13.41	-7.41	39.12	0.25
1.96	76.25	7.57	15.06	-7.81	39.09	0.24
2.12	82.25	9.33	16.93	-8.17	39.06	0.24
2.26	87.44	11.03	18.58	-8.43	38.90	0.22
2.40	92.54	12.85	20.23	-8.65	38.23	0.18
2.55	97.77	14.90	21.95	-8.74	36.71	0.20
2.70	102.73	17.02	23.59	-8.68	35.16	0.29
2.86	107.71	19.34	25.29	-8.55	33.53	0.38
3.00	111.81	21.41	26.71	-8.43	32.10	0.45
3.16	116.22	23.79	28.29	-8.30	30.48	0.52
3.30	119.83	25.87	29.61	-8.22	29.06	0.57
3.46	123.68	28.24	31.06	-8.16	27.44	0.61
3.60	126.82	30.28	32.28	-8.15	26.03	0.64
3.76	130.15	32.56	33.59	-8.17	24.40	0.66
3.90	132.84	34.49	34.69	-8.21	22.98	0.67
4.06	135.68	36.63	35.87	-8.28	21.35	0.67
4.20	137.95	38.42	36.83	-8.35	19.92	0.66
4.36	140.31	40.35	37.86	-8.44	18.28	0.64
4.50	142.19	41.95	38.70	-8.52	16.84	0.62
4.66	144.12	43.64	39.57	-8.61	15.19	0.58
4.82	145.82	45.18	40.36	-8.70	13.55	0.54
4.96	147.13	46.41	40.98	-8.77	12.11	0.50
5.12	148.44	47.66	41.61	-8.85	10.47	0.44
5.26	149.42	48.61	42.08	-8.91	9.03	0.39
5.42	150.35	49.54	42.54	-8.98	7.39	0.33
5.56	151.01	50.20	42.87	-9.03	5.96	0.27
5.72	151.59	50.79	43.16	-9.08	4.32	0.20
5.86	151.94	51.16	43.33	-9.11	2.89	0.15
6.02	152.16	51.40	43.45	-9.13	1.25	0.10

Do you want more output?Y

Total number of output variables (1 to 6)?6

Number(s) of variables you want (1 to 83)?1 2 7 8 9 10

Figure 13-10J

TIME	XO-COORD	YO-COORD	PSIDOT	GAMMADOT	TURN RAD	SIDESLIP
0.00	0.00	0.00	0.00	0.00	0.00	0.00
0.16	6.29	0.01	0.66	-0.62	1435.96	0.10
0.30	11.79	0.03	1.86	-1.69	818.33	0.23
0.46	18.08	0.11	3.52	-3.02	530.94	0.36
0.60	23.58	0.23	5.07	-4.09	397.91	0.45
0.76	29.86	0.47	6.87	-5.13	306.44	0.53
0.90	35.35	0.79	8.45	-5.88	254.42	0.59
1.06	41.61	1.29	10.18	-6.50	224.68	0.63
1.20	47.07	1.88	11.02	-6.30	214.68	0.58
1.36	53.29	2.71	11.46	-5.56	204.62	0.49
1.52	59.47	3.74	11.64	-4.65	198.28	0.43
1.66	64.85	4.80	11.70	-3.88	194.99	0.39
1.82	70.95	6.19	11.73	-3.11	192.80	0.37
1.96	76.25	7.57	11.74	-2.54	191.68	0.35
2.12	82.25	9.33	11.75	-2.01	190.91	0.35
2.26	87.44	11.03	11.77	-1.73	196.85	0.32
2.40	92.54	12.85	11.68	-1.21	181.76	0.27
2.55	97.77	14.90	11.22	-0.06	173.84	0.32
2.70	102.73	17.02	10.78	0.65	170.23	0.47
2.86	107.71	19.34	10.38	0.91	167.05	0.64
3.00	111.81	21.41	10.03	0.88	165.13	0.80
3.16	116.22	23.79	9.64	0.69	163.29	0.97
3.30	119.83	25.87	9.28	0.47	161.85	1.12
3.46	123.68	28.24	8.85	0.20	160.33	1.28
3.60	126.82	30.28	8.47	-0.02	159.06	1.41
3.76	130.15	32.56	8.01	-0.22	157.58	1.55
3.90	132.84	34.49	7.61	-0.36	156.30	1.66
4.06	135.68	36.63	7.12	-0.47	154.90	1.79
4.20	137.95	38.42	6.69	-0.53	153.77	1.90
4.36	140.31	40.35	6.19	-0.57	152.56	2.01
4.50	142.19	41.95	5.73	-0.58	151.57	2.10
4.66	144.12	43.64	5.20	-0.57	150.49	2.20
4.82	145.82	45.18	4.67	-0.53	152.20	2.29
4.96	147.13	46.41	4.19	-0.50	152.59	2.36
5.12	148.44	47.66	3.63	-0.48	148.56	2.43
5.26	149.42	48.61	3.14	-0.44	147.56	2.48
5.42	150.35	49.54	2.58	-0.39	147.20	2.54
5.56	151.01	50.20	2.08	-0.33	146.86	2.58
5.72	151.59	50.79	1.51	-0.25	99.04	2.64
5.86	151.94	51.16	1.01	-0.18	34.30	2.94
6.02	152.16	51.40	0.45	-0.11	2.97	4.53

Do you want more output?Y

Total number of output variables (1 to 6)?6

Number(s) of variables you want (1 to 83)?1 2 16 17 18 19

Figure 13-10K

TIME	XO-COORD	YO-COORD	U-DOT	V-DOT	PSI-DDOT	GAM-DDOT
0.00	0.00	0.00	0.00	0.00	0.00	0.00
0.16	6.29	0.01	-0.01	0.62	7.14	-6.65
0.30	11.79	0.03	-0.02	0.61	9.62	-8.20
0.46	18.08	0.11	-0.04	0.50	10.87	-8.09
0.60	23.58	0.23	-0.07	0.41	11.21	-7.13
0.76	29.86	0.47	-0.10	0.33	11.30	-5.87
0.90	35.35	0.79	-0.14	0.27	11.32	-4.89
1.06	41.61	1.29	-0.15	-0.12	8.46	-1.20
1.20	47.07	1.88	-0.14	-0.38	4.08	3.44
1.36	53.29	2.71	-0.15	-0.33	1.70	5.46
1.52	59.47	3.74	-0.16	-0.22	0.69	5.67
1.66	64.85	4.80	-0.17	-0.14	0.31	5.20
1.82	70.95	6.19	-0.19	-0.07	0.12	4.43
1.96	76.25	7.57	-0.20	-0.04	0.04	3.73
2.12	82.25	9.33	-0.22	-0.02	0.00	3.00
2.26	87.44	11.03	-2.46	-0.32	0.55	0.55
2.40	92.54	12.85	-8.75	0.21	-5.13	10.56
2.55	97.77	14.90	-10.32	0.50	-3.42	6.88
2.70	102.73	17.02	-10.26	0.57	-2.64	2.93
2.86	107.71	19.34	-10.20	0.54	-2.45	0.48
3.00	111.81	21.41	-10.16	0.48	-2.45	-0.76
3.16	116.22	23.79	-10.13	0.39	-2.53	-1.46
3.30	119.83	25.87	-10.12	0.32	-2.62	-1.66
3.46	123.68	28.24	-10.12	0.23	-2.72	-1.60
3.60	126.82	30.28	-10.14	0.16	-2.80	-1.41
3.76	130.15	32.56	-10.16	0.09	-2.89	-1.10
3.90	132.84	34.49	-10.18	0.03	-2.97	-0.83
4.06	135.68	36.63	-10.21	-0.03	-3.06	-0.54
4.20	137.95	38.42	-10.23	-0.08	-3.13	-0.32
4.36	140.31	40.35	-10.26	-0.14	-3.21	-0.13
4.50	142.19	41.95	-10.28	-0.19	-3.27	0.01
4.66	144.12	43.64	-10.31	-0.24	-3.35	0.14
4.82	145.82	45.18	-10.33	-0.31	-3.21	-0.05
4.96	147.13	46.41	-10.22	-0.34	-3.25	-0.15
5.12	148.44	47.66	-10.25	-0.36	-3.47	0.17
5.26	149.42	48.61	-10.25	-0.39	-3.52	0.30
5.42	150.35	49.54	-10.25	-0.41	-3.54	0.40
5.56	151.01	50.20	-10.25	-0.44	-3.56	0.48
5.72	151.59	50.79	-10.25	-0.40	-3.56	0.50
5.86	151.94	51.16	-10.25	-0.33	-3.54	0.47
6.02	152.16	51.40	-10.25	-0.29	-3.53	0.44

Do you want more output?Y

Total number of output variables (1 to 6)?6

Number(s) of variables you want (1 to 83)?1 2 20 21 82 83

Figure 13-10L

TIME	X0-COORD	Y0-COORD	LONG ACC	LAT. ACC	XH	YH
0.00	0.00	0.00	0.00	0.00	0.00	0.00
0.16	6.29	0.01	-0.01	1.08	2.63	-23.17
0.30	11.79	0.03	-0.03	1.89	7.45	-70.75
0.46	18.08	0.11	-0.06	2.91	15.38	-156.40
0.60	23.58	0.23	-0.09	3.88	25.21	-248.57
0.76	29.86	0.47	-0.14	5.03	40.42	-363.51
0.90	35.35	0.79	-0.20	6.06	57.20	-468.05
1.06	41.61	1.29	-0.23	6.85	68.95	-584.47
1.20	47.07	1.88	-0.22	7.16	70.86	-670.85
1.36	53.29	2.71	-0.21	7.51	74.70	-740.26
1.52	59.47	3.74	-0.22	7.74	75.12	-782.86
1.66	64.85	4.80	-0.23	7.86	72.47	-805.48
1.82	70.95	6.19	-0.24	7.94	67.23	-821.07
1.96	76.25	7.57	-0.25	7.97	61.78	-829.24
2.12	82.25	9.33	-0.27	7.99	55.48	-834.86
2.26	87.44	11.03	-2.50	7.68	799.94	-878.88
2.40	92.54	12.85	-8.78	8.00	117.78	-612.99
2.55	97.77	14.90	-10.36	7.69	-433.15	-637.13
2.70	102.73	17.02	-10.31	7.19	-421.02	-601.74
2.86	107.71	19.34	-10.27	6.62	-410.89	-556.57
3.00	111.81	21.41	-10.24	6.10	-408.08	-511.71
3.16	116.22	23.79	-10.22	5.52	-411.37	-456.51
3.30	119.83	25.87	-10.21	5.02	-419.30	-406.06
3.46	123.68	28.24	-10.22	4.47	-432.94	-347.25
3.60	126.82	30.28	-10.23	4.01	-447.72	-295.78
3.76	130.15	32.56	-10.25	3.51	-466.47	-238.25
3.90	132.84	34.49	-10.27	3.08	-483.64	-189.36
4.06	135.68	36.63	-10.29	2.62	-503.32	-135.54
4.20	137.95	38.42	-10.31	2.24	-520.06	-90.58
4.36	140.31	40.35	-10.33	1.83	-538.23	-42.09
4.50	142.19	41.95	-10.35	1.50	-553.12	-2.19
4.66	144.12	43.64	-10.36	1.14	-568.93	40.06
4.82	145.82	45.18	-10.38	0.79	-582.86	67.78
4.96	147.13	46.41	-10.25	0.54	-529.27	99.96
5.12	148.44	47.66	-10.28	0.30	-545.76	143.35
5.26	149.42	48.61	-10.27	0.11	-546.32	170.21
5.42	150.35	49.54	-10.26	-0.08	-547.20	196.74
5.56	151.01	50.20	-10.26	-0.22	-547.94	215.79
5.72	151.59	50.79	-10.25	-0.28	-547.13	225.14
5.86	151.94	51.16	-10.25	-0.28	-545.54	225.52
6.02	152.16	51.40	-10.25	-0.28	-544.53	225.83

Figure 13-10M

```
Do you want more output?N

Stop this problem?
If you answer "Y" to this question, you will be given
the opportunity to store the present input data on a new
version of the old input file (if one exists) or on a new
file; also you may enter a new data set or else terminate the
program.  Any other response will allow you to change any of
the input data without entering a whole new data set.
Enter response: ?Y

Store present input data on a file?Y

Name of new input data file?UMHSRI.TBS


"N" for new TBS problem or "Q" to quit?Q



***   See you next trip.   ***
***   Keep on trucking!!   ***


TBS QUITS AND RETURNS TO EXEC

END OF EXECUTION
CPU TIME: 28.64 ELAPSED TIME: 51:54.77
EXIT
```

Figure 13–10N

runs under different conditions. After this the program is
stopped. The CPU time for the run is listed as 28.64 seconds.
This is considered to be a very nominal expenditure of computer time.

VI. CONCLUSIONS

The use of computer-assist techniques in the reconstruction of
automobile accidents or the evaluation of vehicle stability
under various steer and brake conditions is widely available
to persons interested in the reconstruction of vehicle accidents.
Readily available analytical procedures can be employed that
will significantly improve the accuracy of simpler methods of
reconstruction. With the advent of the interactive computer
programs specifically designed for the accident reconstructionist, and the availability of these services, it is cost effective
to employ these techniques on most accidents that are the
subject of an accident reconstruction effort. These analytical

methods can be useful to the recipient of an accident reconstruction analysis, whether it involves litigation issues, design
safety considerations, automotive engineering research, or
product improvement decisions. The required input parameters necessary for the interactive computer programs are in
fact only a logical and "common-sense" listing of the important features that should be considered in order to reconstruct
properly and accurately an accident. Computer-assist techniques involve the blending of modern technology and scientific knowledge to yield more accurate, valid, and useful
engineering information.

CITATIONS

[1]L. Segel, "Theoretical Prediction and Experimental Substantiation
of the Response of the Automobile to Steering Control." *Proceedings
of the Automobile Division of the Institution of Mechanical Engineers*,
1956–1957, No. 7.
[2]D. M. Severy, J. H. Mathewson, and A. W. Siegel, "Automobile
Side-Impact Collisions Series II." *National Automobile Week*,
No. 491A, March 12–16, 1962.
[3]R. I. Emery, "An Analytical Approach to Automobile Collisions."
SAE paper 680016. Warrendale, PA.: Society of Automotive Engineers, 1968.
[4]R. R. McHenry, D. J. Segal, and N. J. Deleys, "Computer Simulation of Single Vehicle Accidents." SAE paper 670904. Warrendale,
PA.: Society of Automotive Engineers, 1967.
[5]"Graphic Testimony in Automobile Accident Cases." *Scientific
American*, 127(4):255 (1922).
[6]J. Younger, "Retarding of the Automobile." *Transactions of the
Society of Automotive Engineers*, Part 1, Vol. XII, 1917.
[7]CAAAM, P.O. Box 40489, Pasadena, CA. 91104.
[8]MCAUTO, 2990 Telstar Court, Falls Church, VA. 22042.
[9]MCAUTO, Department K242/Building 303, St. Louis, MO. 63166.
[10]GTE Telenet Communications Corporation, 8229 Boone Boulevard,
Vienna, VA. 22180.
[11]R. R. McHenry, *User's Manual for the CRASH Computer Program*.
Performing orgranization—Calspan Corporation, Sponsoring Agency
—NHTSA. Calspan Report No. ZQ-5708-V-3.
[12]R. R. McHenry and J. P. Lynch, *CRASH2 User's Manual*. Performing organization—Calspan Corporation; Sponsoring Agency—
NHTSA. Calspan Report No. ZQ-5708-V-4.
[13]R. R. McHenry, *CRASH3 User's Guide and Technical Manual*.
Performing organization—Calspan Corporation; Sponsoring Agency
—NHTSA.

[14]I. S. Jones, "Results of Selected Applications to Actual Highway Accidents of SMAC Reconstruction Program." SAE paper 741179. Warrendale, PA.: Society of Automotive Engineers, 1974.

[15]A. L. Burgett and M. W. Monk, "Car-to-Car Side Impacts: Computerized CRASH Reconstruction." SAE paper 751154. Warrendale, PA.: Society of Automotive Engineers, 1975.

[16]C. Y. Warner and T. R. Perl, "The Accuracy and Usefulness of SMAC." SAE paper 780902. Warrendale, PA.: Society of Automotive Engineers, 1976.

[17]R. A. Smith and J. T. Noga, "Accuracy and Sensitivity of CRASH." SAE paper 821169. Warrendale, PA.: Society of Automotive Engineers, 1982.

[18]H. T. Moncarz, J. E. Bernard, and P. S. Fancher, *Simplified, Interactive Simulation for Predicting Braking and Steering Response of Commercial Vehicles.* Performing organization—Highway Safety Research Institute, University of Michigan; Sponsoring Agency—Motor Vehicle Manufacturers Association, HSRI. Report No. UM-HSRI-PF-75-8.

IV
HUMAN FACTORS AND BIODYNAMICS

The perceptive lawyer knows that there are significant human factors issues in every personal injury lawsuit. Similarly, in the design and manufacture of most automobile products lurk important human factors issues. Illustrative human factors issues include questions regarding the driver's visual perception and behavioral reaction, the adequacy of warnings and instructions, the appropriate range of human body sizes and reach distances, foreseeable human errors and possible goof-proofing, the effects of fatigue and drugs, human expectations and customary practices, training and sophisticated user behavior, and the effectiveness of human engineering design criteria. Who provides the answers? What is the basis or foundation for the opinions, beliefs, and decisions relating to human factors questions?

Ask a "simple" human factors question and nearly everyone may offer his or her opinion, including almost every engineer and expert witness. It seems only human for humans to be born as "experts" on human behavior. Yet, the scientific discipline of human factors originated because incorrect answers were being vigorously tendered by so-called armchair experts using good common sense, gut reactions, and off-the-top-of-the-head reflections on their own human experiences and behavioral knowledge. For the past 40 years, human factors specialists have conducted and published scientific or experimental research relating to design engineering problems. Many engineers and psychologists receive graduate-level professional training that includes or deals exclusively with what has been called applied experimental psychology, ergonomics, or human factors engineering. There are many professional-level journals, books, and conferences on human factors throughout the world. There are doctorates, board certifications, and other indicia of exposure to the accumulated knowledge, criteria, principles, and techniques of the human factors specialist. Thus, in terms of competency and qualification to answer questions relating to human factors issues, some "experts" may have greater credibility than others. This is no different than the varied opinions that may be heard, from almost anyone, on medical or legal questions. Ultimately, we must distinguish between everyone's right to express an opinion, however right or wrong, in an informal conversational setting and the need to recognize when a professional opinion is required and whether it can be relied upon in matters involving human safety.

Section 14, The Driving Task, illustrates how a behavioral scientist conceptualizes the task performance of an automobile driver, the driver's attributes and limitations, what is required to facilitate human performance, and the kind of research that has been performed and should be performed. Section 15, Visibility Problems in Nighttime Driving, suggests the specificity and precision of the human factors considerations and data necessary for an informed, reliable, and valid professional opinion. Similarly, Motorcycle Conspicuity, Section 17, illustrates the nature and depth of analyses that are being performed by human factors specialists on critical issues relating to human safety. Issues that involve the interface between automotive vehicles and humans in an appropriate environmental setting or tripartite interdependent relationship.

Section 16 on Driver Steering Performance describes the complex human psychomotor performance required to guide automotive vehicles in a diverse mix of vehicles, roadways, environmental conditions, drivers, signals, and objects under high-speed and often dangerous conditions. The opinions are those formulated as a result of cumulative research experience, not as unfounded personal speculation. The emphasis is quantitative, with attempts to define predictive models of human behavior. The concluding section, Biodynamics of Vehicular Injuries (Section 18), contains important tutorial and explanatory information, plus valuable quantitative data that should be of great value to those involved in automotive engineering, research, and litigation.

14

The Driving Task

SLADE HULBERT, Ph.D.
Human Factors Consultant
San Ramon, California

Since 1948 Dr. Slade Hulbert has conducted studies of vehicle operators. Up until 1975 he worked at U.C.L.A. as a Research Psychologist faculty member in the College of Engineering at the Institute of Transportation and Traffic Engineering. Since 1970 he also has been a consultant to various research firms and in 1975 became an employee of TRACOR-MBA as the human factors staff scientist. As a founding member and fellow of the Human Factors Society and member of the Transportation Research Board of the National Academy of Science and Engineering, he has contributed to the increasing use of human behavior as a basis for operator, vehicle, roadway, and traffic control device standards, as well as railroad, maritime, and bicycle operation criteria. He is a licensed psychologist in California and a member of the Institute of Transportation Engineers and the American Psychological Association. The author can be reached at 565 St. George Road, San Ramon, California, 94583 (415-837-6316).

I. INTRODUCTION

The purpose of this section is to acquaint readers with the role of human factors expertise in litigation resulting from street and highway accidents. The basic question is whether, under the circumstances, the behavior of the humans falls within an expectable range based upon what behavioral scientists know or can determine. This centers on an understanding of the human behavior associated with the driving task.

Human factors scientists and practitioners focus their professional activities on the ways humans are capable of interacting with both natural and man-made environments. Transportation environments include, but are not limited to, streets and highways where pedestrians and vehicular traffic occurs. The humans involved in such traffic are referred to as "roadway users" by the Transportation Research Board of the U.S. National Academy of Science and Engineering.

Human factors experts have four types of sources of information about the expectable range of the performance capabilities of the roadway user:

1. Reported studies of persons in the actual act of using a roadway.
2. Reported studies of persons as they reacted to research situations representing a roadway.
3. Reported studies of human behavior in nonroadway environments.
4. Special, nonreported studies conducted for particular lawsuits.

It can be expected that there will be a tendency for jury panel members and judges to place a high degree of confidence in results of actual roadway-use studies, providing the accident circumstances are similar. Thus, the role of the expert is not only to relate the study (studies) results, but *also* to describe their degree of similarity to the accident circumstances.

Results from the study of situations that only "represent" a roadway environment are likely to encounter some resistance by the courts, depending on whether it was or was not possible to conduct the study on an actual roadway. If not, the credibility will likely rest on how "realistic" the artificial roadway environment was.

Studies done in totally "unrealistic" laboratory-type situations are, of course, subject to a great deal of resistance as to the relevance of the results. The courtroom experts bear the burden of convincing the court that there is relevance. This can be done if, for example, there is no other source of information or if the expert is expressing an opinion about an ultimate limit of human capability under any circumstance.

Special studies conducted expressly for a lawsuit will likely have a high degree of relevance; however, they can expect to face some resistance by the court or by the "other side" on the following bases:

1. Is some bias possible?
2. Were the accident circumstances reproduced accurately and adequately?
3. Were adequate measurements made of human performance?
4. What account was taken of such factors as surprise and familiarity with the road scene?

Consequently, the role of the expert is to anticipate such questions and expend effort to provide answers.

II. THE DRIVING TASK

Drivers, as a whole, perform their task very well, considering the difficult nature of the task. Drivers must constantly process a stream of information coming from the environment, primarily through their visual faculties. Since any vehicle (or object) in motion is committed to occupy a certain amount of space directly in its path within the next instant, the driver must make a continuous series of such spatial commitments.

Hulbert and Burg[1] describe the shape of this spatial commitment for automobile drivers as fan-shaped, extending in front of the vehicle, as shown in Figure 14-1. The exact configuration, of course, varies from vehicle to vehicle and is affected by road surface and highway design features. Generally speaking, however, the fan-shaped area grows in size with increased speed and/or reduction in pavement friction. As drivers proceed, they make an unalterable commitment to be somewhere in this fan-shaped zone immediately ahead of their vehicle. The portion of this zone that they actually use is their path.

Both compensatory tracking and predictive tracking are used as the driver follows the roadway. At the time the driver is choosing the immediate path (to which he or she becomes

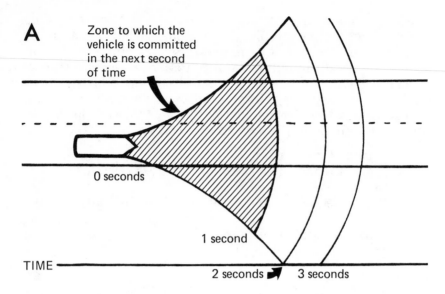

A

Zone to which the
vehicle is committed
in the next second
of time

0 seconds

1 second

TIME

2 seconds   3 seconds

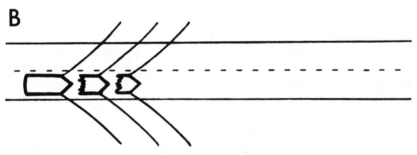

B

Figure 14-1 (A) The exact configuration of the fan-shaped
zone of commitment will depend upon the vehicle speed, turning radius, and stopping distance as they interact with the
driver's reaction time (the zone is not drawn to scale). (B) As
each driver proceeds, the fan-shaped zone extends in front of
the car's path and changes shape as velocity and pavement
conditions vary.

totally committed), he or she is making provisional commitments extending out beyond the immediate zone. There are
various bases upon which these provisional commitments are
made. Some information processing underlies this series of
successive spatial commitments, which are continually being
made and remade as the driver proceeds along the highway.

III. SINGLE-CHANNEL INFORMATION PROCESSING BY DRIVERS

Humans are essentially a single-channel information-processing system, although they may appear otherwise. The ability to shift attention rapidly from one task to another enables us to carry on more than one task simultaneously. The driving task has two major simultaneous elements: namely, tracking and object avoidance. If our single, central processing channel is occupied with one type of information, it cannot process additional information. Time spent reading a highway sign or avoiding a pedestrian is time taken away from the tracking task, and vice versa. For this reason, designers of roadways and vehicles have striven to make the tracking task easier, and traffic control devices have been designed over many years of trial and error to be relatively unambiguous information generators, demanding a minimum of the driver's attention. Nevertheless, a continuous flow of information must be accurately processed by the driver.

Driving a vehicle (except while learning) is an overlearned task that is an extension of our ability to walk and run, in that we learn to anticipate where we will be in the next instant of time and accordingly regulate or control our speed and path so as to move ahead safely. The faster we are moving, the farther ahead our "committed zone" extends and the more likely we are to need traffic control devices to warn us before we can see hazards. As we learn to operate vehicles and to walk and run, we adopt certain general tendencies to look ahead of us about 2 to 2½ seconds of time in order to ascertain if the path is clear. This time of approximately 2½ seconds is recognized by the American Association of State Highway Transportation Officials in their manual.[2] This time estimate also is consistent with measured times of 1.6 to 2.6 seconds for drivers at a crossroad to search visually to see if they can cross safely, 0.8 to 1.6 seconds for drivers to check rearview mirrors, and 0.8 to 1.0 seconds to "look back" to ascertain if it is safe to change lanes.[3] These general values of the time needed to perceive traffic situations must be supplemented with or replaced by more specific and/or precise times associated with the circumstances of any particular accident. Here is where the expert in human factors enters, for the expert has an ability to take into account the detailed nature of the stimuli, the past experience of the human, and the time–space considerations provided by the physical evidence.

Pertinent details of the available stimuli include auditory

as well as visual stimuli and sometimes include vibration cues, bumps, etc. It is essential for the expert to include whatever was there to which reactions could have occurred in his or her study of the human factors aspects of the accident circumstances. There have been landmark research data of this sort compiled. For example, the study entitled "The Visibility and Audibility of Trains Approaching Rail–Highway Grade Crossings"[4] indicates that despite their large size, headlights, and horns or whistles, railroad trains are not very visible and are practically inaudible from inside a moving automobile. Another study[5] revealed that most drivers on the open highway at night overdrive their headlights, or in other words, *are willing to drive at nighttime speeds such that their headlight beams illuminate the roadway less than 2 or 2½ seconds of time ahead.* Traffic engineering data clearly reveal that many *drivers will travel on urban freeways with only 1 second of "headway" at speeds of 60–65 mph.* This was before the 55 mph maximum speed law went into effect in 1973. (The headway of a car refers to the distance from the front bumper of that car to the rear bumper of the car ahead.) Drivers, however, typically only do this *when they can see through the windows of the car ahead.* This way they effectively preview the usual 2 to 2½ seconds ahead of their vehicle.

IV. WHAT IS SAFE?

Research results indicate that drivers will, and often do, drive somewhat faster and follow closer than they would if safety were uppermost in their minds. Clearly, it is not. The reason safety is not uppermost in most driver's minds is that we humans choose our behavior largely on the basis of the probability that we will not harm ourselves. The fact is that there is an extremely high probability we will have a safe journey every time we use an automobile. For this reason, seat belts in the United States are not used by upward of 85 percent of drivers, and are even used less often by passengers.[6] Scare campaigns depicting injured persons have at best only temporary effects on speeding, drinking and driving habits, and associated car crashes.

V. SKILL

Most drivers learn to drive with very little formal training and absolutely no training for emergency avoidance maneuvers. As a consequence, accidents occur that more adequately trained, skillful drivers probably could avoid. For example, one study of skidding accidents revealed that "almost all of these [rear-end collisions] could have been avoided by evasive maneuvers."[7] The law doesn't require or expect an unusual amount of skill on the part of drivers.[8] Therefore, the expert must be able to describe what could be expected of perhaps a 10th or 5th percentile driver, not the "average driver," for if the average driver is used as a standard then 50 percent of drivers will not perform that well. It is up to the expert to describe a "reasonable standard" of roadway-user skill and capability based insofar as possible on research results. However, the capability of skill in operating a vehicle does not necessarily assure accident-free driving. *A study of race drivers[9] reveals them to have significantly higher numbers of both accidents and violations compared to "normal" drivers* in the three states included in the study.

VI. DRIVER VISION

A. How We See

Vision provides the bulk of information to roadway users, and the outcome of many accident lawsuits hinges upon whether or not something could or could not be seen in time to avoid the accident. Objects can be seen only when they contrast against the background. An object must either be sufficiently brighter or darker than its background in order to be detectable by our sense of vision. If a visual target is above our threshold of brightness difference, it is visible. This is not to say that it will therefore be seen (perceived). In order to be seen, an object must also be expected to appear. A common example of persons not perceiving what clearly is visible occurs during performances of legerdemaine (magic). The role of expectation is paramount in deciding whether a roadway user could have been expected to see a visual target at any given distance.

Laboratory studies of vision thresholds provide information about the human nervous system and what energy levels of illumination we are capable of detecting.[10] However, these data cannot be taken directly to apply to nighttime driving scenes without applying a factor of from 3 to 10,[11] which makes it almost *mandatory to actually view the scene and physically measure distances at which the visual targets can be seen.* When using this *reenactment method,* care must be taken to make observations from the same or an exemplar vehicle, at the same eye height, at the same speed, under the same illumination, etc. The more care exercised, the more credible the results, and if forensic photography is also used, the degree of care exercised will form the foundation for admissibility of the resulting movies or still photos. Position of sun or moon can be critical from the standpoint of glare and shadow positions as well as illumination of the visual targets.

The goal of the expert is to reexperience what the persons involved experienced insofar as possible. This endeavor should include observations from the viewpoint of eyewitnesses and police officers in order *to understand and explain the discrepancies* that are certain to exist among the various statements and estimates made by the persons involved.

A key concept of human perception is that it involves some information processing after the target becomes detectable or visible (exceeds contrast threshold)—it must be detected by successfully competing for attention, then it must be recognized by comparison with past experience (memories), and then, and only then, can estimates begin to be made of what the object(s) may do and decisions made as to the degree of risk the object creates. All of this activity is lumped under perception. Then reaction enters, but not until time is allowed for review of several possible reactions and selection of one reaction. This complex chain of events requires time, which can range from ½ second to infinity (if the object is not perceived).

The wide range of times for drivers to react to a simple auditory signal is reported in a study by Johansson and Rumar,[12] who placed a radio receiver in cars and triggered an audible alarm from hidden roadside transmitters as the drivers traveled a route several miles in length. These researchers concluded that if the need for braking occurs unexpectedly, a reaction time of 0.9 seconds or longer would occur for 50 percent of the drivers, 1.5 seconds or longer would occur for 10 percent, and in a few cases, times would be greater than 2.0 seconds. They go on to conclude that while their data reflect differences among drivers, the same range of reaction times could be expected to occur for an individual driver when tested many times.

When a door of a parked car suddenly opens near the path of travel, drivers swerve around it. In one study this technique was used to measure behavior of 1326 cars from a hidden vantage point.[13] From the time the door opened, the average time to swerve was 1.5 seconds. Half of the drivers required 2.5 seconds, and the longest time was almost 4 seconds. These times were independent of approach speeds and lateral placement. Basing his recommendations on these results, which are consistent with earlier studies, the author concludes that "at least 3 seconds should be reserved for drivers to respond, by steering, to changes in the road environment."

These data offer a sharp contrast to the often used general value of 0.75 seconds for driver brake reaction time.

It is the role of the human factors expert to help the court understand the complex nature of perception/reaction and the wide range of times involved because humans are essentially a single-channel information-processing system. This means that while our attention is on one aspect of our environment, we cannot simultaneously attend to any other aspect. What we can do is take samples from our environment and thus give an appearance of being able to attend to more than one thing at a time. The rate at which we can take these samples is limited and is slowed when we are under stress. Senders[14] has determined that normal drivers obtain all the visual information they can process in a ½-second sample. Moskowitz[15] reports that 29 percent fewer glances occur when drivers are at a 0.07 percent blood alcohol level *because it is taking longer to process the information obtained in each glance.* The shortest time for a mental process such as a decision to brake or steer is said to be 0.1 seconds.

These complex human factors (and others) need to be taken into account when reaching conclusions about how drivers see. It is not sufficient merely to determine that a visual target (say a pedestrian) was visible when 3 seconds away, to allow 1½ seconds for perception/reaction time and 1 second to brake to a stop, and then to conclude that the driver should have stopped before striking the pedestrian. It is not that simple.

B. Headlights and Visibility

What can be seen by drivers at night in the beams of their headlights often is a key issue in litigation over nighttime accidents. Researchers in vision refer to visual "targets" when computing or experimentally determining detection distance. Two basically different approaches can be used to estimate how far away a visual target (say a pedestrian) could have been detected. Illumination and photometric measurements can be made of the scene (reconstructed) and then various mathematical formulas can be applied to *calculate* a detection distance. Or, field observations can be made of the scene (reconstructed) in order to determine *empirically* detection distances. The results of these two methods may or may not agree, and the experts will have to convince the court of the merit of their opinion and explain why the two approaches may arrive at different detection distances.

One study provides evidence and results dealing with this issue, although the goal of the work was to develop a basis for evaluating the effectiveness of various headlight beam patterns.[16] The authors conducted field observations of targets that resembled pedestrians in size and shape. They compared these detection distances with computed distances based upon two different math models. The results were critiqued by four other researchers, who pointed out most, if not all, of the shortcomings of any attempt to compute human visual response using our present state of scientific and engineering knowledge and measuring instruments.

C. Glare

Glare is one of the more elusive aspects of human vision, and large individual differences can be demonstrated. Daytime glare usually is created by low sun angle (dawn or sunset) or reflection from a nearby surface. Nighttime glare encountered on roadways usually is from lights on vehicles. Versace[17] states that any light bright enough to be seen in daylight will create glare at night if the viewer is close enough. He also asserts that automobile brake-light intensity typically is about 30 times greater than tail-light intensity.

There are considered to be two major levels of glare: disabling glare and discomfort glare. Research reports refer to glare sources that are so intense that nothing else can be seen when such disabling glare is present. In other words, disabling glare totally prevents visual function because the neurons of the optic nerve are saturated with light energy. Discomfort glare, on the other hand, does not prevent vision. Such glare sources can create distraction of attention and annoyance.

At night, glare from oncoming vehicle headlights does create discomfort glare and, under certain circumstances, can result in disabling glare for a more or less brief time period, depending upon the individual's ability to "recover" from the glare. Two measures of vision under glare conditions were used in a study of over 17,000 motorists in California.[18] Form discrimination was used to learn how bright a visual target had to be in order for the person to identify it in the presence of glare. Glare recovery time was a measure of how many seconds elapsed after two simulated headlight bulbs were extinguished before the driver could "see" the target he had been able to see just before the glare bulbs were illuminated.

Both of these measures of mesopic vision revealed clearcut and increasingly larger values for drivers 45 years and older in age when the study results were accumulated. However, individual differences were large.

For highway and vehicle lighting design standards, the increasing age level of motorists needs to be recognized. *For individual accidents, the vision of the particular person under the particular lighting levels that existed must be considered.*

D. Driver Eye Height

Any consideration of what could or could not have been seen (visible) by roadway users must take account of operator eye height above the pavement. Design standards for vertical curvature of roadways are calculated by formulas that include eye height, speed, perception–reaction time, and stopping distance. As mentioned earlier, *current AASHTO highway design standards use 2½ seconds as a minimum value for perception–reaction time.*

A field study of driver eye height[19] reported a well-known decrease from an average of over 4.5 feet in 1930 to 3.75 feet in 1970 and then presented data to reveal a further decrease in average eye height. The study concludes that "for fully 89 per cent of compact and smaller passenger cars and 73 per cent of the intermediate and full-size passenger cars," *eye heights were less than the standard of 3.75 feet.* Thus, the researchers conclude, "The results of this investigation suggest that *presently calculated safe passing sight distances as well as designs of vertical curves may now be inadequate and unsafe. . . .* [A] value of 3.5 feet found in this study would provide a suitable standard."

The issue of stopping distance and eye height was the key factor in a study of truck driver performance relative to sight distance.[20] This report refers to the 1.14-m AASHTO standard driver eye height for passenger car drivers and a 2.39-m value for cab-over-engine trucks manufactured by three major producers. Cab-behind-engine models average 2.56 m and the newly developed cab-under models place the driver's eye 0.939 m above the road surface.

For motorcycles, the operator eye height is greater than that of passenger car drivers by about 11 inches (author's observations). Bicycle riders eye height varies, of course, with the size of the rider. This vehicle generally is fitted to the operator, and adult bikers eyes will exceed that of motorcyclists as a rule.

Eye height and lateral position on the roadway can be critical within a few inches for several reasons, only one of which is how far over a crest or around a curve can the operator see (sight-distance). Other eye-height visibility factors are, for example, the background against which critical visual targets appear (such as signs, pedestrians, or vehicles), the sun angle related to shadows, vision obstructions due to own vehicle items such as rearview mirrors and corner posts, and vision obstruction due to other vehicles or passengers within own vehicle.

These vision considerations sometimes can help explain why persons involved in a crash often say, "I never saw the other vehicle." In some litigation, the issue of a possible defect of a vehicle or a roadway may hinge directly on a careful measurement of eye location together with a human factors evaluation of its likely significance as a crash causation factor.

VII. HUMAN STRESS AND REDUCED CAPACITY

Stress can be defined to include chemical as well as environmental and situational factors that tend to alter human capabilities. The effects of so-called "life stress" can be totally disabling to roadway users such as those having a difficult divorce, causing them to walk blindly into traffic or drive into a clearly visible object. This is explainable in terms of our limited mental capacity to process information. While we are totally involved in dealing with a life-stress situation (say a death or a dispute), we have little or no mental capacity remaining to carry out other complex functions, and yet we may have enough capacity to drive as long as nothing unusual occurs.

Chemicals in our blood also can result in diminished capacity. The best understood is alcohol (ethanol), but other chemicals known to be depressants of the central nervous system work in a similar fashion. Marijuana has a different, less well understood, impairing effect and is not recommended for drivers.

Fatigue is a scientifically useless term, but it carries a common meaning relating to reduced capacity, such as falling asleep at the wheel. Sleep loss is a major factor, but individual differences are large and must be considered. In extreme cases, narcolepsy may be involved,[21] and blood sugar level definitely plays a role.[22]

Time pressure, such as being late for an appointment, can create stress that alters behavior of roadway users. It may increase or decrease alertness. This human factor has not been measured, but needs to be taken into account categorically as a possible factor influencing a road user's behavior. Time pressure can interact with such other stress factors as traffic delays, reduced visibility (fog, rain, snow, dust, etc.), and ambiguous roadway guidance cues (lack of "positive guidance").[23]

VIII. POSITIVE GUIDANCE

When roadway users do not have "positive guidance," they may inadvertently run off the road without ever realizing why or they may make "last-second" maneuvers that result in overturning or collisions with other vehicles. Whenever roadway users become aware that there is insufficient guidance information, they are likely to suffer from stress, distraction, fear, and, at times, startle.

Clear definitions have been published that define what is meant by positive guidance, and *A Users Guide to Positive Guidance*[24] was published in 1977 for street and highway departments to use in determining improvements in visual cues. In April 1982, two reports[25, 26] were issued documenting trends in accident reductions at two locations where positive guidance was applied.

In brief, positive guidance involves two steps: (1) making the safe path clearly visible far enough ahead for the users to respond appropriately, and (2) spacing the elements of the roadside information far enough apart to avoid overloading the user's capability to process information.

These published guidelines for evaluating whether or not a given section of roadway provides sufficient positive guidance can be used by experts to assist the court in deciding whether or not the roadway was in some degree deficient in design, construction, or traffic control elements. The underlying human factor is that roadway users will not reduce speed or alter their path unless they perceive a reason to do so. For example, in construction zones, speed-reduction signs generally are not effective.[27] And, at a freeway lane closure, field studies showed that "merging is influenced by the perceived urgency to merge."[28]

IX. SPECIAL CONSIDERATIONS

Many human factors should be taken into account when the expert studies the behavior of any particular individual road user involved in an accident. The person's age and vision usually are important. Night vision begins to deteriorate at about age 45,[18] and persons with less than 20/20 visual acuity in daylight will lose a great amount of acuity as the roadway scene becomes darker. This occurs because as the pupil opens to admit more light, the depth of focus decreases and causes a degrading of the sharpness of the image on the retina. Even younger drivers with 20/40 visual acuity in daylight are not likely to be able to read freeway signs at night until they are so close that there is insufficient time to maneuver safely.

When two moving objects (vehicles) are traveling on a collision course, they do not change bearing. Therefore, if such an object is in a "blind spot" (say behind a window pillar), it will remain there until collision.

When we rapidly change the direction in which we are looking, we tend to blink and thus shut off our view of the area lying between our points of vision. In this way drivers waiting to make a left turn will swing their vision quickly (about 90°) as they are making the turn, in order to look at the road ahead. In so doing, they may blank out a large sector and fail utterly to see a sign or anything else located there.

Pedestrians at night believe they can be seen by approaching drivers at far greater distances than the drivers can actually see them. One study[29] showed that pedestrians on an unlighted test road actually became visible to the driver 175 feet away, but the pedestrians estimated that they were visible as far away as 800 feet.

Human abilities to estimate time, distance, and speeds are generally poor and tend to worsen after even a few moments at steady high speeds.[30] Estimates of our vehicle speed tend to result in overestimates at speeds below 35 mph and underestimates at speeds over 35 mph. Time estimates of events that occur rapidly usually are much longer than the actual time elapsed. Distance estimates range greatly from person to person and are generally inaccurate. If possible, persons involved in or witnessing an accident should be asked to recollect landmarks and relative locations (positions) of vehicles from which times and speeds can be calculated by an expert. Carefully conducted interviews (possibly at the accident site) can elicit remembrances of the events that led to the accident. (*Note*: the use of hypnosis may be permitted in some jurisdictions.)

The vision (especially at night) of a witness or participant can be compared by the expert to the expert's own vision. In this way the expert can in a sense become a "calibrated" observer and place himself in a reconstructed scene in order to make estimates of what could be seen, when it became visible, and when it likely could have been perceived. If this is done with sufficient care, the court may allow testimony regarding the results.

X. FAMILIARITY

A major factor in understanding the behavior involved in an accident can be the familiarity of drivers with the vehicles, pedestrians with the roadway, cyclists with the traffic, etc. Therefore, whatever evidence that can be obtained needs to be examined. Unfortunately, familiarity with the road scene can result in a failure to detect an unusual occurrence that the "stranger" would detect because the stranger is noticing "everything." By and large, the stranger will more likely fall victim to a lack of positive guidance, while the familiar road user will more likely fall victim to an unusual event such as encountering a stalled vehicle. Accident studies have not been carried out in sufficient depth statistically to support or refute these conclusions.

XI. DRINKING DRIVERS

Individual differences in alcohol and drug use, drowsiness, driving experience, and night vision are all areas for investigation in order to assess professionally the behavior of accident-involved persons. For example, if a road user is found to have a blood alcohol level (BAL) of 0.20, it is almost certain that person is a chronic heavy drinker because a light drinker typically cannot imbibe that much alcohol without losing consciousness or vomiting or both. This conclusion is based on first-hand experience while conducting research into and demonstrations of alcohol effects on driving.[31]

Night vision can vary markedly in individuals and, if a deficiency is suspected, would have to be either tested by use of special test apparatus[32] or personally assayed in the field by the expert directly comparing what visual details the expert can see with what the road user can see as they view a night scene together. Roadway illumination at night by vehicle headlights and roadside light sources creates a level of light that is greater than that involved in most "night vision" research. Daylight illumination involves scotopic vision, truly dark nighttime scenes involve photopic vision, and road scenes at night typically involve mesopic vision. Unfortunately, relatively little research has been done on mesopic vision. The court should reject attempts to use inappropriate research results merely because a study has the words "night vision" in the title.

XII. BEHAVIOR AT FREEWAY LANE CLOSURES

Driving through roadway construction areas and where maintenance work interferes with the use of the roadway presents an unusual set of roadway and traffic conditions for motorists. Increasing attention has been given to improving the information given to users of roadways under construction or maintenance because not only roadway users are being killed and injured, but also street and highway workers often are involved as victims in these crashes.

A study of freeway construction lane closures[28] is an example of the research interest in this problem. The authors state:

> Normal driving conditions on rural freeways are characterized by uninterrupted free flow of traffic. Lane closures therefore represent a drastic deviation from usual freeway conditions since:
> - All drivers in the closed lane must change lanes and merge into the open lane traffic.
> - The capacity of the freeway is reduced by virtue of the lane closure. At higher flow rates this will result in reduced speeds and increased speed fluctuations.[28]

This research reached the following conclusions:

> [1.] It is generally recognized that the advisory speed
> signs are ineffective in reducing approach speeds
> at work zones.* Average speeds drop no more
> than 3 mph . . . [at] work zones conforming with
> minimum MUTCD [Manual of Uniform Traffic
> Control Devices] standards. . . . However, signifi-
> cant speed reductions have been achieved using
> rumble strips . . .†
>
> [2.] The simulation study indicated that if drivers
> could be induced to merge at the earliest oppor-
> tunity, then, with an advance warning distance
> of 1 mile, 90 per cent of all merges could be
> completed prior to the no recovery zone, even at
> near single lane capacity flows.
>
> [3.] The field study indicated that merging is influ-
> enced by the perceived urgency to merge. . . .
> Many drivers delay the decision until the con-
> struction area is sighted. . . . Changeable mes-
> sage signs . . . [did increase] the amount of early
> lane changes, especially when positioned 3/4 of a
> mile in advance of the lane closure.‡[28]

These results certainly fall in line with other observations
of driver behavior, namely, speeds and choice of lane are
influenced heavily by the appearance of the roadway and less
influenced by signs, although the value of signs for first-time
users is recognized.

Another study that bore out the above conclusions was
done on rural curves in Delaware County, Ohio.[35]

> Two (curves) were given special signing, three special
> pavement markings, one a widening of the inside edge
> marking at the curve and one with markings designed to
> make the curve appear narrower at the beginning of the
> curve. The Wundt illusion. . . . Road user mean speed
> reductions were noted early for the widened inside edge
> marker and inter car speed variation was substantially
> reduced by this treatment although the effect was gone
> (upon retest) thirty days later, suggesting that transient
> rather than local driver behavior would be affected. The
> Wundt illusion produced speed reductions late (at the be-
> ginning of the curve). Signs had little road user effect.
> What was most obvious was a reduction in the high speeds
> as a result of the modifications.

*See citation 27.
†See citation 33.
‡See citation 34.

The general conclusion is that road user's behavior can be modified by altering the visual cues upon which speed and lane use are based; the erection of roadway traffic control signs will be effective only when and where there is some visually observable justification for them.

XIII. ROADSIDE HAZARDS

On any section of roadway there will be errant drivers who run off the road for one reason or another. This "fact of life" has been recognized by highway designers who, under pressure by the U.S. Congress, have created less dangerous roadside "furniture" that breaks away upon impact.

Design standards call for a 30-foot-wide strip at the sides of roadways. These strips should be free of obstructions in order to allow an errant driver to recover vehicle control safely. This ideal design seldom can be achieved on any but the full freeway facilities and not always there.

If a 30-foot clear recovery area is not available, the objects within 30 feet should not be lethal if impacted by errant vehicles. Objects can be of the breakaway type that yield under severe impact. If it is not feasible to make them yielding, the roadside objects can be fronted with either deflecting structures or energy-absorbing structures. Guard rails can deflect errant vehicles. Several types of energy-absorbing devices are in use that are placed in front of fixed object hazards. Plastic "barrels" and "overlapping plastic plates" are but two styles of such devices that are proving effective in slowing errant vehicles at nonlethal rates.

A related device for preventing errant vehicles from crossing the roadway center is the so-called "median barrier." Guard rails and concrete walls are designed to deflect vehicles safely back into the roadway without disabling the vehicle as did earlier styled devices such as steel cables and chain-link fence.

Even with such protection there will be stalled vehicles along the roadway or in the roadway. Approaching motorists need to be able to detect such stopped or slowly moving vehicles in time to slow and avoid collision. Vehicle lighting standards call for four-way flashers to be included on all vehicles. Several research studies verify common experience with these devices and report slowing of vehicle speeds as unsuspecting drivers came upon stalled and slowly moving vehicles on a section of rural two-lane road in Maine. Speeds were measured by roadside detectors every 200 feet and were reported to decrease when four-way flashers were on. At times, speeds decreased even more when reflectorized triangles were placed along the road edge; however, this added decrease did not always occur.[36]

When accidents occur in which a vehicle leaves the roadway and strikes fixed objects or stalled vehicles, the questions before the court are several. For example:

1. What caused the vehicle to leave the roadway?
2. Should the driver have been able to avoid striking objects or stalled vehicles; could he see them in time?
3. Would the results have been different (less severe injuries) if the objects were either not there at all, designed to yield, or protected by deflecting or energy-absorbing structures?

Human factors analysis of such accidents can combine with vehicle, highway, and traffic engineering data and expert opinion to assist the court in answering these questions. A relevant study concluded, "In particular, there was no shift toward less severe accidents on sections with improved roadside design policies. However, although the proportions of fatal, injury, and property damage only accidents did not vary between roadside design policies, the number of accidents occurring for each severity level was found to decrease as the roadside design policy improved."[37]

XIV. BICYCLE USAGE

In general, bicycle users fall into two groups, adult and children. Adult bike riders usually are also automobile drivers, while children never are. Therein lies a large area for human factors considerations. One study of children bike riders observed and carefully rated the biking safety behaviors of 600 elementary school children and more than 3000 junior high school students on two occasions.[38] The study found a "very high error rate for all maneuvers and the greatest numbers of errors occurring on left turns and in search patterns." Head movement was the indicator used to measure search patterns at intersections, after a stop, and before making a lane change.

Adult bike riders as represented by various organizations of riders generally wish to have free use of all roadways. In other words, they resist the creation of bike routes and bike lanes lest they be restricted to those roadways. Other bike riders, unorganized, apply citizen pressure for bike lanes. Bike-lane and bike-path design criteria are in a state of change as various states and communities enact laws and ordinances concerning them.

Intersections pose difficult problems for formulating safe practices and design standards for bicycle riders.[39] For example, if a bike rider crosses within a crosswalk while walking alongside the bike, is he or she a pedestrian or bicyclist? At a railroad crossing should special warnings be posted for bicyclists? What is the safe way for bicyclists to make a left turn at an urban signalized intersection?

These and many other questions are presently unanswered, at least not in ways universally agreed upon. What is agreed to in the United States generally is that on bike paths the traffic control devices should conform to those in use on roadways, although such signs can be smaller in size.

XV. SEAT BELTS

The primary issue pertaining to seat belts is whether or not injuries sustained in a crash would have been less severe if a belt device either had been worn or, in some cases, had *not* been worn. The medical aspects lie outside the realm of human factors considerations. However, there is a human factors issue regarding the likelihood of a reasonable and prudent-acting person failing to put on a belt that was available; and, in at least one case, the issue was how likely was it that a rear-seat passenger made an effort to locate a seat belt but could not because, due to its configuration, the belt(s) had become stuffed down behind the seat.

In the first case, studies of belt use in the United States reveal overall only 10 to 16 percent of drivers observed using belts. Smaller car drivers tend to be more likely than full-size car operators to use belts. Other studies, where drivers are asked by telephone about belt use result in higher estimates. For example, a study by Teknekron Inc., of Washington, D.C., done for the National Highway Traffic Safety Administration picked 1500 drivers at random from telephone books in cities and small towns throughout the United States and found that 24.3 percent said they always wore seat belts.

There are three possible reasons for this telephone survey to yield a higher rate of belt use than did the direct observation type of study. First, the direct observation studies might fail to detect a belt only (no shoulder strap) installation in use; second, a telephone-based survey will not include persons without any phone or those with unlisted phone numbers; and third, it is well known by consumer survey researchers that some respondents will report behavior in ways they believe is "good" or desirable, even though they do not actually behave that way.

At any rate, the overall conclusion is inescapable that most drivers, even though otherwise "average" persons, will not necessarily wear seat belts on any given trip. In fact, the chances are 4 or 5 to 1 that a driver will not be wearing a belt at any given time. This situation may change if, as planned, so-called "automatic" safety belts are installed in cars.[6] Such belt systems come into place with less effort than the so-called "manual" systems.

In those countries where laws mandating use of seat belts have been passed, generally reported usage has been by about 50 percent or less of drivers. A study of 4812 cars and light-duty trucks in Ontario, Canada, and Michigan revealed that 51 percent of drivers used belts in Ontario compared with 17 percent in Michigan.[40] Ontario's seat-belt law went into effect January 1, 1976. Michigan had no such law as of April 27, 1981, when this study was reported in the Insurance Institute for Highway Safety, *Status Report*, Volume 16, Number 6.

Two studies have been made of so-called risk-taking behavior by belted versus nonbelted drivers. Both studies report *nonbelted drivers being observed taking more risks in traffic.* One study defined risk in terms of "headway" between vehicles in "high-flow" freeway traffic. Nonbelted drivers had less headway than belted drivers.[41] Another study defined risk in terms of driving at signalized intersections and found that drivers who "go through red lights are less likely than other drivers to be wearing their shoulder belts: 1 per cent vs. 8 per cent use by other drivers."[42]

These studies are a source of information, but it is likely that they are not nearly sufficient to conclude that a nonbelted driver involved in a crash was more likely to be taking a driving risk. It would be the role of the *expert in human factors* to consider and report the degree of similarity, if any, between the crash circumstances and those included in the above-mentioned studies.

XVI. CONCLUSION

In fact, the general role of the human factors scientist in the field of litigation regarding product defects in vehicles or roadways, roadway-user behavior(s), and behaviors of eye witnesses to crashes is to determine if the behavior falls within expectable ranges, given the circumstances of the accident.

CITATIONS

[1] S. Hulbert and A. Burg, "Human Factors in Transportation Systems," in K. DeGreene (ed.), *Systems Psychology.* New York: McGraw-Hill, 1970, pp. 471–509.

[2] *A Policy on Geometric Design of Rural Highways.* Washington, D.C.: American Association of State Highway Officials, 1965.

[3] G. H. Robinson et al., "Visual Search by Automobile Drivers." *Human Factors,* 14(4):315–323 (1972).

[4] J. P. Aurelius and N. Korborow, *The Visibility and Audibility of Trains Approaching Rail–Highway Grade Crossings.* Incorporated Report No. FRA-RP-71-2. New York: Systems Consultants, May 1971.

[5] C. T. Hare and R. H. Hemion, *Headlight Beam Usage on U.S. Highways.* Report No. AR-66. San Antonio, TX.: Southern Research Institute, December 1968.

[6] P. N. Ziegler and P. R. Knaff, "Improving Safety Belt Acceptability to the Consumer." SAE paper 790681. Warrendale, PA.: Society of Automotive Engineers, June 1979.

[7] L. E. Samuelson et al., *Skid Accident Analysis Study Based on Police Reports.* Report No. 2-01. Swedish Experimental Safety Vehicle Programme: Steerability During Emergency Braking, 1973.

[8] *Driver Behavior and Accident Involvement: Implications for Tort Liability.* Insurance and Compensation Study. Washington, D.C.: Department of Transportation, October 1970, p. 190.

[9] A. S. Willams and B. O'Neill, "On-the-Road Driving Records of Licensed Race Drivers." *Accident Prevention,* 6:260–272 (1974).

[10] H. R. Blackwell and D. M. Blackwell, "Population Data for 140 Normal 20–30 Year Olds for Use in Assessing Some Effects of Lighting upon Visual Performance." *Journal IES,* April 1980.

[11] H. R. Blackwell, "Individual Responses to Lighting Parameters for a Population of 235 Observers of Varying Ages." *Journal IES,* July 1980.

[12] G. Johansson and K. Rumar, "Driver's Brake Reaction Times." *Human Factors,* 12(1):99 (1971).

[13] H. Summala, "Driver/Vehicle Steering Response Latencies." *Human Factors,* 23(6):683–692 (1981).

[14]J. W. Senders, A. Christofeson, W. H. Levison et al., "Attentional Demands of Automobile Driving." *Highway Research Record*, 195:15–32 (1967).

[15]H. Moskowitz, personal communication to the author, 1982.

[16]V. D. Bhise, E. I. Farber, and P. B. McMahan, "Predicting Target Detection Distances with Headlights." *Transportation Research Record*, 611:1–14 (1976).

[17]J. Versace, "University of Michigan Short Course in Engineering," unpublished lecture notes, 1967.

[18]A. Burg, "Light Sensitivity as Related to Age and Sex." *Perceptual and Motor Skills*, 24:1279–1288 (1967).

[19]W. Cunogin and T. Abrahanson, "Driver Eye Height: A Field Study." *Institute of Transportation Engineers Journal*, 49(5):34–36 (May 1979).

[20]D. A. Gordon, *Highway Sight-Distance Requirements: Truck Applications.* Report No. FHWA-RD-79-26. Washington, D.C.: Department of Transportation, Federal Highway Administration, 1979.

[21]R. Yoss, "A Test to Measure Ability to Maintain and Its Application in Driving." *Mayo Clinic Proceedings*, 44(11):769–783 (1969).

[22]S. Hulbert, J. Baers, J. Herzog, and S. Blyden, *Blood Sugar Level and Fatigue Effects on a Simulated Driving Task.* Report No. 63-53. Los Angeles: Institute of Transportation and Traffic Engineering, University of California, 1963.

[23]G. J. Alexander and H. Lunenfeld, "Satisfying Motorists' Need for Information." *Traffic Engineering*, 43(1):46–70 (October 1972).

[24]T. J. Post, G. J. Alexander, and H. Lunenfeld, *A User's Guide to Positive Guidance*, 2nd ed. Report No. FHWA-TO-81-1. Washington, D.C.: Department of Transportation, Federal Highway Administration, December 1982.

[25]J. A. Barsness and M. R. Nesbitt, *Application of Positive Guidance at a Reverse Curve/Narrow Bridge Site in Washington State.* Report No. FHWA-DP-48-2 (Final Report). Washington, D.C.: Department of Transportation, Federal Highway Administration, April 1982.

[26]W. H. Opland, *Application of Positive Guidance at a Freeway Split in Michigan.* Report No. FHWA-DP-48-1 (Final Report). Washington, D.C.: Department of Transportation, Federal Highway Administration, April 1982.

[27]J. L. Graham, R. J. Paulsen, and J. C. Glennon, *Accident and Speed Studies in Construction Zones.* Midwest Research Institute, June 1977.

[28]W. M. Rouphail and Z. A. Nemeth, "A Driver Based Study of Freeway Construction Lane Closures." *Institute of Transportation Engineers Journal*, 51(6):18–21 (June 1981).

[29]M. J. Allen et al., "Actual Pedestrian Visibility and Pedestrian's Estimate of His Own Visibility." *American Journal of Optometry and Archives of American Academy of Optometry*, 47:44–49 (1970).

[30]F. Schmidt and J. Tiffin, "Distortion of Driver's Estimates of Automobile Speed as a Function of Speed Adaptation." *Journal of Applied Psychology*, 7:102–114 (1969).

[31]H. W. Case, S. Hulbert, and H. A. Moskowitz, *Alcohol Level and Driving Performance*. Report No. 71-17. Los Angeles: Institute of Transportation and Traffic Engineering, University of California, April 1971.

[32]R. L. Henderson and A. Burg, *Vision and Audition in Driving*. Report No. TM (L)-5297/000/00. Santa Monica, CA.: System Development Corp., April 1974.

[33]S. Z. Levine and K. W. Crowley, "The Effect of Rumble Strips on Speeds Through a Freeway Lane Closure Work Zone," paper presented at the 61st Annual Meeting of the Transportation Research Board, Washington, D.C., January 1982.

[34]F. R. Hanscomb, "The Effectiveness of Changeable Message Signing at Freeway Construction Site Lane Closures," paper presented at the 61st Annual Meeting of the Transportation Research Board, Washington, D.C., January 1982.

[35]T. H. Rockwell et al., *Improving Driver Performance on Rural Curves Through Perceptual Changes—Phase III*. Report No. OHIO-DOT 08-75 (Final Report). Columbus, OH.: Ohio Department of Transportation, March 1975.

[36]R. W. Lyles, "The Effectiveness of Four-Way Flashers on Stationary and Slow-Moving Vehicles." *Institute of Transportation Engineers Journal*, 52(4):19–22 (April 1982).

[37]J. L. Graham and D. W. Hardwood, *Effectiveness of Clear Recovery Zones*, NCHRP Report No. 247. Washington, D.C.: Transportation Research Board, May 1982.

[38]M. H. Jones, "A Real-World Bicycle Performance Measure." *Transportation Research Record*, 739:26–29 (1979).

[39]*Bikeway Planning Criteria and Guidelines*. Los Angeles: Institute of Transportation and Traffic Engineering, University of California, April 1972.

[40]Evans, Wasielewski, and Von Busek, *Compulsory Seat Belt Usage and Driver Risk Taking Behavior*. Report No. GMR-3413. Warren, MI.: General Motors Research Laboratories, 1981.

[41]Evans and Wasielewski, *Do Accident-Involved Drivers Exhibit Riskier Everyday Driving Behavior?* Report No. GMR-3362. Warren, MI.: General Motors Research Laboratories, 1981.

[42]Deutsch, Sameth, and Akinyemi, "Seat Belt Usage and Risk Taking Behavior at Two Major Intersections." *American Association for Automotive Medicine Quarterly Journal*, January 1981.

15

Visibility Problems in Nighttime Driving

PAUL L. OLSON, Ph.D.
and
MICHAEL SIVAK, Ph.D
The University of Michigan Transportation Research Institute
Ann Arbor, Michigan

Paul L. Olson is associated with the Human Factors Group at the University of Michigan Transportation Research Institute. After graduating from Purdue University in 1959, he joined the staff of the General Motors Research Laboratories. At GM he worked on problems such as vehicle control, lighting, and traffic control. In 1971 he joined the staff of the Highway Safety Research Institute of the University of Michigan (as the Institute was then known) and since then has been involved in projects having to do with vehicle lighting, conspicuity, traffic signs, and driver perception.

Michael Sivak received his Ph.D. in Experimental Psychology from the University of Michigan in 1976. He is currently an Associate Research Scientist at the Transportation Research Institute. His primary research interests are in visual, perceptual, and cognitive aspects of transportation safety. Both authors may be contacted at the University of Michigan Transportation Research Institute, which is part of the Institute of Science and Technology and is located at 2901 Baxter Road, Ann Arbor, Michigan 48109 (313-764-4158).

I. INTRODUCTION

Sometimes the telephone rings and we find ourselves talking to a lawyer, investigator, or "expert" preparing for a trial appearance. The question is typically something like "What visibility distance is provided by automobile headlights?" This is followed by an expectant pause.

The question is simple, and the person on the other end obviously expects a simple answer. One senses a growing impatience while responding with such questions as, "High beam or low beam? What kind of target object? What was the setting like? What were the weather conditions?" When an answer is finally provided in terms of a fairly broad range of distances, we get the feeling that the person on the other end wishes he/she had called someone else.

Estimating the visibility distance provided by headlights is *not* simple because the distance depends on several variables. Some of those can be estimated fairly well, some of them cannot. This section discusses the more important of these variables and their implications for acquiring essential visual information while driving at night.

Many problems are involved in acquiring information visually while driving at night. A dark-clad pedestrian, for example, can be seen only at a short distance. It is a distance much shorter than most persons would expect. This suggests that people think that they can see and be seen at night better than is really the case. And that is a dangerous error.

Broadly speaking, the variables that affect visibility while driving at night fall into four classes:

1. Headlights
2. Target object(s)
3. Atmospheric conditions
4. Human visual system

Before discussing each of these areas, an important point needs to be made. Two things must happen before a driver can respond appropriately to an object or condition in the forward field. These are commonly referred to as *detection* (conscious awareness that something is present) and *identification* (acquiring sufficient information about the object or condition to permit the driver to decide whether any response is called for, and, if so, what).

It is necessary to separate detection and identification because they are different processes. This is not to suggest that identification failures are common. But they do occur (see, for example, Olson and Sivak[1]). Because of the importance of this dual process, in this section we will use the terms detection–identification distance or response distance to describe what is commonly referred to in headlighting literature as "visibility distance."

II. HEADLIGHTS

Conventional automotive headlights have two beams. The upper beam is intended for use in the absence of other traffic, and its design presents no serious problems. The low beam is a different matter. Its design must be based on several criteria, some of which conflict with others.

One of the problems in low-beam design arises from the need to work within rather close tolerances. Figure 15-1 is a road scene as it might appear to a driver. The H and V lines represent planes that intersect at the center of the headlight. At infinite distance they correspond to the horizon and convergence point of the road as shown. The dashed line in quadrant 1 depicts the path of the eyes of an oncoming driver.

The task confronting a designer who is developing a low beam appears fairly straightforward. He/she must provide as much illumination in essential areas as possible without presenting excessive glare to approaching drivers. However, as a glance at Figure 15-1 should make clear, only a small angle separates areas where illumination is desirable and areas where it will cause glare.

There are two approaches to low-beam design in the world today. The "sealed-beam" lamps used in the United States, and in some other parts of the world, have internal shielding together with lens prisms to produce a beam that packs its main intensity in the upper left-hand corner of quadrant 3, while holding quadrant 1 illumination to what is felt to be an acceptable level. The other approach is standard in Europe but also common in other parts of the world. The main control element is a shield between the filament and reflector. This design produces a sharp horizontal cutoff, relatively uniform roadway illumination, and lower glare levels than the sealed beam.

Which low-beam system is best is a matter of controversy. It is not our purpose to contribute to that debate. Each represents a viable approach to the problem. In an ideal world each

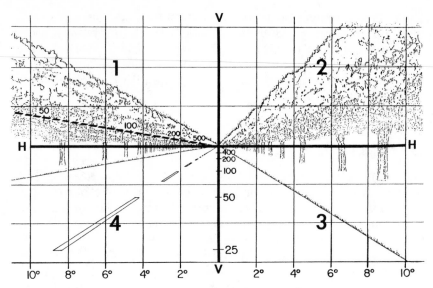

Figure 15-1 Schematic of road scene. Numbers on V line and dashed diagonal line in quadrant 1 represent distance from the headlight in feet.

would work fairly well. One of the main headaches for the lighting engineer is that the world is not ideal, and the lamps must function as well as possible under a number of different conditions. Some examples follow:

Headlights are attached to the front-end sheet metal on cars. Cars, of course, sit on springs. The vertical aim of the lamps may change by one to two degrees, depending on how much fuel is in the tank. Cars haul different passenger and baggage loads and sometimes pull trailers. Any one of these conditions can change vertical aim by several degrees. Consider Figure 15-1. "Several degrees" can make a substantial difference in where the maximum intensity portion of the beam is directed.

Aside from what can happen to the car, the aim of the lamp relative to the car can change for a variety of reasons. Unfortunately, accurate aim as a field service operation is a rather uncertain matter, due to equipment and human problems.[2]

The road depicted in Figure 15-1 is not typical of the roads on which most of us drive most of the time. Thus, while a car is negotiating hills and curves, a lamp designed for this somewhat idealized scenario will not always project its illumination where it will do the driver of its car or an oncoming driver the most good.

Like the rest of the car, headlights get dirty. In bad weather they can get very dirty very quickly. Research indicates that headlight output must drop about 60 percent before the driver is apt to notice.[3] Noticing that the headlights appear dim is no guarantee that the driver will stop and clean them, however. European lamps suffer from an additional problem with dirt. Because they are not hermetically sealed, dirt tends to accumulate inside, causing output to degrade over time.

This list of real-world problems with headlights covers some common concerns but is by no means complete. The key point is that low-beam design is a difficult issue at best, and lamp performance under field conditions is reduced by several factors over which the designer has little or no control.

III. TARGET OBJECTS

A. Contrast

Obviously, some things are easier to see while driving at night than others. For example, a reflectorized sign might be identified a half mile or more away, while a dark-clad pedestrian at the edge of the road may suddenly appear out of the blackness when very close to the car.

Detection requires contrast, and contrast involves both the object or condition of interest and its background. Contrast can take many forms in daylight viewing (e.g., color, texture, and brightness), but under night driving conditions, brightness contrast is of primary importance.

Thus, before an object can be detected under night driving conditions, it must be to some extent brighter or darker than its background. Lighted backgrounds sometimes make it possible to detect silhouetted objects at great distances. Streetlights are intended to help in this regard. However, in many installations, because the illumination is not uniform, the effects are not uniform. The same object at one position may appear brighter and at another position darker than the street behind it. Under some conditions it may not be seen at all, due to insufficient contrast.[4]

Headlights typically function to illuminate an object so that it becomes brighter than its background. In this context it is important to remember that the brightness of anything depends not on how much illumination is reaching it, but on how much is being reflected back toward the driver's eyes.

Imagine two persons walking along the right edge of a road, with a car approaching from behind. One of the pedestrians is wearing blue denim, the other a light gray material. At a distance of 500 feet the car's low beams would project 4000 to 5000 candelas toward these pedestrians. The intensity of illumination (E) on an object varies inversely with the square of the object's distance from the source of illumination:

$$E = I/d^2$$

where I is the amount of light energy (in units such as candelas) directed toward the surface in question. Thus, the illumination measured at the pedestrians would be about 0.02 foot-candelas. However, blue denim will absorb as much as 97 percent of the illumination falling on it, while the gray material may absorb only about 50 percent. These reflectivity characteristics must be considered in calculating the brightness ("luminance" in the terminology of light measurement) of the objects. Luminance (L) is calculated (in units of foot-lamberts) as follows:

$$L = Er$$

where r is the reflectivity of the object in question. Thus, for the blue denim ($r = 0.03$), luminance is 0.0006 ft-L (foot-lamberts), while for the gray material ($r = 0.50$) it is 0.01 ft-L, a difference of about 17:1.

Of course, while the vehicle's headlights are illuminating the pedestrians, they are also illuminating the background. Background reflectivity is variable, ranging from about 2 percent to 10 percent if the background is the road or shoulder surface.[5] Note that this is about the same level of reflectivity as that of dark clothing, so the wearer of blue denim in the hypothetical example given earlier is at a distinct disadvantage in gaining sufficient contrast to ensure detection.

Contrast can be quite variable in a single object. For example, a taller object, such as a pedestrian, will be projected against a varying background. The lower portion (feet and legs) will be seen against that part of the road or shoulder surface that is fairly close and, hence, receiving about the same illumination. As a result, contrast is minimum. The upper portions (chest and head) will be seen against more distant and less illuminated portions of the background. As a result, contrast is maximum. This is fine, except that the distributional characteristics of the low beam are such that the lower portions of the target receive maximum illumination.

While contrast is important, it is not the only object–background characteristic of consequence. Some others are homogeneity and size.

B. Homogeneity

Many target objects and/or backgrounds are not uniform in their reflectivity characteristics. It was noted earlier, for example, that many streetlighting systems provide poor backgrounds, due to large variations in brightness from one point to another.

Virtually all lighting studies have been run with homogeneous targets and backgrounds. For this reason it is difficult to estimate visibility of a specific object under nonhomogeneous conditions, short of recreating the situation. In recreating a situation the danger is that because some portion of an object can be seen at a certain distance, it will be assumed that this represents a reasonable "detection distance." For reasons that will be discussed later, this is not necessarily true. Nonhomogeneous contrast conditions are something like camouflage. They disguise familiar contours and reduce response distances relative to what might be expected based on the maximum contrast available.

C. Size

Two points are relevant concerning object size. First, without sufficient contrast, it does not matter if the object ahead is a brick or a railroad car; it will not be detected. Second, given sufficient contrast, a large object has a greater likelihood of being detected at a given instant than a small one.

In sum, the visibility of an object or condition depends not only on characteristics of the target itself, but also on the background against which it must be seen and other factors such as its size. However, other variables can have a marked effect as well, and they will be considered next.

IV. ATMOSPHERIC CONDITIONS

Certain weather conditions (e.g., rain and fog) have a very significant effect on the acquisition of visual information while driving at night.

A. Rain

Rain produces several effects relevant to vision. Probably the most obvious results from distortion of the optical properties of the windshield due to water droplets. The extent of visual degradation depends on factors such as rainfall rate, vehicle speed, wiper speed, condition of the wiper blade, and condition of the windshield. The problem has been studied to some extent,[6,7] but estimates of visibility in a specific condition are difficult to make.

Water droplets on the windshield also act as lenses, and accentuate the effect of glare from oncoming headlights. Water can also combine with impurities on the windshield surface or flow into scratches and create a film that seems to light up when facing oncoming headlights. This alters the contrast of objects or conditions in the forward field and makes them more difficult to detect.

Rain water also fills in the multitude of small irregularities in a road surface. As a result, the reflective properties of the surface are changed, and much illumination that would normally be reflected back toward the driver is reflected forward instead. As a result, the visibility of the road is reduced and glare for oncoming drivers is increased.

Lane and road edge lines are reflectorized by sprinkling them with tiny glass beads before the paint dries. Moisture alters the reflective characteristics of such a treatment, making it ineffective. The loss of lane markings and reduced visibility of the road surface in general sometimes makes it very difficult to see where the road is going.

Some effects associated with rainfall can be positive. For example, the illumination reflected forward and up from the wet road surface is added to direct illumination from the headlights and can dramatically *increase* the brightness of reflectorized road signs.[8] The same reflected illumination can make it *easier* to detect objects on the roadway, not only by being added to direct illumination, but also because the background does not brighten up as rapidly as if the pavement were dry.

B. Fog

Fog consists of tiny water droplets suspended in the atmosphere. Illumination from headlights cannot penetrate fog very well because each droplet acts like a lens, causing the beam to be scattered. Not only does this reduce the illumination reaching any object of interest in front of the car, but also the intervening atmosphere lights up to some degree, reducing contrast.

While the problem of fog has been studied a great deal (for example, by Koth et al.[9]), there are no real solutions. However, persons who encounter fog regularly may benefit from the use of special fog lamps. The best of these sharply limit upward scatter of light, reducing the problem of contrast loss. Note that the scattering effect of fog is unaffected by the wavelength of light passing through it. Thus, a fog lamp is *not* improved by adding a yellow lens.

The atmosphere is something over which drivers and headlamp designers have little control. It can have a dramatic effect on visibility. Proper equipment, in good condition, and care on the part of the vehicle operator are about the only solutions to severe atmospheric conditions.

V. THE HUMAN VISUAL SYSTEM

In a classic headlighting study in 1938, Roper and Howard[10] asked their subjects to drive a test vehicle to a site where headlight evaluations were to be carried out. Along the way, without the subject's knowledge, a pedestrian-size dummy had been placed in the vehicle's path. Measures were made of the distance from the dummy at which the subject's foot was lifted from the accelerator. With the "surprise" measure concluded, the subjects were briefed on the true purpose of the study and asked to back up and approach the dummy again, lifting their foot from the accelerator when it could be seen. *The distances under the second (alerted) condition averaged twice those under the first (unalerted) condition.*

This appears to be an extraordinary difference in response distance, and it is reasonable to ask how it could come about. Actually, there are several reasons. Understanding these reasons will not only make it clear why the Roper and Howard results came out as they did, but also will provide an appreciation of the difficulties in marking potential roadway hazards so they can be reliably detected and identified by approaching drivers at a safe distance.

In the discussion that follows, the various visual factors will be considered based on whether they affect detection or identification.

A. Detection

A.1. CENTRAL VERSUS PERIPHERAL VISION The light-sensitive portion of the eye is called the retina. In it are found two types of receptors—cones and rods. Cones function at relatively high light levels (called photopic) and are wavelength sensitive, producing the sensation of color. Rods function at low light levels (called scotopic). There is a range of lighting conditions where both rods and cones function, called mesopic. The eyes are typically adapted to this level while driving at night. [11, 12]

The two types of receptors are not evenly distributed across the retina. In particular, cones are found exclusively in a small central area of the retina called the fovea, and less and less frequently as one moves from the fovea into the periphery. Rods predominate in the periphery.

Because of the unequal distribution of cones, one would expect that vision would be best in the foveal portion of the eye and become poorer in the periphery at high light levels. As shown in Figure 15-2, this is exactly what happens. As light levels drop, a point is reached where the rods begin to function, and the differences between foveal and peripheral vision are less. Finally, at sufficiently low light levels the cones cease to function and the fovea becomes blind.

Not only acuity, the function shown in Figure 15-2, but also most other visual functions are better in the fovea than the periphery. These functions include contrast threshold, motion threshold, and color discrimination, all of which are important to the detection and identification of objects or conditions while driving. The problem, and the point of this discussion, is that the foveal area is quite small relative to the entire visual field. From a purely statistical point of view, there is a very good chance that the image of an unexpected object or condition will not fall on the fovea when the separation distance is such that conditions would allow it to be detected. Thus, detection typically occurs peripherally, simply because that area of the eye is so much larger. As should be

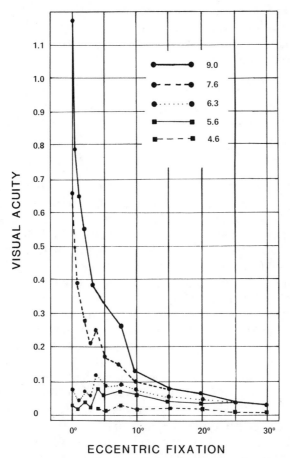

ECCENTRIC FIXATION

Figure 15-2 Acuity as a function of eccentricity and luminance level (in log microlamberts). [From J. Mandelbaum and L. L. Sloan, "Peripheral Visual Acuity." *American Journal of Ophthalmology*, 30:581–588 (1947). Published with permission from The American Journal of Ophthalmology 30: 581–588, 1947. Copyright by The Ophthalmic Publishing Company.]

obvious from Figure 15-2, an object or condition must be more conspicuous if it is to be detected peripherally rather than foveally. In nighttime vehicle operation, something is generally made more conspicuous by getting closer to it.

One of the differences, then, between the alerted and unalerted conditions in the Roper and Howard study[10] was that because the subjects knew where on the road the dummy was located under the alerted conditions, detection was probably foveal, while detection was probably peripheral under the unalerted conditions.

For the same reason, persons seeking to assess the visibility of some object or condition, in order to estimate the distance at which a driver should have seen it, must bear in mind that their estimates will be based on foveal vision, which will yield a significant overestimation of detection distance under normal conditions.

A.2. GLARE A beam of light entering the eye is scattered slightly by the optic media. As a result, some of the illumination ends up on random portions of the retina. Under most conditions the intensity of this stray light is so low relative to the adaptive state of the eye's photoceptors that it has no effect. However, under some conditions, and night driving is a common one, the effect can be quite significant.

The stray light that illuminates the retina under glare conditions produces an effect similar to a veil or screen in front of the eyes.[13] The result is a reduction in contrast for objects and conditions in the forward field so that detection distances become shorter.

The effect just described is known as "disability glare." Glare can also produce a sensation of discomfort. Significant losses in visibility can occur before an observer is apt to describe a glare source as "uncomfortable."[14] Since actions to reduce glare, such as flashing one's lamps to request dimming or switching to the lower setting of a two-level rearview mirror, will probably be based on sensations of discomfort, drivers are often operating under reduced seeing conditions due to glare, without being aware of the fact.

A.3. DARK ADAPTATION The sensitivity of the eye changes (adapts) over a very wide range of lighting conditions. It takes time for the eyes to adapt to a new level, whether up or down. How long depends primarily on the initial state of adaption and the extent of change.[15] For example, the headlights of an oncoming car will cause the eye to light adapt (become less sensitive) to some extent, with re-adaptation typically requiring 5 to 15 seconds.[14] In many night driving situations the eyes are typically adapted to a higher level than is theoretically possible, so that the driver cannot see as well as he/she could were oncoming traffic not present.

A.4. CAPACITY TO PROCESS VISUAL INFORMATION As noted earlier, the total visual field is quite large. Because it is so large, there is typically more than one item of information impinging on the retina at any given time. Often much more. However, although the eyes are marvelously efficient collectors of information, the perceptual system has a limited capacity to transmit information to conscious levels. Thus, most information present on the retina at a given instant does not reach consciousness.

Researchers who have studied this characteristic of visual perception have postulated the existence of a "peripheral filter." No specific mechanism has been identified, but it is apparent that the perceptual system filters information and, by some automatic means, determines what reaches consciousness.[16] The system can be overridden voluntarily. That is, we can focus our attention on something as a matter of choice. It is also true that, although the system has limited information-processing capability at each instant in time, it can process a great deal of information, given enough time.

Given a finite information-processing capability, there is substantial survival value in having some lower-level mechanism prescreen and forward to higher centers the information that is potentially important. By and large, the peripheral filter does this job well.

While the mechanism of the peripheral filter is not understood fully, the characteristics of information it is most likely to pass are well known. In general, these characteristics are ones we say make something "conspicuous." That which is different from its surroundings is most apt to capture our attention. Thus, size, brightness, different coloration or reflectivity, and change (flashing or moving) are attributes that increase the likelihood that something will pass the peripheral filter and reach the conscious level.

What this characteristic of the perceptual system means is that just because something is there to be seen does not mean that it will be detected and certainly not that it will be detected at the same point by all drivers.

The probability that a stimulus will pass the peripheral filter at a given instant in time depends on a great number of factors, one of the most important of which is its conspicuity relative to competing stimuli. Also of consequence is the driver's focus of attention. For example, someone trying to find his/her way through an unfamiliar area may well be concentrating on route markers and street signs to a degree that would make it very difficult for anything else to penetrate the filter.

A.5. SUMMARY Detection is the necessary first step in the process that allows the driver to deal effectively with roadway situations. Under real-world conditions, the likelihood that a reasonably alert driver will detect a given object or condition is governed by several factors, some of the most important of which are the following:

1. Detection can occur at much lower stimulus levels if the image of the object or condition falls on the foveal portion of the retina. However, since the foveal area is small relative to the total visual field, the probability of this happening by chance is small.
2. Glare from the headlights of oncoming cars and other sources can significantly reduce detection distances. Furthermore, there is also the danger that the discomfort associated with glare may cause the driver to look away from the target area.
3. In many typical driving situations the eyes are in a continual state of adaptation. Thus, the level of adaptation at a given instant may be far from optimum for detection of a given object or condition.
4. The ability of the perceptual system to process information is limited. Thus, the presence of the image of some object or condition on the retina of the eye does not guarantee that the information will reach conscious levels immediately. Therefore, assessing something as sufficiently conspicuous based on inspection by an informed person is unrealistic and dangerous.

B. Identification
Detection having occurred, the next necessary stop is identification.

As was noted earlier, identification is not usually a problem. However, some situations present difficulties due to limitations in the perceptual system (see Olson and Sivak.)[1] When crashes occur because of identification failures, they tend to look like and be ascribed to "driver error" since most people apparently do not understand that detection and identification are different processes. This is not only unfair to the involved driver but leads to misdirected corrective efforts. The following discussion will aid in clarifying this problem.

Two levels of identification can be distinguished. They are not equally useful to the motorist, and one does not automatically follow from the other:

1. *What is it?* Typically the first level of identification, this may convey sufficient information for reliable decision making concerning control actions, especially if the object or condition is incapable of movement (e.g., chuckhole, debris in the road). If the object is moving, or capable of movement, more information is required.
2. *What is it doing?* A knowledge of what is ahead and what it is doing is generally all the identification required to enable a driver to infer proper control actions. This level of identification sometimes proves particularly difficult to attain.

The headlights must function to provide sufficient information about the object or condition so that adequate identification can take place. In the real world what typically happens is that detection occurs peripherally, triggering a fixation and inspection by the fovea to complete the identification process. This can be accomplished in a quarter of a second or less and would appear "instantaneous" to the operator.

But, it is not always so simple. All drivers have found themselves wondering if the chuckhole ahead is deep or shallow or if the glob-of-something at the side of the road is harmless junk or a small animal that might dart in the path of the vehicle.

The great bulk of headlighting research has relied on a method much like the alerted portion of the Roper and Howard study.[10] In such studies, detection is with the foveal portion of the retina. Identification is irrelevant, since the target object is known to the subject, and the response is preordained. There have been some attempts to use "identification" measures by having the subjects tell something about the orientation of a portion of the target (e.g., Mortimer and Olson[14]). But this is only a crude approximation of the real-world process.

The primary virtue of the usual type of headlighting study methodology is ease of data collection. Usually, the main interest is in comparing different lighting systems. While it is recognized that the resulting "visibility distances" are long relative to what would be expected under more realistic conditions, it does seem reasonable to assume that a lighting system that does better under these conditions will also do better in the real world.

However, there is the possibility that lighting systems

that rank one way based on traditional testing would rank differently if tested based on their ability to provide essential identification information. Unfortunately, this also means that relatively little is known about what lighting characteristics are required to provide adequate identification. Thus, the following discussion can deal only with general principles.

A key factor in identification is expectancy. In most studies the target is known to the subject, and identification is equivalent to detection. Drivers are seldom so fortunate in the real world. However, it is possible and desirable to warn drivers of certain hazardous conditions in a way that heightens expectancy and facilitates identification. For example, use of a "construction ahead" sign makes it easier for the driver to identify barricades, channelizing devices, etc., in use at the actual site. Warning signs (e.g., stop ahead) are often used in advance of traffic control devices, such as stop signs, increasing the likelihood of detection and facilitating identification.

If expectancy makes identification easier, violations of expectancy make it more difficult. For example, drivers expect vehicles ahead of them on the road to be moving at more or less the same speed. If a vehicle is stopped or moving slowly, the use of some kind of hazard warning is desirable. Lacking a hazard warning, the driver must identify the situation by noting the high closing speed, something people do poorly.[17] Thus, an identification error is more likely.

Detection and identification can be enhanced by a single device. An excellent example is the slow-moving-vehicle symbol, which not only increases the conspicuity of the vehicle but conveys an easily recognized message. The flashing-arrow lane-closure signal commonly used in construction is another good example. Emergency-vehicle warning systems are less effective than they might be because they are more concerned with identifying the agency (e.g., police, fire) than the situation.

Identification remains a difficult issue to quantify for a given situation. In summary, there are three really important points:

1. Correct identification must precede effective action on the part of a driver.
2. Correct identification does not automatically follow detection.
3. Identification can take significant time if the situation is unusual or ambiguous. The likelihood of misidentification increases greatly if cues produce an erroneous expectancy on the part of the driver.

C. Estimating Detection–Identification Distances

Since some time has been spent discussing limitations to human visual information acquisition and processing, it is now appropriate to provide some indication of detection-identification distances that can be expected in a real-world setting using automotive headlights.

The data to be presented will largely be drawn from work in which the authors have been personally involved. This is not to slight others who have done similar work; it merely reflects a preference for data with which we are most familiar.

The reader is also cautioned that the data are based on rather idealized conditions. That is, the lamps were properly aimed and operated at correct voltage, all glass was clean, the subjects were young and alert, and the target contrast conditions were uniform and established by the experimenter. Affairs are not so well organized in the real world, and many of the things that happen tend to reduce system performance.

Figures 15-3, 15-4, and 15-5 are detection–identification distance plots taken from a recent report.[18] Two targets are considered: "debris," which was a short length of lumber 4 inches × 6 inches lying in the road just to the right or left of the vehicle's track, and a dark-clad pedestrian standing

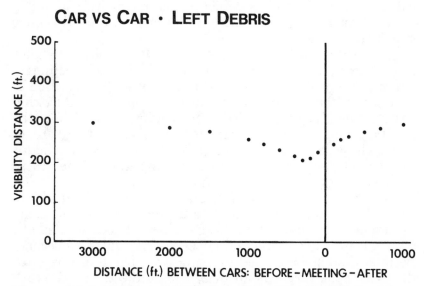

Figure 15-3 Predicted detection–identification distances resulting from two identically equipped cars meeting on a two-lane, flat-straight road—both vehicles on low beam.

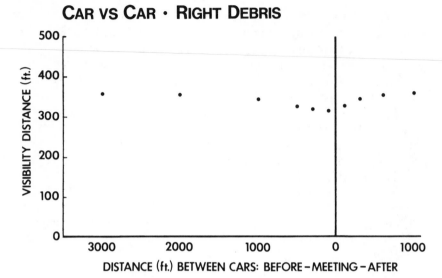

Figure 15-4 Predicted detection–identification distances re-sulting from two identically equipped cars meeting on a two-lane, flat-straight road—both vehicles on low beam.

on the right edge of the road. The car is equipped with stand-ard low beams. The plots depict detection–identification dis-tances through a meeting with a similarly equipped vehicle on a straight, flat two-lane road.

Note that in each plot the detection–identification distance is at a maximum at 3000 feet separation and slowly declines to a minimum just before the two cars pass. The decline is greater for the left debris because the observer is looking closer to the glare source. Recovery begins shortly before the cars pass and continues until the cars are 500 to 1000 feet apart. These data are based on speeds of 40 feet per second for each vehicle, so recovery from low-beam glare under these conditions requires 5 to 10 seconds or more.

Minimum stopping distance at 55 mph is about 150 to 160 feet. The time required for a driver to reach a decision about what to do and put it into effect has not been studied in a driving context. If we assume a decision interval of one second, the total distance required to bring a vehicle to a stop after identifying the target is about 230 to 240 feet. Figures 15-3 and 15-4 indicate that the debris target does not present a problem unless the identification distance is much less than average and/or the decision time is much longer. However, the pedestrian is a different matter.

The data in Figures 15–3 through 15–5 were developed from a computer simulation[19] that, in turn, is based on field studies run under conditions similar to the alerted portion of the Roper and Howard study. Hence, the identification distances depicted are greater than would be expected under realistic conditions. How much greater? It will be recalled that Roper and Howard's data suggest that identification distances obtained under such conditions are about double what could be expected in a realistic setting. However, further verification would be helpful.

The data in these figures were presented originally as part of a study of motorcycle headlighting.[18] Computer simulations for various motorcycle headlights were compared with field response distance measures taken on public roads using realistic targets (including the debris and pedestrian objects). The subjects were told to look for "potential hazards" but did not know what to expect or where. The response distances resulting from this study averaged about one-half the distances predicted by the computer.

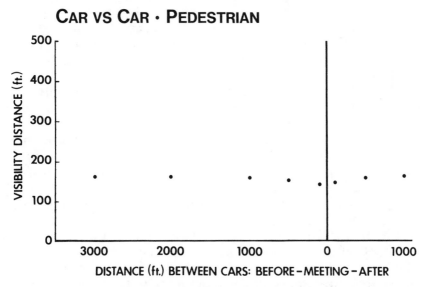

Figure 15–5 Predicted detection–identification distances resulting from two identically equipped cars meeting on a two-lane, flat-straight road—both vehicles on low beam.

Thus, in a real-world setting, under the conditions assessed in Figure 15-5, the expected average response distance (i.e., the distance at which the drivers might initiate a control response) is not 160 to 170 feet, but about 80 feet. Some people will respond at a distance greater than 80 feet, some people at a shorter distance. Given that the average response distance is rather short, it is reasonable to ask about the range of distances expected. Apparently it is substantial. In the motorcycle study the subjects passed the pedestrian target without responding about 10 percent of the time. The longest response distance was 168 feet. Automotive headlights will outperform the best motorcycle headlight, but only by a small amount. So a reasonable range for cars is about 0 to 180 feet.

At this point it would be instructive to compare these response distance data with approximate stopping distances from various speeds:

25 mph: 32 ft
35 mph: 63 ft
45 mph: 105 ft
55 mph: 156 ft

Under the conditions of the test just described, it is apparent that, had the subjects braked instead of pressing a button, the vehicle would have come to a stop past the pedestrian target quite a lot of the time. It is also apparent that if a dark pedestrian or any other low-contrast object is in the path of a vehicle approaching at moderate speed, there is a substantial risk of a collision.

The point was made earlier that more reflective clothing helps. How much? A great deal, it turns out. If the pedestrian is wearing white clothing rather than blue denim, the expected average response distance increases by about 100 percent. Thus, the average response distance to someone in white clothing is about 160 feet. The expected range of response is from about 80 to 260 feet.

The use of high beams also helps, but less than one might think. As a rough rule of thumb, high beams will improve detection–identification distance to objects on the right side by about 50 percent and to objects on the left side by about 100 percent. (The difference is attributable to the fact that low beams direct most of their intensity to the right.)

With these basic comparisons in hand, it is useful to prepare a table summarizing some basic target and beam conditions. This has been done in Table 15-1.

Table 15-1 Expected Response Distances (in Feet) to Pedestrian Targets

HEADLAMP BEAM	TARGET LOCATION[a]	CLOTHING	AVERAGE RESPONSE DISTANCE	RANGE
Low	Right	Dark	80	0-160
		Light	160	80-240
	Left	Dark	60	0-120
		Light	120	50-200
High	Right	Dark	120	60-300
		Light	240	160-400
	Left	Dark	120	60-300
		Light	240	160-400

[a]Defined as the side of the car on which the target appears.

The response distances listed in Table 15-1 should be compared with the stopping distances noted earlier. Doing so, it is apparent that it is difficult to provide a combination of beam, pedestrian location, and clothing that makes for an absolutely safe condition, especially at higher speeds. The pedestrian who is sincerely interested in reaching his/her destination must become an active participant in the collision avoidance process and not rely on the drivers of approaching cars.

VI. CONCLUSION

The acquisition of essential visual information under night driving conditions is sometimes described as difficult, but it is perhaps more accurately described as uncertain. The system works as well as it does because most driving is routine. We can operate under certain assumptions (e.g., the road is clear of fixed objects, the taillights ahead are attached to a vehicle going at about the same speed as we are) that are rarely violated. When assumptions are violated and/or when misleading information is presented, the potential for trouble is substantial because reliably gaining the attention of and adequately informing approaching drivers is not a simple matter.

We know a good deal about the ability of people to receive and process visual information. To a significant extent, these data have influenced the design of the traffic environment and the vehicles that operate in it. But there are still some gaps. We often encounter situations that create unnecessary hazards for want of the application of simple principles such as have been covered in this paper. We hope that a better understanding of the principles will help decrease the frequency of situations in which drivers or pedestrians make unwarranted assumptions about their sight distances or visibility at night.

CITATIONS

[1]P. L. Olson and M. Sivak, *Problems in the Detection and Identification of Significant Roadway Conditions.* Report No. 81-46. Ann Arbor: Highway Safety Research Institute, University of Michigan, October 1981.

[2]P. L. Olson and R. G. Mortimer, *Investigation of Some Factors Affecting the Aim of Headlamps.* Report No. UM-HSRI-73-13. Ann Arbor: Highway Safety Research Institute, University of Michigan, January 1973.

[3]K. Rumar, "Dirty Headlights—Frequency and Visibility Effects." *Ergonomics*, 17(4):529–533 (1974).

[4]A. Ketvirtis and P. J. Cooper, "Detection of Critical Size Objects as a Criteria for Determining Driver's Visual Needs," paper presented at the U.S. Transportation Research Board Annual Meeting, Washington, D.C., February 1977.

[5]V. D. Bhise, E. I. Farber, C. S. Saunby et al., "Modeling Vision with Headlights in a Systems Context." SAE paper 770238. Warrendale, PA.: Society of Automotive Engineers, 1977.

[6]R. S. Morris, J. M. Mounce, J. W. Button, and N. E. Walton, *Study of Driver Visual Performance During Rainfall.* Report No. DOT-HS-802-289. College Station: Texas Transportation Institute, March 1977.

[7]V. D. Bhise, J. F. Meldrum, L. M. Forbes et al., "Predicting Driver Seeing Distance in Natural Rainfall." *Human Factors*, 23(6):667–682 (1981).

[8]H. L. Woltman and W. P. Youngblood, "An Assessment of Indirect Factors Affecting Reflective Sign Brightness." St. Paul: 3M Company, January 1977.

[9]B. W. Koth, W. D. McCunney, C. P. Duerk et al., *Vehicle Fog Lighting: An Analytical Evaluation.* Report No. DOT-HS-803-442. Philadelphia: Franklin Institute Research Labs, March 1978.

[10]V. J. Roper and E. A. Howard, "Seeing with Motorcar Headlamps." *Illumination Engineering*, 33:412–438 (1938).

[11]B. L. Cole, "Visual Aspects of Road Engineering." *Australia Road Research Board Sixth Conference Proceedings. Part I. Principal*

Addresses and Invited Papers. Victoria: Australian Road Research Board, 1972, pp. 102–148.

[12]I. Schmidt, *Visual Consideration of Man, the Vehicle, and the Highway. Part I*. Pub. SP-279. Warrendale, PA.: Society of Automotive Engineers, 1966.

[13]B. L. Cole, "Some Observations on Disability Glare." *Proceedings of Glare Seminar*. Victoria: Australian Road Research Board, 1977.

[14]R. G. Mortimer and P. L. Olson, *Development and Use of Driving Tests to Evaluate Headlamp Beams*. Report No. UM-HSRI-HF-74-14. Ann Arbor: Highway Safety Research Institute, University of Michigan, March 1974.

[15]H. Davson, *The Physiology of the Eye*, 2nd ed. Boston: Little, Brown, 1963.

[16]R. R. Mourant and T. H. Rockwell, "Mapping Eye-Movement Patterns to the Visual Scene in Driving: An Exploratory Study." *Human Factors*, 12:81–87 (1970).

[17]R. G. Mortimer, E. R. Hoffman, A. Poskocil et al., *Studies of Automobile and Truck Rear Lighting and Signaling Systems*. Report No. UM-HSRI-HF-74-25. Ann Arbor: Highway Safety Research Institute, University of Michigan, November 1974.

[18]P. L. Olson and R. A. Abrams, *Improved Motorcycle and Moped Headlamps*. Report No. 82-18. Ann Arbor: Highway Safety Research Institute, University of Michigan, May 1982.

[19]R. G. Mortimer and J. B. Becker, *Development of a Computer Simulation to Predict the Visibility Distance Provided by Headlamp Beams*. Report No. HF-73-15. Ann Arbor: Highway Safety Research Institute, University of Michigan, 1973.

16

Driver Steering Performance

WALTER W. WIERWILLE, Ph.D., P.E.
Professor, Industrial Engineering and Operations Research
Director, Vehicle Simulation Laboratory
Virginia Polytechnic Institute and State University
Blacksburg, Virginia

Walter W. Wierwille is Professor of Industrial Engineering and Operations Research and Director of the Vehicle Simulation Laboratory at Virginia Polytechnic Institute and State University, Blacksburg, Virginia. He also serves as President of Systemetrics, Incorporated, a consulting firm, also located in Blacksburg. He teaches several human factors design courses, and his current research interests include vehicle simulator technology, operator–vehicle systems analysis, and human factors design and evaluation techniques. He has held positions as Manager of the ECM Systems Group at Sanders Associates, Nashua, N.H., and Head of the Dynamics Systems Section at Cornell Aeronautical Laboratory, Buffalo, N.Y. Dr. Wierwille received his B.S.E.E. degree from the University of Illinois, Urbana, in 1958 and his Ph.D. degree from Cornell University in 1961. He is a Fellow of the Human Factors Society, a Senior Member of the IEEE and the IIE, and a member of several professional fraternities. He is a registered professional engineer, the author of more than

*50 publications, and a consultant to a number of govern-
ment and industrial organizations. Dr. Wierwille may be
contacted at the Industrial Engineering and Operations
Research Department, 142 Whittemore Hall, Virginia
Polytechnic Institute and State University, Blacksburg,
Virginia 24061 (703-961-7952).*

I. BACKGROUND

Human control of an automobile represents a complex psychomotor process in which the human functions as the loop-closing element. In general, there are two major subsystems in this process: longitudinal and lateral-directional.[1] Longitudinal control is effected by driver inputs to the accelerator, brake, clutch, and gearshift. Outputs are primarily forward velocity and position, and vehicle pitch. Later-directional control is effected most directly by driver steering wheel inputs. The torque imparted to, and the displacement of, the steering wheel causes changes in front-wheel angle, which, in turn, causes changes in vehicle lateral position, heading, and roll. The process is interactive in the sense that the road condition and vehicle state cause changes in steering forces and displacements as well.

Usually, the two subsystems of automobile control are considered separately, and in this section, the emphasis is on lateral-directional control and steering. However, it should always be kept in mind that there is some interaction between the longitudinal and lateral-directional systems. Whenever the automobile approaches the extremes of its capabilities, the separation into the two subsystems is no longer completely justified. Load and energy transfer effects may make it necessary to consider both subsystems as a single entity. Similarly, when drivers are pushed near the limits of their capabilities, treating steering independent of accelerating and braking may be unjustifiable. In many emergency cases, the driver performs simultaneous or alternate steering, braking, and accelerating maneuvers, and examination of one subsystem in isolation may be misleading.

Nevertheless, there is a great deal of knowledge about driver steering control that can be examined, more or less, in isolation from the longitudinal subsystem. This section is an attempt to summarize that knowledge. Driver steering has been a topic of intense research interest, and it would be possible to write several hundred pages on the subject. Here, however, emphasis will be placed on an overview, with references cited so that the interested reader may obtain additional, detailed information where desired.

As with any other aspect of human behavior, driver steering performance varies. It varies as a function of the driver, vehicular conditions, road, and other environmental conditions. Even if all vehicular and environmental conditions are held constant, as they sometimes can be in a driving simulator, a given driver's performance varies. If experimental runs are repeated, the driver will not exhibit precisely the same performance. There is always some variation in the response traces.

Although this variation in performance is substantial, characterization of a driver's responses is by no means hopeless. There are many constraints on the driver that force him or her to perform in a predictable manner. First, there is the control aspect of steering behavior. There are many steering strategies that would cause the driver–vehicle system to become unstable. For example, if a driver applies a clockwise input to the steering wheel that is proportional to the amount of lane deviation right of center, the vehicle becomes path unstable and ends up in a spiral. To maintain path stability, only certain strategies are acceptable. The driver must select from among the strategies that maintain stability.

Beyond stability, there are legal and social bounds on the operation of a motor vehicle. Driving in the left lane of a two-lane highway with traffic in both directions may produce temporary driver–vehicle stability, but it certainly would not represent acceptable behavior. Generally, a driver must stay in the correct lane, must operate the vehicle at a legal speed, and must otherwise conform to traffic regulations. These regulations also tend to constrain driver responses.

Additionally, it may be assumed that the driver is in command of the vehicle. That is, in most circumstances the driver can make the vehicle go where he or she wants it to go. Another way of saying this is that there is a desired path for the vehicle. The implications of desired or prescribed path are substantial. Because vehicle dynamics can be very precisely determined, and because the path of the vehicle is known, the inputs to the steering system that cause it to follow the given path can be determined mathematically. The driver must apply inputs that are to a great extent determined by the desired path. Again, this is a form of constraint on driver steering performance that tends to make that performance predictable and specifiable.

Thus, while there is variability in steering performance, there are also predictable, specifiable aspects of performance. Research methodologies must be used that take into account both the variability and the predictability. Usually, these will involve application of *statistical methods*, which make it possible to predict reliable differences in mean values as a function of specific independent variables. However, there are research investigators who use the concept of *"normative" models* or responses. The concept in this case is one of specifying or modeling the typical response of drivers in given situations. The review of steering performance to be presented here will rely on both research investigative approaches.

In the way of structure, this review is composed of four parts: normal driving, emergency driving, modeling, and effects of independent variables. The first two parts represent the major portion of the review and describe driver steering performance for ordinary drivers and ordinary vehicles. Although the discussion on the modeling is brief, it does discuss the "servo" aspects of driver performance, thereby providing some additional understanding of driving behavior. The part on the effects of independent variables is merely a listing of references under topics sufficiently complex that review papers could be written on each of them alone. The listing of references by category of independent variable seemed to represent the best compromise between total lack of discussion and a technical paper of book length. As a further surrender to brevity, only automobile driving is considered in this section.

The last known review of driver steering control was done by Hoffman.[2] His emphasis was on mathematical modeling and the effects of vehicle parameters, but the paper also covered the entire subject to an extent.

II. NORMAL STEERING BEHAVIOR

A. Lane Keeping, Effects of Preview, and Comparison with Tracking

In normal lane keeping, a driver relies primarily on visual inputs to judge the lateral position of the vehicle in the lane and the heading of the vehicle relative to the road. The driver does also rely on physical motion to an extent, however. Lateral position and heading are both controlled through steering. The roll axis of the vehicle is only indirectly controlled. As long as the vehicle remains on the highway in normal driving tasks, roll is not excessive and therefore need not be directly controlled. In fact, at a given speed, a driver must accept whatever roll occurs as a price for maintaining desired lateral position and heading.

In normal driving, the steering deflection as a function of time may take on one of two distinct characteristics: (1) a change in position from one setting to another with holds or "flat-tops" between changes or (2) a continuously changing wave form that is somewhat random in appearance. The former is likely to occur in low-disturbance, low-work-load driving on straight or steadily curved roads.[3] The latter is likely to occur when a driver is more intent on precise lane position or is overcoming crosswind disturbances and roadway irregularities.[4]

Because the driver controls both lateral position in the lane and heading, there is some question as to just how this is accomplished. Does the driver perform these operations simultaneously or alternately? If alternately, what is the priority? Modeling efforts by researchers have assumed both simultaneous control[5] and priority control.[4,6,7] Rather than take sides in this controversy, let us examine issues that are resolvable.

First, it should be noted that, to a first approximation, the time derivative of vehicle lateral position is proportional to heading. Therefore, a constant heading angle relative to the roadway tangent causes a linear change in lateral position with time. Because of this relationship, a driver can only effect a change in lateral position by first creating a heading deviation. Similarly, if lateral position is satisfactory, the driver must prevent heading deviations from occurring. Thus, a driver controls heading directly: when lateral error becomes noticeable, a purposeful heading deviation is introduced and then later removed to correct for lateral position.

Second, it is important to recognize that, again to a first approximation, steering deflection is proportional to the time derivative of heading. In other words, a constant steering deflection results in an eventual steady-state increase in heading angle. Therefore, an uncorrected steering deflection angle can result in a very rapid buildup of lateral position error. *Lack of attention to the steering task can cause appreciable lane deviation in a few seconds and may even result in a collision.*

Certain authors have attempted to develop models which integrate the control of lateral translation and heading by the driver.[8-10] These models ordinarily use the concept of a "sight point." The idea is that when the driver senses that either the heading or lateral position of the vehicle is incorrect, he or she turns the vehicle toward a sight point on the roadway in front of the vehicle and drives toward that point. By so doing, the driver eventually corrects for both heading and lateral deviation. The concept is appealing because it appears to coincide with intuitive notions about how drivers control vehicles. Furthermore, it can be shown that when drivers are modeled on this basis, stable driver–vehicle systems result.[10] The major shortcoming of the concept is in the selection of a sight point. Most likely, this point varies from moment to moment.

Driver control of lateral position and heading via steering represents a task that is largely psychomotor in nature. As such, it is related to tracking. In fact, driver lane keeping is sometimes referred to as lane tracking. There is a large difference, however, between lane keeping and pure tracking. In lane keeping the driver has a preview of the future input to the vehicle, whereas in pure tracking no information about the future input is given. If one wished to study pure tracking using the lateral-directional dynamics of an automobile, one could do so by cutting a hole in the floor of an automobile and then having drivers track a center line through that hole. Hopefully, this experiment would be performed on a test track closed to the public!

The relationship between driving and tracking may at first appear academic. However, when one observes that tracking can be considered as a limiting case of restricted preview, tracking then aids in the understanding of driving. Many authors have examined the effects of restricted preview, including Wierwille, Gagne, and Knight,[3] McLean and Hoffmann,[11] Allen and McRuer,[12] Helander, Merritt, and Abrams,[13] Thompson,[10] and MacAdam.[14] In general, results indicate that as preview is reduced, the driver's equivalent internal time delay increases. In other words, the driver with preview can overcome his or her own perceptual and neuromuscular lags by looking ahead in time, so to speak. *When preview is severely restricted, the driving task becomes more difficult, steering motion somewhat more erratic, and vehicle control less precise.* It is important to note that as preview becomes severely restricted, a driver can no longer accurately estimate vehicle direction relative to the road. Under these circumstances, the driver must rely more heavily on physical motion cues and on lateral position error accumulation rate to control heading. McLean and Hoffman[11] have used power spectral densities to examine changes in driver steering performance as preview is restricted. They conclude that peak frequencies shift from the 0.1 to 0.3 Hz region (for driving) to the 0.35 to 0.6 Hz region (for severely restricted preview). *Changes in perform-*

ance begin to occur when preview distance is shortened below 70 feet (at a speed of 30 mph). Restricted preview driving occurs in rain, snow, fog, night driving, and with certain types of windshield and glare conditions.

In lane keeping on a highway, quite often another vehicle or object is positioned on the road shoulder, but not in lane. When this occurs, it has been found that drivers steer away from the object and toward the unobstructed side of the lane in an apparent effort to maximize clearance between their vehicle and the obstruction.[15,16] It has similarly been found that when there is oncoming traffic in the adjacent lane to the left, drivers will move toward the right edge of their own lane. In fact, two studies have shown that *drivers begin their lateral movements to the right approximately 3 seconds before the oncoming traffic is abreast,* and that at the instant of passage, lane deviation (and therefore clearance) is maximized.[17,18]

There is a general consensus among researchers that a *shift in steering strategy occurs as roads become narrower or bridges are approached.* The change usually consists of more steering movements per unit time, which is perhaps indicative of the driver's desire for tighter control of lateral position.

When roads contain curves, drivers must rely more heavily on preview to maintain control of their vehicles. Modeling procedures by Thompson[10] indicate that instabilities may occur if preview distances are too short in simulated S-curves. Proper signing of curves with posted advisory speeds, however, have been found helpful.[19,20] As an additional aid, Witt and Hoyos[21] have developed a road-marking concept for curved roads. They decreased the length of lane-edge marking segments and gaps as curvature increased. According to the authors, this marking created smoother, more predictable driver steering performance in negotiating short radius curves.

B. Lane Changing and Passing

In lane changing and passing, the driver must effect a substantial shift in lateral position. However, this still involves the same principle as that used for a small correction of lateral position. Basically, the driver introduces a heading deviation that results in buildup of lateral deviation. Then as the vehicle approaches the correct lateral position in the adjacent lane, the driver removes the heading deviation by applying a steering correction in the direction opposite that of the initial steering input.

Passing differs from lane changing in that the above-described maneuver occurs twice, once to place the vehicle in the adjacent lane and once to return it to the original lane. In passing, then, there are really four segments to the steering waveform: initiation of the heading deviation in one direction, removal of heading deviation in that direction, initiation of heading deviation in the other direction, and removal of heading deviation in that direction.

Weir, Alex, and Ringland,[22] Jaksch,[23] McRuer, Allen, Weir, and Klein,[24] and Matsushita, Takanami, Takeda, and Takahashi[25] have all studied lane change and passing maneuvers. For expert drivers, passing maneuvers show a marked symmetry in steering (see Weir et al.,[22] Figures 3.1 and 3.2; and McRuer et al.,[24] Figure 8). A pulse of steering to the left is followed by a pulse of steering to the right, placing the vehicle in the left lane. Subsequently, a pulse of steering to the right is followed by one to the left, returning the vehicle to the right lane. Less experienced drivers tend to be less precise in their steering inputs, resulting in somewhat more noiselike responses. However, when averaged over several runs, a smoothed, pulselike structure emerges.

The rates at which lane change and passing maneuvers occur vary. For example, on four-lane highways, where there is no concern about oncoming traffic, passing maneuvers are sometimes performed over periods of up to perhaps 1 minute. In contrast, passing maneuvers on two-lane highways with oncoming traffic may take place in as little as a few seconds. The more rapidly the lane changes take place, the larger are the peaks of the steering waveform. In addition, if the time in the passing lane is sufficiently short, the second and third segments of the steering waveform may overlap in time.

III. EMERGENCY STEERING BEHAVIOR

Occasionally, drivers find themselves in situations that they had not anticipated and that contain an element of risk or danger. Usually, these situations require that quick judgments be made and that rapid actions be taken. In this subsection, research results will be reviewed for those situations in which steering inputs may be required. Obviously, many emergency situations require braking, but these will not be covered in this paper.

There are, of course, experimental difficulties in dealing with emergency steering behavior. Usually, tests must be performed on a closed course or track, or possibly in a simulator. Any full-scale experiment, even though conducted off the public roads, must still take all necessary safety and ethical precautions. Questions of validity then arise.

A. Loss of Driver Visual Input

Occasionally, drivers are faced with the loss of visual input. These situations can occur as a result of blinding snow squalls, headlight glare from an oncoming vehicle, sun glare on a dirty, frosted, or broken windshield, sudden puddle splashing onto the windshield, or hood latch failure. It was stated earlier that inattention of the driver to the steering task can result in the rapid buildup of lateral error. Therefore, potentially, loss of visual input is just as serious, since the driver does not know what steering action is the correct action.

Zwahlen[26] appears to have been the only researcher to have performed a study on path deviations resulting from occlusion. (Senders et al.[27] did, however, work with a model of driver uncertainty for occluded vision.) Zwahlen found, surprisingly, that path standard deviation increased as a function of *distance* as speed decreased. In other words, lower speeds caused greater lateral deviation as a function of distance (not time). He further found that permitting drivers to steer with no visual input produced smaller lane deviations than release of the steering wheel (no steering input). Since the vehicles used were properly aligned, the results suggest that drivers can use their kinesthetic senses to reduce path deviation.

Zwahlen's data indicate, for example, that for an occlusion distance of 300 feet and a speed of 30 mph, the corrected standard lateral deviation is approximately 18 inches with steering and 30 inches without steering. Clearly, one could expect substantially larger deviations in an operational environment where initial deviation would be uncorrected, road crown and curvature may exist, and surprise may cause an incorrect steering input.

B. Gust Responses and Blowouts

Occasionally, drivers encounter wind-shear-type crossgusts. These gusts can be very severe and may result in hundreds of pounds of force being applied to the side of the vehicle. They may occur when exiting bridges or tunnels, when crossing mountain passes, or when large trucks and buses are abreast. These step gusts are more dangerous than random amplitude gusts because they may be unexpected and can be higher in peak amplitude.

Research has been directed at determining lane deviations and reaction times for typical drivers. Both issues are important from the standpoint of vehicle design and in certain instances from the standpoint of litigation.

Tire blowouts are similar to step gusts in that they are unanticipated, they create vehicle disturbances, and they will usually require some corrective steering action by the driver. They differ, however, in that the vehicle itself undergoes a rapid deterioration in dynamics and, therefore, may respond in a manner unpredictable to the driver.

In regard to crossgusts, Iacovoni[28] appears to have been the first to examine their effects on driver–vehicle steering performance. Using a gas nozzle mounted sideways on the hood of a vehicle, he applied step side forces to the vehicle and recorded responses. He found that drivers initiated steering corrections in approximately 0.3 seconds. Lane deviations of approximately 0.5 feet and heading deviations of approximately 0.7° were noted for a step side force of 150 pounds. Later, Mahig[29] attempted to combine a driver model and a vehicle model in an effort to study the stability of such a driver–vehicle system to side gusts.

More recently, Repa, Zucker, and Wierwille[30] and Alexandridis, Repa, and Wierwille[31] examined peak lateral deviation resulting from crossgusts. For side forces of approximately 300 pounds, peak lateral deviations between 30 and 60 inches were observed, depending on vehicle characteristics. Their results support the indication that crossgusts can be dangerous because in some cases vehicles will exceed lane boundaries. These cases will occur even though the driver makes a concerted effort to correct for them.

In a follow-up study, Wierwille, Casali, and Repa[32] examined driver steering reaction time to crossgusts. They found that reaction times were relatively short, that is, between 0.3 and 0.6 seconds. Apparently, the driver relies heavily on motion cues and triggered learned responses for control of crossgusts.

In regard to *truck- and bus-induced aerodynamic disturbances*, similar results have been obtained[33]; that is, in certain cases lane boundaries may be exceeded despite corrective efforts by the driver. Weir, Hoh, and Teper[33] studied two distinct cases: passing situations in still air and passing situations with steady crosswinds. In general, their results show that passing a large vehicle in calm air *pushes the driver's vehicle away from the large vehicle by as much as 1½ feet*. However, when passing a large vehicle in a negative crosswind condition, *the driver's vehicle is pulled toward the large vehicle and may easily exceed lane boundaries*, even though corrective action is taken by the driver. *This represents a distinct hazard and is worthy of remedial research and design effort.*

Despite its importance, very little research literature has been found on driver steering response to tire blowouts. Perhaps this is because of the danger and expense associated with such research. Sussman, Sugarman, and Knight[34] did simulate tire blowouts as part of a simulator study on driver fatigue. They did not, however, present the values of peak lane deviations even though those data were used in their experimental analyses. It must be remembered, however, that blowout behavior of automobiles may be highly variable. Consequently, driver–vehicle control must also be expected to vary substantially. Little definitive information appears to be available on this long-term potentially dangerous problem. Tire manufacturers are known to fail their tires purposely in testing, but results are not generally published. Similarly, driving schools do fail tires in some advanced training procedures, but responses of ordinary drivers to these failures have apparently not been studied.

C. Shoulder Climbing

There are some roads on which there is a sudden drop-off at the edge of the lane (usually at the edge of the pavement). Most state highway departments have endeavored to eliminate these hazards or have put up signs warning of their existence where they could not be eliminated. Occasionally, however, drivers still fall victim to them. Therefore, it is important to understand the nature of driver–vehicle performance associated with returning the vehicle to the driving lane.

Nordlin, Parks, Stoughton, and Stoker[35] appear to have been the first to examine this problem systematically. They found that as long as the tire that is off the shoulder does not scrub the shoulder (meaning the tire and shoulder edge are separated and come in contact with one another at an angle and with some lateral velocity), recovery is possible. *The cor-*

*rect procedure is to slow the vehicle, obtain some separation of
the shoulder and tire, and then turn back onto the pavement.*

Klein and Johnson[36] subsequently did additional full-scale
tests of shoulder climbing. Their results verified the earlier
ones, but their results also showed that if scrubbing occurs
and the driver persists in climbing the shoulder, an unstable
situation will result. Specifically, the tire eventually climbs
the shoulder, but because of the larger steering wheel deflection, the car crosses the lane rapidly and enters the adjacent
lane before the driver can recover (even though reverse steering
wheel correction is applied). *This situation is likely to occur
when unitiated drivers attempt to reenter their driving lanes
from shoulder drops of 4 inches or more.* (For a typical time
history of an unstable maneuver due to shoulder climbing, see
Klein and Johnson,[36] Figure 3.) Reverse steering following the
climb *does not* provide vehicle recovery, and *the vehicle literally
shoots into the adjacent lane and may spin out.* Clearly, these
results indicate that driver steering performance must be
taught for shoulder climbing.

D. Obstacle Avoidance, Evasive Maneuvers

One of the most important and frequent emergency situations
encountered by drivers is obstacle avoidance or evasive maneuvering. This situation differs from normal passing and
lane-change maneuvers in that the element of surprise is
present and some action must usually be taken to avoid a
collision. In many cases, as indicated earlier, drivers use
braking rather than steering. However, here it will be assumed
that the driver attempts to steer out of the difficulty.

It is important to recognize that in performing a given
evasive maneuver, drivers must achieve certain vehicle trajectories if they are to avoid a collision. This in turn constrains
the steering behavior that drivers may exhibit. Sheridan,[37]
Roland and Sheridan,[38] and Kroll[39] showed by means of preview modeling that obstacle avoidance can be considered as
an optimal trade-off relation between control effort and error.
In other words, drivers will attempt to miss an obstacle by a
safe margin, but not more. Furthermore, if this safe margin
cannot be attained, they will apply what they believe to be the
best steering strategy to obtain whatever remaining margin
can be achieved.

Unfortunately, substantial full-scale testing reported by
Koppa and Hayes[40] indicates that drivers rarely use the full

capabilities of their vehicles in emergencies and that, therefore, their impressions of the best steering strategy are usually incorrect. Koppa and Hayes used five different emergency situations and equipped vehicles with outriggers so that they could not be rolled over. They found that inexperienced drivers often lost control following evasive maneuvers and that drivers tended to level any differences that existed in vehicles.

Emergency steering maneuvers can often be characterized as having three distinct portions if they are successful in evading an object. These are described in the paper by Maeda, Irie, Hidaka, and Nishimura[41] (their Figures 9, 10, and 11). First there is a large steering input that results in rapid buildup of heading and lateral deviation. This first portion is used to avoid a collision with the object. As soon as the object is evaded, the second and third portions follow. In the second portion, a reverse steering input is applied. Its purpose is to stop the continued buildup of lateral deviation and to correct for vehicle heading. It represents a short-term holding action, so to speak, in which an attempt is made to reduce the likelihood of running off the road or of creating a potential collision situation with, perhaps, other vehicles or roadway objects. The third portion of the maneuver is the attempt to regain vehicle control and is termed control steer. Here the driver attempts to return to an appropriate lane and to reinstitute lane keeping.

Obviously, there may be some variation in the above scenario resulting from circumstances. For example, if a driver finds on evading one obstacle that there is a second obstacle in the way, he or she may have to produce at least two evasive steering inputs or use steering and braking together. One of these inputs is used to avoid the first obstacle, and the other is used to avoid the second obstacle. Furthermore, in the third portion, the driver may not be able to regain control of the vehicle and may end up off the road or spinning out. Usually, however, even when this loss of control occurs, it is less risky than collision with an obstacle.

Several other investigators have examined emergency steering maneuvers and have come to conclusions aligned with statements made earlier in this section. Fancher, Segel, Bernard, and Ervin[42] reviewed steering performance for emergency lane change maneuvers and concluded that there is some variability in these responses. However, the responses that Fancher et al. (see their Figures 5, 6, and 7) obtained clearly show the underlying four segments described in our discussion on lane changing. Barrett, Kobayashi, and Fox,[15] Summala,[16] and Reid, Graf, and Billing[43] dealt with obstacles partially blocking the lane of an approaching vehicle. They found similar characteristic steering waveforms, and they noted that maximum lane deviation usually occurs when the driver's vehicle is alongside the obstacle.

IV. MODELING OF THE DRIVER

In this section, emphasis has been on driver steering performance, not on modeling the driver. Nevertheless, the two subjects are related. Several times in this presentation, mention has been made of models, where additional insight into performance could be obtained by considering them.

There are, however, some aspects of modeling that are important but do not have internal validity. In other words, while the models may provide responses similar to the driver's, internally the models and the driver have different strategies. This is particularly true of the transfer-function models of the driver. This discussion is intended to provide additional insight by describing these transfer-function models very briefly.

Wierwille, Gagne, and Knight[3] showed in an experimental simulator study that drivers could be modeled in lane keeping or on winding roads by means of transfer functions. Their model included a predictor–corrector transfer function and a stabilizing transfer function (closed-loop). They found in comparing driving and tracking that the usual delays that occur in tracking models did not exist in driving models (see their Figures 11 and 12). They also found that tracking resulted in much greater amounts of lead compensation by the human operator than did driving. Therefore, fundamentally, *preview has the effect of eliminating effective time delay and of reducing lead compensation.*

The idea of using transfer-function models for driving occurred to several investigators in the late 1960s, and a great deal of work followed. One of the best summaries was presented by McRuer, Allen, Weir, and Klein.[24] They indicated that there are two basic modes and one advanced mode of control in driving and that at any given time a driver may exhibit one or more of these modes.

The three proposed modes are compensatory, pursuit, and precognitive. The compensatory mode would ordinarily be used for normal lane keeping. In this mode the driver overcomes wind gusts, road disturbances, and road crown and maintains the vehicle in the lane. According to McRuer et al., the following rules are applicable to the compensatory situation:

1. In adjusting to different vehicle dynamics, typical drivers adopt equalization which can be accounted for by the crossover model of manual control theory.
2. Driver lead equalization increases directly with and compensates for the vehicle effective time delay.
3. For a wide range of vehicle dynamic configurations, system crossover frequency is held substantially constant at about 4 rad/sec in full scale tests and 2 rad/sec in simulations . . .
4. System phase margins and system stability increase and effective system latency decreases as the effective vehicle time constant is decreased. [McRuer et al., p. 390[24]]

The pursuit mode is believed to be used for precise course following for turns, merges, drops, and exits. In this case the driver takes advantage of the preview to obtain a precise lane position and to follow curvature. The transfer-function models for the pursuit mode (see Figure 7 of McRuer et al.[24]) have a substantially higher driver/vehicle overall open-loop gain and less phase lag. Consequently, more precise directional and lateral control is achieved.

The precognitive mode of driver control is believed to be an open-loop mode in the sense that a driver applies a pre-learned command of steering input. The concept here is similar to that described earlier. Applying a pulse of steering to the left and another to the right to change lanes is an example. Yet another example is the first portion of the evasive maneuver in which a single large steering deflection is used to avoid an obstacle.

Transfer-function models do not adequately fit the precognitive mode. However, other methods of modeling do fit this mode and have been recognized from the beginning of driver modeling.[38] Knowing the approximate trajectory that the vehicle must take in an evasive maneuver determines to a great extent the inputs the driver must apply to miss the obstacle. However, reaction time and steering deflection do interact, and, thus, driver response cannot be uniquely determined without experimentation.

In regard to other aspects of modeling, most recent investigators have recognized that driver models must contain vehicle heading information and vehicle lateral position information as inputs and must produce steering deflection as an output. Obviously in any pursuit or precognitive model, additional input information must also be provided. Further information on modeling approaches can be found in Hoffmann's review.[2]

V. EFFECTS OF SPECIFIC INDEPENDENT VARIABLES ON STEERING PERFORMANCE

A large number of research studies have been directed at determining the effects of specific independent variables on driver steering performance. These studies may have involved both normal and emergency driving. Also, they vary substantially in terms of measures, methods, and results.

To avoid an overly lengthy presentation, typical references are cited here by category of independent variable, but without commentary. The full citations for these studies appear at the end of this section under the heading References on Steering Performance (pp. 429–434).

Alcohol and Other Drugs
Allen and Schwartz (1978)
Allen, Jex, McRuer, and DiMarco (1975)
Betts, Clayton, and Mackay (1972)
Clayton (1976)
Clayton, Betts, and Harvey (1974)
Crancer, Dille, Delay et al. (1969)
Dott and McKelvey (1977)
Howat and Mortimer (1978)
Huffman, Florio, Payne, and Boys (1963)
Landauer, Laurie, and Miller (1973)
Landauer, Miller, and Patman (1969)
Landauer, Pocock, and Prott (1974)
Linnoila and Mattila (1973)
Miller and Landauer (1971)
Mortimer and Sturgis (1979)
Patman, Landauer, and Miller (1969)
Salvendy and McCabe (1975)
Schroeder, Ewing, Rouse et al. (1972)
Smiley, Ziedman, and Moskowitz (1981)
Sugarman, Cozad, and Zavala (1973)
Ziedman, Smiley, and Moskowitz (1979)

Attentional Demand, Work Load
Blaaw, Godthelp, and Moraal (1976)
Farber and Gallagher (1972)
Helander, Merritt, and Abrams (1978)
Hicks and Wierwille (1979)
McDonald and Ellis (1975)
McDonald and Hoffmann (1980)
McLean and Hoffmann (1975)
Matsushita, Takanami, Takeda, and Takahashi (1980)
Senders, Kristofferson, Levison et al. (1967)
Wierwille and Gutmann (1978)
Wierwille, Gutmann, Hicks, and Muto (1977)

Fatigue, Long-term Driving
Attwood and Scott (1981)
Brown, Simmonds, and Tickner (1967)
Dureman and Boden (1972)
Greenshields (1966)
Muto and Wierwille (1982)
Platt (1964)
Riemersma, Biesta, and Wildervanck (1977)
Snook and Dolliver (1976)
Sussman, Sugarman, and Knight (1971)
Wierwille and Muto (1981)

Learning, Experience, Age, and Instruction
Attwood (1979)
Blaaw (1981)
Blaaw, Godthelp, and Moraal (1976)
Maeda, Irie, Hidaka, Nishimura (1977)
Rackoff (1975)
Smiley, Reid, and Fraser (1980)

Physical Motion
Casali and Wierwille (1980)
McLane and Wierwille (1975)
Repa, Leucht, and Wierwille (1981)

Sex Differences
Clayton, Betts, and Harvey (1974)
Hagen (1975)
Koppa and Hayes (1976)

Vehicle Parameters
Alexandridis, Repa, and Wierwille (1978)
Dugoff, Segel, and Ervin (1971)
Eaton and Dittmeier (1970)
Flanagan (1971)
Gillies (1979)
Good (1976)
Good (1979)
Hoffmann and Joubert (1966)
Hoffmann and Joubert (1968)
Jaksch (1978)
Koppa and Hayes (1976)
Lincke, Richter, and Schmidt (1973)
McLean and Hoffmann (1971)
Matsushita, Takanami, Takeda, and Takashashi (1980)
Olson and Thompson (1970)
Pierce, Woodson, and Selby (1973)
Repa, Alexandridis, Howell, and Wierwille (1978)
Repa, Leucht, and Wierwille (1981)
Repa, Leucht, and Wierwille (1982)
Repa and Wierwille (1976)
Repa, Zucker, and Wierwille (1977)
Richter (1974)
Stoudt (1969)
Sweatman and Joubert (1976)
Wierwille and Gutmann (1978)
Wierwille, Gutmann, Hicks, and Muto (1977)
Yoshimori (1976)

Other Independent Variables and Models
Biggs (1966)
Casali and Wierwille (1980)
Crossmann and Szostak (1968)
Hayhoe (1979)
Helander (1978)
Helander, Merritt, and Abrams (1978)
KLD Associates, Inc. (1980)
Konz and McDougal (1968)
Reddy and Ellis (1981)
Ritchie, McCoy, and Welde (1968)
Wohl (1961)

CITATIONS

[1] L. Segel, "Theoretical Prediction and Experimental Substantiation of the Response of the Automobile to Driver Steering Control." *Proceedings of the Automobile Division, Institution of Mechanical Engineers*, London, 1956-1957, Vol. 7, pp. 310-330.

[2] E. R. Hoffmann, "Human Control of Road Vehicles." *Vehicle System Dynamics*, 5:105-126 (1975-1976).

[3] W. W. Wierwille, G. A. Gagne, and J. R. Knight, "An Experimental Study of Human Operator Models and Closed-Loop Analysis Methods for High-Speed Automobile Driving." *IEEE Transactions on Human Factors in Electronics*, HFE-8:187-201 (1967).

[4] J. M. Carson and W. W. Wierwille, "Development of a Strategy Model of the Driver in Lane Keeping." *Vehicle System Dynamics*, 7:233-253 (1978).

[5] D. H. Weir and C. H. Wojcik, "Simulator Studies of the Driver's Dynamic Response in Steering Control Tasks." *Highway Research Record*, 364:1-15 (1971).

[6] E. Donges, "A Two-Level Model of Driver Steering Behavior." *Human Factors*, 20:691-707 (1978).

[7] H. Godthelp and H. Konings, "Levels of Steering Control: Some Notes on the Line to Line Crossing Concept as Related to Driving Strategy." *Proceedings of the First European Annual Conference on Human Decision Making and Manual Control*, Delft, The Netherlands, May 1981, pp. 343-356.

[8] J. G. Wohl, "Man-Machine Steering Dynamics." *Human Factors*, 3:222-228 (1961).

[9] N.L. Biggs, "Directional Guidance of Motor Vehicles—A Preliminary Survey and Analysis." *Ergonomics*, 9:193-202 (1966).

[10] A. G. Thompson, "Parameter Plane Studies of Car Steering Stability with Combined Lateral and Previewed Error Sensing by the Driver." *Journal of Mechanical Engineering Science*, 21:139-152 (1979).

[11] J. R. McLean and E. R. Hoffmann, "The Effects of Restricted Preview on Driver Steering Control and Performance." *Human Factors*, 15:421-430 (1973).

[12] R. W. Allen and D. T. McRuer, "The Effect of Adverse Visibility on Driver Steering Performance in an Automobile Simulator." SAE paper 770239. Warrendale, PA.: Society of Automotive Engineers, February/March, 1977.

[13] M. Helander, J. O. Merritt, and C. Abrams, "Effect of Headlight Illumination on Driver Behavior." *Proceedings of the Twenty-second Annual Meeting of the Human Factors Society*, Detroit, October 1978, pp. 51-55.

[14] S. C. MacAdam, "Application of an Optimal Preview Control Method for Simulation of Closed-Loop Automobile Driving." *IEEE Transactions on Systems, Man, and Cybernetics*, SMC-11:393-399 (1981).

[15]G. V. Barrett, M. Kobayashi, and B. H. Fox, "Feasibility of Studying Driver Reaction to Sudden Pedestrian Emergencies in an Automobile Simulator." *Human Factors*, 10:19–26 (1968).

[16]H. Summala, "Driver/Vehicle Steering Response Latencies." *Human Factors*, 23:683–692 (1981).

[17]T. J. Triggs, "The Influence of Oncoming Vehicles on Automobile Lateral Position." *Human Factors*, 22:427–433 (1980).

[18]H. Summala, M. Leino, and J. Vierimaa, "Drivers' Steering Behavior When Meeting Another Car: The Case of Perceptual Tropism Revisited." *Human Factors*, 23:185–189 (1981).

[19]C. G. Hammer, "Evaluation of Minor Improvements." *Highway Research Record*, 286:33–45 (1969).

[20]K. S. Rutley, *Advisory Speed Signs for Bends*. Report No. LR 461, 27S. Transport and Road Research Laboratory, 1972.

[21]H. Witt and C. G. Hoyos, "Advance Information on the Road: A Simulator Study of the Effect of Road Markings." *Human Factors*, 18:521–532 (1976).

[22]D. H. Weir, F. R. Alex, and R. F. Ringland, *Driver Control During Overtaking and Passing Under Adverse Conditions*. Report No. 174-1. Hawthorne, CA.: Systems Technology, Inc., May 1969.

[23]F. O. Jaksch, "Driver–Vehicle Interaction with Respect to Steering Controllability," in A. Slibar and H. Springer (eds.), *The Dynamics of Vehicles on Roads and on Tracks*. Amsterdam: Swets and Zeitlinger, 1978, pp. 301–319.

[24]D. T. McRuer, R. W. Allen, D. H. Weir, and R. H. Klein, "New Results in Driver Steering Control Models." *Human Factors*, 19:381–397 (1977).

[25]A. Matsushita, K. Takanami, N. Takeda, and M. Takahashi, "Subjective Evaluation and Vehicle Behavior in Lane-Change Maneuvers." SAE paper 800845. Warrendale, PA.: Society of Automotive Engineers, June 1980.

[26]H. T. Zwahlen, "A Theoretical and Experimental Investigation of Automobile Path Deviations When Driver Steers with No Visual Input." *Highway Research Record*, 520:25–37 (1974).

[27]J. W. Senders, A. B. Kristofferson, W. H. Levison et al., "The Attentional Demand of Automobile Driving." *Highway Research Record*, 195:15–33 (1967).

[28]D. H. Iacovoni, "Vehicle–Driver Simulation for a Cross-Wind Disturbance Condition." SAE paper 670609. Warrendale, PA.: Society of Automotive Engineers, February 1967.

[29]J. Mahig, "Effects of Variation of Speed on Vehicle Handling During Wind Gust." ASME paper 73-ICT-3. New York: American Society of Mechanical Engineers, September 1973.

[30]B. S. Repa, R. S. Zucker, and W. W. Wierwille, "The Application of Integral Performance Criteria to the Analysis of Discrete Maneuvers in a Driving Simulator." *Proceedings of the Thirteenth Annual Conference on Manual Control*, Cambridge, Massachusetts, June 1977, pp. 81–100.

[31]A. A. Alexandridis, B. S. Repa, and W. W. Wierwille, "The Influence of Vehicle Aerodynamic and Control Response Characteristics on Driver–Vehicle Performance." *Proceedings of the Fourteen Annual Conference on Manual Control*, Los Angeles, April 1978, pp. 279–294. (NASA Conf. Pub. 2060.)

[32]W. W. Wierwille, J. G. Casali, and B. S. Repa, "Driver Steering Reaction Time to Abrupt-Onset Crosswinds, as Measured in a Moving-Base Driving Simulator." *Human Factors*, 25(1):103–116 (February 1983).

[33]D. H. Weir, R. H. Hoh, and G. L. Teper, "Driver–Vehicle Control and Performance in the Presence of Aerodynamic Disturbances from Large Vehicles." *Transportation Research Record*, 520:1–12 (1974).

[34]E. D. Sussman, R. C. Sugarman, and J. R. Knight, "Use of Simulation in a Study Investigating Alertness During Long-Distance, Low Event Driving." *Highway Research Record*, 364:27–32 (1971).

[35]E. F. Nordlin, D. M. Parks, R. L. Stoughton, and J. R. Stoker, *The Effect of Longitudinal Edge of Paved Surface Drop-off on Vehicle Stability*. Report No. CA-DOT-TL-6783-1-76-22. Sacramento: California Department of Transportation, March 1976.

[36]R. H. Klein and W. A. Johnson, "Vehicle Controllability in a Pavement/Shoulder Edge Climb Maneuver." SAE paper 780620. Warrendale, PA.: Society of Automotive Engineers, September 1978.

[37]T. B. Sheridan, "Three Models of Preview Control." *IEEE Transactions on Human Factors in Electronics*, HFE-7:91–102 (1966).

[38]R. D. Roland and T. B. Sheridan, *Simulation Study of the Driver's Control of Sudden Changes in Previewed Path*. MIT Report No. DSR-74920-1. Cambridge: M.I.T., Department of Mechanical Engineering, 1967.

[39]C. V. Kroll, "Preview-Predictor Model of Driver Behavior in Emergency Situations." *Highway Research Record*, 364:16–26 (1971).

[40]R. J. Koppa and G. G. Hayes, "Driver Inputs During Emergency or Extreme Vehicle Maneuvers." *Human Factors*, 18:361–370 (1976).

[41]T. Maeda, N. Irie, K. Hidaka, and H. Nishimura, "Performance of Driver–Vehicle Systems in Emergency Avoidance." SAE paper 770130. Warrendale, PA.: Society of Automotive Engineers, 1977.

[42]P. Fancher, L. Segel, J. Bernard, and R. Ervin, "Test Procedures for Studying Vehicle Dynamics in Lane Change Maneuvers." SAE paper 760351. Warrendale, PA.: Society of Automotive Engineers, February 1976.

[43]L. D. Reid, W. O. Graf, and A. M. Billing, *A Preliminary Simulator Study of the Obstacle Avoidance Maneuver*. Report No. CVOS-TR-80-07. Toronto: Ontario Ministry of Transportation and Communication, May 1980.

REFERENCES ON STEERING PERFORMANCE

1. A. A. Alexandridis, B. S. Repa, and W. W. Wierwille, "The Influence of Vehicle Aerodynamic and Control Response Characteristics on Driver–Vehicle Performance." *Proceedings of the Fourteen Annual Conference on Manual Control*, Los Angeles, April 1978, pp. 279–294. (NASA Conf. Pub. 2060.)
2. R. W. Allen and S. H. Schwartz, "Alcohol Effects on Driver Risk Taking." *Proceedings of the Twenty-second Annual Meeting of the Human Factors Society*, Detroit, October 1978, pp. 579–582.
3. R. W. Allen, H. R. Jex, D. T. McRuer, and R. J. DiMarco, "Alcohol Effects on Driving Behavior and Performance in a Car Simulator." *IEEE Transactions on Systems, Man, and Cybernetics*, SMC-5:498–505 (1975).
4. D. A. Attwood, "The Effects of Driving Experience on Objective Measures of Driving Performance." *Proceedings of the Twenty-third Annual Meeting of the Human Factors Society*, Boston, October 1979, pp. 277–281.
5. D. A. Attwood and P. L. Scott, "The On-Line Use of Performance Measures to Predict Driving Fatigue." *Proceedings of the Twenty-fifth Annual Meeting of the Human Factors Society*, Rochester, N.Y., October 1981, pp. 726–730.
6. T. A. Betts, A. B. Clayton, and G. M. Mackay, "Effects of Four Commonly Prescribed Tranquillizers upon Low-Speed Vehicular Handling Tests." *British Medical Journal*, 4:580–584 (1972).
7. N. L. Biggs, "Directional Guidance of Motor Vehicles—A Preliminary Survey and Analysis." *Ergonomics*, 9:193–202 (1966).
8. G. J. Blaaw, "Driver's Internal Representation and Supervisory Control: A First Model Verification in Relation to Driving Experience Task Demands and Deteriorated Vision." *Proceedings of the First European Conference on Human Decision Making and Manual Control*, Delft, The Netherlands, May 1981, pp. 315–327.
9. G. J. Blaaw, J. Godthelp, and J. Moraal, "Driver's Lateral Control as Affected by Task Demands and Driving Experience." SAE paper 770876. Warrendale, PA.: Society of Automotive Engineers, September 1976.
10. I. D. Brown, D. C. V. Simmonds, and A. H. Tickner, "Measurement of Control Skills, Vigilance, and Performance on a Subsidiary Task During Twelve Hours of Car Driving." *Ergonomics*, 10:665–679 (1967).
11. J. G. Casali and W. W. Wierwille, "The Effects of Various Design Alternatives on Moving-Base Driving Simulator Discomfort." *Human Factors*, 22:741–756 (1980).
12. A. B. Clayton, "The Effects of Psychotropic Drugs upon Driving-related Skills." *Human Factors*, 18:241–252 (1976).
13. A. B. Clayton, T. A. Betts, and P. G. Harvey, "The Influence

of Sex and Personality Factors upon the Effects of Tranquil-lizers on Driving Performance." *Proceedings of the Sixth International Conference on Alcohol, Drugs, and Traffic Safety,* Toronto, 1974, pp. 415-422.

14. A. Crancer, J. M. Dille, J. C. Delay et al., "Comparison of the Effects of Marijuana on Simulated Driving Tasks." *Science,* 164:851-854 (1969).

15. E. R. F. W. Crossman and H. Szostak, "Man–Machine Model for Car Steering." *Proceedings of the Fourth Annual NASA-University Conference on Manual Control,* Ann Arbor, Michigan, March 1968, pp. 171-195. (NASA Special Pub. 192.)

16. A. B. Dott and R. K. McKelvey, "The Influence of Ethyl Alcohol in Moderate Levels on the Ability to Steer a Fixed Base Shadograph Driving Simulator." *Human Factors,* 19:295-300 (1977).

17. H. Dugoff, L. Segel, and R. D. Ervin, "Measurement of Vehicle Response in Severe Braking and Steering Maneuvers." SAE paper 710080. Warrendale, PA.: Society of Automotive Engineers, January 1971.

18. E. I. Dureman and C. Boden, "Fatigue in Simulated Car Driving." *Ergonomics,* 15:299-308 (1972).

19. D. A. Eaton and H. J. Dittmeier, "Braking and Steering Effort Capabilities of Drivers." SAE paper 700363. *International Automobile Safety Conference Compendium,* Detroit, May 1970, pp. 153-158.

20. E. Farber and V. Gallagher, "Attentional Demand as a Measure of the Influence of Visibility Conditions on Driving Task Difficulty." *Highway Research Record,* 414:1-5 (1972).

21. W. Flanagan, "Data Indicate Lower Steer Ratio Promotes Better Emergency Action." *Automotive Engineering,* 79:30-32 (1971).

22. G. J. Gillies, "Human Factors Assessment of Vehicle Power Steering." *Ergonomics,* 22:253-262 (1979).

23. M. C. Good, "Sensitivity of Driver–Vehicle Performance to Vehicle Characteristics Revealed in Open-Loop Tests." *Vehicle System Dynamics,* 6:245-277 (1976).

24. M. C. Good, "Effects of Free-Control Variables on Automobile Handling." *Vehicle Systems Dynamics,* 8:253-285 (1979).

25. B. D. Greenshields, "Changes in Driver Performance with Time in Driving." *Highway Research Record,* 122:75-88 (1966).

26. R. E. Hagen, "Sex Difference in Driving Performance." *Human Factors,* 17:165-171 (1975).

27. G. F. Hayhoe, "A Driver Model Based on the Cerebellar Model Articulation Controller." *Vehicle System Dynamics,* 8:49-72 (1979).

28. M. Helander, "Driver's Steering Behavior During Traffic Events: A Case of Perceptual Tropism?" *Human Factors,* 20:681-690 (1978).

29. M. Helander, J. O. Merritt, and C. Abrams, "Effect of Headlight Illumination on Driver Behavior." *Proceedings of the Twenty-*

second Annual Meeting of the Human Factors Society, Detroit, October 1978, pp. 51–55.

30. T. G. Hicks and W. W. Wierwille, "Comparison of Five Mental Workload Assessment Procedures in a Moving-Base Driving Simulator." *Human Factors,* 21:129–143 (1979).

31. E. R. Hoffmann and P. N. Joubert, "The Effect of Changes in Some Vehicle Handling Variables on Driver Steering Performance." *Human Factors,* 8:245–263 (1966).

32. E. R. Hoffmann and P. N. Joubert, "Just Noticeable Differences in Some Vehicle Handling Variables." *Human Factors,* 10:263–272 (1968).

33. P. A. Howat and R. G. Mortimer, "Review of Effects of Alcohol and Other Licit Drugs on Driving-related Performance." *Proceedings of the Twenty-second Annual Meeting of the Human Factors Society,* Detroit, October 1978, pp. 564–572.

34. W. J. Huffmann, R. B. Florio, J. L. Payne, and F. E. Boys, "The Influence of Two Selected Tranquillizers on Driving Skills." *American Journal of Psychiatry,* 19:885–886 (1963).

35. F. O. Jaksch, "Driver–Vehicle Interaction with Respect to Steering Controllability," in A. Slibar and H. Springer (eds.), *The Dynamics of Vehicles on Roads and on Tracks.* Amsterdam: Swets and Zeitlinger, 1978, pp. 301–319.

36. KLD Associations, Inc., *A Review of the Driver–Vehicle Effectiveness (DRIVEM) Model.* Report No. TM-62. Huntington Station, N.Y.: KLD, November 1980.

37. S. Konz and D. McDougal, "The Effect of Background Music on the Control Activity of an Automobile Driver." *Human Factors,* 10:233–254 (1968).

38. R. J. Koppa and G. G. Hayes, "Driver Inputs During Emergency or Extreme Vehicle Maneuvers." *Human Factors,* 18:361–370 (1976).

39. A. A. Landauer, W. Laurie, and G. Miller, "The Effect on Benzoctamine and Alcohol on Motor Skills Used in Car Driving." *Forensic Science,* 2:275–283 (1973).

40. A. A. Landauer, G. Miller, and J. Patman, "Alcohol and Amitriptyline Effects on Skills Related to Driving Behavior." *Science,* 163:1467–1468 (1969).

41. A. A. Landauer, D. A. Pocock, and F. W. Prott, "The Effects of Medazepam and Alcohol on Cognitive and Motor Skills Used in Driving." *Psychopharmocologia,* 37:158–168 (1974).

42. W. Lincke, B. Richter, and R. Schmidt, "Simulation and Measurement of Driver Vehicle Handling Performance." SAE paper 730489. Warrendale, PA.: Society of Automotive Engineers, May 1973.

43. M. Linnoila and M. J. Mattila, "Drug Interaction on Psychomotor Skills Related to Driving: Diazepam and Alcohol." *European Journal of Clinical Pharmacology,* 5:186–194 (1973).

44. L. B. McDonald and N. C. Ellis, "Driver Work Load for Various

Turn Radii and Speeds." *Transportation Research Record*, 530: 18–30 (1975).

45. W. A. McDonald and E. R. Hoffmann, "Review of Relationships Between Steering Reversal Rate and Driving Task Demand." *Human Factors*, 22:733–739 (1980).

46. R. C. McLane and W. W. Wierwille, "The Influence of Motion and Audio Cues on Driver Performance in an Automobile Simulator." *Human Factors*, 17:488–501 (1975).

47. J. R. McLean and E. R. Hoffmann, "Analysis of Drivers Control Movements." *Human Factors*, 13:407–418 (1971).

48. J. R. McLean and E. R. Hoffmann, "Steering Reversals as a Measure of Driver Performance and Steering Task Difficulty." *Human Factors*, 17:248–256 (1975).

49. T. Maeda, N. Irie, K. Hidaka, and H. Nishimura, "Performance of Driver–Vehicle Systems in Emergency Avoidance." SAE paper 770130. Warrendale, PA.: Society of Automotive Engineers, March 1977.

50. A. Matsushita, K. Takanami, N. Takeda, and M. Takahashi, "Subjective Evaluation and Vehicle Behavior in Lane-Change Maneuvers." SAE paper 800845. Warrendale, PA.: Society of Automotive Engineers, June 1980.

51. G. Miller and A. A. Landauer, "Alcohol, Thioridazine and Chlorpromazine Effects on Skills Related to Driving Behavior." *British Journal of Psychiatry*, 118:351–352 (1971).

52. R. G. Mortimer and S. P. Sturgis, "Some Effects of Alcohol on Car Driving on Two-Lane and Limited-Access Highways." *Proceedings of the Twenty-third Annual Meeting of the Human Factors Society*, Boston, October 1979, pp. 254–258.

53. W. M. Muto and W. W. Wierwille, "The Effects of Repeated Emergency Response Trials on Performance During Extended Duration Simulated Driving." *Human Factors*, 24(6):693–698 (December 1982).

54. P. L. Olson and R. R. Thompson, "The Effect of Variable-Ratio Steering Gears on Driver Preference and Performance." *Human Factors*, 12:553–558 (1970).

55. J. Patman, A. A. Landauer, and G. Miller, "The Combined Effect of Alcohol and Amitriptyline on Skills Similar to Motor-Car Driving." *Medical Journal of Australia*, 2:946–949 (1969).

56. B. Pierce, W. Woodson, and P. Selby, *Human Force Considerations in the Failure of Power-assisted Devices*. Report No. DOT-HS-230-2-396. Washington, D.C.: National Highway Traffic Safety Administration, 1973.

57. F. N. Platt, "A New Method for Evaluating the Effects of Fatigue on Driver Performance." *Human Factors*, 6:351–358 (1964).

58. N. J. Rackoff, "An Investigation of Age-related Changes in Drivers' Visual Search Patterns and Driving Performance and the Relation to Tests of Basic Functional Capacities." *Proceed-*

ings of the Nineteenth Annual Meeting of the Human Factors Society, Dallas, October 1975, pp. 285-288.

59. R. N. Reddy and J. R. Ellis, "Contribution to the Simulation of Driver-Vehicle-Road System." SAE paper 810513. Warrendale, PA.: Society of Automotive Engineers, February 1981.

60. B. S. Repa and W. W. Wierwille, "Driver Performance in Controlling a Driving Simulator with Varying Vehicle Response Characteristics." SAE paper 760779. Warrendale, PA.: Society of Automotive Engineers, October 1976.

61. B. S. Repa, P. M. Leucht, and W. W. Wierwille, "The Influence of Motion Cues on Driver-Vehicle Performance in a Simulator." *Proceedings of the Seventeenth Annual Conference on Manual Control,* Los Angeles, June 1981, pp. 157-169.

62. B. S. Repa, P. M. Leucht, and W. W. Wierwille, "The Effect of Simulator Motion on Driver Performance." SAE paper 820307. Warrendale, PA.: Society of Automotive Engineers, February 1982.

63. B. S. Repa, R. S. Zucker, and W. W. Wierwille, "The Application of Integral Performance Criteria to the Analysis of Discrete Maneuvers in a Driving Simulator." *Proceedings of the Thirteenth Annual Conference on Manual Control,* Cambridge, Massachusetts, June 1977, pp. 81-100.

64. B. S. Repa, A. A. Alexandridis, L. J. Howell, and W. W. Wierwille, "Study of Vehicle Steering and Response Characteristics in Simulated and Actual Driving." SAE paper 780011. Warrendale, PA.: Society of Automotive Engineers, March 1978.

65. B. Richter, "Driving Simulator Studies: The Influence of Vehicle Parameters on Safety in Critical Situations." Report No. DOT-HS-4-00944. *Proceedings of the International Automobile Tire Conference,* Toronto, October 1974, pp. 91-99.

66. J. B. J. Riemersma, P. W. Biesta, and C. Wildervanck, "Fatigue and Stress Due to Prolonged Driving and Changing Task Demands." SAE paper 770134. Warrendale, PA.: Society of Automotive Engineers, February 1977.

67. M. L. Ritchie, W. K. McCoy, and W. L. Welde, "A Study of the Relation Between Forward Velocity and Lateral Acceleration in Curves During Normal Driving." *Human Factors,* 10:255-258 (1968).

68. G. Salvendy and G. P. McCabe, Jr., "Marijuana and Human Performance." *Human Factors,* 17:229-235 (1975).

69. S. A. Schroeder, J. A. Ewing, B. A. Rouse et al., *Synergistic Effects of Alcohol, Methapyriline, and Chlordiazepoxide on Driver's Eye Movements and Tracking Errors in Simulated Dangerous Situations.* Chapel Hill: Highway Safety Research Center, University of North Carolina, September 1972.

70. J. W. Senders, A. B. Kristofferson, W. H. Levison et al., "The Attentional Demand of Automobile Driving." *Highway Research Record,* 195:15-33 (1967).

71. A. Smiley, L. Reid, and M. Fraser, "Changes in Driver Steering Control with Learning." *Human Factors*, 22:401–415 (1980).
72. A. Smiley, K. Ziedman, and H. Moskowitz, "Manual Control Analysis of Drug Effects on Driving Performance." Jet Propulsion Lab. Report No. 81–95. *Proceedings of the Seventeenth Annual Conference on Manual Control*, Pasadena, California, October 1981, pp. 503–514.
73. S. H. Snook and J. J. Dolliver, "Driver Fatigue: A Study of Two Types of Countermeasures." *Proceedings of the Twentieth Annual Meeting of the Human Factors Society*, College Park, Maryland, July 1976, pp. 304–311.
74. H. Stoudt, *Vehicle Handling: Force Capabilities from Braking and Steering*. Boston: Harvard School of Public Health, May 1969.
75. R. C. Sugarman, C. P. Cozad, and A. Zavala, "Alcohol-induced Degradation of Performance on Simulated Driving Tasks." SAE paper 730099. Warrendale, PA.: Society of Automotive Engineers, January 1973.
76. E. D. Sussman, R. C. Sugarman, and J. R. Knight, "Use of Simulation in a Study Investigating Alertness During Long-Distance, Low-Event Driving." *Highway Research Record*, 364: 27–32 (1971).
77. P. F. Sweatman and P. N. Joubert, "Automobile Directional Characteristics and Driver Steering Performance." *Vehicle System Dynamics*, 5:155–170 (1976).
78. W. W. Wierwille and J. C. Gutmann, "Comparison of Primary and Secondary Task Measures as a Function of Simulated Vehicle Dynamics and Driving Conditions." *Human Factors*, 20:233–244 (1978).
79. W. W. Wierwille and W. M. Muto, "Significant Changes in Driver-Vehicle Response Measures for Extended Duration Simulated Driving Tasks." *Proceedings of the First European Annual Conference on Human Decision Making and Manual Control*, Delft, The Netherlands, May 1981, pp. 298–314.
80. W. W. Wierwille, J. C. Gutmann, T. G. Hicks, and W. M. Muto, "Secondary Task Measurement of Workload as a Function of Simulated Vehicle Dynamics and Driving Conditions." *Human Factors*, 19:557–565 (1977).
81. J. G. Wohl, "Man–Machine Steering Dynamics." *Human Factors*, 3:222–228 (1961).
82. K. Yoshimori, "Vehicle Controllability and Human Response Characteristics." SAE paper 760780. Warrendale, PA.: Society of Automotive Engineers, October 1976.
83. K. Zeidman, A. Smiley, and H. Moskowitz, "The Effects of Drugs on Driving: Driving Simulator Tests of Diazepam and Secobarbital." *Proceedings of the Twenty-third Annual Meeting of the Human Factors Society*, Boston, October 1979, pp. 259–262.

17

Motorcycle Conspicuity

PAUL L. OLSON, Ph.D.
The University of Michigan Transportation Research Institute
Ann Arbor, Michigan

*Paul L. Olson is associated with the Human Factors
Group at the University of Michigan Transportation
Research Institute. After graduating from Purdue
University in 1959, he joined the staff of the General
Motors Research Laboratories. At GM he worked on
problems such as vehicle control, lighting, and traffic
control. In 1971 he joined the staff of the Highway Safety
Research Institute of the University of Michigan (as the
Institute was then known) and since then has been involved
in projects having to do with vehicle lighting, conspicuity,
traffic signs, and driver perception. He may be contacted
at the University of Michigan Transportation Research
Institute, which is part of the Institute of Science and
Technology and is located at 2901 Baxter Road, Ann
Arbor, Michigan 48109 (313-764-4158).*

I. INTRODUCTION

One of the major changes in the traffic scene in recent years has been an increase in the number of motorcycles. Since 1961, motorcycle registrations have increased at a rate about four times that of all other vehicles, reaching a total of nearly 6 million in 1980.[1]

In 1980 motorcycles comprised about 3.5 percent of the total vehicle population. An examination of the general accident statistics suggests that motorcyclists do no worse than the operators of other vehicles in terms of crash involvement. They are ridden fewer miles per unit time than most other vehicles, but motorcycles still accounted for only about 1.7 percent of all motor vehicle crashes in 1980. However, when a crash occurs with a motorcycle, its rider(s) are much more likely to be injured. For example, in 1981 there were 21,800,000 crashes involving passenger cars and 510,000 involving motorcycles, a difference of about 45 to 1. But, the automobile crashes resulted in 28,800 occupant fatalities versus 4000 for motorcycles, a difference of about 7 to 1. Overall, in 1980 the death rate for motorcycles was estimated at 21 per 100 million miles, while that for all other vehicles was only about 3.5 per 100 million miles.[1]

Motorcyclists and their passengers are at a disadvantage when a mishap occurs because the vehicle itself offers little protection. There are no prospects for improving this situation, so the emphasis in motorcycle safety has been on protective gear (e.g., helmets) and accident-reducing strategies, such as rider's courses and improved licensing procedures.

II. ACCIDENT DATA

Motorcyclists learn early to "look out for cars," the drivers of which often seem to behave as though the motorcycle was not present. Gradually, statistical evidence has accumulated indicating that this was not simply paranoia on the part of bikers. For example, Harano and Peck[2] compared car-car and motorcycle-car crashes that occurred in California in 1966. *They found that motorcycle-car crashes were more likely to occur at intersections than were car-car crashes.*

A short time later, two other studies—Waller[3] and Reiss, Berger, and Vallette[4]—were reported that examined culpability in motorcycle-car crashes. Waller's analysis was based on 630 crashes that occurred in 1973. Reiss' was based on 400 Maryland crashes that also occurred in 1973. *The results of these two studies are virtually identical, the driver of the car being judged culpable in 62.2 percent of the cases by Waller and in 61.1 percent of the cases by Reiss et al.*

Several studies have examined motorcycle-car crashes from a point of view of the precrash maneuvers of each vehicle—for example, Griffin,[5] who examined 1267 crashes, and Reiss, Berger, and Vallette,[4] who analyzed a subsample of 100 of their crashes. Both studies found that the motorcycle was traveling straight most of the time (about 60 percent) and at a higher incidence than the involved cars. The disparity in precrash actions comparing cars and motorcycles is consistent with the findings concerning culpability just described and suggests that auto drivers occupied with a maneuver such as turning across or merging with traffic may have more of a chance of failing to detect or incorrectly identifying a motorcycle than a car.

It has been hypothesized that the problem of inappropriate response on the part of motorists toward motorcycles may stem in part from lack of experience. That is, motorcycles are a relatively new phenomenon in the United States and motorists are not used to looking for them. If true, then the accident experience should be different in other parts of the world where motorcycles have been a significant part of the traffic mix for a longer period of time. Available evidence suggests this is not the case. For example, Smith,[6] in Australia, found that in motorcycle-car crashes, the car driver most often erred by turning right (corresponding to a left turn in the United States) without sufficient room, or failed to yield at an intersection. Nagayama, Morita, Miura, Watanabem, and Murakami[7] analyzed precrash maneuvers in Japan and noted that the motorcycle was traveling straight in 86 percent of the cases in their example.

The most comprehensive look at precrash activity in motorcycle-car crashes was carried out by Olson, Halstead-Nussloch, and Sivak.[8] The analysis was based on 6467 motorcycle-car crashes in Texas in 1975. A sample of car-car crashes (total of 16,353), also drawn from 1975 Texas data, was used for a comparison. For purposes of this discussion, the most important data are summarized in Table 17-1. Each row in this table gives the percentages of times each vehicle was engaged in each of six different types of maneuvers just prior to a crash.

Table 17-1 Percent of Precrash Maneuvers by Each Vehicle in Motorcycle–Car and Car–Car Crashes (Texas Data, 1975)[a]

CRASH SITUATION	VEHICLE	MANEUVER						
		TRAVELING STRAIGHT	TURNING RIGHT	TURNING LEFT	BRAKING	STOPPED	PARKED
Motorcycle–car	Motorcycle	87.2	2.8	6.2	0	3.4	0
	Car	46.4	7.0	36.7	1.7	7.2	0.9
Car–car	Car	39.7	7.6	22.9	2.7	24.4	2.7

[a]Adapted from P. L. Olson, R. Halstead-Nussloch, and M. Sivak, *Development and Testing of Techniques for Increasing the Conspicuity of Motorcycles and Motorcycle Drivers.* DOT-HS-805-143. Ann Arbor: University of Michigan, Highway Safety Research Institute, October 1979.

In Table 17-1, three columns are of special interest. First, as other investigators have noted, in motorcycle–car crashes, the motorcycle is usually traveling straight, while the car is much less likely to be doing so. Second, the car is more likely to be turning left if the impacting vehicle is a motorcycle than if it is a car. Third, motorcycle–car crashes rarely involve stopped vehicles, while it is a major category in car–car crashes.

Another analysis of these data is provided in Table 17-2. These data are only for crashes in which one vehicle (car or motorcycle) was turning left at the time. For all three relative travel directions (angle, same, and opposite), the car was many times more likely to be turning left than the motorcycle. The difference was especially large when the initial travel directions were opposite.

These data should be contrasted with those in Table 17-3, which is an identical analysis for car–truck collisions in the same state (Texas) for the same year (1975). The differences are striking. Table 17-3 is remarkably homogeneous whether comparing rows or columns. There is no evidence that the drivers of these two types of vehicles had any special problem reacting to one another.

Thus, a great deal of accident data from a variety of sources suggests that motorcycles, more so than cars and other large vehicles, are apt to be involved in crashes where the other driver is judged at fault and where the other vehicle was in the process of making a maneuver at the time (generally

Table 17-2 Motorcycle-Car Crashes in Which One Vehicle Was Making a Left Turn at the Time—Percent Involvement for Each Vehicle as a Function of Direction of Travel Prior to Crash (Texas Data, 1975)[a]

| LEFT-TURNING VEHICLE | RELATIVE TRAVEL DIRECTION | | | ROW TOTAL |
	ANGLE	SAME	OPPOSITE	
Motorcycle	5.2	4.5	3.0	12.7
Car	20.1	17.7	49.5	87.3
Column total	25.3	22.2	52.5	100.0

[a]Adapted from P.L. Olson, R. Halstead-Nussloch, and M. Sivak, *Development and Testing of Techniques for Increasing the Conspicuity of Motorcycles and Motorcycle Drivers*. Report No. DOT-HS-805-143. Ann Arbor: University of Michigan, Highway Safety Research Institute, October 1979.

Table 17-3 Car–Truck Crashes in Which One Vehicle Was Making a Left Turn at the Time—Percent Involvement for Each Vehicle as a Function of Direction of Travel Prior to Crash (Texas Data, 1975)[a]

LEFT-TURNING VEHICLE	RELATIVE TRAVEL DIRECTION			ROW TOTAL
	ANGLE	SAME	OPPOSITE	
Car	17.7	18.6	16.3	52.6
Truck	17.3	16.5	13.6	47.4
Column total	35.0	35.1	29.9	100.0

[a]Adapted from P. L. Olson, R. Halstead-Nussloch, and M. Sivak, *Development and Testing of Techniques for Increasing the Conspicuity of Motorcycles and Motorcycle Drivers*. Report No. DOT-HS-805-143. Ann Arbor: University of Michigan, Highway Safety Research Institute, October 1979.

a left turn). Specifically, two motorcycle–car precrash scenarios stand out as most overrepresented relative to car–car involvements. These are diagrammed in Figure 17-1. In each case the car tries to cross the path of the motorcycle when there is insufficient room for such a maneuver. As a consequence, the motorcycle typically runs into the side of the car. In some cases the motorcyclist may be able to maneuver clear of the car, only to impact something else or spill the bike.

III. WHY SUCH CRASHES OCCUR

One hypothesis for the phenomenon discussed above is that it reflects hostility on the part of car drivers toward motorcyclists. While many motorists are hostile toward motorcyclists, this is not a likely explanation, since the problem only seems to occur in a limited number of situations, and these are situations that are likely to result in significant damage to the involved car.

A different hypothesis has been advanced by Nagayama and his colleagues.[7] They speculate that part of the problem may be attributable to unawareness on the part of motorcyclists of the presence of vehicles seeking to maneuver across their path. The researchers made recordings of eye fixations while their subjects were driving a car and a motorcycle. The results indicate that, *while riding a motorcycle, these persons*

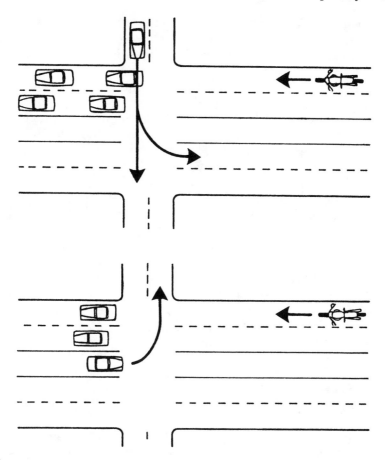

Figure 17-1 Two precrash configurations most overrepresented in motorcycle crash statistics.

may indeed have been visually less effective and more prone to overlook significant conditions in the forward field.

This is an intriguing study. The sample (three subjects) is very small, so the results are tentative. However, the implications are very important and further work is desirable.

The usual explanation for car–motorcycle crashes is that "drivers have trouble seeing motorcycles." It is popularly assumed that because motorcycles are small relative to most other vehicles having similar speed capability, they are more apt to be overlooked by a driver scanning approaching traffic for an opportunity to make a turn or crossing maneuver. This may well be a true and complete explanation of the problem. It accounts for the interest in "motorcycle conspicuity"—the effort to make the vehicle and/or its rider more attention-getting to car drivers.

However, there are reasonable explanations other than failure to detect. For example, there might be some tendency for motorists to misidentify the motorcycle as a bicycle or even a pedestrian. In a hurried glance, at a distance of some hundreds of feet, this would be an easy mistake to make. It could lead to an assumed lower speed and consequent over-estimation of available gap size.

Another possible explanation is speed–spacing judgment error. The motorcycle, being smaller, may be judged further away than a larger vehicle at the same distance. In addition, all other factors being equal, the angular size of a motorcycle will change at a slower rate than that of a car as it is driven toward an observer. Assume, for example, a 6-foot-wide car and a 2-foot-wide motorcycle first seen at 300 feet. The car subtends a horizontal angle of 1.15°, compared to 0.38° for the motorcycle. At 50 feet/second, 2 seconds later the car has increased to 1.72°, the motorcycle to 0.57°. The average increase in horizontal size during that time is about 0.28 degrees/second and 0.10 degrees/second for the car and motorcycle respectively. This difference may tend to cause drivers to err toward lower speed estimates if the approaching vehicle is a motorcycle.

It is possible that the special problem that motorcyclists seem to have can be traced to all of the above possibilities. The point is, *no one knows for certain*. To maximize effectiveness, "conspicuity-enhancing" treatments should not only be good attention-getters, they should aid in identifying the vehicle as a motorcycle.

IV. RESEARCH

In recent years there have been a number of studies of ways in which motorcycle conspicuity might be improved. Before reviewing these data, it is important to point out that there is a great deal of data on the effectiveness of one treatment, daytime headlights on. Several states enacted laws requiring motorcycles to have their headlights on at all times, starting in the late 1960s. Analysis of accident experience in states with and without such laws (e.g., Waller and Griffin[9]) indicates that use of low-beam lamps in daytime reduces accidents significantly.

There have been a number of suggestions for ways in which motorcycle conspicuity might be improved. For daytime use recommendations include the wearing of light-colored clothing and helmets and the use of fluorescent materials both on the rider and the bike. Fluorescent materials may have limited appeal to many bikers, but they should have excellent attention-getting properties, since they are so bright and contrast well with almost any background.

For nighttime use various retroreflective treatments have been proposed, ranging from tire sidewalls to the entire bike and rider.

For both day and night riding, a number of lighting techniques have been suggested. Beside continuous operation of the low beam already mentioned, they have included a wide variety of steady burning and flashing lamps in various locations, including the rider's helmet.

A key question is the relative effectiveness of the proposed treatments. The ultimate criterion is reduction in crashes, but such analyses are slow, costly, and difficult. For example, Hurt[10] noted few crashes involving riders wearing light-colored clothing. However, it is hard to rule out the possibility that riders who "dress light" are more cautious in their riding habits.

A number of approaches short of actual crash involvement have been used to evaluate conspicuity-enhancing techniques. These fall into four general categories.

1. *Observations and subjective appraisal.* This is a good technique for obtaining rapid initial appraisals of the attention-getting capabilities of various treatments. Its relationship to results obtained by other means is unknown, and total reliance on it is undesirable.

2. *"Laboratory" studies, with controlled presentations and reaction-time and/or percent-correct identification criteria.* Such studies may be run indoors (e.g., Williams and Hoffman[11]), typically using photographs, or outdoors (e.g., Burg and Beers[12]) using full-scale vehicles. The studies mentioned found greater detection and identification distances with the use of flourescent and retroreflective materials.

This technique has several advantages, including close control and economy. The use of alerted subjects and the relationship of criteria such as are customarily employed to the real-world situation in which crashes occur are the major unresolved questions.

3. *Exposing drivers in normal traffic to conspicuity treatments of interest and stopping them shortly thereafter (e.g., at a toll booth) to ask if they recall seeing a motorcycle recently.* Studies of this type have been reported by Janoff, Cassel, Fartner, and Smierciak,[13] Janoff and Cassel,[14] and Janoff,[15] concerned with headlights on; and by Ramsey and Brinkley,[16] concerned with strobe and flashing lights.

The theory is that the more conspicuous the treatment, the more likely the motorist is to perceive it and remember having done so a short time later. The technique is inexpensive and comes much closer to a real-life setting than the two previously described, but there is a question whether techniques that cause something to be remembered are necessarily those which will prove most effective in reducing crashes.

4. *A gap-acceptance measure.* It was noted earlier that in a common form of motorcycle–car crash the car driver was attempting to make a maneuver across the path of a motorcycle when there was not sufficient room. This suggests that a gap-acceptance measure would be useful. In such a study motorcycles with the treatments of interest are operated in normal traffic. Measures are made of gap sizes in front of the bike that are accepted and rejected by cars seeking to maneuver across its path. It is expected that good treatments will reduce the probability of short gaps being accepted.

The first such study was carried out by Kirkby and Stroud[17] to evaluate the effects of *headlights on* and *fluorescent clothing*. The test was carried out in a traffic circle in Great Britain. All measures were made on cars trying to turn left in front of the motorcycle. *No significant differences were found.*

Schuldt[18] evaluated *lights, auxiliary lighting,* and a *control car* in a nighttime study. He reports *significant differences between all conditions for all maneuvers studied.*

The largest study to date using gap-acceptance was by Olson, Halstead-Nussloch, and Sivak.[8] They evaluated nine daytime treatments and three nighttime treatments, plus a control motorcycle and car, for three car maneuvers (the two shown in Figure 17–1 plus a case where the car turned right). They found *significant daytime differences favoring: headlights on, a modulating headlight, and wearing of fluorescent clothing.* At night, running lights and wearing of retroreflective clothing reduced the incidence of short gaps being accepted.

V. CONCLUSIONS

Available research evidence makes it clear that *motorcyclists are involved in a significant number of accidents that seem to arise from perceptual limitations on the part of other drivers.* This is generally thought of as a failure to detect, but it may be attributable, at least in part, to other causes as well. Countermeasures should certainly focus on improvements in conspicuity, but they should also aid in identifying the vehicle as a motorcycle.

A great number of conspicuity techniques have been suggested and tested by various means. Several can be recommended as effective. *The simplest countermeasure is to ride with the low-beam head lamp on at all times. Wearing light-colored clothing and helmet is probably helpful. The use of fluorescent materials during the day and retroreflective materials during the night is probably more helpful.* Curiously, the effect of high-visibility materials seems greater when it is worn by the rider than when attached to the bike.[8] *Devices that cause the headlight to modulate in intensity seem quite effective. Use of the turn signal lamps as running lights also seem to help.*

With the available evidence it is surprising that more states have not enacted lights-on laws. True, all motorcycles sold in the country are now equipped so the headlight comes on with the ignition. However, some owners disable this system to reduce lamp burnout and/or to ensure that the battery will stay charged. Only legislation coupled with enforcement can discourage such unwise practices.

Motorcycles are surely here to stay. The toll they exact each year can be significantly reduced in several ways that will not impose an undue burden on the riders or reduce the pleasure of ownership. Among these are widespread use of conspicuity-enhancing techniques such as have been described in this section.

CITATIONS

[1]*Accident Facts—1981.* Chicago: National Safety Council, 1981.
[2]R. M. Harano and R. C. Peck, *The California Motorcycle Study; Driver and Accident Characteristics.* Inglewood: California Department of Motor Vehicles, Division of Administration, 1968.

[3]P. F. Waller, *An Analysis of Motorcycle Accidents with Recommendations for Licensing and Operation.* Chapel Hill: Highway Safety Research Center, University of North Carolina, 1972.

[4]M. L. Reiss, W. G. Berger, and G. R. Vallette, *Analysis of Motorcycle Accident Reports and Statistics.* Falls Church, VA.: BioTechnology, February 1974.

[5]L. I. Griffin, *Motorcycle Accidents: Who, When, Where, and Why.* Chapel Hill: Highway Safety Research Center, University of North Carolina, 1974.

[6]D. I. Smith, *An Investigation to Determine Whether the Daytime Usage of Motorcycle Headlights and Taillights Should Be Made Compulsory in Western Australia.* Perth: Road Traffic Authority, July 1975.

[7]Y. Nagayama, T. Morita, T. Miura, J. Watanabem, and N. Murakami, "Motorcyclists' Visual Scanning Pattern in Comparison with Automobile Drivers." SAE paper 790262. Warrendale, PA.: Society of Automotive Engineers, 1979.

[8]P. L. Olson, R. Halstead-Nussloch, and M. Sivak, *Development and Testing of Techniques for Increasing the Conspicuity of Motorcycles and Motorcycle Drivers.* Report No. DOT-HS-805-143. Ann Arbor: University of Michigan, Highway Safety Research Institute, October 1979.

[9]P. F. Waller and L. I. Griffin, "The Impact of a Motorcycle Lights-on-Law," in D. F. Huelke (ed.), *Proceedings of the 21st Conference of the American Association for Automotive Medicine.* Morton Grove, IL.: American Association for Automotive Medicine, 1977.

[10]H. H. Hurt, Jr., "Motorcycle Accident Cause Factors and Identification of Countermeasures." Interim Report, Contract DOT-HS-5-01160. Los Angeles: University of Southern California, January 1979.

[11]J. J. Williams and E. R. Hoffmann, *The Influence of Motorcycle Visibility in Traffic Accidents.* Parkville, Australia: Melbourne University, Department of Mechanical Engineering, July 1977.

[12]A. Burg and J. Beers, "Reflectorization for Nighttime Conspicuity of Bicycles and Motorcycles." *Journal of Safety Research*, 10:69–77 (1978).

[13]M. S. Janoff, A. Cassel, K. S. Fartner, and E. S. Smierciak, *Daytime Motorcycle Headlight and Taillight Operation.* Report No. F-C 2588, DOT-HS-800-321. Philadelphia: Franklin Institute Research Laboratories, August 1970.

[14]M. S. Janoff and A. Cassel, "Effect of Daytime Motorcycle Headlight Law on Motorcycle Accidents." *Highway Research Record*, No. 377, pp. 56–63 (1971).

[15]M. S. Janoff, "Motorcycle Noticeability and Safety During the Daytime." *Proceedings of the 2nd International Congress on Automotive Safety.* Paper No. 73034. Washington, D.C.: Motor Vehicle Safety Advisory Council, Department of Transportation, 1973.

[16]J. D. Ramsey and W. A. Brinkley, "Enhanced Motorcycle Notice-ability Through Daytime Use of Visual Signal Warning Devices." *Journal of Safety Research*, 9:77–84 (1977).

[17]C. Kirkby and P. G. Stroud, "Effects of Motorcyclists' High-Visibility Aids on Driver Gap-Acceptance." *Traffic Engineering and Control*, 19(9):401–403 (1978).

[18]R. C. Schuldt, *An Evaluation of Motorcycle Front Lighting on Visibility*. Linthicum, MD.: Motorcycle Safety Foundation, 1978.

18

Biodynamics of Vehicular Injuries

ANTHONY SANCES, JR., Ph.D.
DENNIS J. MAIMAN, M.D.
JOEL B. MYKLEBUST, Ph.D.
SANFORD J. LARSON, M.D., Ph.D.
and
JOSEPH F. CUSICK, M.D.
Department of Neurosurgery
Medical College of Wisconsin
Marquette University
Milwaukee, Wisconsin

and

Veterans Administration Medical Center
Wood, Wisconsin

Dr. Anthony Sances, Jr., is Professor and Chairman of Biomedical Engineering at Marquette University and the Medical College of Wisconsin (Department of Neurosurgery). He teaches courses for life and physical scientists including bioengineering neurology, bioengineering analysis of trauma, analytical and clinical biomechanics of the spine, biomaterials and biomechanics, and analysis of neural systems. He has published six books and more than 200 scientific articles. He serves as a consultant for the National Science Foundation and was a member of the Study Section, Surgery and Biomedical Engineering for the

National Institutes of Health. He was Past President of the Alliance for Engineering in Medicine and Biology, is a Registered Professional Engineer and a Certified Clinical Engineer, and belongs to 24 national and international medical and engineering societies. Dr. Sances may be contacted at the Department of Neurosurgery, Medical College of Wisconsin, 8700 West Wisconsin Avenue, Milwaukee, Wisconsin 53226 (414-257-5307).

Dr. Dennis J. Maiman is an Assistant Professor of Neurosurgery at the Medical College of Wisconsin and a Fellow in Spinal Cord Injury at the Veterans Administration Spinal Cord Injury Unit. His research interests include the experimental analysis and modification of spinal cord injury, including models of production, metabolic changes, neurophysiology, and biomechanics.

Dr. Joel B. Myklebust is a biomedical engineer in the Neuroscience Laboratory of the Veterans Administration Medical Center at Wood, Wisconsin. His research interests include the therapeutic application of electrical current to the nervous system and the recording of neuroelectric potentials for diagnostic purposes. He is a Registered Professional Engineer in the state of Wisconsin.

Dr. Sanford J. Larson was appointed Director of Neuro-surgical Education at Cook County Hospital, Chicago, in 1962. The following year he was appointed Associate Professor and Chairman of the Department of Neuro-surgery, Marquette School of Medicine (now Medical College of Wisconsin), Milwaukee, and is currently Professor and Chairman of that department.

Dr. Joseph F. Cusick is a member of the faculty of the Medical College of Wisconsin in Milwaukee and a Professor in the Department of Neurosurgery.

I. EPIDEMIOLOGY

Accidents in which deaths or disabling injuries occurred, together with noninjury motor vehicle accidents and fires, cost the nation approximately $83.2 billion in 1980. Of this, motor vehicle accidents are estimated to have cost approximately $39.3 billion.[1] This figure includes wage losses, medical expenses, insurance administration, and property damage. Motor vehicles are the leading cause of all deaths from 1 to 44 years of age.[1] Crash injuries impose a huge burden on Americans of all ages; however, the most devastating impact falls upon the nation's teenagers. Nearly half of the 16- to 19-year-old deaths are produced by injuries sustained in motor vehicle crashes.[1,3,4] In 1980 there were 52,600 fatalities and 2 million disabling injuries that occurred for 164,900,000 registered vehicles in the United States. For 146 million licensed drivers in the United States, a death rate of 3.48 per 100 million vehicle miles was calculated.[1] Drivers and front-seat passengers routinely impact windshields, dashboards, or steering columns with their faces; as a result, approximately 45 percent of facial fractures and 44 percent of facial lacerations occur in vehicles. It is estimated that there are approximately 175,000 severe facial lacerations and fractures seen in the United States per year.[148]

The findings of The National Head and Spinal Cord Injury Survey[3] indicate that there are approximately 10,000 new cases of acute spinal cord injury each year in the United States. Costs of medical treatment for all spinal cord injuries is estimated to be in excess of $380 million per year.

Acute head injury occurs in approximately 1 million persons in the United States who require hospitalization and are stressing already overburdened health care facilities. It is estimated that the societal costs of head injury exceeded $4 billion in 1980.[148] The occurrence of catastrophic spinal or head injury in the young is a social and economic burden— particularly tragic because of the many years of permanent disability, psychological trauma, and familial involvement.[3,89]

Automobile steering columns are implicated in severe chest or abdominal injury. The assemblies most commonly used are the axial compression columns or the self-aligning wheel. The injuries probably occur because the shaft of the steering column is deformed during the crash or binds when the driver strikes the wheel.[148]

Head injuries are the predominant cause of death in bicycle accidents. The bicyclists are most often killed in collisions with motor vehicles rather than in collisions with roadside objects or secondary to falls from the bicycle.[30] Surveys indicate that over 500 excess deaths occurred in 1980 in the 28 states that repealed or weakened their laws requiring motorcycle riders to wear helmets. Approximately 2000 fatalities involving motorcycle riders occurred in these states.[47]

Available and proposed safety devices can improve these statistics. Manual seat belts substantially reduce the likelihood of death or injury during crashes. However, the air bag is by far the most effective vehicle safety technology developed. It provides protection in violent front and front-angle crashes, the type that account for the majority of deaths in vehicle occupants.[96] Belts and child restraints, like helmets, are engineered to protect persons in crashes from injury. State laws requiring the use of existing manual belts and restraints in motor vehicles would be effective in reducing motor vehicle crash injuries in children and at a relatively low cost to the taxpayer. Cars with simple midline brakelights mounted on their trunks in addition to their standard brakelights had less than one-half of the rear-end crashes in contrast to those without lights.[83] Protrusion injuries could be reduced with improved design of instrument panels. Most exterior styling aggravates serious injury to pedestrians and cyclists struck by cars, even at low to moderate impact speeds. Furthermore, materials and design innovations can reduce vehicular repair costs due to low-velocity impacts.[96]

The National Highway Traffic Safety Administration (NHTSA) has begun to reexamine the safety program to determine whether more effective occupant protection can be provided in motor vehicles. This study has resulted in a five-year plan.[83] The plan is designed to upgrade automobile crashworthiness by developing comprehensive performance standards that will deal with the four major impact modes (frontal, side, rear, and rollover). Because of the increased number of vehicles, the decrease in their size, and the increasing density of traffic and miles driven, the development of an advanced test dummy is planned to evaluate these various modes of impact in the passenger cars.[5]

It is interesting to compare traffic fatalities for selected countries (see Table 18-1).

The abbreviated injury scale (AIS) is routinely used to classify injuries. In this scale, 0 = no injury, 1 = minor, 2 = moderate, 3 = severe, 4 = serious, 5 = critical to life, 6 = currently untreatable.

Table 18-1 Comparative Traffic Fatality Rates for Selected Countries in 1976[a]

COUNTRY	FATALITIES	ESTIMATED TRAVEL (10^8 MILES)	DEATHS PER 10^8 MILES
Federal Republic of Germany	14,820	1,804	8.2
Italy	8,921	1,331	6.7
Netherlands	2,432	404	6.0
United Kingdom	6,570	1,561	4.1
United States	45,422	14,082	3.22

[a]Adapted from S. Backaitis and M. Haffner, "Development of the NHTSA Advanced Dummy for the Occupant Protection Standard Upgrade." *Proc. 7th Int. Experimental Safety Vehicle Conf.*, 1979, pp. 395–407.

Table 18-2 shows the fatality distribution by body regions as a function of equal AIS level injury score. This data was obtained from the National Crash Severity Study (NCSS), a major accident data collection program of the National Center for Statistics and Analysis of the National Highway Traffic Safety Administration. The injury distribution by body regions is a function of equal AIS level injury count, as given in Table 18-3.

The above data, also collected from the NCSS, were used to estimate injuries to the various body regions and were ranked as a function of probability of fatality and societal cost models. The results indicate that the four principal body regions for injury are thorax, head, abdomen, and neck. Injuries to the extremities are of much lower consequence.[48] Furthermore, frontal and side crashes and rollovers are the

Table 18-2 Percent Fatality Distribution by Body Regions as a Function of Equal AIS Injury Score[a]

BODY REGIONS	SINGLE COUNT	TWO COUNTS	THREE COUNTS
Head/face	43.9	37.8	36.4
Thorax	26.7	28.9	29.1
Neck	18.0	16.4	15.7
Abdomen	10.2	15.8	17.6
Extremities	1.2	1.1	1.2

[a]Adapted from S. Backaitis and M. Haffner, "Development of the NHTSA Advanced Dummy for the Occupant Protection Standard Upgrade." *Proc. 7th Int. Experimental Safety Vehicle Conf.*, 1979, pp. 395–407.

Table 18-3 Percent Injury Distribution (AIS ≥ 4) by Body Regions as a Function of Equal AIS Injury Score[a]

BODY REGIONS	SINGLE COUNT	TWO COUNTS	THREE COUNTS
Head/face	36.1	33.5	32.7
Thorax	19.5	20.6	21.1
Neck	11.7	10.9	10.5
Abdomen	20.7	24.2	24.9
Extremities	12.0	10.9	10.8

[a]Adapted from S. Backaitis and M. Haffner, "Development of the NHTSA Advanced Dummy for the Occupant Protection Standard Upgrade" *Proc. 7th Int. Experimental Safety Vehicles Conf.*, 1979, pp. 395–407.

modes in which injuries are most prominent. Head injuries include brain trauma and skull fractures, with cerebral concussions and contusions more common than other manifestations. Cervical spine injuries occur in all crash directions, but they are most prominent in frontal and side impacts. Occupants between 16 and 25 years of age suffered these injuries more than twice as often as those in other age groups. Indeed, there are 500 new quadriplegics each year as a result of automobile accidents.[50] Even more sobering is that there are 6000 deaths per year as a result of cervical injuries incurred in vehicular trauma.[50]

Within the abdominal region, liver, kidney, and spleen are the principal organs to be considered. In the thoracic region, rib fractures, lung, and great vessel trauma are prominent. In general, the liver was the primary organ injured in the abdominal region in the four-crash-directions studies (frontal, side, rollover, and rear). Furthermore, the spleen ranked high in all four crash directions.[48] The kidney was high in side and rollover crashes, while the digestive system ranked higher than the kidney in frontal crashes. There is a high incidence of rib fractures occurring with abdominal injuries. In general, the injuries to body system ranked versus crash direction[48] are (1) thorax (front), (2) head (side), (3) head (front), (4) abdomen (front), (5) thorax (side), (6) neck (rollover), and (7) head (rollover).

A. A Review of Injuries at Our Institutions

The teaching institutions of the Medical College of Wisconsin (MCW), including the Milwaukee County Medical Complex and Froedtert Memorial Lutheran Hospital, are the primary trauma centers for southeastern Wisconsin. They provide care for over 350 patients with head injuries annually. A review of nonfatal head injury patients admitted indicate that approximately 25 percent of the total occurred in automobiles. Of all severe head injuries admitted to our institution, 40 percent occurred in motor vehicles. The average age of nonsevere injuries was 31 years, and the average age of the severe injuries was 24 years. Of the total number of motor-vehicle-related head injuries, 20 percent were severe and required prolonged hospitalization and/or surgery. The majority of the severely injured patients had residual disabilities. On a national basis, the National Safety Council indicates that approximately 23 percent of the severe head injuries occurred in motor vehicles.[1]

Between 1975 and 1980, 152 cervical spine injury patients and 105 patients with thoracolumbar trauma were admitted (see Figures 18–1 and 18–2). Additionally, over 350 spinal cord

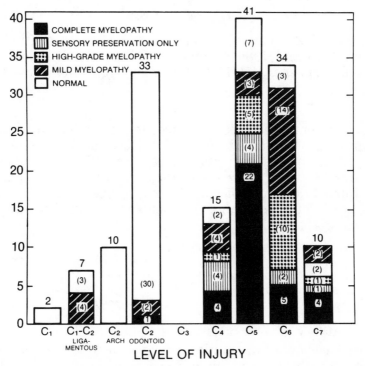

Figure 18–1 Cervical spine fractures admitted between 1975 and 1980. [Reprinted with permission of *CRC Crit. Rev. Bioeng.*, Vol. 11(1), 1984. Copyright CRC Press, Inc.]

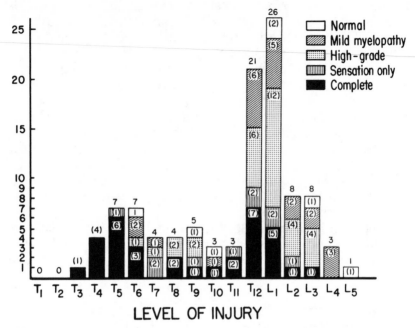

Figure 18-2 Thoracolumbar spine fractures admitted between 1975 and 1980. [Reprinted with permission of *CRC Crit. Rev. Bioeng.*, Vol. 11(1), 1984. Copyright CRC Press, Inc.]

injury patients per year were cared for at the Regional Spinal Cord Injury Center at the Wood V.A. Hospital. Approximately 50 percent of the patients represented by the statistics of Figures 18-1 and 18-2 were motor vehicle related; nationally, one-third to one-half of spinal cord injuries occur in motor vehicles.[3] The average age of patients with spine injuries was 26 years.

II. THE HEAD

A. Anatomy

A brief review of anatomic principles will be done prior to discussing the clinical manifestations of head injury. More detailed descriptions can be found elsewhere in anatomy or neuroanatomy books.[43, 64, 72, 133, 140]

The scalp consists of five layers and is generally 5 to 7 mm thick. The skin of the scalp is thin and firmly connected to underlying tissue layers, in contradistinction to skin elsewhere in the body. A dense layer of connective tissue that is richly endowed with blood vessels lies under the skin. The third layer consists mainly of muscle and fascia, including the frontal and occipital muscles. Between them is a membranous sheet known as the galea apeneurotica, which provides much of the tensile strength of the scalp. Underneath the galea is loose connective tissue, which allows the free movement of the upper portions of the scalp. The innermost layer is the pericranium, which, unlike other periostea of the skeleton, is only loosely connected to the skull.

The skull consists of two components: the base where the brain rests and the surrounding bone, the calvarium. The calvarium is composed of several curved, flattened bones opposing each other at the sutures. The frontal bone forms the anterior aspect of the skull, including the roofs of the orbits and extending back to the coroneal suture (Figures 18-3 and 18-4). The posterior calvarium is formed primarily by the

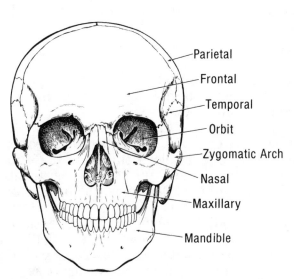

Figure 18-3 Diagram of skull, anterior view. (See anterior skull radiograph, Figure 18-4.) [Reprinted with permission of *CRC Crit. Rev. Bioeng.*, Vol. 11(1), 1984. Copyright CRC Press, Inc.]

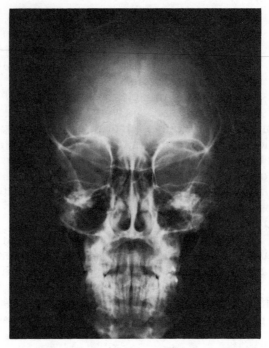

Figure 18-4 Anterior-posterior (AP) radiograph of the skull. [Reprinted with permission of *CRC Crit. Rev. Bioeng.*, Vol. 11(1), 1984. Copyright CRC Press, Inc.]

occipital bone. The lateral skull is formed primarily by the temporal bone and its divisions and by the parietal bone (Figures 18-5 and 18-6).

The calvarium has three layers: a thick outer layer of cortical bone (outer table), a middle layer of softer cancellous bone incorporating the blood supply to the skull and some vessels to the dura, and a thin layer of cortical bone (inner table). The thickness of the temporal bone averages about 4 mm and at the vertex is about 7 mm; the other areas of the skull are intermediate. The inner surface of the calvarium is smooth and contoured. The base of the skull, on the other hand, is irregular in contour and has several depressions and ridges. The bone is mainly membranous bone, with cortical bone in some areas.

The floor of the cranium is divided into the anterior, middle, and posterior fossae (see Figure 18-14, page 472). The anterior fossa is formed by the frontal and sphenoid bones and

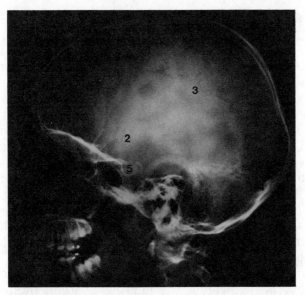

Figure 18-5 Lateral radiograph of skull (1, frontal bone; 2, temporal bone; 3, parietal bone; 4, occipital bone; 5, sella). Reprinted with permission of *CRC Crit. Rev. Bioeng.*, Vol. 11(1), 1984. Copyright CRC Press, Inc.]

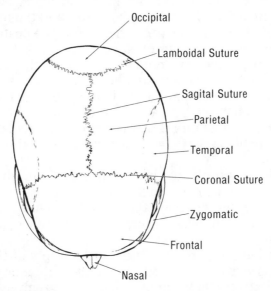

Figure 18-6 Diagram of top of skull. Several bones and sutures are labeled.

forms the seat of the frontal lobe. The middle fossa is formed mainly by the sphenoid and temporal bones, with the posterior margins marked by the petrous bones. Herein lie the temporal lobes of the brain, pituitary gland, and important vascular connections. The border between the anterior and middle fossae is formed by the lesser wing of the sphenoid bone, whose sharp edges may cause frontal and temporal lobe injuries. The posterior fossa, which is formed by the petrous and occipital bones, contains the cerebellum and parts of the brain stem. In the posterior fossa is an opening, the foramen magnum, through which goes the brain stem, spinal cord, and several blood vessels. The foramen magnum is particularly important as a focus of forces and brainstem movement in head injury. Distributed throughout the three cranial fossae are several openings for nerves and blood vessels supplying various aspects of the head, face, and brain.

Immediately inside the skull are the meninges, three layers serving to protect the nervous system, including the brain. The dura mater is a thick fibrous layer enclosing the brain, spinal cord, and spinal nerves. It may be adherent to the inner table of the skull, especially in older people. Several sinuses directing the venous supply of the brain are formed of dural folds. The dura also forms structural separations between specific areas of the brain, including the falx, which separates the left and right hemispheres, and the tentorium, a tent-shaped structure forming the roof of the posterior fossa. The tentorium is often implicated in trauma to the brainstem. The arachnoid is immediately under the dura. It is a loose layer of connective tissue, beneath which is located the circulating cerebrospinal fluid. This fluid provides some of the nutrition for the surface of the brain. The innermost layer is called the pia mater. It is a thin delicate layer, which includes the blood vessels of the surface of the brain and spinal cord.

The blood supply to the meninges is mainly from the middle meningeal artery, which enters the skull through a middle fossa foramen, and other small vessels. They are frequently injured in head injury patients and cause serious ramifications.

A detailed description of the blood supply of the brain is beyond the scope of this discussion. It should be briefly noted, however, that vessels branching from the great vessels of the thorax supply most of the blood flow to the brain. These include the two carotids and two vertebral arteries; the latter

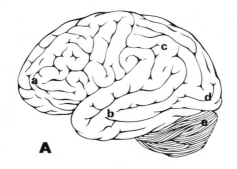

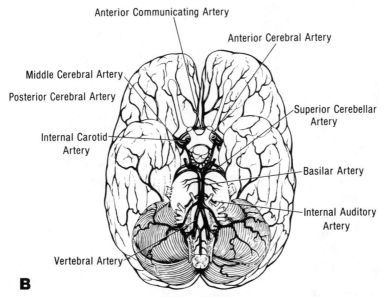

Figure 18-7 Gross anatomy of the brain. On the lateral view (A), the lobes of the brain are labeled (a, frontal; b, temporal; c, parietal; d, occipital; e, cerebellum). Base view (B) diagrams some of the main blood vessels of the brain, as they interconnect on the brain surface. [Reprinted with permission of *CRC Crit. Rev. Bioeng.*, Vol. 11(1), 1984. Copyright CRC Press, Inc.]

combine to form the basilar artery (Figure 18-7B). The carotid artery extends from the neck to enter the skull in the middle fossa and divides to form the anterior and middle cerebral arteries, supplying the frontal and medial areas and the lateral surfaces of the brain, respectively. The basilar artery and its branches supply the brainstem, posterior areas of the deeper structures, and occipital lobes, the latter as the posterior cerebral artery. The cerebral arteries branch and anastomose over the surface of the brain under the pia.

The anatomy of the brain is extremely complex; however, several principles are important for an understanding of head injury. The cerebral cortex can be conveniently divided into general areas based on both location and function (Figure 18-7A).

The frontal lobes encompass several different functional regions. Anteriorly and mainly on the left (dominant) side in most people are areas for thought processes and socialization. Further posteriorly, areas concerned with communication are present. The posterior border of the frontal lobe is comprised by the areas responsible for motor control. Immediately behind the frontal lobes are the parietal lobes. The parietal lobes, especially on the left side, are concerned with integrating sensory information and complex motor activities. The dominant temporal lobe is concerned especially with communication skills and memory. The nondominant temporal lobe is also concerned with communication, etc., but to a lesser degree. The occipital lobes, located behind the parietal lobes, subserve the sense of vision and the integration of visual perception.

Inside the cerebral hemispheres underneath the cerebral cortex are located several functional groups of structures. The thalamus consists of several nuclei that receive and project fibers to various areas of the cerebral cortex. It predominantly functions as a switchboard to other areas of the brain, although some perception of sensation, especially pain, is evident here. The basal ganglia, continuous with the thalamus, are important in the integration of motor function. The cerebellum, located underneath the occipital lobe in the posterior fossa (Figure 18-7A), maintains equilibrium, helps regulate muscle tone, and coordinates complex motor activities.

The ventricular system comprises four cerebrospinal fluid-filled reservoirs in the midst of the brain and brainstem (Figure 18-8). These spaces communicate with the subarachnoid space and provide some of the nutrients for the cerebral cortex. Their characteristic shapes are often modified by brain swelling or masses. The cisterns are also fluid-filled spaces around the brain structures, within the dura (see Figure 18-8).

The brainstem, divided into pons and medulla, contains a collection of nuclei subserving motor, sensory, and basic autonomic functions. Twelve pairs of cranial nerves that supply

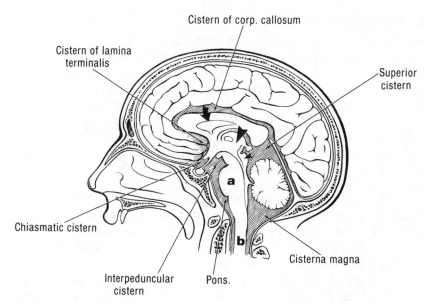

Cistern of corp. callosum

Cistern of lamina terminalis

Superior cistern

Chiasmatic cistern

Interpeduncular cistern

Pons.

Cisterna magna

Figure 18-8 Mid-sagittal view of brain. The cisterns are labeled. The ventricular system is also demonstrated: the lateral ventricles are lateral to the region marked by the angled arrow, large arrowhead points to the third ventricle, small arrowhead to the fourth [a, brainstem (pons); b, spinal cord]. The lateral ventricles are well demonstrated as the boomerang-shaped low densities on the normal CT cut (see Figure 18-9). [Reprinted with permission of *CRC Crit. Rev. Bioeng.*, Vol. 11(1), 1984. Copyright CRC Press, Inc.]

motor and sensory fibers to the face, auditory fibers, and visual fibers are present. Additionally, autonomic fibers, which join several cranial nerves, emanate from the brainstem. These autonomic functions include reflexes for breathing, heart rate, blood pressure, and gastrointestinal functions. The spinal cord represents the caudal continuation of the medulla (Figure 18-8).

B. Clinical Aspect of Head Injuries
Head trauma is the most common type of injury seen in motor vehicle accidents. Seemingly minor episodes of trauma may cause manifestations ranging from trivial loss of consciousness to coma and death.

C. Clinical Evaluation

A medical history, when obtained, can be of value; conscious patients may relate amnesia for the event, nausea, vomiting, and headache. In the unconscious or confused patient, witnesses, including passengers or bystanders, may be helpful in providing information regarding the patient's initial and subsequent neurologic status, position in the vehicle, or impact sites. A certain number of patients who had apparent head injuries may actually have had a medical event precipitating the accident, such as a cerebrovascular accident or myocardial infarction.

The most important factor in the clinical evaluation of the head-injured patient is the assessment of the level of consciousness.[95] Deterioration in the level of consciousness is one of the earliest signs of a progressive mass lesion; therefore repeated neurologic evaluations are crucial.[60,62]

The vital signs, including blood pressure, pulse, and respirations, are frequently altered.[60,95] Hypertension is common; it represents a protective mechanism for maintaining cerebral blood flow in the presence of cerebral edema. Bradycardia (slow heart rate) is also a classical finding in severe head injuries with cerebral edema. These changes may not be seen because associated injuries, including visceral or spinal cord injury, may cause shock syndromes with hypotension and tachycardia.

There are also classical breathing patterns for certain levels of coma. Hyperventilation is characteristic of midbrain injuries, while slow irregular breathing rates are seen in trauma to the pons. With injuries to the low medulla, there is complete cessation of breathing due to loss of respiratory reflexes.

Careful evaluation of eye movements can be of great value in determining the severity of injury in the unconscious patient. As the centers controlling eye movements are located in the upper levels of the brainstem, abnormalities of eye movement may indicate brainstem compression. Additionally, changes in the size of pupil may also suggest this. There are also reflex eye movements that have prognostic value in head injury.[95]

Motor responses will vary according to the level of the injury. The most appropriate response will consist of the patient following commands from the examiner. At higher levels of injury, the patient may maintain the ability to withdraw actively from painful stimuli. As the level of injury becomes lower, characteristic types of posturing become evident, until at the lowest levels of injury (i.e., lower brainstem) there is no response to noxious stimuli whatsoever.

In the evaluation of the head-injured patient, assessment must always be made of possible alcohol or drug overdose. Alcohol intoxication is seen in 60 to 70 percent of patients with coma and head trauma admitted to our institution. Substance intoxication, therefore, may not always be an adequate explanation for coma.[95]

D. Diagnostic Studies in Head Injury

Once the clinical evaluation has been completed, the physician must assess what further studies are indicated. The indications for skull x-rays are frequently subjective and may be related to the physician being comfortable with the management of head injury, medicolegal factors, and local standards.[34] It is generally agreed, however, that any patient with obtundation or coma, other abnormalities in the neurologic exam, past history of neurosurgical problems, or penetrating head injuries such as gunshot wounds should have skull x-rays performed. It is also the practice in our institutions to perform skull x-rays on patients with true loss of consciousness lasting for more than 30 seconds or on patients with full thickness scalp lacerations or sizeable scalp contusions. As will be discussed later, cervical spine radiography is also of primary importance in patients with head injuries.

In the presence of more severe head injury, other radiographic procedures may be indicated. Computerized axial tomography (CT) is a radiographic technique that has been available for approximately 10 years. During that time, it has revolutionized the evaluation and management of head-injured patients. The CT scan gives a rapid, noninvasive, and accurate documentation of the presence of mass lesions such as blood clots and brain swelling; it even allows evaluation of bony anatomy (Figure 18-9). Because of these advantages, it has almost completely replaced other means of secondary x-ray investigation. Examples of the utility of CT scanning will be presented with the specific types of head injury. Recently, nuclear magnetic resonance methods have been advanced for neurologic evaluations.[7, 46, 99]

Other types of radiography used to a lesser extent include cerebral angiography and ventriculography.[130] Cerebral angiography is an examination that, by injecting dye into the

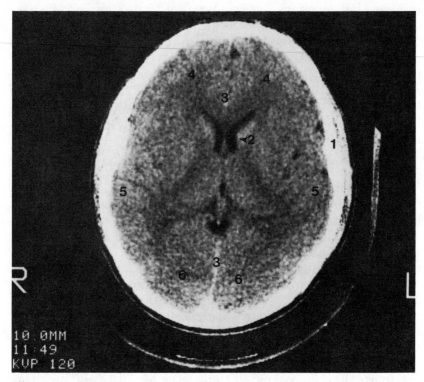

Figure 18-9 Normal CT scan of the head, upper cut (1, cranium (bone); 2, lateral ventricles; 3, falx; 4, frontal region; 5, parietal regions; 6, occipital region). [Reprinted with permission of *CRC Crit. Rev. Bioeng.*, Vol. 11(1), 1984. Copyright CRC Press, Inc.]

blood vessels of the brain, allows their visualization and helps outline masses. This procedure may be of particular value if there is evidence of trauma to the blood vessels. The disadvantages of cerebral angiography are that it is an invasive procedure, generally requires a longer period of time to perform than CT, and may miss blood clots in the brain that are not large enough to cause shifting of blood vessels.

Ventriculography has been largely supplanted by CT scanning. This procedure consists of drilling a small hole through the skull, passing a needle into the ventricular system of the brain, and then injecting either air or contrast media, followed by skull x-rays. This will show shifts of brain substance due to either blood clots or brain swelling. This procedure is invasive and has some risk associated with it because displacement of the ventricular system may make localization of the ventricle difficult.

Nonradiographic methods of evaluation include investigation of intracranial pressure, evoked potentials, EEGs, and echoencephalography.[2] Determination of the intracranial pressure and treatment based on the results have become routine in the management of head injury.[13,61,62,131] The pressure is monitored either by a catheter placed into the ventricular system through a burr hole or by placement of a measuring bolt or catheter into the epidural space. While these are invasive procedures, the risks of placement of these devices are usually minimal; brain infection, however, may occur after they have been in place for several days.

Elevations of intracranial pressure are commonly seen in patients with head injury. Several investigators have suggested that elevated intracranial pressure will cause brain destruction and have therefore devised therapies to decrease it.[13,61] This is a controversial area, and there have been no definitive data to this point that indicate that management on the basis of intracranial pressure has an effect on the outcome of head-injured patients.[131]

In recent years, observation of the evoked potential has become increasingly popular. Briefly, the evoked potential measures the brain's response to either a peripherally delivered stimulus to a nerve or an auditory or visual stimulus.[8,23-25,29,67,103,105-111,113,114] It has been helpful in investigating the status of specific systems, and for research purposes it has a prognostic value in head injury. The electroencephalogram, or EEG, is another electrical technique utilized in the neurosciences, but only peripherally in neurotraumatology. It is primarily utilized for the evaluation of seizure disorders and cortical function. Echoencephalography, which has to a major degree been replaced by CT scanning, is a noninvasive technique utilizing echo waves to determine shift of midline brain structures as a gross indication of the presence of mass lesions.

E. Specific Types of Injuries

E.1. SCALP INJURIES The head is a closed container; forces delivered to its exterior are reflected to varying degrees in the interior. Consequently, scalp and skull injuries can be important not only in themselves, but may reflect cerebral injury. The scalp may dampen a substantial amount of the force of an impact delivered to the head and is therefore commonly injured.[43] Because of the scalp's extensive vascular supply, even trivial lacerations may cause major blood loss. Scalp lacerations may be linear, stellate, flap, or even degloving in nature. The latter three are particularly associated with more severe blows and depressed skull fractures. Whatever the other factors in each particular case, skull x-rays are generally indicated in most of these latter types of lacerations.

If it is determined that there are no injuries, such as fractures beneath the scalp laceration, repair of the scalp can generally be carried out in the emergency room. Care to remove foreign material and closure in two layers, including the deeper tissues and the skin, are indicated.

E.2. SKULL FRACTURES Basic types of skull fracture include linear, depressed, comminuted, and basilar fractures (Figure 18-10). Linear fractures are incurred by generalized blows to the skull; often they extend some distance from the impact and occasionally to the opposite site of the head[43] (see Figures 18-10 and 18-11). They are significant from two standpoints: one, they may be related to underlying brain injury; two, in children they may cause dural cysts, known as "leptomeningeal cysts" or "growing fractures," as a result of entrapment of the dura in the fracture margins.

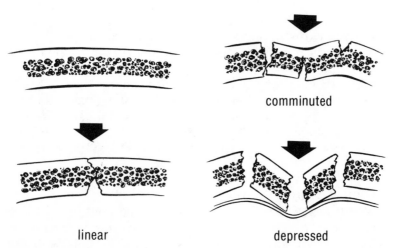

comminuted

linear   depressed

Figure 18-10 Representation of the three types of cranial vault fractures typically seen.

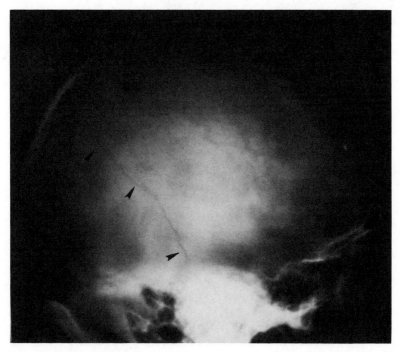

Figure 18-11 Lateral radiograph showing linear skull fracture (*arrowheads*).

Depressed skull fractures are inward displacements of localized areas of the skull due to focal impacts[10,43,57] (see Figures 18-10 and 18-12). Fragments of bone and scalp may be pushed into the cerebral substance with the associated likelihood of neurologic deficits and seizures (Figure 18-13). Laceration of the meninges by the depressed fragments may increase the risk of meningitis. Depressed fractures may be comminuted; that is, there may be fragmentation of the fractured bone (Figure 18-10). Commonly, depressed fractures are associated with scalp lacerations, exposing the brain and meninges to the air. The management of depressed skull fractures usually includes operative procedures for the removal of all foreign material, destroyed brain and blood clots, and careful wound closure.[10,57] Postoperative antibiotics are used to prevent infection. Additionally, many neurosurgeons routinely use anticonvulsants in these patients because of an increased risk of late seizure disorders.

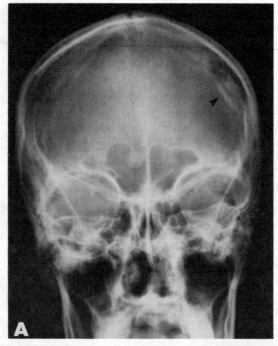

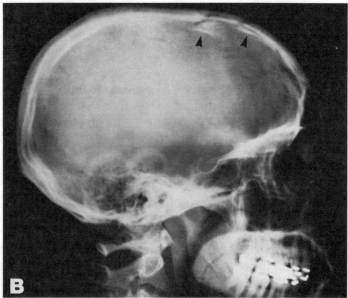

Figure 18-12 Depressed skull fracture. AP (A) and lateral
(B) radiographs show inward displacement of the inner table
of the skull (*arrowheads*).

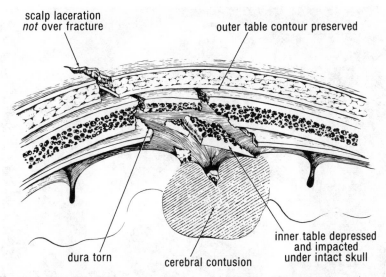

scalp laceration
not over fracture

outer table contour preserved

dura torn

cerebral contusion

inner table depressed
and impacted
under intact skull

Figure 18-13 Diagram of depressed skull fracture, demonstrating the cerebral pathology. [Adapted from B. Jennett, *An Introduction to Neurosurgery*, 3rd ed. Chicago: Year Book Medical Publishers, 1977.]

Basilar skull fractures may also be linear, comminuted, or depressed, especially in the anterior fossa and in association with facial trauma.[43, 58] Most are extensions of linear fractures of the calvarium due to impacts. They are more commonly diagnosed clinically than radiographically. Clinical findings of basilar fractures includes spinal fluid leaks through the nose or ears, evidence of blood either behind the ear drum or in the ear canal, and ecchymosis around the eyes or the mastoid region. Cranial nerve abnormalities may be evident if the fracture runs across neural foramina. Leakage of spinal fluid is of particular importance because this is related to a high incidence of meningitis. X-rays in patients with suspected basilar skull fractures are positive in only approximately 50 percent of cases because the fracture lines are horizontal and therefore are often not seen on routine x-rays. Basal views are required for demonstration of these (Figure 18-14).[130] Surgery may be indicated in cases of persistent spinal fluid leakage to prevent meningitis.

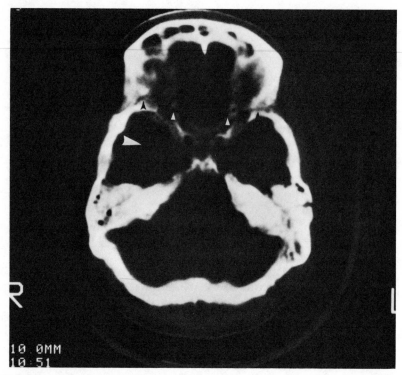

Figure 18–14 CT (base cut) of patient with basilar skull fracture and CSF leak through nose. Small arrowheads show fracture line through base of skull. The base of the temporal lobe in the middle fossa is also marked (*large white arrowhead*). The frontal fossa is anterior to the fracture line.

E.3. VASCULAR HEAD INJURIES The blood vessels of the head and neck are commonly injured in severe head injury.[43] Hematomas may be created by lacerations of meningeal or cerebral arteries or veins; these will be discussed later, since their importance is as mass lesions. Direct trauma to cranial arteries and veins may create fistulas between them, with abnormal shunting of blood and potential cerebral ischemia.[60] Aneurysms, balloonlike dilatations of the vessel walls, may occur. These frequently rupture, causing subarachnoid hemorrhage and potential neurologic deficits. Blood vessels may also be injured by compression from masses.[60] The carotids and vertebral arteries may also be injured in the neck. The carotid may be torn or kinked anywhere from its origins to its entrance into the skull. Although the vertebral artery may also be affected anywhere along its course, it is most likely to be compressed or lacerated at the base of the skull. Hyperextension–hyperflexion forces characteristically produce these injuries.[43]

E.4. INTRACRANIAL INJURIES Brain injuries can be conveniently divided into two broad categories based on clinical findings and pathology—concussion and contusion. Concussions are loosely defined as traumatic losses of consciousness with resolution of most complaints completely within 24 hours.[135] Examination of brains of patients suffering concussions and dying of other causes generally fail to show evidence of brain injury. The term contusion includes a broad group of intracranial injuries with hematomas, gross destruction of brain tissue, or cellular injuries to the brain. These patients classically have focal findings or changes in consciousness lasting for periods longer than 24 hours. While these definitions of concussion and contusion have been rendered somewhat inaccurate by modern radiographic and histologic techniques, they have persisted in the literature.[43,61,62]

The biomechanics of head injury are important for an understanding of the pathophysiology; a few general concepts will be presented here.[43] Coup injuries are cerebral injuries that underlie the region of impact. These are secondary to skull deformation, when seen in the absence of fracture, and to direct compression by bone fragments in depressed fractures. In linear fractures, the skull edges may transiently be pushed into the brain. Contrecoup injuries involve trauma to the brain some distance from the impact, usually on the opposite side of the brain (Figure 18-15). These can be due to relative movements of the brain following impact against rough surfaces of the skull, usually in the anterior edges of the frontal and middle fossae or due to negative intracranial pressures.

Rotational forces are also important in head injury. Several researchers have suggested that these forces are responsible for many hematomas and contusions. Rotation may be associated with impact injury, in addition to producing a contrecoup. These forces also figure prominently in injuries to the blood vessels of the head and neck, especially the veins connecting the brain surface and the dura, the "bridging veins."[43,108]

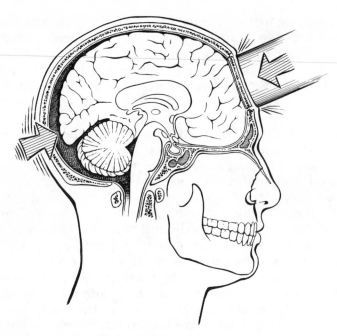

Figure 18-15 Mechanism of contrecoup injury. The piston is delivering the force that is reflected through the brain: the rear of the brain moves toward the impact site. A negative pressure occurs that may produce cavitation followed by a rebound.

Coma, as manifested in head injury, is usually produced by trauma to the reticular activating system (RAS). This poorly defined group of nuclei and fibers extends from the hypothalamus, located below the thalamus, into the mid brainstem. The RAS in the brainstem may be compressed by brain shifts caused by mass lesions such as blood clots or brain edema. Contusions of the brainstem may be produced by any of the forces associated with severe head injury, including coup, contrecoup, and rotational forces. These contusions are related to unequal brain movements during and after impact, both in horizontal and downward directions, the latter in association with changes in intracranial pressure dynamics.[95]

E.5. CEREBRAL HEMATOMAS There are three types of hematomas that occur in response to head trauma: epidural hematomas, subdural hematomas, and intracerebral hematomas.

Epidural hematomas (Figure 18-16) are usually related to skull fractures, most commonly in the temporal region but occurring in other areas in about 20 percent of patients.[19] Bleeding is generally secondary to trauma to dural blood vessels caused by slapping of the dura by the margins of linear fractures, but bleeding may also be due to bone bleeding and trauma to dural sinuses, the last most commonly in

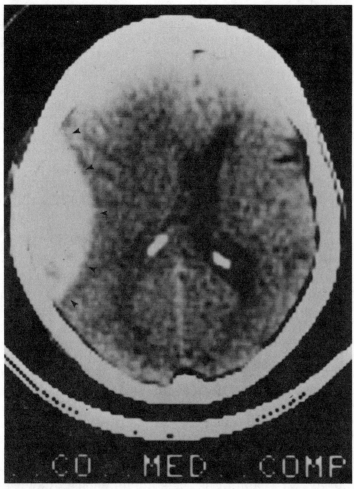

Figure 18-16 Epidural hematoma. CT scan cut shows convex-shaped mass (*arrowheads*), white in color (high density), which is appearance of fresh blood. There is some shift of the ventricular system.

children. Epidural hematomas tend to occur in younger people because the dura has not yet scarred down to the skull as happens in older patients.

The classical history for epidural hematoma is an initial brief period of loss of consciousness, followed by a lucid period, and, as the hematoma enlarges, a progressive loss of consciousness and signs of brainstem compression, including paralysis of the opposite side of the body and abnormalities of eye movements and pupil size. In reality, however, this history is not often obtained, since the initial lucid period may not occur or be witnessed. Generally, the presentation to the emergency room is of a young person who is comatose and has a linear skull fracture across the temporal region. Epidural hematomas without skull fractures have been reported.

Because these patients may deteriorate rapidly, often there is time only to obtain lateral skull and cervical spine x-rays prior to going to the operating room for potential removal of the hematoma without definite diagnosis. If the patient is not rapidly deteriorating, CT scanning can be of benefit in defining and localizing the mass lesion.

Prognosis for these patients, if managed promptly and if no other brain pathology is present, is frequently quite good. This is because epidural hematomas are caused by injuries to tissues outside the brain and therefore the brain itself is not necessarily injured. If management is delayed, prolonged compression of the brain and brainstem may cause permanent coma and neurological deficits or death.[58, 61, 102, 127]

Subdural hematomas occur in all age groups with head injury. They are, however, somewhat more common in older individuals where the outer surface of the dura has scarred down to the inside of the skull and where there may be some atrophy of the brain, creating a larger subdural space.[60]

Acute subdural hematomas (Figure 18–17) are most commonly caused by lacerations of the brain cortex with trauma to cortical arteries and/or veins produced by coup or contrecoup forces.[118] In the absence of severe impacts, rotational forces are thought to be important in causing tearing of the bridging veins. Skull fractures are common and are often contralateral to the hematoma. If the patient is not deteriorating rapidly, CT scanning is the study of choice. As with epidural hematomas, the most common presentation is that of altered level of consciousness in addition to varying degrees of paralysis. Seizures may also be present with subdural hematomas.

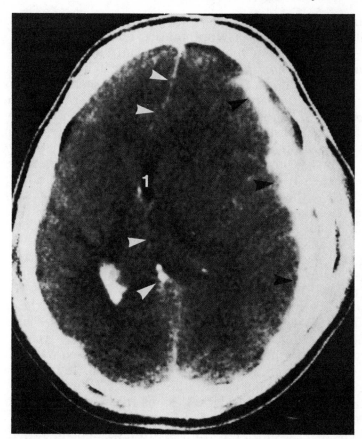

Figure 18-17 Acute subdural hematoma. CT cut demonstrates a crescent-shaped hematoma extending the entire length of the cerebral hemisphere (*dark arrowheads*). The left lateral ventricle is occluded (right *marked 1*) by severe edema; also noted is marked shift of midline structures (*white arrowheads*).

As with epidural hematomas, prompt surgical evacuation offers the best prognosis for sizeable lesions. The mortality rate, however, may be as high as 60 percent, depending on the severity of the injury, and in survivors residual neurologic deficits are common. It has been suggested that the reasons for the poor prognosis of subdural hematomas are related to the primary brain injury. Additionally, subdural hematomas often are associated with disproportionately high amounts of brain swelling and edema, even in the presence of small clots.

In patients with small clots or large subdural spaces, subdural hematomas may be asymptomatic. The patients may later present liquified hematomas and complaints of headaches or neurologic changes. Chronic subdural hematomas often develop vascularized membranes around them and may enlarge after further trauma due to fresh bleeding from the membranes. In these instances, surgery is often required.

Intracerebral hematomas are caused by intraparenchymal brain injuries.[37] They may be seen in any age group, are particularly common in motor vehicle accident victims, and are frequently multiple. They may be associated with skull fractures either in the region of impact or on the opposite side of the skull.

Intracerebral hematomas and cerebral contusions are most commonly related to coup and contrecoup forces.[43] In the former, they may be caused by depressed skull fractures or by bone edges. However, traumatic intracerebral hematomas are related to contrecoup mechanisms. Brain trauma is explained on the basis of the relative movements of the brain against the walls of the base of the anterior fossa and the anterior border of the middle fossa. These are rough and irregular in nature. This relates to the increased incidence of intracerebral hematomas in the frontal and temporal lobes (Figure 18-18) as opposed to the occipital lobe, which is surrounded by smooth borders. Lesions in the occipital lobe are more likely to be caused by coup mechanisms.

The presenting signs and symptoms depend largely on the size and location of the mass. Because of the typical frontal and temporal locations, patients may demonstrate changes in affect, level of consciousness, abnormalities in communication skills, and focal motor deficits. CT scanning is the radiographic study of choice and, indeed, has largely supplanted other modalities for defining the extent of intracerebral hematomas.

The management of these lesions is somewhat subjective. Surgery may be indicated acutely if the patient is actively deteriorating; however, this may be dangerous, as there is usually a significant degree of edema secondary to the trauma, which may be worsened by surgical manipulation. Second, the deep brain blood vessels that caused the hematoma initially may be difficult to control acutely. Hematomas may completely resolve after a period of weeks. If the hematomas persist, removal after one to two weeks can speed recovery. The prognosis for these lesions may be good if there is not extensive brain destruction.

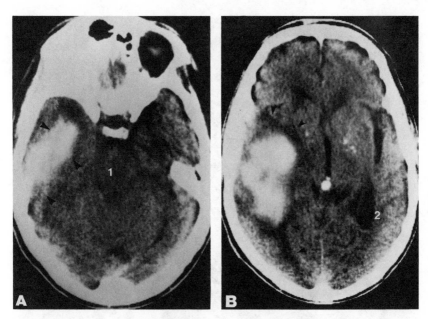

Figure 18-18 (A) Traumatic intracerebral hematoma involving the right temporal and parietal lobes. This CT cut demonstrates the oval-shaped mass in the temporal lobe (*arrowheads*). There is slight asymmetry of the brainstem (*1*), suggesting compression of the mass. (B) Higher CT cut of same patient. There is evidence of cerebral edema presenting as a low-density border to the hematoma (*small arrowheads*). Also seen is occlusion of the right occipital horn of the lateral ventricle (left occipital horn *marked 2*).

Closed head injury, in the absence of hematoma, represents the largest category of serious head injuries. Rotational forces are important in producing these injuries, although translation and impact mechanisms are often involved.[108] This type of head injury is particularly common in younger age groups. Skull fracture is present in about one-half of cases, and CT scanning generally demonstrates cerebral edema with decreased size of the lateral ventricles and other radiographic evidence of cerebral edema (Figure 18-19). The most prominent clinical finding is usually the altered level of consciousness, but any number of focal neurologic deficits may coexist. Intracranial pressure is often elevated.

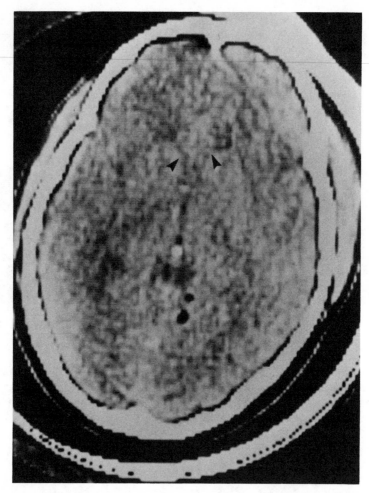

Figure 18-19 Closed head injury without hematoma. The lateral ventricles are reduced to slits (*arrowheads*). Compare to normal CT of Figure 18-9.

The management of these patients is almost exclusively medical, with respiratory and metabolic support. As noted earlier, in some institutions control of intracranial pressure is utilized in the hopes of preventing brain injury; this is still controversial. The prognosis for patients with closed head injuries without hematoma is considered to be better than that for patients with hematomas, especially in patients under the age of 40. [13, 16, 61, 127, 135]

TABLE 18-4 Glasgow Coma Scale

EYE OPENING		BEST VERBAL RESPONSE		BEST MOTOR RESPONSE	
4	Spontaneous	5	Oriented	6	Obey Commands
3	To speech	4	Confused	5	Localized Pain
2	To pain	3	Inappropriate	4	Withdraws
1	None	2	Incomprehensible	3	Flexion to Pain
		1	None	2	Extension to Pain
				1	None

E.6. NEUROLOGIC INJURY SCALES Various coma scales have been developed to standardize the neurologic examination. The best known of these is the Glasgow Coma Scale (Table 18-4).[61,62] This scale records three general areas: eye opening, verbal response, and motor response. It principally tests the level of consciousness and motor response. Some investigators have criticized the Glasgow Scale for attributing similar importance to eye opening as to the verbal response, since the latter is a better measure of the level of consciousness.

While the Glasgow Coma Scale remains in popular use, others have been developed. The Maryland Scale investigates the various aspects of the neurologic exam in a more detailed manner.[102] It has, therefore, gained some popularity. In our institution, we prefer to evaluate repeatedly each particular aspect of the neurologic exam, thereby providing a more accurate evaluation of the overall clinical status and allowing a more systematic observation of changes. This method is used to determine the clinical normality of the patient on a 100 percent scale for comparison with the analysis provided from our computer-automated head injury monitoring system.

III. THE SPINE

A. Anatomy

A.1 VERTEBRAL COLUMN The spinal column is composed of 33 vertebrae joined by ligaments and cartilage. There are 7 cervical, 12 thoracic, 5 lumbar, and 5 fused sacral vertebrae (Figure 18-20). Additionally, there are 4 coccygeal vertebrae that are fused into one bone. Normal curves of the spine include a forward convex curve in the cervical region (the

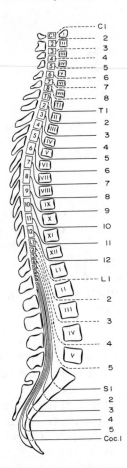

Figure 18-20 Diagram of the spinal cord within the vertebral canal. The vertebral segments (*roman numerals*) and spinal cord segments (*arabic numbers*) are compared. Note that the spinal cord terminates at L1. Also note the normal curvatures of the spine. [Reprinted with permission of *CRC Crit. Rev. Bioeng.*, Vol. 11(1), 1984. Copyright CRC Press, Inc.]

cervical lordosis), a concave curve in the thoracic region (thoracic kyphosis), and another convex curve in the lumbar region (lumbar lordosis).[38] See Figure 18-20 above.

The head rests on C1, otherwise known as the atlas. The atlas consists of a bony ring with anterior and posterior arches, and with large lateral masses containing the articular surfaces or facets. The superior facets articulate with the occipital condyles of the skull, and the inferior facets to the body of C2 (the axis). The axis is similar in design to the atlas, with the prominent exception of the odontoid process. This process extends from the middle of the anterior arch into the anterior half of the opening of the atlas (Figure 18-21).

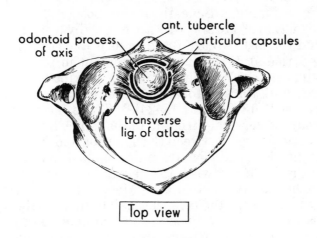

Top view

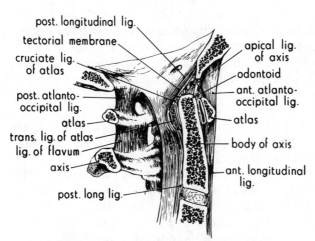

Median section through occipital skull
and upper cervical vertebrae

Figure 18-21 Anatomy of the C1-2 region. [Reprinted with permission from *CRC Crit. Rev. Bioeng.*, 5(2):79–122 (1981). Copyright CRC Press, Inc.]

The bony anatomy of the spine becomes unitary below C2. Between C2 and C3 is the first intervertebral disc. Discs are seen between each of the vertebral bodies in the rest of the cervical, thoracic, and lumbar spines (Figure 18-20). They are basically fibrocartilagenous pads between the vertebral bodies. The vertebral bodies gradually increase in width through the cervical and upper thoracic spine. Here they decrease in size somewhat but then increase again down to the lumbosacral junction. Beneath the lumbosacral junction, the next five sacral vertebral bodies are generally fused into the sacrum, and the last two are fused to form the coccyx.

The articulating facets are important in providing posterior support for the spine, yielding a tripod effect when considered with the vertebral bodies and intervertebral discs (Figures 18-22, 18-23, and 18-24).[143] These facets change in shape from the cervical through lumbar spine but at all levels provide articulations between the superior and inferior levels of the spine. The pedicles are pillar-shaped masses just anterior to the facets, between the neural foramina.

Posterior to the articulating facets are the vertebral arches, which encase the posterior half of the spinal canal and provide attachments for muscles and ligaments. The posterior arches consist of the transverse processes, the lamina, and the spinous process (Figures 18-22 and 18-24). The transverse processes, located laterally on the arch, and the spinous processes, located posteriorly, are the sources of attachment for the muscles and ligaments of the posterior aspects of the spine. The lamina are flattened bones between the transverse and spinous processes. They overlap like shingles in most of the spine.

Motion in the spine between one vertebra and another is allowed by the facet joints, which are within synovia, and by the intervertebral discs. The discs, in addition to supporting bending loads, are also able to absorb compression. The effectiveness of the discs in performing these tasks is dependent on the condition of the individual discs, with decreasing mobilities in older individuals due to disc degeneration and partial collapse of the disc space. Eventually, ossification of the disc occurs with formation of osteophytes and loss of the characteristics of the normal disc.[108, 112]

A.2. SPINAL LIGAMENTS Ligaments are important structures in that they not only add stability to the bony elements of the spine, but also allow a requisite amount of spinal motion. They

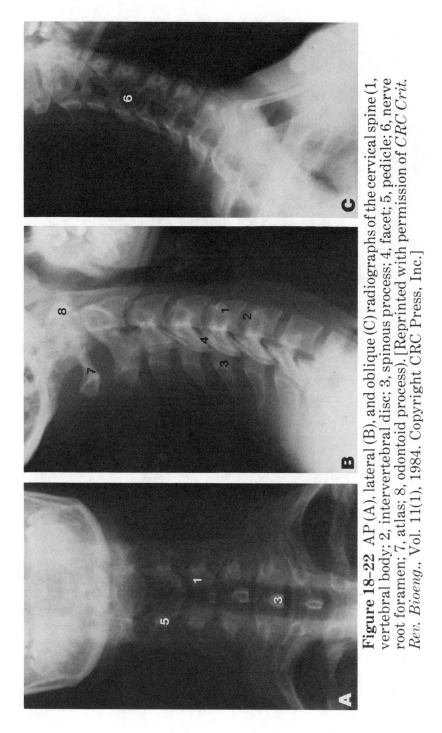

Figure 18–22 AP (A), lateral (B), and oblique (C) radiographs of the cervical spine (1, vertebral body; 2, intervertebral disc; 3, spinous process; 4, facet; 5, pedicle; 6, nerve root foramen; 7, atlas; 8, odontoid process). [Reprinted with permission of *CRC Crit. Rev. Bioeng.*, Vol. 11(1), 1984. Copyright CRC Press, Inc.]

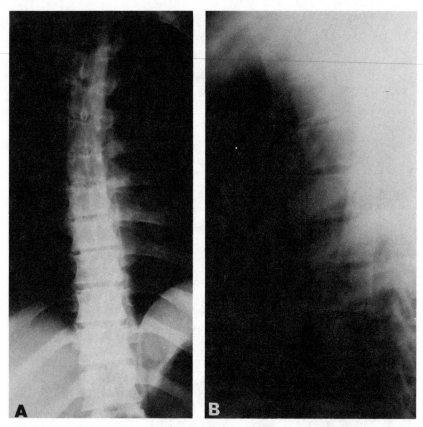

Figure 18-23 AP (A) and lateral (B) radiographs of the thoracic spine. The vertebral bodies can be seen. Anatomic details are difficult to appreciate because they are obscured by structures such as the ribs and heart. [Reprinted with permission of *CRC Crit. Rev. Bioeng.*, Vol. 11(1), 1984. Copyright CRC Press, Inc.]

are composed primarily of two substances: elastin, which allows ligaments to stretch and return to original length, and collagen fibers, which provide tensile strength.[143]

The occipital-atlantal-axial region has a unique set of ligamentous structures well suited to the functional requirements of this region (Figure 18-21). The transverse atlantal ligament is a strong band that attaches to the lateral masses of the atlas. It serves to hold the odontoid process against the anterior arch of the atlas, thereby maintaining the stability of the C1-2 region. The apical ligament, which extends from

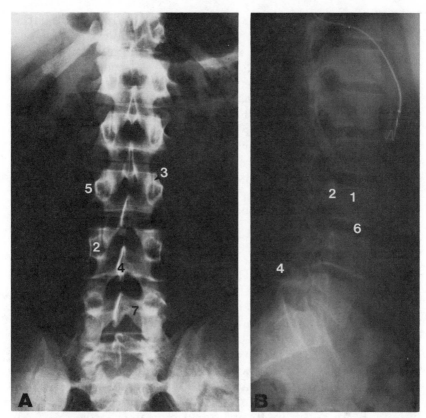

Figure 18-24 AP (A) and lateral (B) radiographs of the lumbar spine (1, vertebral body; 2, pedicle; 3, facet; 4, spinous process; 5, transverse process; 6, intervertebral disc; 7, lamina). [Reprinted with permission of *CRC Crit. Rev. Bioeng.*, Vol. 11(1), 1984. Copyright CRC Press, Inc.]

the apex of the odontoid to the base of the occipital bone, also serves to hold the odontoid anteriorly. This is assisted by the alar ligaments, which are on each side of the apical ligament and attached to the medial side of the occipital condyles. The tectorial membrane is the most cranial extension of the posterior longitudinal ligament. An important ligament in this region is the transverse atlantal ligament. It is extremely stout and is often stronger than the bone of the odontoid process. In addition to their roles in maintaining the position of the odontoid process, the alar ligaments limit the rotation of the neck somewhat.[73, 108]

In addition to these special ligaments, there are three other groups of ligaments that extend through most of the spine (Figure 18-25). The anterior longitudinal ligament extends from the occiput of the skull to the anterior aspect of the sacrum. It thins out between vertebra, but it is continuous. It is most firmly connected to the margins of the vertebral bodies and the intervertebral discs, those elements that limit hyperextension of the spine. The posterior longitudinal ligament is located on the posterior surface of the vertebral body, from C1 to the sacrum. It attaches to the posterior margins of the vertebral bodies and to the intervertebral discs. It helps to limit hyperflexion of the spine and is often stretched up to 1 cm between vertebral bodies without disruption.[112]

The posterior elements of the spine also have characteristic groups of ligaments. The ligamentum flava connect the lamina of the spine. They arise from the ventral surface of the lower lamina and attach to the dorsal aspects of the lamina above. While allowing flexion of the spine, they encourage return of the lamina to their normal position when forces are relieved. Supraspinous and interspinal ligaments extend between the spinous processes. The ligamentum nuchae is the continuation of the superspinous ligament in the cervical region, extending from the skull base to C7. The intertransverse ligaments connect adjacent transverse processes. All these ligaments serve to limit flexion, and the intertransverse ligaments, in addition, limit lateral motion (Figure 18-25A).

A.3. MUSCLES IN THE SPINAL REGION The muscles of the spinal regions provide further stability to the spine, especially in the cervical and lumbar regions.[108, 140, 143, 146] There are several superficial muscles that extend over the upper back and neck, including the trapezius, latissimus dorsi, and rhomboidius groups. Functionally, they are most important in motion of the arm and scapula but may have some role in lateral movement of the neck. Additionally, there are several deeper muscles that extend from the posterior aspects of the skull to insert on the spinous processes and lamina of the cervical spine. These muscle groups not only aid in the maintenance of position against gravity, but also assist in both the rotation and limitation of excess rotation of the spine; as a group they are called the erector spinae muscles.

There are also muscles present anterior to the spine, although these are of lesser significance than the posterior musculature in the cervical region (see Figures 18-25C and D). Several muscles of the neck are related to internal aspects of

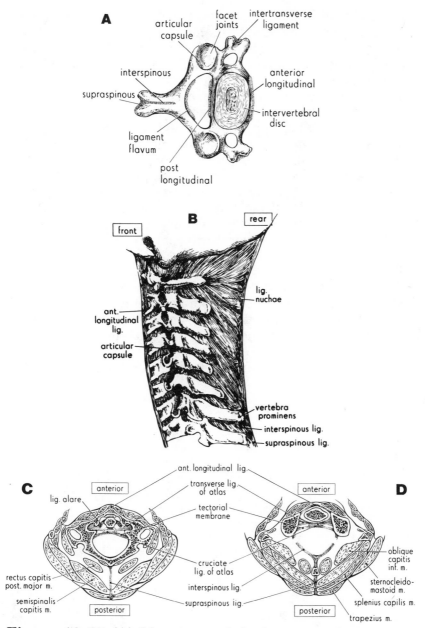

Figure 18-25 (A) Ligaments of the lower cervical spine—cross-sectional view. (B) Lateral view of the posterior spinal ligaments. (C) Muscles and ligaments of the C1-2 region. (D) Cross-sectional view of the muscles of the cervical region. [A, B, C, and D: Reprinted with permission from *CRC Crit. Rev. Bioeng.*, 5(2):79–122 (1981). Copyright CRC Press, Inc.]

rotation. In addition, the longus coli group is densely adherent to the anterior longitudinal ligament.

In the thoracic region, the intercostal structures provide a measure of stability to the thoracic spine (Figure 18-23). Again, posteriorly are the erector spinae group, here also known as the paravertebral muscles, and, to a lesser extent, anterior vertebral muscle groups. Several abdominal muscles, including the oblique groups and the transverse abdominus, extend from the more posterior aspects of the thorax around to the anterior abdominal wall. Important muscles in the lumbar spine region include the psoas and quadratus lumborum muscles. These muscles arise from the lateral vertebral bodies and the transverse processes of all the lumbar vertebra. The soleus muscles is particularly important in flexing and bending the lumbar vertebral column.[146]

B. Motion of the Spine

When discussing motion of the spine, one must consider both movement at the single vertebral body level and movement over the entire spine. If the discs are in good condition, motion is allowed in several directions, limited by the anterior and posterior ligaments and the facets (Figures 18-26 and 18-27).

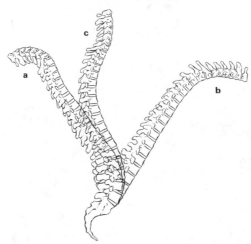

Figure 18-26 Diagrammatic representation of extremes of spine motion. Extension (a); flexion (b); neutral (c). [Reprinted with permission of *CRC Crit. Rev. Bioeng.*, Vol. 11(1), 1984. Copyright CRC Press, Inc.]

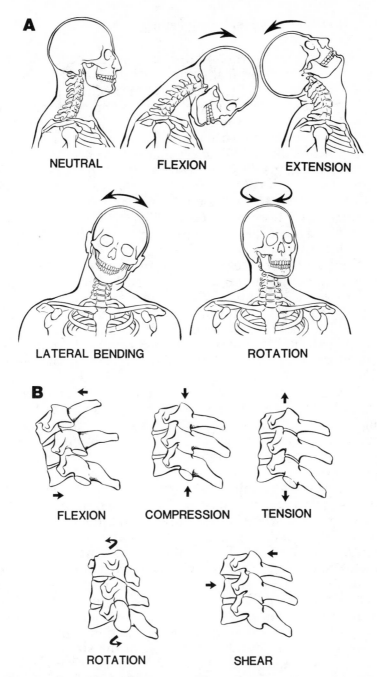

Figure 18-27 (A) Motions of the head and neck on the torso. (B) Potential forces involved in spinal injury. [A and B: Reprinted with permission of *CRC Crit. Rev. Bioeng.*, Vol. 11(1), 1984. Copyright CRC Press, Inc.]

As noted earlier, the complex ligamentous and bony anatomy of the upper cervical spine is ideally suited to the functional requirements of the region. In most of the spine, motion is in part based on the status of the discs and requires activity of multiple layers of the spine. In the upper cervical spine, however, lateral motion occurs primarily at C1–2. The cervical spine will flex up to 60 degrees and extend up to 75 degrees; lateral flexion, usually in association with some rotation, ranges from 35 to 70 degrees. Isolated rotation is usually 70 to 80 degrees to each side. The apex of motion is at the C5–6 and, to a lesser degree, at C6–7. Therefore, the major strain is at these levels, and here occurs the highest percentage of cervical spine injuries.[108, 115]

Similar differences between regions are noted in the thoracic spine. Maximum flexion–extension motions are about 65 to 80 degrees, limited by the anterior and posterior longitudinal ligaments, posterior elements, muscles, and the rib cage.[143] The motion is least between T3 and T5 and is three times higher at T12. Lateral bending, coupled to some degree to rotation, occurs to a lesser degree than in the cervical spine.[143]

In the lumbar spine, flexion–extension motions are in the range of 60 to 80 degrees, with maximum forces at the L4–5 and L5–S1 levels. Lateral bending, again coupled with rotation, is only about 30 degrees for the entire lumbar spine and also with flexion and extension with little movement at the L5–S1 level.

The size of the spinal canal, wherein lies the spinal cord and its coverings, is variable.[38] It is largest in the upper cervical region, where it measures approximately 24 mm in width, 17 mm in depth, and at lower lumbar levels a width of 23 mm and a depth of 17 mm. The canal is narrowest in the upper to mid thoracic region, with an average width of 17.2 mm and depth of 16.8 mm. In the low thoracic to upper lumbar areas, diameters of 21 × 17 mm are expected. With flexion of the spine, the spinal canal is lengthened; during extension, the canal is shortened and narrowed and the ligamentum flavum folds within. Considerable variation in the size of the canal can exist; as a consequence, persons with narrow canals are at a greater risk for cord damage. Degenerative diseases of the spine (including cervical spondylosis), metabolic bone diseases, and lumbar stenosis will often reduce the size of the spinal canal.

C. Spinal Cord

The spinal cord, its investing layers, and the nerve roots extend as the continuation of the brainstem to the sacrum in the spinal canal. The average width of the cord in the cervical region is 13.0 mm and 7.7 mm in depth. In the smallest (thoracic) region the width is 8.0 mm and depth 6.5 mm, and 9.5 mm in width and 8.0 mm in depth in the lumbosacral region. There are enlargements in the cervical and lumbar regions corresponding to the origin of the nerve roots supplying the arms and legs. The spinal cord thickens in extension and lengthens in flexion. The cord is suspended in the spinal canal by the dentate ligaments, which arise from the pia and attach to the dura (Figure 18-28). Ordinarily, the spinal cord terminates at the level of L2. The lumbar termination is termed the conus medullaris, from which extends the L1 to S5 nerve roots. Nerve roots are composed of a dorsal sensory portion and a ventral motor root merging distal to the spinal cord. With the exception of the C1 and C2 nerve roots, the

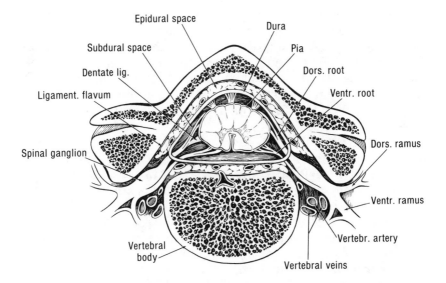

Figure 18-28 Cross-sectional anatomy of the spine and spinal cord. The dorsal (sensory) and ventral (motor) rootlets are seen exiting the cord and merging at the level of the spinal ganglion to form the nerve root going through the neural foramen.

nerve roots leave the spinal canal via the neural foramina. The reader is referred to textbooks of neuroanatomy for a discussion of tracts and functional considerations of the spinal cord.[64,133,140]

D. Clinical Evaluation of the Cervical Spine

Serious cervical injuries routinely occur following vehicular ejection or with interior impact with the roof, header, pillar, steering wheel, instrument panel, windshield, roof rail, seat back, side window, or rearview mirror (Figure 18-26). The initial field evaluation of the potential spinal cord injury patient is of paramount importance. In our institution, a review showed 10 percent of patients admitted comatose had spine injury. Immobilization in the field may limit damage to the spinal cord if spinal trauma is present. Consequently, if possible, all unconscious patients and conscious patients with neck pain and/or motor or sensory loss should be immobilized on a back board with the head restrained.[9]

Once the potential spinal injury patient is admitted to the trauma center, the priorities of management are similar to those in other kinds of multiple trauma. Initial attention should be addressed to maintenance of the airway; if intubation is necessary, it should be carried out with minimal neck manipulation. In the conscious patient, a careful neurologic exam can be carried out, documenting motor and sensory function; even in the unconscious patient, response to pain can sometimes be assessed.

In most patients with severe trauma or loss of consciousness and certainly in all awake patients complaining of neck pain, a lateral cervical spine x-ray should be taken early in the evaluation, prior to movement of the patient. All seven cervical vertebrae should be visualized, because of the high percentage of fractures at the C6-7 region. Special techniques may be necessary to make this visualization possible. Flexion-extension radiographs for abnormal motion may be of benefit to determine instability.[38]

Once the fracture has been diagnosed, secondary procedures, such as myelography or CT scanning, are often carried out to evaluate the anatomic status of the spinal cord. In some institutions, these may be carried out immediately.[17] Myelography is a radiographic technique, involving injection of a substance into the subarachnoid space to provide contrast with the spinal cord, allowing its definition. Common materials include water- and oil-soluble dyes or air, each of which have advantages (see Figure 18-37, page 503).[130] CT scanning of the spine has become increasingly important in the evaluation of spinal trauma. It is particularly valuable in documenting compression of the spinal cord by bone or disc material (see Figure 18-47, page 513).

Following definition of the fracture, tension is routinely applied to the spinal column to obtain spinal realignment in the presence of instability or dislocation. A traction device is applied to the outer table of the skull, using either tongs or the halo apparatus, with weights applied to provide distraction. Following reduction, it is our general practice to carry out the more definitive radiographic procedures after a period of several days to allow stabilization of other injuries and resolution of spinal cord edema. In some institutions, however, these procedures are performed immediately, followed by definitive therapy such as spinal fusion.[17] The advantages of immediate definite therapy have yet to be demonstrated.[136] Monitoring of the evoked potential may be of value in the management of spinal cord injury, particularly in indicating early deterioration or functional return.

The rational management of spine injuries is best accomplished according to location and mechanism, although multiple bones may be involved within a given injury. The directions of motion involved in spinal cord injuries are shown in Figure 18-27. Characteristically, the most common locations of automobile-related fractures are at C6-7 and lower thoracic and upper lumbar regions.

Jefferson fractures are burst fractures of the atlas produced by axial compression loads on the vertex of the skull (Figure 18-29). Generally seen are combined fractures of both the anterior and posterior arches of the atlas, with lateral dislocation of the lateral masses (Figures 18-29 and 18-30). These are rarely associated with spinal cord compression; they are generally treated with external immobilization consisting of minerva jackets or halo devices. Atlantooccipital dislocation is caused by extreme forces, thought to include both flexion and extension. It is usually fatal because of disruption of the spinal cord (Figure 18-31).

Odontoid fractures or fractures through the dens of the axis are fairly common (Figure 18-32). The mechanism of these fractures is thought to include either flexion or extension in association with rotation. The location of the fracture may have prognostic value; fractures occurring at the base of

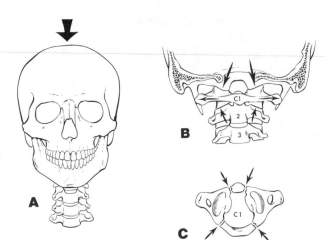

Figure 18-29 Representation of forces in production of the Jefferson fracture. Upon delivery of the axial load to the vertex of the skull (A), forces are transmitted to the occipital condyles and articulations of C1 (B). This causes explosion of the arch with lateral propulsion of the lateral masses (B: *lower arrows*) and arch. Four fractures are seen (C). [A, B, and C: Reprinted with permission of *CRC Crit. Rev. Bioeng.*, Vol. 11(1), 1984. Copyright CRC Press, Inc.]

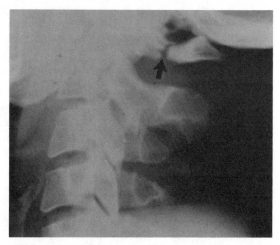

Figure 18-30 Jefferson fracture. Lateral cervical film reveals fracture of the arch of the atlas (*arrow*). [Reprinted with permission of *CRC Crit. Rev. Bioeng.*, Vol. 11(1), 1984. Copyright CRC Press, Inc.]

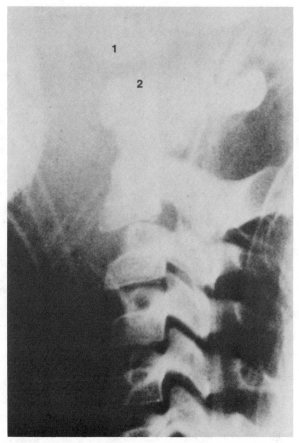

Figure 18–31 Atlanto-occipital dislocation. Note gap between occipital condyles of the skull (1) and the articulating facets of C2 (2). This lesion is almost always fatal. [Reprinted with permission of *CRC Crit. Rev. Bioeng.*, Vol. 11(1), 1984. Copyright CRC Press, Inc.]

the odontoid are unlikely to heal without surgery.[74] Patients with odontoid fractures usually present only neck pain; the rare patient with neurologic compromise may have a profound quadriparesis or quadriplegia and respiratory paralysis. While many of these fractures will be demonstrated on the lateral cervical spine x-ray, lateral skull or anterior-posterior "open-mouth" views are considered ideal to show these lesions. Polytomography may be of benefit in further defining odontoid fractures (Figure 18–32C). The management of these lesions

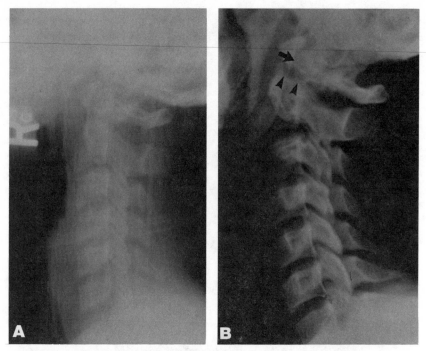

Figure 18-32 (A) Apparently normal cervical spine film in comatose 19 year old. (B) Cervical film of same patient seven weeks later, when he complained of neck pain. Fracture through base of odontoid is present (*arrowheads*) with posterior dislocation of the odontoid process (*arrow*). (Normal position is at end of arrow.) (C) A-P polytomogram of same case showing fracture line through base of odontoid process (*arrowheads*). [A, B, and C: Reprinted with permission of CRC Crit. Rev. Bioeng., Vol. 11(1), 1984. Copyright CRC Press, Inc.]

is controversial, although most agree that these lesions are unstable and require immobilization. Some would suggest that prolonged immobilization in minerva jacket or halo apparatus is adequate therapy. Others consider that surgical fusion is indicated for most odontoid fractures, since healing rates are low.[74]

Atlantoaxial dislocation is an instability of the C1-2 region caused by weakening of the transverse atlantal ligament. It may be caused or precipitated by trauma, although

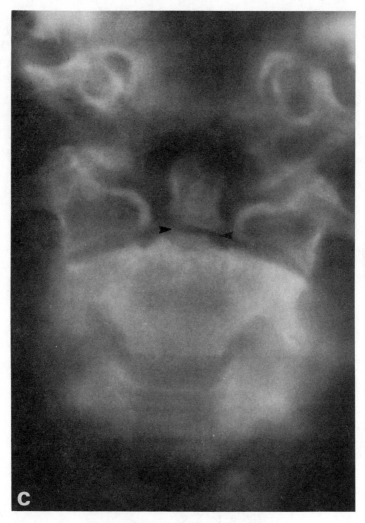

Figure 18-32 (*Continued*)

weakness of the ligament may be congenital or related to degenerative diseases. Neurologic abnormalities, including numbness and tingling in the arms and legs, may be associated with movement of the neck. Radiographic diagnosis with flexion–extension x-rays often will show an abnormal distance between the arch of the atlas and the odontoid process in flexion. Management includes posterior cervical fusion to restore stability to the upper cervical spine.[73]

With hyperextension injuries, fractures of the posterior elements and spinal dislocation may occur.[75] Commonly, hyperextension causes "Hangman's fracture,"[116] which is traumatic spondylolisthesis of C2 on C1. These fractures frequently occur upon impact of the face with the header-visor area or windshield (Figure 18-33). If conscious, patients will generally

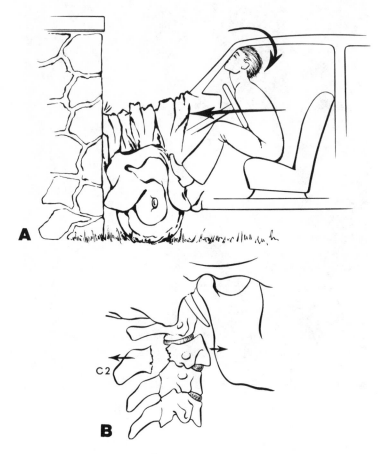

Figure 18-33 (A) Diagrammatic representation of forces involved in the production of Hangman's fracture. There is hyperextension of the head on the neck, associated with shear forces related to inertial movement of the torso. (B) Representation of forces on C2 (see the radiograph in Figure 18-34). [A: Adapted from E. L. Seljeskog and S. N. Chou, *J. Neurosurg.*, 45:3-8, 1976. B: Reprinted with permission of *CRC Crit. Rev. Bioeng.*, Vol. 11(1), 1984. Copyright CRC Press, Inc.]

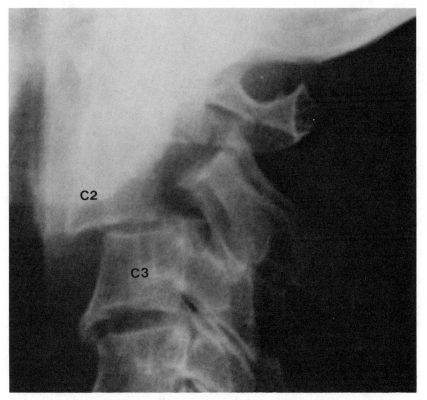

Figure 18-34 Hangman's fracture. There is a fracture through the arch of C2 and an interior subluxation of the body of C2 on C3. [Reprinted with permission of *CRC Crit. Rev. Bioeng.*, Vol. 11(1), 1984. Copyright CRC Press, Inc.]

present neck pain; associated head injury and coma are common. Lateral cervical spine x-rays will show a fracture through the arch of C2 and anterior dislocation of the bodies of C1 and C2 (Figure 18-34). Generally, these will heal with external immobilization and only rarely require surgery.

Rear impacts may produce hyperextension with anterior ligamentous disruption and avulsion of the anterior surface of the vertebral body or disruption of the disc space (Figure 18-35). It should be emphasized that flexion of the neck may occur as a secondary event after hyperextension, especially when the neck is wrapped around the seat (Figure 18-36; see also Figure 18-52, page 525). The same forces discussed above are involved throughout the rest of the cervical spine.

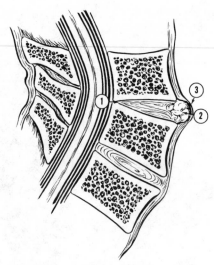

Figure 18-35 Mechanism of anterior longitudinal ligament disruption, in this instance in extension. As the posterior aspect of the disc space collapses, with buckling of the posterior longitudinal ligament (1), the traumatized disc (2) pushes anteriorly, tearing the attenuated anterior longitudinal ligament (3). A similar process may occur in burst fractures and even flexion injuries. Note the buckling of the posterior elements, which may stimulate their fracture. [Reprinted with permission of *CRC Crit. Rev. Bioeng.*, Vol. 11(1), 1984. Copyright CRC Press, Inc.]

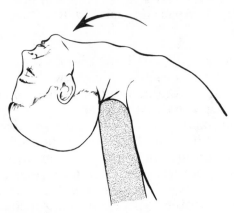

Figure 18-36 Hyperextension injuries of the cervical spine may occur with the top of the seat functioning as a fulcrum. [Reprinted with permission of *CRC Crit. Rev. Bioeng.*, Vol. 11(1), 1984. Copyright CRC Press, Inc.]

Axial compressive forces may occur in rollover and frontal or side vehicle impacts to cause burst fractures of lower cervical spine levels (Figure 18-37). More commonly, however, the compressive injuries are associated with flexion of the spine due to impacts with various interior structures. If hyperflexion is present, especially in the presence of additional shearing forces, significant dislocation of the vertebral bodies may be seen (Figure 18-38).

Burst fractures with or without flexion are commonly associated with severe neurologic deficits due to displacement of bone and disc fragments into the spinal canal. X-rays will demonstrate flattening or wedging of the vertebral body and will often show the compromise of the spinal canal. There may be angulation or frank dislocation of the spine depending on

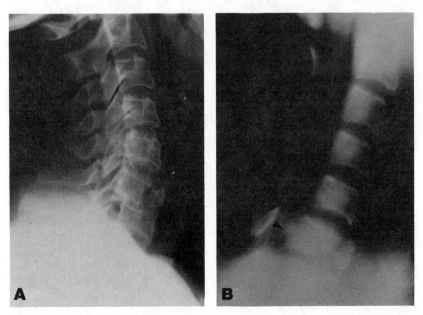

Figure 18-37 (A) Burst fracture. The body of C6 has been compressed. The fracture anterior component is moved forward. The remaining body is moved posteriorly into the spinal canal (see Figure 18-48). (B) Air myelogram shows the spinal cord compressed by the posterior aspect of the fractured vertebral body (*arrowhead*). [A and B: Reprinted with permission of *CRC Crit. Rev. Bioeng.*, Vol. 11(1), 1984. Copyright CRC Press, Inc.]

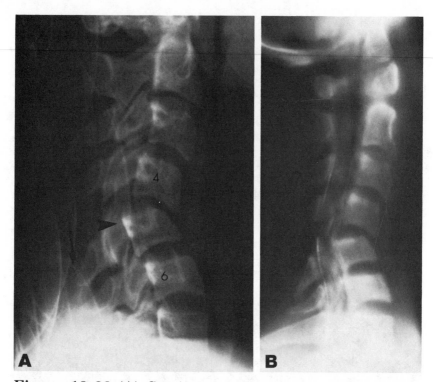

Figure 18-38 (A) Cervical dislocation due to flexion. The posterior aspect of the vertebral body is in the spinal canal on this lateral cervical film (*arrowhead*). There is fanning of the spinous processes (*large arrow*), indicating disruption of the posterior ligaments. Note absence of significant bony injury. (B) Air myelogram of same patient showing compression and distortion of the spinal cord. [A and B: Reprinted with permission of *CRC Crit. Rev. Bioeng.*, Vol. 11(1), 1984. Copyright CRC Press, Inc.]

the degree of flexion or other forces involved (Figures 18–38 and 18–39).[9] Myelography or CT scanning can demonstrate compression of the spinal cord by bone and disc. Management will generally include reduction of angulation or relocation if possible. Immobilization, followed by spinal decompression and fusion to restore the spinal canal and vertebral stability, are usually performed.

Flexion injuries may occur in the absence of compressive forces. Forced flexion, in addition to causing wedgelike fractures of the vertebral body, is likely to cause dislocation and

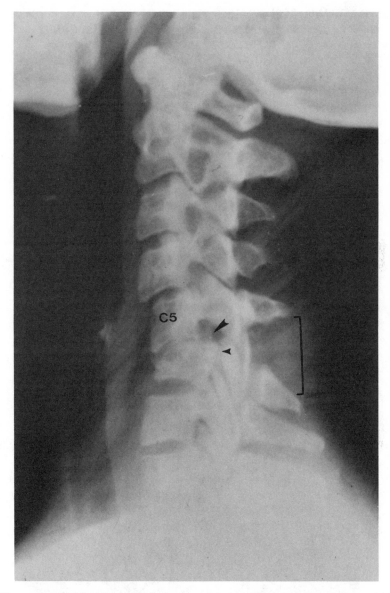

Figure 18-39 Flexion injury with wedge compression of C6. There is a spicule of bone in the C5-6 neural foramen (*large arrowhead*). Small arrowhead shows the border of the vertebral body, which is into the spinal canal. There is also fanning of the posterior elements (*bracket*). [Reprinted with permission of *CRC Crit. Rev. Bioeng.*, Vol. 11(1), 1984. Copyright CRC Press, Inc.]

locking of the facet joints.[9] Because of disruption of the posterior ligaments, fanning of the posterior elements is often seen. As noted in the anatomy subsection, the facet joints are important in maintaining the lateral stability of the cervical spine. With flexion, in association with slight rotational forces, a facet joint may jump out of position and move anteriorly (Figure 18-40).[115] If unilateral, this may cause neck pain and compression of nerve roots. With hyperflexion, there can be complete dislocation of the spine and the facets may lock

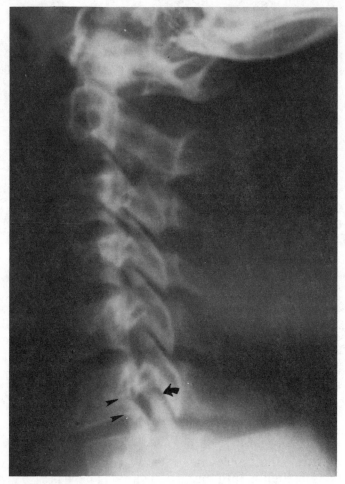

Figure 18-40 Unilateral locked facet. The facet marked by the arrow is in normal position. The other facet (*arrowheads*) has rotated anteriorly. [Reprinted with permission of *CRC Crit. Rev. Bioeng.*, Vol. 11(1), 1984. Copyright CRC Press, Inc.]

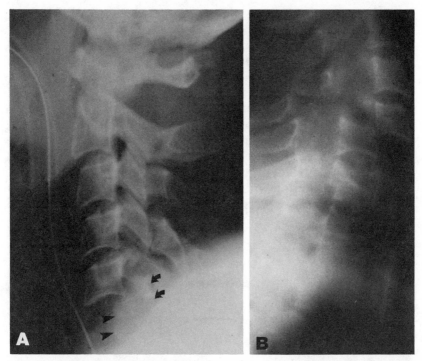

Figure 18-41 (A) Bilateral locked facets with complete dislocation. Arrowheads define anterior border of body of C6 and
arrows the posterior border. (B) Air myelogram cut demonstrates obliteration of the spinal canal by the vertebral body.
[A and B: Reprinted with permission of *CRC Crit. Rev. Bioeng.*, Vol. 11(1), 1984. Copyright CRC Press, Inc.]

bilaterally (Figure 18-41). Characteristically, in these cases,
the spine above the level of the locked facets moves anteriorly,
with severe injury to the spinal cord as a result. The radiographic diagnosis of bilateral locked facets is readily made on
routine lateral cervical spine film because of the dislocation
produced. Unilateral locked facets may be difficult to diagnose. Oblique views of the cervical spine may be required to
demonstrate the abnormality of the facet and narrowing of
the neural foramen. In either case, reduction is generally
carried out by traction. In many centers, open (surgical)
reduction is carried out immediately, although there is some
evidence that even late surgery may be of benefit in producing
neurologic recovery. Generally, the outlook for neurologic recovery for patients with bilateral locked facets is poor.

Flexion injuries may also create fractures of the spinous processes, commonly called "clay shoveler's" syndrome (Figure 18-42). In cases of unilateral flexion of the spine, isolated fractures of the lateral masses, including the facets, may occur. These may be unstable, and diagnosis is best made by tomography.

Extension injuries of the lower cervical spine can also cause injuries to the posterior elements, including the facets, primarily by compression.[75] These fractures, seen on routine radiography with oblique views, are generally stable and often produce no neurologic deficits. Additionally, the anterior longitudinal ligament may be torn or the anterior surface of the vertebral body can be avulsed by the anterior longitudinal ligament. Often movement of one vertebral body relative to another is seen (Figures 18-35 and 18-43). Routine x-rays in

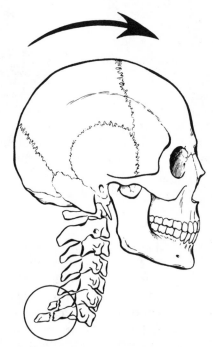

Figure 18-42 Mechanism of "clay-shoveler's" fracture. The spinous processes in the lower cervical spine fractures. Avulsion of the spinous processes due to tension from the posterior ligaments and muscles of attachment. [Reprinted with permission of *CRC Crit. Rev. Bioeng.*, Vol. 11(1), 1984. Copyright CRC Press, Inc.]

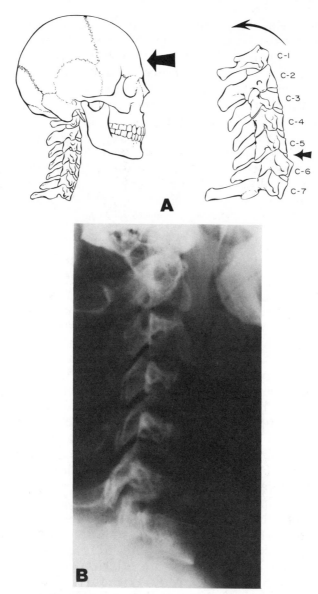

Figure 18-43 (A) At C5-6, the bodies C1-5 have moved posteriorly, with dislocation of the spine. (B) Dislocation of cervical spine due to shear force, in association with some compression. There is also an anterior vertebral body fracture. The spinal canal is occluded by the upper vertebral body. [A and B: Reprinted with permission of *CRC Crit. Rev. Bioeng.*, Vol. 11(1), 1984. Copyright CRC Press, Inc.]

the presence of ligamentus injuries may be normal, and flexion–extension views are often required. This dislocation of the cervical spine is often associated with severe neurologic deficit due to spinal cord compression or transection. These will be evident on routine cervical radiography and are managed as other unstable fractures of the cervical spine. It is important to note that many injuries of the cervical column may be due to combined flexion or extension with rotation or shear. Tension injuries of the cervical spine are uncommon. Patrick demonstrated that high loads are necessary to produce injury.[90] When it occurs, generally all ligaments are injured and spinal cord transection may be seen (Figures 18–44 18–45).

E. Clinical Analysis of the Thoracolumbar Spine

The thoracic spine is restricted in its curvature by the ribs and associated musculature. While the lumbar spine does not have the protection of the ribs, it instead has a significant body of muscles providing some additional strength. Hyperextension and hyperflexion injuries of the thoracic spine are less common than in the cervical or lumbar region.[143] The most common mechanisms for fracture are axial compression or compression with additional flexion or anterior–posterior shear forces. These are routinely seen in the lower thoracic and upper lumbar regions, presumably because of the decreasing effects of the rib cage and the increasing magnitude of shear forces. There is also a fairly high incidence of fractures in the T4 to T6 region associated with high-speed injuries with violent flexion.

A well-defined series of events occurs in the production of flexion deformities of the spine (see Figure 18–46). Associated with the initial compression, the discs flatten and press back into the spinal canal.[38,143] With continuing compression, the vertebral body is fractured and a fulcrum is set up through the middle of the vertebral body. With further anterior compression, there is shattering of the bone and retropulsion of both bone fragments and disc into the spinal canal with compression of the spinal cord. Severe neurologic deficit may result, although occasionally severe bony injuries are unassociated with para spinal cord damage. Burst or vertical compression fractures are similar in their effects on the spinal cord (Figures 18–47 and 18–48). In the burst fractures, there may or may not be injuries to the ligamentous structures.

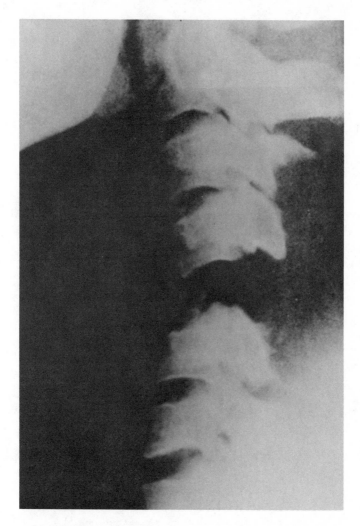

Figure 18-44 Distraction injury between C4 and C5 causing complete separation of the spine. [Reprinted with permission of *CRC Crit. Rev. Bioeng.*, Vol. 11(1), 1984. Copyright CRC Press, Inc.]

While many thoracolumbar fractures will be stable, they are usually initially treated as unstable, and patients are carefully immobilized for transport and early evaluation. This early evaluation includes routine anterior and lateral radiographs. Initial therapy in most institutions consists of bed rest, although some prefer to use pelvic traction in an

Figure 18-45 Study carried out by Patrick on himself at two times his body weight[90]: substantial forces are required for the production of spine injuries due to tension. [Reprinted with permission of *CRC Crit. Rev. Bioeng.*, Vol. 11(1), 1984. Copyright CRC Press, Inc.]

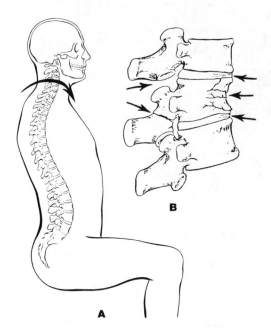

Figure 18-46 Flexion injury of the thoracolumbar spine in sitting position. (A) Direction of the overall forces for trauma to upper thoracic spine; (B) progression of injury in flexion. [Reprinted with permission of *CRC Crit. Rev. Bioeng.*, Vol. 11(1), 1984. Copyright CRC Press, Inc.]

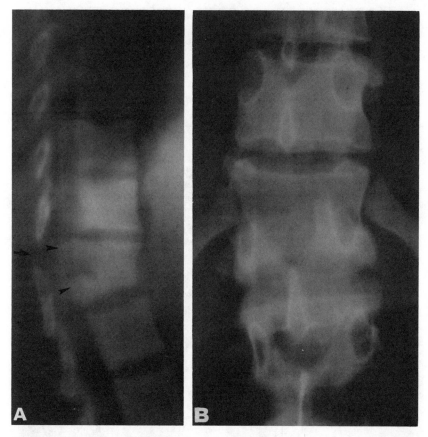

Figure 18-47 (A) Thoracic compression fracture (air myelogram). There is a wedge deformity of the vertebral body, and the fragmented posterior aspect of the body is in the spinal canal (*arrowheads*). A fracture of the posterior elements is seen (*arrow*). (B) AP film of same patient showing variation in vertebral body height. (C) CT scan through level of fracture. Arrowheads emphasize fragmentation of the vertebral body. The spinal cord (1) is outlined by metrizamide contrast media (2). Note compression of the spinal cord by the anterior fragment and fractured posterior elements. AP (D) and lateral (E) postoperative radiographs. Spinal decompression, anterior bone fusion, and posterior instrumentation using Weiss springs has been performed. The extent of the vertebral body removal is defined by the surgical clips; the bone graft is also seen (*arrows*). [A, B, C, D, and E: Reprinted with permission of *CRC Crit. Rev. Bioeng.*, Vol. 11(1), 1984. Copyright CRC Press, Inc.]

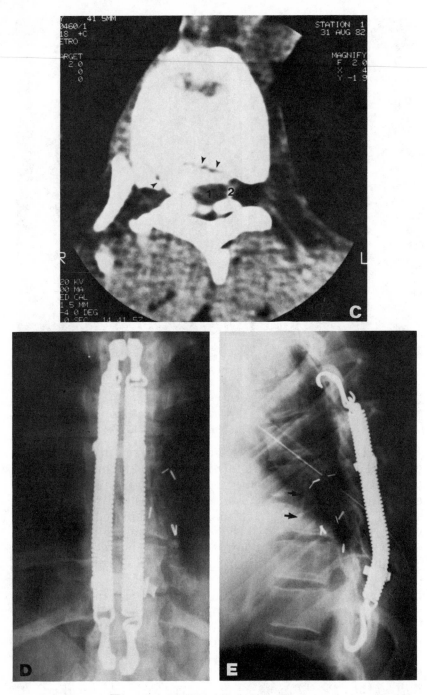

Figure 18-47 (*Continued*)

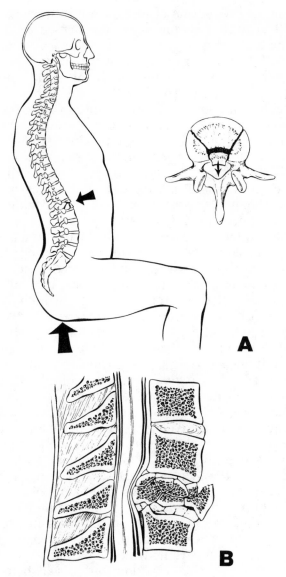

Figure 18-48 Representation of burst fractures of the thoracolumbar spine. (A) The axial load, most commonly due to rollovers, is delivered from the buttocks. Retropulsion of bone and disc into the spinal canal occurs as a result. Final result is diagrammed in B. The radiographic appearance is similar to that seen in the cervical region (Figure 18-42). [A and B: Reprinted with permission of *CRC Crit. Rev. Bioeng.*, Vol. 11(1), 1984. Copyright CRC Press, Inc.]

attempt to obtain reduction of angulation if present. Myelography or CT scanning is commonly performed to define the fracture anatomy and determine spinal cord compression (Figures 18–47A and C). In many institutions immediate surgical approaches are done, including posterior element instrumentation (i.e., Harrington rods), with or without laminectomy as the procedure of choice.[31] While some have suggested that this improves neurologic outcome, other studies show little long-term neurologic improvement produced by the procedure.[88] Other investigators consider that maximal neurologic recovery will be obtained by removal of the mass compressing the spinal cord. Therefore, surgical approaches have been developed to remove the vertebral body and provide anterior bony fusion (Figures 18–47D and E).[68]

Unstable injuries of the thoracolumbar spine associated with severe neurologic deficits are often associated with rotational or horizontal shear forces. Shear forces associated with forward movement in the lap-belted restrained spine may produce injuries called "Chance fractures," which are linear fractures through the middle of the vertebral body, with or without spinal dislocation.[53] These are characteristically unstable because they are fractures not only through the vertebral body, but also through the posterior elements of the spine.[143] Clinically, patients frequently complain of severe pain, and neurologic deficits may be evident. The radiographic diagnosis can generally be made on routine AP and lateral spine radiography, and myelography is performed to define further the anatomy of the lesion. Ligamentous injuries are common in association with flexion injuries of the thoracolumbar spine, but they rarely occur as isolated phenomena. When they do, they are likely to be due to extension injuries, with damage to the anterior longitudinal ligament, and sometimes compression fractures of the posterior elements, similar to those seen in the cervical region. These extension injuries are characterized by severe neurologic deficit.

Injuries below the L2–3 region due to seat belts have a lower incidence of spinal cord injury because they occur below the level of the termination of the cord.[38,120] Instead, they produce cauda equina syndromes with isolated or multiple nerve root deficits. Management is similar to that of the lesions discussed earlier.

Minor injuries of the thoracolumbar spine, such as transverse or spinous process fractures, are common. These are generally due to violent muscle tension, especially by the quadratus lumborum and soleus muscles. They are significant in that they might indicate more severe fractures of the thoracolumbar spine.

The lumbar or lower thoracic spine may be injured during rollover or bottoming out of the seats upon loading following lift off.[18,55,103] Intrusion of the roof has also been implicated. Sacral and coccygeal fractures are not unusual in severe motor vehicle accidents.[63] Characteristically, they are seen in patients with trauma to the pelvis and may occur either unilaterally or bilaterally. Sacral fractures may be produced by shear forces transmitted when the knee hits the dashboard (Figure 18-49). Sacral and coccygeal fractures often result in low back and rectal pain. In upper sacral fractures, there may be some loss of function of the S1 nerve root, with weakness of dorsiflexion of the foot and lateral foot paresthesias. Bowel and bladder dysfunction may be seen, because of injury to the lower sacral nerve roots. Associated visceral injuries, such as bladder lacerations, are sometimes present. Diagnosis is best made on anterioposterior and lateral views of the sacrum, but oblique views may be required to better

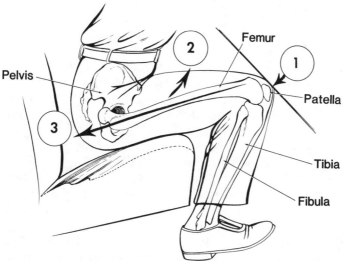

Figure 18-49 Mechanisms of sacral and pelvis fractures. Injuries to the patellar (knee) are typically due to direct impact (1); these forces may be also transmitted through the femur to the pelvis and/or sacrum, causing fractures here (3), or buckling and fracture of the femur (2).

document the fracture line. Again, myelography or CT scanning may be helpful in determining the status of the spinal canal in the upper sacral area and neural foramina in the lower regions. Treatment usually consists of bed rest to reduce pain; in the presence of neurologic deficit, laminectomy and decompression of nerve roots may be indicated.

Degenerative diseases may predispose the spine to injury. Diseases or congenital weakness of the transverse ligament may increase the likelihood of atlantoaxial dislocation.[73] In the presence of spondylosis in the cervical region, severe neurologic deficits may be produced by trivial trauma. In these instances, the spinal canal becomes narrowed by the development of osteophytes in the area of the disc interspace. In association with extension injuries, there is a pulping of the central part of the spinal cord, causing disproportionate weakness in the upper arms and a mantle-type sensory loss, a constellation of signs known as the central cord syndrome.[115] Initial x-rays in these patients may reveal no abnormalities other than chronic degenerative disease. Myelography or CT scanning with dye enhancement, however, will demonstrate compromise of the spinal cord.[130] Frequently, management is conservative with physical therapy and rehabilitation, but often laminectomy is required to decompress the spinal cord fully. The central cord syndrome may also rarely be seen in younger people with burst or compression fractures and flexion-type deformities.

At all levels of the spine, herniated discs may be produced by trauma. Characteristically, these are most common in the cervical region at C5 and C6 and in the lumbar region at L4–5 and L5–S1. These are produced by mild flexion and rotational forces, causing initial bulging at the disc. If there is some weakness in the annulus, disc material may rupture through and compress the nerve root directly. The characteristic findings will be weakness of the muscles innervated by the compressed nerve root and radicular pain and hypesthesia. Routine radiographs will generally be normal, and myelography or CT scanning will aid in making the radiographic diagnosis. Initial therapy is frequently conservative, although surgical treatment may ultimately be required to relieve pain and restore neurologic function.

Several types of bone disease may increase the propensity to and severity of spinal trauma. Osteoporosis is a common condition involving millions of women over the age of 40 and small groups of others. The disorder is characterized by decreased strength of the bony matrix and markedly increased propensity to fracture. Even relatively trivial trauma, therefore, can cause fracture of vertebral bodies. Similar problems are seen in patients with cancer that has spread to the bone (Figure 18-50). Paget's disease of the spine is a metabolic disease of bone characterized by decreased strength of the

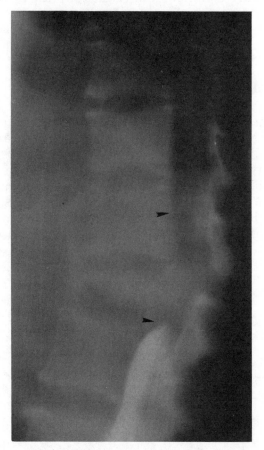

Figure 18-50 Thoracic compression fracture. Minor auto accident produced this fracture in a 67-year-old man with multiple myeloma. Myelogram cut shows complete blockage of spinal canal by fractured vertebral body. Air injected above the fracture does not pass through, nor does positive contrast dye. The extent of the block is marked (*arrowheads*). [Reprinted with permission of *CRC Crit. Rev. Bioeng.*, Vol. 11(1), 1984. Copyright CRC Press, Inc.]

vertebral bodies and soft tissue development compressing the spinal cord, and a similar propensity to collapse. In ankylosing spondylitis, on the other hand, a "bamboo spine" is created by a pseudofusion at the level of the discs. Patients with severe ankylosing spondylitis characteristically suffer shearing or hyperextension fractures, with the injury occurring through the mid vertebral body or at the level of the disc.   Gross dislocations are common, and reduction may be difficult.

IV. THE THORAX

A. Anatomy

The thorax is composed of the rib cage and the viscera that are enclosed by it.[140,146] Figure 18-51 gives a diagrammatic view of the thorax and abdomen. The rib cage consists of the thoracic spine, the sternum, and the twelve pairs of ribs extending between the two. The upper nine pairs of ribs articulate with both the thoracic spine and the sternum; the bottom three pairs, called floating ribs, have free ends. The intercostal muscles, extending in different directions and organized optimally for respiration, extend between each of the ribs.

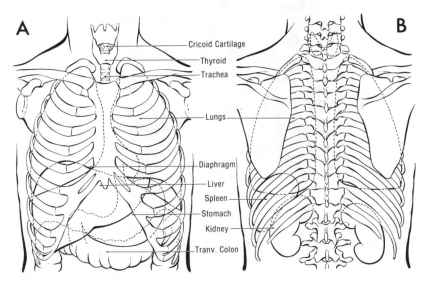

Figure 18-51 Diagrammatic anatomy of the thorax and abdomen. (A) Front view; (B) rear view.

The border between the thoracic and abdominal cavities is formed by the diaphragm, a dome-shaped muscular structure important in respiration. Because the diaphragm is dome shaped and extends as high as the seventh rib, several of the abdominal contents (including the liver, stomach, spleen, pancreas, and to a lesser extent the kidneys) are incorporated in the rib cage.

Two membranes, the parietal and the visceral pleura, line the thoracic cavity and cover the lungs. Between the layers of the pleura is a potential space that may fill with blood in responses to trauma. The lungs are multilobulated organs that are broken down into smaller functional units. At the smallest, or alveolar, level, air exchange takes place with the capillary system.

Between the pleural sacs is located the mediastinum; this space can be viewed on chest radiography and can be an important indication of trauma to the heart or great vessels.

The heart, encased in a membranous sac called the pericardium, is located in the mediastinal region. The heart is divided into four chambers, the venous inflow coming via the superior and inferior vena cavae to the right atrium. Outflow is through the pulmonary vasculature in the right ventricle, and arterial outflow through the aorta that exits from the left ventricle. The great vessels most prominently include the superior and inferior vena cavae and the aorta, which are posterior to the heart and adjacent to the vertebral bodies of the spine by which they may be injured.

B. Chest Trauma

Rib fractures are common in impact injuries to the chest. They may be singular or multiple. Characteristically, they produce sharp chest pain, which may be increased with respiration. Their major significance, however, is that rib fractures may be diagnostic indicators of more severe injuries to the thoracic contents.[49]

Invasion of the space between the pleural layers by blood or air (hemothorax or pneumothorax) represents the most common thoracic manifestation of motor vehicle accidents. Generally, these are caused by fractured ribs cutting through the pulmonary pleura. The rib fragment may puncture the lung or may lacerate the small blood vessels overlying the ribs or on the pulmonary surface. These injuries may cause severe respiratory compromise and chest pain. They are usually managed by placement of a chest tube into the pleural space to evacuate the blood or air and to allow the lung to expand and the leak to seal.

In the presence of multiple rib fractures, a flail chest may be produced. This implies that a segment of the chest wall is moving paradoxically to the normal chest movements that occur during respiration. Flail chest may create serious respiratory difficulties with hypoxia and, if severe or unrecognized, cardiac arrest. As soon as the diagnosis is made, prompt intubation should be carried out; mechanical ventilation is generally required. Pulmonary edema and pneumonia are common sequelae to the flail chest syndrome.

Pulmonary contusions are common events in victims of flail chest and in patients with multiple rib fractures. Clinically, respiratory distress may be evident, but this may be missed in the presence of altered level of consciousness or other injuries. The initial chest x-rays may demonstrate some patchy infiltrates, which are not necessarily evident until several days posttrauma. Additionally, there may be evidence of hypoxia on the blood gas determinations. The most serious complication of lung contusion is the high likelihood of secondary pneumonia, which represents the most common cause of death in patients with thoracic trauma. Ideal management of pulmonary contusions frequently includes intubation and mechanical ventilation with delivery of high oxygen levels. In spite of this, permanent lung damage including restrictive disease is likely.[79,90]

Injuries of the heart may be seen in severe thoracic trauma, often in association with pulmonary injuries. Tears of the pericardial sac of the heart are common in patients dying of blunt chest trauma. Of much greater significance, however, are large tears of the heart muscle wall. This most commonly occurs in the right ventricle, followed by the left ventricle. Survival long enough to reach appropriate medical care is uncommon.

In patients with small tears of the heart muscle wall, different clinical manifestations may be present. Cardiac tamponade is produced by bleeding into the pericardial sac. Under these circumstances, there is compression of the heart cavities and compromise of blood flow. This is an immediately life-threatening process: surgical puncture of the pericardium and removal of this blood is necessary. A chronic complication of small muscle wall tears is the production of ventricular aneurysms. In these, the wall is thinned out significantly and may rupture some time after the trauma.

Injuries to the great vessels are particularly common in patients with sternal and upper rib fractures. They may be manifested as ruptures of the aorta, in which case only a small percentage survive to the hospital, or as aneurysms of the aorta or its branches, in which case clinical manifestations may range from the asymptomatic patient to hypotension. Routine chest x-rays may reveal a widened mediastinal shadow, and aortography is required for diagnosis. When recognized, surgery is generally required to correct the lesion.

In addition to the structures of the thorax, the upper abdominal viscera may be injured by impacts during automobile accidents. In lower rib fractures, the liver, spleen, or pancreas may become perforated by bony fragments. Additionally, blunt trauma to the area may cause rupture of the spleen or liver lacerations, with profuse bleeding and shock. Surgical exploration is usually required in these cases. Similarly, blunt trauma to the lower abdomen may produce injuries to these organs and to the other viscera of the abdominal cavity and retroperitoneum, including the intestines and their blood supply, bladder, and kidneys.[79,124]

V. BIOMECHANICAL FAILURE LEVELS

An accurate crash reconstruction of the accident is important for a biomechanical investigation. Computer reconstruction of crashes are generally accepted in court. The current programs—Calspan Reconstruction of Accident Speeds on the Highway (CRASH) and Simulation Model of Automobile Collisions (SMAC)—are typically used to determine changes in velocity upon impact. Impact velocities and accelerations as a function of time can also be obtained if sufficient information is available. These programs are generally applicable to planar accidents with impacts ranging from head-on to rear. Several occupant dynamic programs are in development. For example, our group has developed programs to determine the forces secondary to impact upon occupants with seat belts. If an estimate of the deceleration can be obtained, then forces upon the occupant can be calculated. It is important to examine carefully the vehicle and the injuries to determine impact areas.

The knowledge accumulated in the areas of head and spinal injuries are derived from measurements made on experimental animals, cadavers, instrumented dummies, mathematical models, or retrospective clinical evaluations. Animal studies allow the determination of changes in physiologic function in the living preparation while human cadavers provide a means to determine the strength of bones and soft tissues with extrapolation to the living human.

It is generally agreed that fresh human cadaver tissues are more closely representative of living tissues than those that have been embalmed. Our group has conducted biomechanical studies on over 50 fresh human cadaver subjects to determine the forces and energies required for head, cervical, thoracic, and lumbar spinal damage.[104,108,112]

Various mathematical approaches that have been advanced to understand injury mechanisms include lumped parameter systems, distributed models, and finite element analysis.[104,108,109,139,142] Anthropomorphic dummies provide another means for studying forces of impact and acceleration. Various dummies have evolved that can measure forces upon lower limbs, head and neck, and thorax and are often used in crash studies. The early studies with human volunteers were essentially conducted by the military. A review of these dynamic studies has been given elsewhere.[108,112] The Appendix at the end of this section (pages 544–550) gives a review of the physics of injury analysis.

A rich literature exists that is based upon retrospective clinical evaluations of injuries. Unfortunately, few instances have occurred where the treating physicians have observed or recorded the physical mechanisms of injury. It has, therefore, been necessary to postulate the mechanisms based on biomechanical extrapolations and clinical findings. Consequently, advanced mathematical models and biomechanical studies with sophisticated instrumentation to measure the physical mechanisms of trauma in the living animal and human cadaveric tissues are essential.

The goal of biomedical research is to extend the observations on human volunteers to determine injury tolerance levels with suitable scaling techniques and information derived from mathematical or experimental studies. Typically, force, pressure, velocity, linear and angular acceleration, torque, momentum, energy, and severity index or head injury criterion (HIC) are referenced (see the Appendix, pages 544–550).

A. Head and Neck Measurements

Because the head and neck are coupled to the torso, they move backward, forward, sideways, or they rotate (Figure 18-27A). Acceleration injuries may differ from those resulting from direct impacts to the body. Injuries can be produced without impact to the spine.[50,56,108] Furthermore, injuries to the brain may also be produced when the head is rapidly rotated and the brain fails to follow. In acceleration and deceleration injuries the forces are proportional to the weight of the system multiplied by the acceleration. With flexion, the head is often stopped when the chin hits the chest. Extension injuries often occur without a headrest, when there is nothing to stop the backward movement until the occiput hits the posterior chest wall or seat. With whiplash, there is often a recoil from extension into flexion (Figure 18-52). It is important to differentiate between forces applied directly to the head in contrast to those produced secondary to acceleration or deceleration.

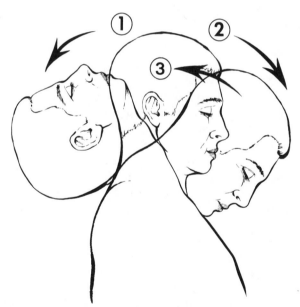

Figure 18-52 Mechanism of whiplash. Extension (1) followed by flexion (2) prior to resuming the neutral position (3). [Reprinted with permission of *CRC Crit. Rev. Bioeng.*, Vol. 11(1), 1984. Copyright CRC Press, Inc.]

B. Brain Injury Levels

Various criteria have been advanced recently based on finite element analysis to suggest mechanisms of brain injury.[139] Typically a head injury criterion of 1000 or a Gadd severity index of 1500 are routinely used as levels where closed impact head injury can occur (see Appendix). Various levels of deceleration from maximum levels of 400 G are suggested as injury producing. The Wayne State Acceleration Versus Time Duration Curve is sometimes referenced.[29] Another measure often referred to is the injury developed at the pole of the head opposite to the impact area. Typically, at the contrecoup injury site, negative pressure levels of approximately one atmosphere have been suggested to produce tissue destruction.[43,139]

The brain can suffer hemorrhage of the bridging vessels and white matter with rotation. It has been suggested that a pure angular acceleration of 1800 rad/sec^2 will produce a concussion 50 percent of the time in man.[86] This study is based upon a calculation extrapolated from studies in the subhuman primate. In contrast, Ewing demonstrated no adverse effects in humans following an angular head velocity of 38 rad/sec and an angular head acceleration of 2675 rad/sec^2 measured during 15 G_{-x} sled accelerations.[28]

C. Skull Fracture Levels

An intrusion of the skull into the brain can produce direct damage beneath the depressed site or destruction of other areas secondary to propogated influences. Furthermore, once the skull has penetrated the overlying tissues of the brain, a route for infection is available. Human slow skull loading produces a skull deflexion with less force than with rapid loading.[43,108] An empty human skull will fracture with an energy absorption of 2.0 foot-pounds (ft lb), while the intact head with scalp requires approximately 32 to 48 ft lb for fracture. In human head studies with the scalp intact, dropped onto a heavy steel slab, fractures were observed at energies of approximately 51 ft lb. Using a 8.8-lb striker, fractures were produced at energies of 25 ft lb with forces of approximately 1000 lb. The peak accelerations ranged from 150 to 360 G. An acceleration time tolerance curve for human linear skull fracture based on a drop test demonstrates that approximately 90 G are required for an average 5-millisecond (ms) duration acceleration pulse and approximately 50 G for a duration of 30 ms or greater.[42,43]

Depressed or comminuted skull fractures have been produced at the temporal parietal area with 500 lb, 900 lb at the frontal area, and 200 lb at the zygoma, with a 1-inch² impactor. Penetration of the parietal skull with an impactor of 0.3 to 0.15 inch² can be produced by forces of approximately 250 lb.[76,77] Soft tissues did not affect peak penetration force if the device had sufficient energy to penetrate. In summary, large surfaces produce linear fractures and small impactors produce penetration fractures; medium-size impactors produce comminuted depressed fractures (Figure 18-53). An excellent clinical follow-up of patients with skull fractures is given by Braakman,[10] Jamieson,[57-59] and others.[127,135,137]

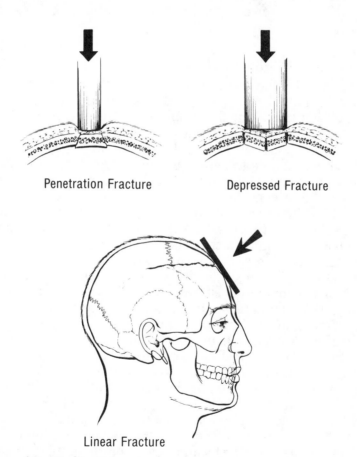

Penetration Fracture   Depressed Fracture

Linear Fracture

Figure 18-53 Skull fractures versus impactor type. [Adapted from J. W. Melvin and F. G. Evans, *Proc. 15th Stapp Car Crash Conf.*, 1971, p. 666.]

D. Spine Loads

The majority of the early works to determine the breaking loads of the cervical vertebral bodies and discs was conducted with isolated tissues.[112] Typically, the vertebral bodies are weaker in compression than the discs while the reverse is true in tension. The compressive breaking load for cervical vertebral bodies is less than those in the lower regions. The intervertebral discs are somewhat stronger. The vertebral bodies and discs become progressively stronger under direct compression because of their increasing size from the thoracic through the lumbar areas. The strength of the lumbar vertebral body is also less than the disc. These strength figures vary with age since the materials deteriorate in the later decades.

E. Cervical Failure Levels

Several studies have been conducted on the entire fresh cervical column.[22, 39, 85, 104, 109, 110, 112, 113] Studies from our laboratory indicate that the cervical vertebrae fractures in vertical compression at 1000 to 1500 lb but is weaker in flexion and extension.[104, 109, 110, 112, 113] The anterior ligaments of the cervical column, which include the anterior longitudinal, annulus fibers and disc, and posterior longitudinal ligament are considerably stronger than the posterior ligaments. The posterior complex includes the ligamentum flavum intraspinous ligament supraspinous ligament (Figure 18-25). Selective ablation studies in our laboratory indicate that the posterior ligament complex disrupts in tension with approximately 150 lb. The anterior ligament complex ruptures with application of approximately 300 lb of tension. Other studies in the lower cervical region indicate that the anterior longitudinal ligament and the anterior fibers of the annulus can withstand approximately 200 lb of force prior to avulsion. The ligaments of attachment from the upper cervical elements to the skull are extremely strong, and in several fresh cadaver studies it was found that ring fractures of the base of the lower skull occur in tension without substantial ligamentous disruption of the cervical column.[110] These fractures can occur during high-speed crashes when the chin is captured by the interior of the vehicle, producing tension at the basilar region of the skull. In general, it has been our finding that with extension the majority of the ligamentous disruptions are in the lower cervical column.

In football helmet studies conducted in our laboratory it was demonstrated that substantially higher forces were produced in the disrupted anterior compartment of the cervical column with a force applied to the face mask than with the same force applied to the chin or forehead. Furthermore, lower cervical disruptions were always observed. Consequently, any lever effect upon the cervical column may exacerbate injuries to anterior spinal column.

Studies done on one or two isolated spinal segments should be applied with caution to the intact spinal column because moment arms exist within the normal head–neck complex that are not present in isolated studies. In general, approximately 10 percent of the body weight is supported by the cervical column, with the head weighing approximately 10 lb and the neck several pounds. Several shear studies on the cervical column of the human cadaver indicate that the posterior complex can be disrupted with application of approximately 200 lb on the posterior side of the column. Approximately twice this value was required to disrupt the anterior complex, with forces applied from the anterior to posterior direction. The odontoid was fractured with direct application of approximately 200 lb.[104] Typically, the cervical column is strongest in compression and tension, and weakest in rotation and shear (see Figure 18-27B, page 491).

F. Thoracolumbar Spine Failure Loads

Studies on isolated thoracolumbar segments of the human cadaver demonstrate fracture of the vertebral bodies at loads ranging from several hundred to over one thousand pounds.[104, 109, 112] Typically, the shorter segments required more force for compressive fracture and disruption of the ligaments. A long column is weaker due to bending than a shorter column. This column effect was also observed in the intact cadaver studies in our laboratory when forces were applied directly to the head. In the intact cadaver, thoracolumbar fractures were produced with approximately 400–600 lb applied to the base of the neck with the subject in the sitting position.[81, 112] Typically, thoracolumbar injuries occur secondary to ejection of the passenger from the vehicle, with impact to the shoulders or chest or with impact to the buttock. Forces can be applied to the buttock secondary to seat bottoming out, which typically occurs when the vehicle contacts the ground after lift off or with impacts with the interior of the vehicle. Rotational injuries of thoracolumbar column can be produced with side impact rollover or other modes and are almost always attendant with injuries to the thorax. A considerable body of knowledge exists in the area of ejection-seat studies that can be helpful in analysis of impacts applied from below the thoracolumbar column.[108, 112]

G. Thorax Failure Loads

The thorax incorporates many of the body organs and has been implicated as a site of more severe and fatal injuries to automobile accident victims than any other area. Typically, frontal or side impact is often associated with thorax trauma. Rib fractures have been sited following chest impacts with deflection of 1 inch and loads of approximately 1000 lb.[90] It is important to review carefully each of the studies of the literature to determine the type of impactors used in the experimental protocol. A review of the history of the standards developed in this area is given elsewhere.[26, 91, 92, 124, 125] The stiffness factors are in the range of approximately 500 pounds per inch with forces applied to the chest wall. Rib fractures have been reported with application of 500 lb/inch with a chest deflection of 3 inches using a 6-inch diameter impactor.[49] Mechanisms of cardiovascular injury in side impact collisions are probably caused by direct impact with the side door or arm rest. The mechanisms are a potential problem. They probably produce shearing of vessels at their attachments to the heart or direct compression causing bruising or other damage when the heart is displaced, or fluid pressure increases within the closed cardiovascular system. These mechanisms are also observed with impact to the steering column or during collision. Some authors have suggested that thoracic injury criteria should be based on the actual internal injury to the lungs, liver, and aorta in contrast to rib fracture only.[82] Federal Motor Vehicle Safety Standard No. 208 currently specifies as acceptable any acceleration pulse that does not exceed 60 G except for intervals whose cumulative duration is not more than 3 ms. Federal Motor Vehicle Safety Standards 203 and 204 define the performance of different steering assemblies along with their European equivalent Regulation 12. In studies conducted on 108 frontal crash 3-point seat-belted cadavers, Eppinger determined that a force of 1300 to 1500 pounds in the upper torso belt would produce a minimum number of rib fractures due to the webbing tension.[26] He chose the age and weight distribution of United States automotive fatality population in frontal crash situations at 30 miles/hr. For side impacts to the chest, it has been suggested that a lateral chest deflection of 3.72 inches produced by a blunt surface would result in an AIS injury level of 3, which is severe but not life threatening.[125]

H. Abdomen Tolerance

The organs most frequently injured as a result of blunt abdominal trauma are liver, kidney, spleen, intestines, pancreas, and bladder. The majority of the early works were conducted with hogs to determine the effect of abdominal impact against improperly worn lap belts.[145] A force of approximately 1000 lb against a 10-inch square surface was considered survivable. Studies with a control wheel, 10-inch square block, projecting peg, and abdominal seat belt at various velocities are described elsewhere.[79] Various studies have also been carried out on isolationed organs.[78]

I. Lower Extremity Failure Loads

The elements of the lower extremities include the pelvis, the femur, the tibia, fibula, ankle, foot bones, and patella (the bony kneecap). Also the head of the femur where it articulates in the ball and socket joint of the pelvis is a frequent area of injury. Injuries typically occur with knee impact with the frontal interior region of the vehicle. Impact with the dashboard typically causes dislocation of the hip joint with fractures of the pelvis, femur, patella, or the ligaments of attachment. Levels of force for fractures of the femur are approximately 1500 lb while those of the patella are often somewhat greater than those of the pelvis. They are in a similar range as those of the femur (Figure 18-49). Various studies have been conducted with knee impacts using padded or unpadded devices. The majority of the loading that occurs to an occupant, contained within the compartment of the vehicle, is axial and is associated with bending of the bones. In contrast, pedestrian injuries occur with transverse loading secondary to being struck by a bumper or other surfaces of a vehicle. The injury forces which produce trauma to the lower legs are approximately 1000 to 1500 lb.[63,92]

VI. SEAT BELTS

A large body of information exists in this area. It has been statistically demonstrated that seat belts help prevent injuries when properly used. Table 18-5 gives a historical review.

A good review of seat belts is given in the *Proceedings of the 6th International Conference of the International Association for Accident and Traffic Medicine*.[100] Various other studies focus upon models, retrospective clinical evaluations, or experimental investigations (those interested are referred to the following studies in the Citations listing at the conclusion of this section—16, 20, 32, 35, 40, 45, 52–55, 84, 120, and 141). Part 571, Federal Motor Vehicle Safety Standards, based on 1975 statistics, indicates that 100 percent lap belt usage would prevent 10,900 fatalities and 96,000 (AIS 2–5) injuries per year. In contrast, 100 percent usage of lap and shoulder belts would prevent 16,300 fatalities and 231,000 (AIS 2–5) injuries annually.

Table 18-5 Seat-Belt Applications, Installations, and Standards[a]

YEAR	EVENT
1885	Seat belts used on early vehicles on rough roads.
1917	Leather seat belt used in United States Army Spad III fighter.
1922	Seat belt used by Barney Oldfield in his race car.
1935	Factory installation of seat belts advocated by C. J. Strickland, President, Automobile Safety League.
1949	Factory-installed automobile seat belts offered as option by Nash.
1956	Factory-installed seat belts offered as option by Ford.
1961	American Seat Belt Council organized; SAE issued Standard J4, "Motor Vehicle Seat Belt Assemblies."
1962	Seat-belt anchorages factory-installed in front outboard seating positions.
1963	Congress enacted Public Law 88-201 to provide that seat belts sold in interstate commerce meet certain safety standards.
1964	Seat belts factory-installed in front outboard seating positions— with delete option.
1966	Congress enacted Public Law 89-563 to "reduce traffic accidents and deaths and injuries resulting from traffic accidents."
1967	"Initial Federal Motor Vehicle Safety Standards" issued, including FMVSS No. 208 and No. 209
1968	FMVSS No. 208, effective January 1, 1968, required factory-installed seat belts in all forward-facing occupant seating positions and shoulder straps in front outboard positions.

[a]Adapted from "Seat Belt Systems Continue to Evolve." *Automotive Eng.*, 90(9):61 (1982).

Seat belts often prevent the occupant from making contact with the interior of the vehicle or from being ejected. Typically, the lap belt prevents forward movement of the lower region of the body and ameliorates injuries to the lower limbs. Contact with the dash or windshield is often prevented during frontal and oblique frontal impacts in the pelvis and upper restrained occupant. Whiplash is also a mechanism for injury (Figure 18-52). Typically, soft tissue damages can be produced due to nonphysiological extension and flexion.

Smith and Kaufer[120] suggest that seat-belt injuries produce disruption of the posterior spinous element and Chance fractures and that the point of rotation is the seat belt. Consequently, the posterior spinal column is in tension. Minimum or no compression fracture or anterior wedging was observed in the lumbar vertebral bodies. However, the majority of their cases were high-speed barrier type or head-on collisions. Another potential problem is submarining with improper design or if the seat belt is not sufficiently low on the abdomen. Additional studies on seat-belt and crash analysis that are relevant can be found in the Citations listing at the end of this section (see citations 6, 11, 12, 14-16, 18, 21, 27, 33, 36, 41, 42, 44, 53-56, 65, 66, 69-71, 80, 87, 93, 94, 97, 98, 101, 117, 119, 121, 123, 126, 128, 129, 132, 134, 144, and 147).

ACKNOWLEDGMENTS

This reseach was supported in part by the Office of Naval Research Contract No. 00014-77-C-0749.

CITATIONS

[1]*Accident Facts.* Chicago: National Safety Council, 1981.

[2]J. J. Ackmann, S. J. Larson, A. Sances, Jr., and R. E. Barr, "Non-invasive Monitoring Techniques in Neurosurgical Intensive Care." *J. Clin. Eng.*, 4(4):329 (1979).

[3]D. W. Anderson and R. L. McLaurin (eds.), "Report on the National Head and Spinal Cord Injury Survey." *J. Neurosurg.*, 53(Suppl): 1-43 (1980).

[4]J. F. Annegers and L. T. Kurland, "The Epidemiology of Central Nervous System Trauma," in G. L. Odom (ed.), *Central Nervous System Trauma Research Status Report*, 1979, pp. 1-10.

[5]S. Backaitis and M. Haffner, "Development of the NHTSA Advanced Dummy for the Occupant Protection Standard Upgrade." *Proc. 7th Int. Experimental Safety Vehicle Conf.*, 1979, pp. 395–407.

[6]S. P. Baker, J. Wong, and W. C. Masemore, "Fatal Tractor Trailer Crashes: Considerations in Setting Relevant Standards." *Proc. 4th Int. Cong. Automotive Safety.* Washington, D.C.: U.S. Government Printing Office, 1976, p. 25.

[7]J. H. Battocletti, R. E. Halbach, S. X. Salles-Cunha, and A. Sances, Jr., "The NMR Blood Flowmeter—Theory and History." *Med. Physics*, 8(4):444–451 (1981).

[8]M. D. Berger, M. S. Weiss, A. Sances, Jr., P. R. Walsh, and S. J. Larson, "Evaluation of Changes in CNS Function Due to Impact Acceleration." *Proc. Aerospace Med. Assoc. 50th Ann. Scientific Mtg.*, Washington, D.C., May 14–17, 1979, pp. 135–136.

[9]H. H. Bohlman, "Acute Fractures and Dislocations of the Cervical Spine." *J. Bone Joint Surg.*, 61A(8):1119–1142 (1979).

[10]R. Braakman, "Depressed Skull Fracture: Data, Treatment, and Follow-up in 225 Consecutive Cases." *J. Neurol. Neurosurg. Psychiatry*, 35:395–402 (1972).

[11]P. W. Braunstein, "Medical Aspects of Automotive Crash Injury Research." *JAMA*, 163(4):249 (1957).

[12]P. W. Braunstein, J. O. Moore, and A. W. Preston, "Preliminary Findings on the Effect of Automotive Safety Design on Injury Patterns." *Surg. Gynecol. Obstet.*, 105(3):257 (1957).

[13]D. A. Bruce, T. A. Gennarelli, and T. W. Langfitt, "Resuscitation from Coma Due to Head Injury." *Crit. Care Med.*, 6(4):254–269 (1978).

[14]J. M. Burkes, J. R. Cromack, and H. Ziperman, "Impact Testing of Allied Chemical 'Inflataband' with Dummies and Human Volunteers." Technical Report No. SWRIP-11-4020. *NTIS*, Vol. 2, February/May, 1975.

[15]B. J. Campbell et al., "Comparative Injuries to Belted and Unbelted Drivers of Sub-compact, Compact, Intermediate, and Standard Cars." *Proc. 3rd Int. Cong. Automotive Safety*, San Francisco, July 1974.

[16]H. E. Campbell, "Deceleration, Highway Mortality, and the Motorcar." *Surgery*, 36:1056–1058 (1954).

[17]M. Carol, T. B. Ducker, and D. P. Brynes, "Minimyelogram in Cervical Spinal Cord Trauma." *Neurosurg.*, 7(3):219–224 (1980).

[18]D. Cesari and M. Ramet, "Comparison Between In-the-Field Accidents and Reconstructed Accidents with Dummies and with Cadavers." *Proc. 19th Stapp Car Crash Conf.* Warrendale, PA.: Society of Automotive Engineers, 1975, p. 167.

[19]F. Cordobes, R. D. Lobato, J. J. Rivas et al., "Observations on 82 Patients with Extradural Hematoma: Comparison of Results Before and After the Advent of Computerized Tomography." *J. Neurosurg.*, 54:179–186 (1981).

[20]F. M. Council and W. W. Hunter, *Seat Belt Usage and Benefits in*

North Carolina Accidents. Chapel Hill: Highway Safety Research Center, University of North Carolina, July 1974.

[21]J. E. Cowley and M. H. Cameron, "Prediction of Motor Vehicle Occupant Fatality Trends Following Seat Belt Wearing Legislation." *ARRB Proc.*, 8:20–30 (1976).

[22]R. H. Culver, M. Bender, and J. W. Melvin, *Mechanisms, Tolerances and Responses Obtained Under Dynamics of Superior Inferior Head Impact*. PB-299292. Ann Arbor: Highway Safety Research Institute, University of Michigan, May 1978.

[23]J. F. Cusick, J. Myklebust, S. J. Larson, and A. Sances, Jr., "Spinal Evoked Potentials in the Primate: Neural Substrate. *J. Neurosurg.*, 49(4):551–557 (1978).

[24]J. R. Cusick, J. B. Myklebust, S. J. Larson, and A. Sances, Jr., "Spinal Cord Evaluation by Cortical Evoked Responses." *Arch. Neurol.*, 36(3):140–143 (1979).

[25]J. F. Cusick, J. Myklebust, M. Zyvoloski, A. Sances, Jr., et al., "Effects of Vertebral Column Distraction in the Monkey." *J. Neurosurg.*, 57:651–659 (1982).

[26]R. H. Eppinger, "Prediction of Thoracic Injury Using Measurable Experimental Parameters." *Report on the 6th Int. Technical Conf. on Experimental Safety Vehicles*. Washington, D.C.: U.S. Department of Transportation, October 12–15, 1976.

[27]*Evaluation of Research on Surrogates for Humans in Motor Vehicle Crashes*. Washington, D.C.: Committee on Evaluation of Research on Surrogates for Humans in Motor Vehicle Crashes, Assembly of Life Sciences, National Academy of Sciences, 1978.

[28]C. L. Ewing, "Injury Criteria and Human Tolerance for the Neck," in K. Salczalski (ed.), *Aircraft Crashworthiness*. Charlottesville: University Press of Virginia, 1975.

[29]C. L. Ewing, D. L. Thomas, A. Sances, Jr., and S. J. Larson (eds.), *Impact Injury of the Head and Spine*. Springfield, IL.: Thomas, 1983.

[30]D. Fife, A. F. Williams, J. K. Wells et al., *Fatal Injuries to Bicyclists*. Washington, D.C.: Insurance Institute for Highway Safety, 1982.

[31]K. R. Flesch, L. L. Leider, D. L. Erickson et al., "Harrington Instrumentation and Spine Fusion for Unstable Fractures and Fracture-Dislocations of the Thoracic and Lumbar Spine." *J. Bone Joint Surg.*, 59A:143–153 (1977).

[32]L. A. Foldvary and J. C. Lane, "The Effectiveness of Compulsory Wearing of Seat Belts in Casualty Reduction (with an appendix on chi-square partitioning-tests of complex contingency tables)." *Accid. Anal. Prev.*, 6:59–81 (1974).

[33]*Report to the Public on the National Safety Forum*. Dearborn, MI.: Ford Motor Company, 1955.

[34]H. A. Freed, "Skull X-ray Criteria Endorsed by the Food and Drug Administration: Some Flaws and Proposed Modifications." *Neurosurg.*, 7:636–638 (1980).

[35]G. D. Frisch, J. O'Rourke, and L. D'Aulerio, "The Effectiveness of Mathematical Models as a Human Analog." *Mathematical Modeling Biodynamic Response to Impact*, SAE National Auto Engineering and Manufacturing Meeting, Dearborn, MI., October 1976, p. 61.

[36]G. D. Frisch, L. D'Aulerio, and J. O'Rourke, "Mechanisms of Head and Neck Response to $-G_x$ Impact Acceleration: A Math Modeling Approach." *Aviat. Space Environ. Med.*, 48(3):223 (1977).

[37]S. Galbraith and G. Teasdale, "Predicting the Need for Operation in the Patient with an Occult Traumatic Intracranial Hematoma." *J. Neurosurg.*, 55:75-81 (1981).

[38]J. A. Gehweiler, R. L. Osborne, and R. F. Becker, *The Radiology of Vertebral Trauma*. Philadelphia: Saunders, 1980.

[39]C. Got, A. Patel, A. Fayon et al., "Results of Experimental Head Impacts on Cadavers: The Various Data Obtained and Their Relations to Some Measured Physical Parameters." *Proc. 22nd Stapp Car Crash Conf.*, Society of Automotive Engineers, Ann Arbor, October 24-26, 1978, p. 55.

[40]G. Grime, "Seat Harness. Effect of a Harness on the Movement of the Occupant of a Car During a Head-on Collision." *Automob. Eng.*, January 1963, p. 12.

[41]E. S. Gurdjian and L. M. Thomas (eds.), *Neckache and Backache*. Springfield, IL.: Thomas, 1970.

[42]E. S. Gurdjian, W. A. Lane, L. M. Patrick, and L. M. Thomas (eds.), *Impact Injury and Crash Protection*. Springfield, IL.: Thomas, 1970.

[43]E. S. Gurdjian, *Impact Head Injury: Mechanistic, Clinical and Preventive Correlations*. Springfield, IL.: Thomas, 1975.

[44]W. Haddon, Jr., "Reducing the Damage of Motor-Vehicle Use." *Technology Review*, 77(8), 1975 (Massachusetts Institute of Technology).

[45]J. L. Haley, Jr., "Fundamentals of Kinetics and Kinematics as Applied to Injury Reduction," in E. S. Gurdjian et al. (eds.), *Impact Injury and Crash Protection*. Springfield, IL.: Thomas, 1970, p. 423.

[46]R. E. Halbach, J. H. Battocletti, T. A. Knox, A. Sances, Jr., et al., "Blood Flow Imaging Techniques Using NMR." *IEEE 1982 Frontiers of Engineering to Health Care*, Philadelphia, September 20-21, 1982.

[47]N. S. Hartunian, C. N. Smart, T. R. Willemain, and P. L. Zador, *The Economics of Safety Deregulation: An Analysis of Excess Deaths and Costs Due to Motorcycle Helmet Law Repeat in the United States*. Washington, D.C.: Insurance Institute for Highway Safety, 1982.

[48]G. E. Hedstrom, *Analysis of Injuries Utilizing NCSS Data*. Washington, D.C.: Office of Passenger Vehicle Research, National Highway Traffic Safety Administration, August 1980.

[49]R. L. Hess, K. Weber, and J. W. Melvin, "Review of Research

on Thoracic Impact Tolerance and Injury Criteria Related to Occupant Protection." *Proc. Occupant Crash Interaction with the Steering System*, International Congress and Exposition, Detroit, February 22-26, 1982.

[50]D. F. Huelke, J. O'Day, and R. A. Mendelsohn, "Cervical Injuries Suffered in Automobile Crashes." *J. Neurosurg.*, 54:316-322 (1981).

[51]D. F. Huelke, W. C. Grabb, and R. O. Dingman, "Automobile Occupant Injuries," in *Striking The Windshield*. Ann Arbor: Highway Safety Research Institute, University of Michigan, 1967.

[52]D. F. Huelke and W. A. Chewning, "Comparison of Occupant Injuries with and Without Seat Belts." *Int. Automotive Engineering Cong.*, Society of Automotive Engineers, Detroit, January 13-17, 1969.

[53]D. F. Huelke and H. Kaufer, "Vertebral Column Injuries and Seat Belts." *J. Trauma*, 15(4):304 (1975).

[54]D. F. Huelke and R. G. Synder, "Seat Belt Injuries: The Need for Accuracy in Reporting of Cases." *J. Trauma*, 15:20-23 (1975).

[55]D. R. Huelke, T. E. Lawson, R. Scott, and J. C. Marsh, "The Effectiveness of Belt Systems in Frontal and Rollover Crashes." SAE paper 770148. Warrendale, PA.: Society of Automotive Engineers, 1977.

[56]D. F. Huelke, R. A. Mendelsohn, J. D. States et al., "Cervical Fractures and Fracture-Dislocations Sustained Without Head Impact." *J. Trauma*, 18:533-538 (1978).

[57]K. G. Jamieson and J. D. N. Yelland, "Depressed Skull Fractures in Australia." *J. Neurosurg.*, 37:150-155 (1972).

[58]K. G. Jamieson, "Surgical Lesions in Head Injuries: Their Relative Incidence, Mortality Rates and Trends." *Aust. N.Z.J. Surg.*, 44(3): 241 (1974).

[59]K. G. Jamieson and D. Kell, "Traffic Injuries in Brisbane Hospitals over One Decade." *Aust. N.Z.J. Surg.*, 44(2):150 (1974).

[60]B. Jennett, *An Introduction to Neurosurgery*, 3rd ed. Chicago: Year Book Medical, 1977.

[61]B. Jennett, G. Teasdale, R. Braakman et al., "Prognosis of Patients with Severe Head Injury." *Neurosurg.*, 4(4):283-289 (1979).

[62]B. Jennett, G. Teasdale, J. Fry et al., "Treatment for Severe Head Injury." *J. Neurol. Neurosurg. Psychiatry*, 43:289-295 (1980).

[63]M. Kramer, K. Burow, and A. Heger, "Fracture Mechanism of Lower Legs Under Impact Load." SAE paper 730966. *Proc. 17th Stapp Car Crash Conf.*, Society of Automotive Engineers, Oklahoma City, November 12-13, 1973.

[64]J. S. Krieg, *Functional Neuroanatomy*, 3rd ed. Bloomington, IL.: Pantagraph Printing, 1966.

[65]C. K. Kroell, D. C. Schneider, and A. M. Nahum, "Comparative Knee Impact Response of Part 572 Dummy and Cadaver Subjects." *Proc. 20th Stapp Car Crash Conf.*, Society of Automotive Engineers, Dearborn, MI., 1976, p. 583.

[66]J. Kulowski, "Residual Motor-Skeletal Disabilities Among 215 Motorist Casualties." *Ind. Med. Surg.*, 24(1):395 (1955).

[67]S. J. Larson, P. R. Walsh, A. Sances, Jr., J. F. Cusick et al., "Evoked Potentials in Experimental Myelopathy." *Spine*, 5(4): 299–302 (1980).

[68]S. J. Larson, "Unstable Thoracic Fractures: Treatment Alternatives and the Role of the Neurosurgeon." *Clin. Neurosurg.*, 27: 624–640 (1980).

[69]D. N. Levine and B. J. Campbell, *Effectiveness of Lap Seat Belts and the Energy Absorbing Steering System in the Reduction of Injuries.* Chapel Hill: Highway Safety Research Center, University of North Carolina, November 1971.

[70]R. D. Lister, "Safety Glass for Windscreens." *Automob. Eng.*, 51:341–347 (1961).

[71]R. G. Livingstone, "Automobile Collision Injuries." *Surgery*, 36(6): 1059 (1954).

[72]R. D. Lockhart, G. F. Hamilton, and F. W. Fyfe, *Anatomy of the Human Body.* Philadelphia: Lippincott, 1959.

[73]D. J. Maiman and J. F. Cusick, "Traumatic Atlanto-Axial Dislocation." *Surg. Neurol.*, 18(5):388–392 (1982).

[74]D. J. Maiman and S. J. Larson, "Management of Odontoid Fractures." *Neurosurgery*, 11(4):471–476 (1982).

[75]B. C. Marar, "Hyperextension Injuries of the Cervical Spine: The Pathogenesis of Damage to the Spinal Cord." *J. Bone Joint Surg.*, 56A(8):1655–1662 (1974).

[76]J. W. Melvin and F. G. Evans, "A Strain Energy Approach to the Mechanics of Skull Fracture." *Proc. 15th Stapp Car Crash Conf.*, Society of Automotive Engineers, New York, 1971, p. 666.

[77]J. W. Melvin, P. M. Fuller, and V. L. Roberts, *Frangible Head Form Development Phase I: A Six Month Study of the Effects of Localized Impact on Tissue.* Report PO No. NP-47-356319. Ann Arbor: Highway Safety Research Institute, University of Michigan, February 1969.

[78]J. W. Melvin, R. L. Stalnaker, V. L. Roberts, and M. L. Trollope, "Impact Injury Mechanisms in Abdominal Organs." *Proc. 17th Stapp Car Crash Conf.*, Society of Automotive Engineers, Oklahoma City, November 12–13, 1973.

[79]H. J. Mertz, Jr., and C. K. Kroell, "Tolerance of the Thorax and Abdomen," in E. S. Gurdjian et al. (eds.), *Impact Injury and Crash Protection.* Springfield, IL.: Thomas, 1970.

[80]J. O. Moore, "The Epidemiological Aspects of Automobile Accidents." *Bull. N.Y. Acad. Med.*, 32(11):784 (1956).

[81]J. B. Myklebust, A. Sances, Jr., D. Maiman, F. Pintar et al., "Experimental Spinal Trauma Studies in the Human and Monkey Cadaver." *Proc. 27th Stapp Car Crash Conf.*, Society of Automotive Engineers, San Diego, CA., October 17–19, 1983 (in press).

[82]A. M. Nahum, C. W. Gadd, D. C. Schneider, and C. K. Kroell, "Deflection of the Human Thorax Under Sternal Impact." SAE

paper 700400. *1970 International Automobile Safety Conf. Compendium*, Society of Automotive Engineers, Detroit, May 13–15, 1970, pp. 797–807.

[83]National Highway Traffic Safety Administration, *Five-Year Plan for Motor Vehicle Safety and Full Economy Rulemaking 1980–1984*, Washington, D.C.: NHTSA, April 1979.

[84]I. D. Neilson, "The Dynamics of Safety Belts in Motor Car Head-on Impacts." *Proc. Inst. Mech. Eng.*, 181:19–33 (1966).

[85]G. S. Nusholtz, J. W. Melvin, D. F. Huelke et al., "Response of the Cervical Spine to Superior-Inferior Head Impact." *Proc. 25th Stapp Car Crash Conf.* Warrendale, PA.: Society of Automotive Engineers, 1981, pp. 197–237.

[86]A. K. Ommaya et al., "Comparative Tolerances for Cerebral Concussion by Head Impact and Whiplash Injury in Primates." *1970 International Automobile Safety Conf. Compendium*, Society of Automotive Engineers, Detroit, May 13–15, 1970, pp. 808–817.

[87]B. O'Neill et al., "Relationships Between Car Size, Car Weight, and Crash Injuries in Car-to-Car Crashes." *Proc. 3rd Int. Cong. Automotive Safety*, Vol. 1, Suppl. 2-1. Springfield, VA.: National Technical Information Service, 1974.

[88]W. R. Osebold, S. L. Weinstein, and B. L. Sprague, "Thoraco-Lumbar Spine Fractures: Results of Treatment." *Spine*, 6:13–34 (1981).

[89]J. Overgaard et al., "Prognosis After Head Injury Based on Early Clinical Examination." *Lancet*, September 22, 1973, pp. 631–639.

[90]L. M. Patrick, J. J. Mertz, and C. K. Kroell, SAE paper 670913. *Cadaver Knee, Chest, and Head Conference Proceedings*, Anaheim, California, October 10–11, 1967, pp. 106–117.

[91]L. M. Patrick, "Impact Force-Deflection of the Human Thorax." *Proc. 25th Stapp Car Crash Conf.* Warrendale, PA.: Society of Automotive Engineers, 1981, pp. 471–496.

[92]L. M. Patrick and H. J. Mertz, "Human Tolerance to Impact." SAE paper 700195. *Conference on Human Anatomy, Impact Injuries and Human Tolerances*, Detroit, January 15, 1970.

[93]N. Perrone, "Biomechanical Problems Related to Vehicle Impact," in Y. C. Fung, N. Perrone, and M. Anliker (eds.), *Biomechanics, Its Foundations and Objectives*. Englewood Cliffs, N.J.: Prentice-Hall, 1972, pp. 567–583.

[94]P. G. Petty, "The Influence of Seat Belt Wearing on the Incidence of Severe Head Injury." *Med. J. Aust.*, 2:768–769 (1975).

[95]F. Plum and J. B. Posher, *The Diagnosis of Stupor and Coma*, 2nd ed. Philadelphia: F. A. Davis, 1980.

[96]*Policy Options for Reducing the Motor Vehicle Crash Injury Cost Burden*. Washington, D.C.: Insurance Institute for Highway Safety, May 1981.

[97]H. Powiertowski, "Most Frequent Causes and Mechanisms of Brain Injuries in Traffic Accidents." *Patol. Pol.*, 25(3):328–338 (1974).

[98]F. Preston, "A Comparison of Contacts for Unrestrained and Lap-belted Occupants in Automobile Accidents." *Proc. 17th Conf. Am. Assoc. Automotive Medicine*, American Association for Automotive Medicine, Oklahoma City, November 14–17, 1973, p. 116.

[99]*Proc. First Annual Scientific Meeting, The Society of Magnetic Resonance in Medicine*, Boston, August 16–18, 1982.

[100]*Proc. 6th Int. Conf. Int. Assoc. Accident Traffic Medicine*, International Association of Accident and Traffic Medicine, Melbourne, Australia, 1977.

[101]K. S. Rutley and J. A. Cook, "Crash Injuries. A Survey of the Incidence of Head Injuries to the Occupants of Cars and Commercial Vehicles." *Automob. Eng.*, 52:55–57 (1962).

[102]M. Salcman, R. S. Schepp, and T. B. Ducker, "Calculated Recovery Rates in Severe Head Trauma." *Neurosurg.*, 8(3):301–308 (1981).

[103]B. Saltzberg, W. D. Burton, Jr., M. S. Weiss et al., "Dynamic Tracking of Evoked Potential Changes in Studies of Central Nervous System Injury Due to Impact Acceleration," in C. Ewing, D. J. Thomas, A. Sances, Jr., and S. J. Larson (eds.), *Impact Injury of the Head and Spine*. Springfield, IL.: Thomas, 1983, pp. 310–323.

[104]A. Sances, Jr., J. B. Myklebust, C. Houterman et al., "Head and Spine Injury Studies." *AGARD Conf. Proc. No. 322 on Impact Injury Caused by Linear Acceleration: Mechanism, Prevention, and Cost*, Koln, Germany, April 26–29, 1982, pp. 13-1–13-34.

[105]A. Sances, Jr., J. Myklebust, S. J. Larson, J. F. Cusick, and P. R. Walsh, "Theoretical Investigations and Clinical Application of the Evoked Potential." *IEEE 1979 Frontiers of Engineering in Health Care*, Institute of Electrical and Electronic Engineers, Denver, October 6–7, 1979, pp. 228–232.

[106]A. Sances, Jr., S. J. Larson, J. F. Cusick, J. Myklebust et al., "Early Somatosensory Evoked Potentials." *Electroencephalogr. Clin. Neurophysiol.*, 45(4):505–514 (1978).

[107]A. Sances, Jr., J. Myklebust, S. J. Larson, and J. F. Cusick, "The Evoked Potential and Early Studies of Bioelectricity." *J. Clin. Eng.*, 5(1):27–32 (1980).

[108]A. Sances, Jr., J. B. Myklebust, S. J. Larson, J. F. Cusick et al., "Bioengineering Analysis of Head and Spine Injuries." *CRC Crit. Rev. Bioeng.*, 5(2):79–122 (1981).

[109]A. Sances, Jr., J. Myklebust, S. Larson, J. Cusick, and R. Weber, "The Evoked Potential—A Biomechanical Tool," in C. L. Ewing, D. J. Thomas, A. Sances, Jr., and S. J. Larson (eds.), *Impact Injury of the Head and Spine*. Springfield, IL.: Thomas, 1983, pp. 231–285.

[110]A. Sances, Jr., J. Myklebust, J. Cusick et al., "Experimental Studies of Brain and Neck Injury." *Proc. 25th Stapp Car Crash Conf.* Warrendale, PA.: Society of Automotive Engineers, pp. 149–194, 1981.

[111]A. Sances, Jr., S. J. Larson, J. Myklebust et al., "Evaluation of Electrode Configurations in Cerebellar Implants." *Appl. Neurophysiol.*, 40(2-4):160–174 (1977–1978).

[112]A. Sances, Jr., "The Biomechanics of Spinal Injuries." *CRC Crit. Rev. Bioeng.*, 11(1), February 1984.

[113]A. Sances, Jr., R. Weber, J. Myklebust, J. Cusick, S. Larson et al., "The Evoked Potential: An Experimental Method for Biomechanical Analysis of Brain and Spinal Injury." *SAE Trans.*, 89:3815–3836 (1980).

[114]A. Sances, Jr., J. Myklebust, D. Kostreva, J. F. Cusick et al., "Pathophysiology of Cervical Injuries." *Proc. 26th Stapp Car Crash Conf.* Warrendale, PA.: Society of Automotive Engineers, 1982, pp. 41–70.

[115]B. R. Selecki and H. B. L. Williams, *Injuries to the Cervical Spine and Cord in Man.* Australian Medical Association, Mervyn Archdall Medical Monograph 7. South Wales: Australian Medical Publishers, 1970.

[116]E. L. Seljeskog and S. N. Chou, "Spectrum of the Hangman's Fracture." *J. Neurosurg.*, 45:3–8 (1976).

[117]D. M. Severy, J. H. Mathewson, and A. W. Siegel, "Automobile Head-on Collisions—Series II." *SAE Trans.*, 67:239 (1959).

[118]H. A. Shenkin, "Acute Subdural Heomatoma: Review of Thirty-nine Consecutive Cases with Incidence of Cortical Artery Rupture." *J. Neurosurg.*, 57:254–257 (1982).

[119]C. N. Smart and C. R. Saunders, *The Costs of Motor Vehicle Related Spinal Cord Injuries.* Washington, D.C.: Insurance Institute for Highway Safety, 1976.

[120]W. S. Smith and H. Kaufer, "Patterns and Mechanisms of Lumbar Injuries Associated with Lap Seat Belts." *J. Bone Joint Surg.*, 51A: 239 (1969).

[121]R. G. Snyder, C. C. Snow, J. W. Young et al., "Pathology of Trauma Attributed to Restraint Systems in Crash Impacts." *Aerosp. Med.*, 39:812 (1968).

[122]R. G. Snyder, W. M. Crosby, C. C. Snow et al., "Seat Belt Injuries in Impact," in M. L. Selzer et al. (eds.), *The Prevention of Highway Injury.* Ann Arbor: Highway Safety Research Institute, University of Michigan, 1967, pp. 188–210.

[123]W. W. Snyder, *An Engineering Pilot Study to Determine the Injury Potential of Basic Automotive Interior Design.* Aberdeen, MD.: Human Engineering Laboratory, U.S. Proving Grounds, 1953.

[124]R. L. Stalnaker, J. H. McElhaney, V. L. Roberts, and M. L. Trollope, "Human Torso Response to Blunt Trauma." *Proceedings of the Symposium on Human Impact Response*, Warren, Michigan, October 1972.

[125]R. L. Stalnaker and D. Mohan, "Human Chest Impact Protection Criteria." SAE paper 740589. *Proceedings of the Third Inter-*

national Conference on Occupant Protection, Troy, Michigan, July 10–12, 1974.

[126]H. J. H. Starks, *Research on Injuries Sustained in Road Accidents*. Road Research Technical Paper No. 37. London: Department of Scientific and Industrial Research, 1956.

[127]S. L. Stover and H. E. Zeigler, "Head Injury in Children and Teenagers: Functional Recovery Correlated with the Duration of Coma." *Arch. Phys. Med. Rehabil.*, 57:201 (1976).

[128]C. L. Straith, "Automobile Injuries." *JAMA*, 109(12):940 (1937).

[129]C. L. Straith, "Guest Passenger Injuries." *JAMA*, 137(4):348 (1948).

[130]J. M. Taveras and E. H. Woods, *Diagnostic Neuroradiology*, 2nd ed., 2 vols. Baltimore: Williams & Wilkins, 1976.

[131]S. C. Tindall, A. S. Fleischer, and G. T. Tindall, "Intracranial Pressure Monitoring in the Head-injured Patient—Comparative Study of Outcome in Monitored and Non-monitored Patients." Presented at the American Association of Neurological Surgeons Meeting, Boston, 1980, pp. 128–130.

[132]G. W. Trinca and B. J. Dooley, "The Effects of Seat Belt Legislation on Road Traffic Injuries." *Aust. N.Z. J. Surg.*, 47(2):150 (1977).

[133]R. C. Truex and M. B. Carpenter, *Human Neuroanatomy*, 6th ed. Baltimore: Williams & Wilkins, 1969.

[134]P. J. Van Eck, D. B. Chaffin, D. R. Foust et al., *A Bibliography of Whiplash and Cervical Kinematic Measurement*. Washington, D.C.: Insurance Institute for Highway Safety, 1973.

[135]M. Vapalahti and H. Troupp, "Prognosis for Patients with Severe Brain Injuries." *Br. Med. J.*, 3:404 (1971).

[136]F. C. Wagner and B. Chehrazi, "Spinal Cord Injury: Operative Intervention." *Surg. Clin. N. Am.*, 60:1049–1054 (1980).

[137]A. E. Walker, W. F. Caveness, and M. Critchley (eds.), *The Late Effects of Head Injury*. Springfield, IL.: Thomas, 1969.

[138]P. R. Walsh, S. J. Larson, A. Sances, Jr., et al., "Experimental Methods for Evaluating Spinal Cord Injury During Impact Acceleration," in F. M. Wageneder and R. H. Germann (eds.), *Electrotherapeutic Sleep and Electroanesthesia*, Vol. V. Graz: University of Graz, 1978, pp. 19–23.

[139]C. Ward, "Finite Element Modeling of the Head and Neck," in C. L. Ewing, D. J. Thomas, A. Scances, Jr., and S. J. Larson (eds.), *Impact Injury of the Head and Spine*. Springfield, IL.: Thomas, 1983, 421–474.

[140]R. Warwick, P. L. Williams et al. (eds.), *Gray's Anatomy*, 35th British ed. Philadelphia: Saunders, 1973.

[141]J. R. Weaver, "A Simple Occupant Dynamics Model." *J. Biomech.*, 1:185 (1968).

[142]R. Weber, "An Introduction to the Elements of Linear Biomechanical Modeling," in C. L. Ewing, D. J. Thomas, A. Sances, Jr., and S. J. Larson (eds.), *Impact Injury of the Head and Spine*. Springfield, IL.: Thomas, 1983, pp. 391–420.

[143]A. A. White and M. M. Panjabi, *Clinical Biomechanics of the Spine*. Philadelphia: Lippincott, 1978.

[144]J. Williams and J. Kirkpatrick, "The Nature of Seat Belt Injuries." *J. Trauma*, 11(3):207 (1971).

[145]P. G. Windquist, P. W. Stumm, and R. Hansen, *Crash Injury Experiments with the Monorail Decelerator*. AF Technical Report No. AFFTC-53-7. Air Force Flight Test Center, April 27, 1953.

[146]R. T. Woodburne, *Essentials of Human Anatomy*, 5th ed. New York: Oxford University Press, 1973.

[147]F. D. Woodward, "Medical Criticism of Modern Automotive Engineering." *JAMA*, 138(9):627 (1948).

[148]*The Year's Work 1981–1982*. Washington, D.C.: Insurance Institute for Highway Safety.

Appendix: Review of the Physics of Vehicular Injury Analysis

In analyzing vehicular injuries, force, energy, acceleration, momentum, or various indices are often referred to. Therefore, a brief review is given here.

DEFINITION OF TERMS

Abbreviations and Symbols

F = force (pounds)
R = reaction force (pounds)
t = time (seconds)
S = distance (feet)
m = mass (slugs)
V = velocity (feet per second)
a = acceleration (feet per second per second)
g = acceleration of gravity = 32.2 ft/sec^2
G = acceleration expressed in G-units
W = weight (pounds)
KE = kinetic energy (foot-pounds)
Δ = delta, used to indicate a change in magnitude or quantity
Σ = summation
CG = center of gravity

Definitions and Basic Relationships

Force: The cause of the acceleration of any mass. A vector quantity, having magnitude and direction.

$$F = ma \text{ (lb)}$$

Weight: A force caused by gravity, acting toward the center of the earth.

$$W = mg \text{ (lb)}$$

Mass: The quantity of matter in a body. Mass remains constant.

$$m = W/g \text{ (lb} \cdot \text{sec}^2/\text{ft, or slugs)}$$

Velocity: Rate of motion, a vector quantity having both magnitude and direction. (The velocity of a body changes if there is a change of speed, or direction, or both.)

$$V = \Delta S / \Delta t \text{ (ft/sec)}$$

Acceleration: Rate of change of velocity:

$$a = \Delta V / \Delta t \text{ (ft/sec}^2)$$

Acceleration may increase or decrease speed and/or change the direction of motion. An acceleration which produces a decrease in speed is a deceleration.

Acceleration of Gravity: Acceleration caused by the attraction between masses. A free falling body, subjected only to this attraction, will accelerate at the rate of 32.2 feet per second per second on earth.

$$g = 32.2 \text{ ft/sec}^2$$

G-Units: The ratio of acceleration to the acceleration of gravity.

$$G = a/g$$

Kinetic Energy: Energy, or ability to do work, due to motion of a mass or masses.

$$KE = mV^2/2 \text{ (ft lb)}$$

An object has potential energy due to its height above a surface. When it falls, it is converted to kinetic energy. The potential energy is WS (ft lb) where S = height of fall in feet, and W = weight in pounds. Energy is often used to determine injury levels as well as force, where $F = ma$. If an acceleration of 10 G acts upon a weight of 10 pounds, this produces a force equal to 100 pounds upon the object.

Work: Work is the expenditure of energy: the product of force multiplied by the distance through which the force acts.

$$w = FS \text{ (ft lb)}$$

Change in Momentum:

$$m(V_2 - V_1) = \sum R \cdot \Delta t = \int_{t_1}^{t_2} R \cdot \Delta t$$

Momentum Conservation Law:

$$m_1 V_1 + m_2 V_2 + \ldots = m_1 V_1' + m_2 V_2' + \ldots$$

This equation is used to calculate the initial velocity of objects (unprimed) if their final velocities after a collision (primed) are known (or vice versa).

Work-Energy Principle

Newton's first law of motion states: "Bodies in motion will remain in motion unless acted upon by an opposing or unbalanced force." The "body of motion" possesses *energy*, while the "opposing force" does *work* on the body to decrease its velocity; this is the work–energy principle. This principle can be expressed as

$$\int_{S_1}^{S_2} F \cdot \Delta S = m(V_2^2 - V_1^2)/2$$

where

F = opposing force acting on the CG of the mass (m)
S = distance traversed by CG of mass (m) while force (F) is acting
m = mass of body on which force (F) is acting
V_2 = velocity of mass (m) subsequent to the opposing force application
V_1 = velocity of mass (m) prior to the opposing force application

If the force (F) acting on the mass (m) is constant, the equation becomes the following:

$$F \cdot S = m(V_2^2 - V_1^2)/2$$

This equation is helpful in determining the force–distance relationship when the velocity difference is known. The work–energy equation is easier to use when the opposing force is expressed in terms of the mass being decelerated. The equation is as follows:

$$F \times S = m(V_2^2 - V_1^2)/2$$

since $F = ma$, therefore

$$ma \times S = m(V_2^2 - V_1^2)/2$$

$$S = (V_2{}^2 - V_1{}^2)/2a$$

and $a = gG = 32.2G$, then

$$G = (V_2{}^2 - V_1{}^2)/64.4S$$

This equation is used to calculate the G forces on a subject when the mass, initial velocity, final velocity, and the stopping distance are known. The equation becomes

$$G = (V_2{}^2 - V_1{}^2)/30S$$

for $V =$ miles/hr and $S =$ ft. Clearly, the larger the stopping distance, the smaller the G level. However, the G value increases as the square of the velocity. For example: If a vehicle going 30 mph hits a fixed barrier and crushes in 2 feet, it is decelerated

$$G = (30 \text{ mph})^2/(30)(2 \text{ ft}) = 15 \text{ G}$$

Momentum

In certain impact situations, it is difficult to determine the *distance* moved by the moving mass or masses because of excessive deformation in the masses. In these cases, where a mass or body is deformed and stops in a distance only a fraction of its own depth, it is helpful to determine the force versus time relationship. If the total reaction force (R) is desired due to an impact by mass (m), it may be obtained from Newton's second law as follows:

$$R = ma \quad \text{and} \quad a = \Delta V/\Delta t$$

Eliminating a,

$$\sum R \cdot \Delta t = \sum m \cdot \Delta V$$

The expression $\Sigma R \cdot \Delta t$ is known as the resultant *linear impulse*, while the expression $\Sigma m \cdot \Delta V$ is called the resultant *linear momentum change*.

All impacts involve at least two masses even though one mass may be stationary. The impulse–momentum equation for two masses is expressed in terms of their momentum before and after the impact. Newton's third law states the following: "Action and reaction forces between two particles are always equal and oppositely directed." This principle applied to the momentum problem indicates that the total momentum of two masses before impact must be identical to their momentum after impact. This relationship is called the Momentum Conservation Law and is stated as follows for two masses:

$$m_1 V_1 + m_2 V_2 = m_1 V_1' + m_2 V_2'$$

where

    m_1 and m_2 = mass of bodies under study
    V_1 and V_2 = velocity of masses prior to impact
    V_1' and V_2' = velocity of masses after impact

For example: If vehicle 1 (m_1 = 4000 lb) going 40 mph (V_1) hits into the rear of vehicle 2 (m_2 = 2000 lb), which is stopped (V_2 = 0), then the combined velocity of the two vehicles after the impact is

$$V_c = (4000 \text{ lb}) \ (40 \text{ mph})/(6000 \text{ lb}) = 26.6 \text{ mph}$$

The velocity of impacting masses prior to impact and their velocities after impact can be related as follows:

$$e = \frac{Relative\ velocity\ between\ two\ masses\ after\ impact}{Relative\ velocity\ between\ two\ masses\ before\ impact}$$

$$e = (V_2' - V_1')/(V_1 - V_2) = \text{coefficient of restitution}$$

Perfectly elastic bodies would have exactly the same relative velocity after impact as before, and the value of e would be one. On the other hand, perfectly inelastic (plastic) bodies would cling together after impact and the final relative velocity between the bodies would be zero and the value of e would be zero.

Circular Motion

An object rotating in a circle has a constant centripetal force of

$$F_c = m V^2/r$$

to hold it in the circular path, where

    V = tangential velocity along the circle
    m = mass
    r = radius of the circle

The tangential acceleration along the circular path is $a_T = R\alpha$, where α is the angular acceleration (rad/sec^2). The tangential force is therefore

$$F_T = ma_T$$

The velocity along the circular path is $V = r\omega$, where ω is angular velocity (rad/sec). A body rotating with angular velocity ω has kinetic energy due to its rotation:

$$KE = I\omega^2/2$$

where I is the moment of inertia of the body.

Torque

A pair of equal and opposite parallel forces F_p acting on a body and separated by a distance D produces a "couple" equal to

$$\text{couple} = F_p \times D$$

The torque T or moment is defined as the product of a perpendicular force F acting over a distance D:

$$T = F \times D$$

HEAD INJURY CRITERIA

The Motor Vehicle Safety Standard No. 208 states that the resultant acceleration at the center of gravity of the head shall be such that the head injury criteria (HIC)

$$HIC = \left[\frac{1}{t_2 - t_1} \int_{t_1}^{t_2} a\,dt \right]^{2.5} (t_2 - t_1)$$

is less than 1000 (where a is the resultant acceleration expressed as a multiple of the acceleration of gravity (G) and t_1 and t_2 are any two points in time during the impact that maximize the HIC). Furthermore, the resultant acceleration at the center of gravity of the upper thorax shall not exceed 60 G, except for intervals whose cumulative duration is not more than 3 milliseconds.

The Gadd severity index is

$$SI = \int a^{2.5}dt$$

for face/head impacts.

The Gadd severity index preceded the HIC and includes the effects of rebound. A value of 1500 is often approximately equivalent to a HIC = 1000.

V

RISK REDUCTION

If a potential safety or quality problem has been identified, should corrective or preventive action be undertaken to preclude future accidents, injuries, or other losses? The answer is sometimes "yes," sometimes "no," and often "we need more information." These responses are generally based upon a preliminary question, "Is there a significant risk that could be materially reduced?" For example, "Is the risk trivial, acceptable, or of a nature that there is no safer alternative?"

All of life's experiences involve risk, from the very process of birth until the final cause of death. Some people believe that all of life's risks are just part of some immutable fate, predetermined destiny, or act of a higher power; each person merely takes his chances and trusts to luck without too much worry or attempted human intervention in the inevitable fatalistic sequence of events that comprise human life. The consequence of such beliefs, overtly or impliedly expressed, is that no action is warranted for most safety problems.

Other people prefer a comparative risk approach to safety. Based upon some risk estimate (frequency and severity of injuries or monetary damage), how does one risk compare to others? Comparisons are made to "normal" everyday natural risks (such as crossing a roadway intersection), some other background determinant for added "excess" lifetime-imposed risks (such as being above the "safe" threshold exposure to a toxic chemical), or some derivative of the "pareto" principle (let's focus our efforts on the vital few and solve the most important problems first). This approach compares or relates one risk to another and may serve as a basis for the producer's assessment of the "acceptability of the risk" and the reasonableness of the consumer's "expectations" relative to risk. Unfortunately, the risk estimate and assessment procedures may become so complex, uncertain, argumentative, and cumbersome as to forestall any timely action. Yet, how can intelligent decisions be made without adequate information?

The plaintiff trial lawyer may assess the risk in a very different fashion. Even if the risk is comparatively minor and would injure only a few people, shouldn't the hazard be eliminated if there exists a low-cost, known, and effective remedy or product improvement? If the risk is comparatively high and there is no known remedy to reduce those risks, is there a safer product already on the market and does the product really serve a useful social purpose? Does the product needlessly induce high-risk behavior without appropriate design safeguards, training or supervision, warnings or instructions, or other controls that could preclude an inadvertent assumption of excessive and needless risks? The lawyer may utilize legal criteria as to what constitutes a defective and unsafe product. Such criteria may include definitions of risk–benefit analyses, consumer expectations, social utility concepts, a substandard condition or deviation from the manufacturer's intended result, or merely the question, "Was there a defect that caused the injury?" The emphasis may be on "preventable danger," but there are, generally, considerations of gravity (severity), exposure (likelihood), remedies (technical feasibility), cost (economic), effectiveness (alternatives), adverse consequences (new problems), and social utility (perceived need). Therefore, arguable concepts of risk pervade the law as well as engineering and science.

The opening section of this part, entitled How Safe Is Reasonable? describes several risk assessment concepts and demonstrates their application in the area of roll bars, seat belts, air bags, and warning devices. It illustrates how important questions can arise during the conduct of such analyses, questions that may be more important than the quantitative end results of such analytic risk evaluations, particularly when uncertain data and conceptual biases require caution and considerable judgment in relying upon their conclusions.

Exactly how can an identified risk be reduced to a reasonable or acceptable level? Section 20, Warnings in Automotive Systems, presents information on how to design a legally adequate and sufficient warning. There is usually a presumption that warnings will be read and heeded and thus will serve some risk reduction purpose. There are other remedies for reducing risk, as indicated in Section 21, Product Recall and Recall Prevention. It is important to remember that costly recalls are a corrective remedy but that product-recall planning is a preventive (loss control) remedy.

Proper organizational planning includes contingencies for both design (engineering) and quality (manufacturing) defects or discrepancies that affect either the safety or the quality attributes of the product (as defined by the user). System Safety Engineering, Section 22, describes the design-oriented engineering and management techniques and programs intended to prevent defects from becoming manifest from the cradle to the grave of a particular product or system. This design safety approach, used widely during the past two decades, is complementary to the preventive countermeasures that have evolved in the disciplines of human factors, quality and product assurance, reliability and system effectiveness, and the more traditional safety and health specialties. In essence, there are known preventive and corrective methods to eliminate or minimize unreasonable risks from avoidable hazards. These methods should be properly utilized to reduce the present level of injuries and their associated costs to individual citizens, commercial enterprises, and society in general.

REFERENCES

1. G. A. Peters, "The Human Factors in Automobile Accidents. Symposium on Automobile Accidents." *International Record of Medicine*, Vol. 171, No. 9, September 1958, pp. 558-562.
2. G. A. Peters and F. S. Hall, "Design for Safety." *Product Engineering*, September 13, 1965, pp. 125-128.
3. G. A. Peters, *Product Liability and Safety*. Washington, D.C.: Coiner Publications, 1971.
4. G. A. Peters, "Systematic Safety." *National Safety News*, September 1975, pp. 83-90.
5. G. A. Peters, "Why Only a Fool Relies on Safety Standards." *Hazard Prevention*, November/December 1977, pp. 12-14.
6. G. A. Peters, "New Product Safety Legal Requirements." *Quality Progress*, August 1978, pp. 34-36.
7. G. A. Peters, "Personal Liability and Your Future Role." *Quality Progress*, May 1979, pp. 28-30.
8. G. A. Peters and B. J. Peters, *Sourcebook on Asbestos Diseases*. New York: Garland STPM Press, 1980. (See Chapters 3, 4, and 5.)

SUPPLEMENTAL REFERENCES

1. *Trials of War Criminals Before the Military Tribunals Under Control Council Law No. 10*, Vol. 2, October 1946–April 1949. Washington, D.C.: U.S. Government Printing Office, 1947, pp. 181–183. [The Nuremberg war trials served to internationalize the concept that each person must consent to his personal exposure to risk and that such consent must be informed, voluntary, and *revocable.*]
2. *Safety Engineering of Systems and Associated Systems, and Equipment, General Requirements for.* Military Specification MIL-S-38130 (USAF), September 30, 1963. [Required design failure mode analysis (including prediction of personnel errors), a *risk classification* of hazards (as safe, marginal, critical, or catastrophic), an operational safety analysis, the identification of *risk reduction actions* (safety devices, warnings, elimination of hazards during early stages of design, etc.), and written plans that specifically define who, when, and how such analytic and risk reduction efforts would be accomplished.]
3. W. W. Lowrance, *Of Acceptable Risk.* Los Altos, CA.: William Kauffman Inc., 1976. [Provides a general review of risk concepts and safety decision making.]
4. R. B. Hubbard and G. C. Minor (eds.), *The Risks of Nuclear Power Reactors.* Cambridge, MA.: Union of Concerned Scientists, 1977. [Provides an example of a critical review of validity of a risk assessment, in this case the NRC Reactor Safety Guide, WASH-1400 (NUREG-75/014), in a public attempt at risk reduction.]
5. *Barker* v. *Lull Engineering Co.*, 20 C. 3d 413, 143 Cal. Rptr. 225, 573 P. 2d 443 (1978). [Provides an illustrative legal definition of risk-benefit analysis (patterned after the design review tradeoff procedures and failure mode analyses that had been routinely performed by engineers during the prior two decades).]
6. *Bashada* v. *Johns-Manville Products Corp.*, 90 N.J. 191, 447 A. 2d 539 (1982). [Provides two tests for determining whether a product is safe: (1) does its utility outweigh its risk (more good than harm) and, if so, (2) has the risk been reduced to the greatest extent possible consistent with the product's utility (that is, could it have been made or marketed more safely)? It restates the legal policy of risk spreading, where the price of a product should reflect all costs including costs of injuries, which is accomplished by imposing strict liability on manufacturers and distributors who can insure against such risks. The court held that presumed unawareness of dangers, the state-of-the-art defense in failure-to-warn litigation, is not an allowable defense to strict liability actions. This serves the goal of "simplifying tort trials," and in terms of risk reduction, by imposing on the manufacturer the costs of failure to discover hazards, an incentive is created for them to invest more actively in safety research.]

19

How Safe Is Reasonable?

KENNETH A. SOLOMON, Ph.D., P.E.
CHARLES L. BATTEN, JR., Ph.D.
and
CHARLES E. PHELPS, Ph.D.
Rand Corporation
Santa Monica, California

Dr. Kenneth A. Solomon, a senior engineer at the Rand Corporation and an Adjunct Associate Professor at the University of California, Los Angeles, has conducted numerous safety assessments of technologies that range from power plants (nuclear, coal, hydroelectric, and gas) and transportation (air and automotive) to mining, manufacturing, and processing. During the past several years he has particularly focused on using risk assessment to answer the question, "How safe is reasonable?"

Dr. Charles L. Batten, Jr., is a communications analyst at the Rand Corporation and an Associate Professor at the University of California, Los Angeles. His most recent work has focused on the costs of closing nuclear power plants and on improvements to electronic equipment on board fighter aircraft.

Dr. Charles Phelps, a senior staff economist, is Director of Rand's Regulatory and Institutions Program. He has worked in a number of areas including health and water studies. All three authors may be contacted at the Rand Corporation, located at 1700 Main Street, Santa Monica, California 90406 (213-393-0411).

I. INTRODUCTION

In a world of unlimited resources, no one would need to ask "How safe is reasonable?" The answer would be obvious: "The greatest protection technologically possible against all conceivable dangers."

In such an ideal world, an automobile buyer would face no quandary when choosing between a 5000-pound luxury sedan and an 1800-pound mini-compact. Assuming he has average driving skills, his chances of suffering a driving fatality in the minicompact could be four to five times greater than in the luxury sedan. Setting aside issues other than safety, the luxury sedan is his obvious choice.

But his easy choices do not end here. The buyer would now load his automobile with all conceivable safety extras: watertight fittings to protect against floods, bulletproof glass and side panels to protect against assailants, a backup system to protect against heating failures occurring during subzero weather. . . . The list could continue almost infinitely.

Ours, however, is scarcely a world of unlimited resources, and thus we encounter serious problems when we try to answer the question, "How safe is reasonable?" No one likes calculating the probabilities of fatalities, and no one likes placing prices on human life. Yet, such must at least implicitly be done whenever we attempt to define a reasonable level of safety.

Using principles derived from a wide range of recent literature, this paper aims at providing a brief introduction to ways of answering the question, "How safe is reasonable?" It focuses exclusively on fatalities—not because it assumes injuries are unimportant, but rather because injuries are more difficult to calculate, because they involve various shades of injury, and because they also tend to be a function of fatality rates.

Subsection II uses information involving the safety of nuclear power plants and the costs of various kinds of safety measures to arrive at two criteria that ought to be used when we contemplate introducing a new safety measure into an already existing technology, industry, or product. A new safety measure should be introduced if either of the following criteria is met:

- *Risk/Safety Criterion.* A new safety device in an existing technology, product, or industry should be considered for use if it reduces the fatality rate of the industry so that the industry contributes less than 0.1% of the total fatality rate of background risk. (This "background risk" level currently stands at 0.5 accidental fatalities per 1000 people per year.)

- *Cost/Safety Criterion.* For those technologies, products, or industries that fail the Risk/Safety Criterion, the new safety device should be mandated for use if its costs are roughly equal to or less than similar safety measures per fatality averted. (For automotive safety equipment, this cost currently stands at $260,000 per annual fatality averted.)

Subsection III then applies these criteria to three problems in automotive design (as well as one outside of automotive design) that are of current legal interest:

1. Should roll bars be installed on all utility vehicles?
2. Should the wearing of seat belts be legally enforced?
3. Should air bags be required in all passenger vehicles?
4. Should warning devices be installed on trains?

This paper lacks adequate data to answer any of these questions. Rather, it deals with a broad spectrum of available data—ranging from fairly extensive data on roll bars to less thorough data on air bags—to show how risk assessments can determine acceptable levels of safety in various kinds of situations.

Subsection IV provides a selected bibliography of works that deal with the acceptance of various levels of risk.

II. WHAT DOES "REASONABLY SAFE" MEAN?

Only after considering not only cost but also realistic need can the question, "What does 'reasonably safe' mean?" be answered. This point was forcefully made by a three-part, unscientific experiment conducted by a Los Angeles consumer reporter. To test the breaking point of the 2-liter bottles used by a particular soft-drink manufacturer, this reporter loaded a few dozen in the back of a station wagon. After a rough ride over potholes and around sharp curves at high speeds, each of the bottles emerged intact. Thus the bottles met some nominal level of safety. Next, the reporter dropped a few dozen of them from a helicopter hovering about 100 feet above an asphalt pavement. Only one broke. Thus a fraction failed to meet a higher level of safety. Finally, he placed one bottle under a baby elephant's foot. It broke. Thus—at least in theory—none of the bottles could meet this highest level of safety.

Manufacturers can conceivably construct soft-drink bottles that will consistently withstand 100-foot drops and the feet of baby elephants. However, two questions arise: Can consumers afford soft drinks bottled in such a fashion? Do consumers need this degree of protection? Infinite safety is neither affordable nor reasonable; finite safety can be.

A. Acceptable Risks in Achieving Finite Safety

Focusing specifically on nuclear power plants, two recent studies[1,2] have surveyed a broad spectrum of proposals that address the question of a reasonable level of safety. In particular, Solomon and Nelson[1] look at over 90 safety criteria proposed by a wide array of groups including national laboratories, nuclear reactor vendors, architect–engineers, universities, private research organizations, and public interest groups. Though these groups approach and define the criteria often in strikingly different ways, Solomon and Nelson have been able to derive from them a current rough, and admittedly very subjective, consensus concerning acceptable risk for the nuclear power industry. This paper applies this consensus to other technologies, industries, and products.

A.1. NEW TECHNOLOGIES, INDUSTRIES, OR PRODUCTS According to the Solomon–Nelson consensus,[1] the introduction of a new technology, industry, or product is justified if it *increases* the fatality rate (rate of fatalities from all accidents for average members of the population) by no more than a factor of 0.1 percent. For the average adult in the United States, the risk of immediate death per year due to accidents is about 0.5 in 1000. As a consequence, a new technology, industry, or product is reasonably safe if it adds no more than 0.0005 in 1000 to the annual risk of immediate mortality.*

---

*For the average adult in the United States, the risk of *delayed* death per year is more difficult to estimate. If we consider (1) that most delayed deaths result from cancer, (2) that cancer accounts for about 20 percent of all deaths, (3) that 50 percent of all cancers are due to exposure to some risk, and (4) that an average lifetime can be roughly calculated at 80 years, then the average delayed cancer risk due to exposure is 1 in 800 per year. Thus, a tolerable increase in the level of delayed risk due to the addition of a technology, industry, or product is about 0.001 in a 800 mortalities per year (or about 0.00125 in 1000 per year).

A.2. NEW SAFETY MEASURES FOR EXISTING TECHNOLOGIES, INDUSTRIES, OR PRODUCTS From this rough consensus, a corollary can be asserted concerning the introduction of safety measures. A new safety measure for an already existing technology, industry, or product is justified if it *reduces* the risk of fatality so that the technology, industry, or product contributes no more than 0.1 percent of the total accident risk. Currently, this "background risk" level is 0.5 accidental fatalities per 1000 people per year; 0.1 percent of it is 0.0005 fatalities per 1000 people per year. We call this the Risk/Safety Criterion.

Effective safety measures conceivably fall into three classes:

1. Measures that reduce risk below the Risk/Safety Criterion level.
2. Measures that reduce risk, but the risk already stands below the Risk/Safety Criterion level.
3. Measures that reduce risk, but the risk remains above the Risk/Safety Criterion level.

Increased maintenance procedures for commercial aircraft is an example of Class 1 (see Figure 19-1). Before changes in maintenance occurred in the 1960s, the risk of fatality in a commercial aircraft accident stood at perhaps 0.2 to 0.4 percent of the background risk (Class 1, Level A). This risk is computed by dividing the annual deaths in the United States caused by commercial aircraft accidents (roughly 200 to 400) by the annual deaths in the United States caused by all accidents (roughly 100,000). With changes in maintenance procedures, the risk decreased generally below 0.1 percent of the background risk (Level B). (Two problems should be noted concerning these calculations: these risks are averaged over the entire population even though less than 20 percent of the population flies in commercial airplanes during any given year; the occurrence of a major accident during a given year can significantly alter these averages.)

The use of protective roofs against meteorites is an example of Class 2. Without such roofs, the risk of dying as a result of a meteorite crashing into a home stands at less than 0.00001 percent of the background risk (Class 2, Level A). This is computed by dividing the annual deaths in the United States caused by meteorites crashing into homes (less than one in 100 years) by the annual deaths in the United States caused by all accidents (100,000). With the use of protective roofs, this risk will decrease by some trivial percent (Level B).

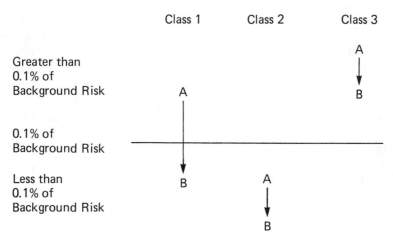

Figure 19-1 Effects of safety measures on levels of risk (not drawn to scale).

A law enforcing the wearing of seat belts is an example of Class 3. Without the law, the risk of dying in an automobile accident stands at roughly 50 percent of the background risk (Class 3, Level A). This is computed by dividing the annual deaths in the United States caused by automobile accidents (50,000) by the annual deaths in the United States caused by all accidents (100,000). With the introduction of the law enforcing the wearing of seat belts, we assert in our hypothetical example that the risk will decrease to roughly 47.5 percent (Level B). (For particulars, see Subsection III.)

To apply these rules, we first need to know the Risk/Safety Criterion as it applies to a given product, technology, or industry (hereafter, for brevity, a "product"). If that product poses risks greater than the criterion justifies, then the costs per life saved of the new safety technology must be investigated. The new technology should be mandated—by this rule—if the product currently fails the Risk/Safety technology, and if the costs are not too large. Thus, products already in Class 2 would never be evaluated for cost because they would pass the criterion. Products in either Class 1 or Class 3 would "rise or fall" on their costs. Presumably, if the effectiveness of the safety device varied with its cost, then the criterion would suggest stopping investment when the Risk/Safety Criterion were met.

It is important to note here that we are not advocating this rule as a normative goal, but rather attempting to infer how one would behave in parallel to the normative rule inferred from previous risk choices made by individuals and groups.[1] And this standard differs from one minimizing expected costs of saving lives because it deliberately introduces criteria other than cost per life saved. For example, a new technology might have very low cost per lives saved, but fall into Class 2 (current risk of the product lies below the Risk/Safety Criterion). *The rule we discuss would not require introduction of that new safety device, whereas a rule requiring introduction of the cheapest (marginal) lifesaving devices would force adoption of such a safety device.*

B. Acceptable Costs in Achieving Finite Safety

As we have seen, costs must somehow be considered in risk assessments. Although accurate and equitable values on human life have eluded our grasp, Cohen[3] has arrived at a number of useful estimates involving the costs actually expended on saving human life. Begun in 1975, Cohen's work has been used frequently in the field of risk assessment (for example, NUREG/CR-2040[4]) and portions of his findings have been validated by other researchers.[5,6] Although Cohen's approach scarcely solves all methodological problems, it does provide a widely agreed-upon basis for estimating the costs of safety measures in specific activities.

Table 19-1 illustrates the cost per fatality averted (in 1982 dollars) of various medical and safety measures. From

Table 19-1 Value of Fatality Averted[a]

ACTIVITY	COST PER FATALITY AVERTED (1982 DOLLARS)[b]
Medical screening and care	
Cervical cancer	$50,000
Breast cancer	160,000
Lung cancer	140,000
Colorectal cancer/fecal blood test	20,000
Colorectal cancer/proctoscopy	60,000
Multiple screening	52,000
Hypertension control	150,000
Kidney dialysis	400,000
Mobile intensive care units	60,000

(Continued)

Table 19-1 (*Continued*)

ACTIVITY	COST PER FATALITY AVERTED (1982 DOLLARS)[b]
Traffic safety	
Auto safety equipment: 1966–1970	$260,000
Steering column improvement	200,000
Air bags (driver only)	640,000
Tire inspection	800,000
Rescue helicopters	130,000
Passive 3-point harness	500,000
Passive torso belt-knee bar	220,000
Driver education	180,000
Highway construction/maintenance practice	40,000
Regulatory and warning signs	68,000
Guardrail improvements	68,000
Skid resistance	84,000
Bridge rails and parapets	92,000
Wrong-way entry avoidance	100,000
Impact-absorbing roadside device	216,000
Breakaway sign, lighting posts	232,000
Median barrier improvement	456,000
Clear roadside recovery	586,000
Radiation-related activities	
Radium in drinking water	$5,000,000
Medical x-ray equipment	7,200
ICRP recommendations	640,000
OMB guidelines	14,000,000
Radwaste practice—general	20,000,000
Radwaste practice—iodine 131	200,000,000
Defense high-level waste	400,000,000
Civilian high-level waste	36,000,000
Miscellaneous nonradiation	
Food for overseas relief	$10,600
Sulfur scrubbers in power plants	1,000,000
Smoke alarms in homes	480,000
Coal mine safety	44,000,000
Other mine safety	68,000,000
Coke fume standards	9,000,000
Air Force pilot safety	4,000,000
Civilian aircraft (France)	2,400,000

[a]Adapted from B. L. Cohen, "Society's Evaluation of Life Saving in Radiation Protection and in Other Contexts." *Health Physics*, 38:33–51 (1980).
[b]To convert Cohen's 1975 dollars to 1982 ones, a 10 percent discount rate for nonchronic risks and a 0 percent discount rate for chronic ones was assumed. The wide diversity among costs is discussed in S. L. Salem, K. A. Solomon, and M. S. Yesley, *Issues and Problems in Inferring a Level of Acceptable Risk*. R-2561-DOE. Santa Monica, CA.: The Rand Corporation, August 1980.

this table we can derive a Cost/Safety Criterion: a safety measure is justifiable if it costs roughly the same or less than similar safety measures per fatality averted.

III. APPLICATION TO SPECIFIC EXAMPLES

The best way to demonstrate the concepts in the previous discussion is to apply them to specific cases.

The numbers in the following examples involve a mix of *hypothetical* and *factual* data. They are used merely to demonstrate the method of estimating reasonable safety. As a consequence, the reader should infer from these examples no conclusions about specific safety measures.

Moreover, the reader should be aware of the uncertainty involved in all such estimations. Indeed, in some instances the high degree of uncertainty may overwhelm all other issues. Accounting for uncertainty is difficult at best, impossible at worst. (Solomon[7] provides the special measures that must be taken to account for uncertainty.)

A. Should Roll Bars Be Installed on Utility Vehicles?

A utility vehicle is a multipurpose vehicle designed for use both on and off road.* It has a 5 to 11 times higher probability per mile of rolling over than does a conventional passenger automobile. Though rolling over is the major cause of death in utility vehicle accidents, neither federal regulations nor federal performance standards provide for roll bars.[8]

This analysis uses annualized data based on an assumed driving rate in utility vehicles of 10,000 miles per year. (Much of these data are derived from Snyder[8]; the balance are assumed.) The annual fatality rate resulting from rollovers assumed where *no roll bar is installed* is 0.12 per 1000 people; where the *roll bar is installed*, this rate is 0.03 per 1000 people. Thus the reduction in fatality rate resulting from installation of roll bars is 0.09 per 1000 people (0.12 minus 0.03). As a consequence, the addition of a roll bar reduces the annual fatality

---

*Utility vehicles include various models of the Willys Jeep, AMC Jeep, Ford Bronco, International Scout, Toyota Land Cruiser, Chevrolet Blazer, GMC Jimmy, Dodge Ramcharger, Plymouth Trail Duster, and Volkswagen Thing.

rate by 400 percent (0.12 divided by 0.03).

Without roll bars, the annual risk of fatality for a person in a utility vehicle stands at roughly 24 percent of the background risk. With roll bars, it stands at roughly 6 percent—still above the background risk. Thus, a roll bar is not justified on the Risk/Safety Criterion.

Because utility vehicle driving is inherently risky (i.e., it contributes more than 0.1 percent of the background risk) we now apply the Cost/Safety Criterion. If we calculate that the cost of a roll bar is approximately $100 and that approximately 1000 of them will be needed to save one life (or 1000 divided by 0.09), then the cost of roll bars per fatality averted is $1 million (or 10,000 times $100). Table 19-1, however, shows that the average cost of automobile safety equipment per fatality averted is $260,000.

As a consequence, *while roll bars can save lives, other safety equipment can save more lives per dollar spent.* Based on this mix of hypothetical and factual data, roll bars ought not to be made mandatory equipment on utility vehicles.

B. Should the Wearing of Seat Belts Be Legally Enforced?

As of 1966, seat belts are required on all passenger vehicles. Few states, however, enforce the wearing of these seat belts.

It has been asserted that if all occupants in passenger vehicles wore seat belts, approximately 5000 lives would be saved annually (or 10 percent of the 50,000 lives lost annually). Currently, less than one-third of passengers and drivers in passenger vehicles regularly wear seat belts. For the purposes of demonstration, let us assume that a law enforcing the wearing of seat belts would be only 50 percent efficient. Thus it would increase the fraction of people wearing seat belts from one-third to two-thirds, it would save roughly 2500 lives per year, and it would reduce the fatality rate by 5 percent relative to automotive accidents and 2.5 percent relative to all accidents.

Without enforcement of wearing seat belts, the risk of fatality in a passenger vehicle stands at roughly 50 percent of the background risk. With enforcement, it stands at roughly 47.5 percent—still considerably above 0.1 percent of the background risk.

Having failed the Risk/Safety Criterion and because automobile driving is inherently risky (i.e., it contributes more than half of all accident mortalities), we now apply the Cost/ Safety Criterion. If we assume that enforcing this law would cost $50 million dollars per year, then it would cost $200,000 per life saved—which is $60,000 less than the average cost of automobile safety equipment per fatality averted (see Table 19-1, pp. 562–563).

Based on this mix of hypothetical and factual data, *the legal enforcement of wearing seat belts is justified.* We must note, however, that *these costs would be borne by different people*: society as a whole would pay for enforcement, while only the owners of automobiles would pay for specific automobile safety equipment.

If the additional policemen and equipment for this enforcement were financed from automobile user fees, such as licenses and gasoline taxes, or from traffic fines, this disparity could at least partly be alleviated.

C. Should Air Bags Be Required in All Passenger Vehicles?

Air bags have distinct advantages and disadvantages. Though they can cause a reduced rate of injury or fatality following a collision, they also can cause accidents by inflating prematurely and/or erroneously. In addition, they provide little or no protection against side crashes, multiple collisions, and rollovers.

It has been asserted that if every passenger vehicle contained self-inflating air bags, from 6000 to 9000 lives could be saved annually, assuming that air bags will be used in conjunction with seat belts or passive belts (see NUREG/CR-2226[9]). Thus, air bags would reduce the fatality rate by 12 to 18 percent relative to automotive accidents and 6 to 9 percent relative to all accidents.

Without air bags, the risk of fatality in a passenger vehicle stands at roughly 50 percent of the background risk. With air bags, it stands at roughly 41 to 44 percent—still considerably above the background risk. With or without air bags, automobile driving is a highly risky event.

Because the risk of accident still remains high in automobiles, we now apply the Cost/Safety Criterion. Table 19-1 indicates that air bags in passenger vehicles would cost $640,000 for each driver fatality averted. This makes air bags the least cost-effective traffic safety measure in the table— aside from tire inspections.

As a consequence, while air bags can save lives, other safety equipment can save more lives per dollar spent. Based on this mix of hypothetical and factual data, *air bags ought not to be made mandatory equipment on passenger vehicles.*

D. Should We Have Warning Devices on Board Passenger Trains?

Here we generate an example where the risk of the technology is equal to the Risk/Safety Criterion cutoff. For this example we go outside of the automotive industry. The death rate for train passengers averaged over the entire population of the United States was only about 5 in 100 million per year, according to the *World Almanac* of 1979. Assuming that only 10 percent of the population are regular users of trains, then the mortality risk to exposed individuals (only train users) is about 5 in 10 million per year, or equal to the Risk/Safety Criterion cutoff.

Now let us suppose that we could install a special signal device that would eliminate train crashes, and suppose it could be installed for $2 million. Such a simple device might couple on to the existing communication network. So for $2 million we could save 10 lives (an average of 10 people per year are killed due to train collisions in the United States). The cost per fatality averted is merely $200,000.

What should be done? By the first criterion, the signaling device need not be added; yet, by the second criterion, it would be cost effective to do so. Under such circumstances it would make sense to add the device.

IV. RISK ACCEPTANCE: A SELECTED BIBLIOGRAPHY

The subject of diverse interpretations, risk acceptance has been treated in numerous books and papers. These works tend to fall into four often overlapping categories:

1. Psychological and sociological
2. Legal and regulatory
3. Economic
4. Technical

A. Psychological and Sociological Literature

While very rich in observations, the psychology and sociology studies provide inadequate pragmatic solutions to the question, "How safe is safe enough?" The literature for both disciplines suggests the following social norms involving risk acceptance:

1. For high-consequence, low-probability events (i.e., accidents), members of society are generally far more concerned with consequences than with probabilities.
2. For low-consequence, high-probability events (i.e., routine exhaust emissions), members of society are less uniform. Some are more concerned with consequences, others with probabilities, and yet others with uncertainties.
3. Members of society generally have varying tolerances for and perceptions of risk. What some individuals regard as acceptable, others perceive as unacceptable.
4. Some risks, although equally probable and equally consequential, are less desirable than others. The nature of the risk is an important consideration.
5. The acceptability of a risk is generally proportional to the level of resulting benefit and to the degree of control a member of society has over the risk—that is to say, whether the individual voluntarily or involuntarily incurs the risk.
6. The members of society generally cannot conceive of risk in absolute terms. He or she is far more concerned with reductions in probabilities than in consequences.
7. When members of society select between two competing alternatives, they will more often select the one that is superior in a single characteristic regardless of the degree of its superiority.

- C. Lindblom, "The Science of Muddling Through," in W. J. Gore and J. W. Byson (eds.), *The Making of Decisions*. New York: Free Press, 1964.
- W. W. Lowrance, *Of Acceptable Risk: Science and the Determination of Safety*. Los Altos, CA.: William Kaufman, 1976.
- J. G. March and H. A. Simon, *Organizations*. New York: Wiley, 1968.
- P. Slovic, B. Fischoff, and S. Lichtenstein, "Behavioral Decision Theory." *Annual Review of Psychology*, 28:1–39 (1977).
- L. Tribe, "Policy Science: Analysis or Ideology?" *Philosophy and Public Affairs*, 66:12–16 (1972).
- R. I. Youden and E. T. Joiner, *Risk, Choice, and Prediction*. Boston: Duxbury Press, 1974.

- R. Zeckhauser, "An Approach to the Analysis of Societal Decision." *Colloques Internationaux, Centre National de la Recherche Scientifique*, No. 171, pp. 317–333, 1979.
- J. M. Ziman, *Public Knowledge: An Essay Concerning the Social Dimension of Science.* Cambridge, Engl.: Cambridge University Press, 1968.

B. Legal and Regulatory Literature

The legal and regulatory literature provides us merely a basis for answering questions about acceptable levels of risk. This literature frequently raises two questions:

1. What are the legal, regulatory, and institutional constraints affecting the formulation of risk-acceptance criteria?
2. In what way can we use the experience gained in the legal process to formulate risk-acceptance criteria?

- W. Bordas, *Problems of State and Local Risk Management: An Overview.* UCLA-ENG-8246. Los Angeles: UCLA School of Engineering and Applied Sciences, December 1981.
- H. Crean, "The Essence of Congressional Decision Making," in *Risk Acceptance and Public Policy*, Proceedings of Session IV of the International System Safety Society Symposium, Denver, July 17–20, 1973, pp. 56–60.
- M. Crenson, *The Un-Politics of Air Pollution: A Study of Non-Decisionmaking in the Cities.* Baltimore: Johns Hopkins Press, 1971.
- Federal Insurance Admininstration, *Full Insurance Availability.* Washington, D.C.: Department of Housing and Urban Development, 1974.
- P. K. Fife, "Professional Liability and the Public Interest," in *Risk Acceptance and Public Policy*, Proceedings of Session IV of the International System Safety Society Symposium, Denver, July 17–20, 1973, pp. 88–100.
- R. N. McKedan, *Efficiency in Government Through Systems Analysis.* New York: Wiley, 1958.
- R. O. Mason, "A Dialectical Approach to Strategic Planning." *Management Science*, 15:B403–B414 (1969).
- M. W. Meyer and K. A. Solomon, *Risk Management Practices in Local Communities: Five Alternates.* UCLA-ENG-8242. Los Angeles: UCLA School of Engineering and Applied Sciences, December 1981.
- D. Okrent et al., *Final Report, Alternative Risk Management Policies for State and Local Governments.* UCLA-ENG-8240. Los Angeles: UCLA School of Engineering and Applied Sciences, December 1981.

- A. Wildavsky, "The Political Economy of Efficiency: Cost-Benefit Analysis, Systems Analysis, and Program Budgeting." *Public Administration Review*, 26:292 (1966).

C. Economic Literature:
Studies of Management and Economics

Four major areas concerning risk are addressed in economic literature:

1. How much is an individual willing to pay to reduce a risk by either a known or an unknown amount? How much will society pay?
2. How sensitive are those amounts to the nature of the risk?
3. Can we develop an economically feasible safety program to satisfy and assure adequate levels of safety in some specific activities or industries?
4. What is the value of human life?

- R. F. Baker, R. M. Michels, and E. Preston, *Public Policy Development: Linking the Technical and Political Processes*. New York: Wiley, 1975.
- R. Bauer (ed.), *Social Indicators*. Cambridge, MA.: MIT Press, 1966.
- V. Bauer and M. Wegener, "Simulation, Evaluation and Conflict Analysis in Urban Planning." *Proceedings of the IEEE*, 63:405–413 (1975).
- W. J. Baumol and E. Oates, *The Theory of Environmental Policy: Externalities, Public Outlays, and Quality of Life*. Englewood Cliffs, N.J.: Prentice-Hall, 1975.
- J. Bennington and P. Skelton, "Public Participation in Decision Making by Governments," in *Benefit-Cost and Policy Analysis 1974*. Chicago: Aldine, 1975, pp. 417–454.
- L. K. Caldwell (ed.), *Science, Technology, and Public Policy: A Selected and Annotated Bibliography*, 3 vols. Bloomington: Program in Public Policy for Science and Technology, Department of Government, Indiana University, 1968–1972.
- R. L. Crain, E. Katz, and D. B. Rosenthal, *The Politics of Community Conflict: The Fluoridation Decision*. Indianapolis: Bobbs-Merrill, 1969.
- H. M. Ellis and R. L. Keeney, "A Rational Approach for Government Decisions Concerning Air Pollution," in A. W. Drake, R. L. Keeney, and P. M. Morse (eds.), *Analysis of Public Systems*. Cambridge, MA.: MIT Press, 1972.
- R. Haveman and J. Margolis (eds.), *Public Expenditure and Policy Analysis*. Chicago: Markham, 1970.

- R. Howard, "Power of Pricing Mechanisms." *Management Science*, 13:10 (June 1967). (Section titled "Free for All.")
- L. B. Lave, "Safety in Transportation: The Role of Government." *Law Contemporary Problems*, 33:512–535 (Summer 1968).
- R. C. Lind, *Optimal Resource Allocation, Markets, and Public Policy: An Introduction*. New York: Wiley, 1971.
- A. Maass, "Benefit-Cost Analysis: Its Relevance to Public Investment Decisions." *Quarterly Journal of Economics*, 80:208 (1966).
- R. McKean, *Public Spending*. New York: McGraw-Hill, 1968.
- R. G. McManus, "Comments on the General Theory of Second Best." *Review of Economic Studies*, 26:209 (1958–1959).
- S. A. Marglin, *Public Investment Criteria*. Cambridge, MA.: MIT Press, 1967.
- B. M. Moriarty, "Safety Quantification for Insurance Premiums," in *Risk Acceptance and Public Policy*, Proceedings of Session IV of the International System Safety Society Symposium, Denver, July 17–20, 1973, pp. 66–85.
- A. Wildavsky, "If Planning Is Everything, Maybe It's Nothing." *Policy Sciences*, 4:127–153 (1973).
- P. Wright, "The Harassed Decision-Maker: Time Pressures, Distractions, and the Use of Evidence." *Journal of Applied Psychology*, 59:555–561 (1974).

D. Technical Literature

The literature is very rich in technical studies. The basic technical approach consists of defining a series of events or scenarios leading to an accident or chronic situation, estimating the consequence of these undesired events, and then estimating their probabilities.

One observation stands out in much of this literature: The ability to provide quantitative risk assessments is limited by the quality of the data rather than by available technical methods. It is presently unclear the extent to which uncertainty and error propagation can be mastered.

- *Accident Facts—1979*. Chicago: National Safety Council, 1979.
- M. R. Gelpe and A. D. Tarlock, "The Uses of Scientific Information in Environmental Decisionmaking." *Southern California Law Review*, 48:371–427 (1974).
- D. Nelkin, "The Political Impact of Technical Expertise." *Social Studies of Science*, 5:35–54 (1975).
- K. A. Solomon and S. C. Abraham, "The Index of Harm." *Journal of Health Physics*, 38:375–391 (1979).
- K. A. Solomon and M. W. Meyer, *Classification of Risks*. UCLA-ENG-8245. Los Angeles: UCLA School of Engineering and Applied Sciences, December 1981.

- K. A. Solomon and M. W. Meyer, *Management of Risks Associated with Drinking Water at the Local and State Levels*. UCLA-ENG-8243. Los Angeles: UCLA School of Engineering and Applied Sciences, December 1981.
- K. A. Solomon and D. Okrent, *Catastrophic Events Leading to De Facto Limits on Liability*. UCLA-ENG-7732. Los Angeles: UCLA School of Engineering and Applied Sciences, May 1977.

V. SUMMARY

Drawing on numerous prior studies dealing with the question, "How safe is reasonable?" this section has focused specifically on four issues of current interest:

1. Should roll bars be installed on all utility vehicles?
2. Should the wearing of seat belts be legally enforced?
3. Should air bags be required in all passenger vehicles?
4. Should warning devices be installed on trains?

Using a mix of hypothetical and factual data, the authors demonstrate the method whereby risk assessments could determine acceptable levels of safety in various kinds of situations. Specifically, the two criteria used should be employed whenever a new safety measure is being considered for an already existing technology, industry, or product. A new safety measure is justified if it meets *either* of the following requirements:

1. *Risk/Safety Criterion.* It should reduce the risk of fatality so that the technology, industry, or product to which the safety measure is added does not contribute more than 0.1 percent of the total accident risk experienced by the population as a whole.
2. *Cost/Safety Criterion.* It should cost roughly equal to or less than similar safety measures per fatality averted.

If we accept this consensus, we may wish to ask how to apply this concept in the case where a new safety device emerges in the market for an industry, technology, or product that already exists. Examples might include a new air pollution control device for electric utilities, a self-locking seat belt for automobiles, or a child-proof cap for medicine bottles. The analog rule for these existing products would be:

Require that the new safety enhancement be employed for any industry, product, or technology that currently constituted more than 0.1 percent of the background risk for a representative individual *unless* the cost per life saved exceeds some critical value K.

Presumably, K would represent the cost per life saved of other lifesaving innovations under consideration by the relevant political body. The intuition behind this rule is that, if society were willing to defer introduction of a new technology that increased background risk noticeably (i.e., more than 0.1 percent), then it should be willing to require that a new safety device be adopted for currently risky products or technologies, unless it were unreasonably expensive to do so.

CITATIONS

[1]K. A. Solomon and P. F. Nelson, *An Evaluation of Alternative Safety Criteria*. N-1806-ORNL. Santa Monica: The Rand Corporation, May 1982.

[2]*Safety Goals for Nuclear Power Plants: A Discussion Paper*. Draft of Report No. NUREG-0880. Washington, D.C.: U.S. Nuclear Regulatory Commission, February 1982.

[3]B. L. Cohen, "Society's Evaluation of Life Saving in Radiation Protection and in Other Contexts." *Health Physics*, 38:33–51 (1980).

[4]*A Study of the Implications of Applying Quantitative Risk Criteria in the Licensing of Nuclear Power Plants in the United States*. Report No. NUREG/CR-2040. Washington, D.C.: U.S. Nuclear Regulatory Commission, March 1981.

[5]W. S. Cool, *Occupational Radiation Exposure at NRC-Licensed Facilties*. Washington, D.C.: U.S. Nuclear Regulatory Commission, 1975.

[6]R. B. Minogue, *Further Action to Control Risks Associated with Radiation Exposure*. Paper No. SECY-78-415, prepared for NRC Commissioners, July 31, 1978.

[7]K. A. Solomon, *Dealing in Uncertainty*. Report No. R-3045-ORNL. Santa Monica: The Rand Corporation, August 1983.

[8]R. G. Snyder et al., *On-Road Crash Experience of Utility Vehicles*. Report No. UM-HSRI-80-14. Ann Arbor: Highway Safety Research Institute, University of Michigan, February 1980.

[9]*A Survey of Safety Levels in Federal Regulation*. Report No. NUREG/CR-2226. Washington, D.C.: U.S. Nuclear Regulatory Commission, June 1981.

20

Warnings in Automotive Systems

LORNA MIDDENDORF, Ed.D.
Grosse Pointe Park, Michigan

*Dr. Lorna Middendorf is a human factors consultant
specializing in warnings. For 15 years she was a
consultant to the General Motors Design Staff. She has
published many research reports and has performed human
factors evaluations in facilities in North America, South
America, and Asia. A registered professional engineer
(Safety—California) and board certified in forensic
psychology, the author maintains an office at 1040 Berk-
shire Road, Grosse Pointe Park, Michigan 48230
(313-343-0609).*

I. INTRODUCTION

Automotive warnings function as part of automotive system safety efforts to safeguard drivers, passengers, bystanders, and automotive service personnel. Warnings also serve to fulfill the automotive manufacturer's legal duty to warn in the presence of product hazards. Millions of persons are injured and thousands are killed each year using automotive products for work or leisure activities. The purpose of warnings is to reduce the risk or likelihood of injuries. Statistics document the presence of hazards and risks of harm associated with automotive use, and the need for adequate automotive warnings (U.S. National Traffic and Motor Vehicle Safety Act, 1966[1]) has been documented.

In this section warnings have been defined. The purposes and requirements for warnings are explained. What types of warning are appropriate and effective in passenger cars is discussed. The process of generating warnings is outlined. Examples of automotive warnings are given. Illustrative regulatory requirements for various automotive warnings are listed. Methods of evaluating and testing warnings are discussed. Some legal issues pertaining to warnings are examined in light of selected cases. While the focus of this section is warnings on passenger cars, the information has applicability for a wide range of automotive products.

Automotive warnings may appear in written, graphic, visual, or auditory form or some combination of forms. This examination of automotive warnings applies to such common warnings as labels, placards, signs, embossed or molded lettering on vehicles or vehicle components, tags, legends, brochures, recall notices, add-on notices, portions of operating manuals, training or instructional texts, service or maintenance bulletins and shop manuals, buzzers and tones, and static or flashing lights.

II. LANGUAGE OF WARNINGS

Warnings constitute a unique language with compelling communication purposes. As a language, warnings have structure, defined relationships to specific referents, special meanings, and potency. Warning messages encode a sense of urgency, peril, misfortune, a need to be cautious, to be on guard, and to be informed.

They take the form of imperatives ranging from basic information or instructions to alarms that signal imminent danger. As imperatives, warnings telegraph by words, symbols, graphics, layout, location, color, sounds, form, and emphasis the need to be aware, to attend, to be ready to alter behavior in specific ways. Warnings are meant to be—by design—obtrusive, interruptive, distinct, attention-gaining, arousing, strong, separate, and dynamic. At the same time, warnings are tailored for a specific hazardous condition or set of circumstances, and need to be, by design, integrated and permanent for a location or purpose. The fire engine siren, instrument panel warning lights, railroad grade crossing signals, the skull and crossbones on poisonous substances, the placard with **DANGER** in bold, white letters with a red and black background fixed to a battery are examples. Warnings express the active mode, that is, doing something, arresting or actively not doing something.

A warning is a message in warning language. It is a message sent to a person to assist in the avoidance of harm, to provide information in the presence of harm that may not be in awareness and that enables the receiver to make the decision with appropriate behavior to avoid the harm.

A warning emphatically calls attention to itself. A warning clearly reveals a hazard and the relative magnitude of risk of injury. A written warning details specific behaviors necessary to avoid harm and the consequences of failing to heed the warning. A warning concisely spells out what must be done if injury occurs to minimize the harm.

A warning is a commanding instruction that begins with a signal word, light, color, form, or some combination of these to reinforce the message. To be effective, warning messages must be space or time-linked, that is, warnings require space or time sufficient to adequately inform a person.

Warnings need to be seen or heard and understood not only by an ordinary person, but also by a person who may have a handicap of language, age, or some foreseeable condition.

The object of a warning is a person who needs to be informed of a hazard with injury potential. The object, as with most imperatives, is you—the viewer or person within its range. In written warnings, the verb is active—commanding, requesting, or prohibiting action. The purpose of the message is disclosure of a hazard or danger (an unreasonable or unacceptable risk of serious injury or death to the person).

III. ADEQUACY OF WARNINGS

Determination of the adequacy of warnings is a legal question based on human factors requirements. Legal determination of adequacy is based on whether there has been sufficient disclosure of all unexpected risks of serious avoidable injury so that a person can make an informed choice as to behavioral alternatives. The human factors determination of adequacy draws on human behavioral research to measure whether a warning message significantly modifies or controls behavior by reducing the likelihood of unsafe behaviors and by enhancing the probabilities of safe behaviors for persons at risk most of the time.[2]

An adequate warning, then, will be a message in warning language that meets social, moral, and legal requirements. The message will disclose the risks so that an informed choice can take place in the presence of known hazards, so that safe behaviors can be shaped and used and unsafe behaviors can be halted or altered by the user, purchaser, or bystander. The adequate warning will be an exhortation as to the nature of the hazard and the gravity of the risk for efficient risk reduction. It will provide the user with sufficient information and intensity to determine intellectually and emotionally how further risk reduction or harm avoidance can take place. It will serve as a reminder to someone who knows the danger but whose awareness and attention have been diverted by other activities or situational circumstances. In essence, the adequate or sufficient warning as part of the safeguarding system will result in minimal risk of harm and fewer injuries.

IV. CURRENT AUTOMOTIVE WARNINGS

Passenger car warnings signal the presence of hazards and the likelihood of personal injury or death should dangerous conditions or circumstances emerge during ordinary vehicle operation, maintenance, and repair. For the typical driver or passenger, warnings provide opportunities to be informed, to make reasoned choices as to personal behavior in light of injury potentials, and to avoid harm associated with hazards.

Present passenger car warnings take various forms. A bank of indicators on the instrument panel illuminated when the ignition key is turned on. A buzzer or bell sounding concurrently with a lighted symbol until the seat belt is fastened.

A colored label on the battery informing of explosive gases, caustic substances, and electrical shock. Embossed letters on the fan belt shroud forming the words: CAUTION FAN. A placard fixed to the driver's door indicating load limits for tires and the vehicle. A series of paragraphs appearing in the owner's manual set off from text by lines, signal words, and typeface. A letter sent to passenger car owners requesting return of the vehicle to the agency service center for replacement of a defective part or correction of a defective condition. Red tail lamps actuated when the brakes are applied.

An analysis of a 1982 passenger vehicle owner's and driver's manual identified a number of hazards and hazard consequences associated with ordinary vehicle use, servicing, repair, and misuse. These include loss of vehicle control, occupants being thrown from the vehicle, objects or occupants being thrown about within the vehicle, the vehicle falling on a person; burns, inhalation of dangerous (poisonous) substances, laceration, electrical shock; increasing injury severity during an accident; and vehicle or property damage.

A particular hazard consequence, such as loss of vehicular control, can result from various hazards such as mechanical malfunctions, incorrect handling, mismatched parts, or improper procedures. Table 20–1 lists selected passenger car hazards, possible antecedents, and consequences.

The automotive manufacturer identifying hazards with attendant risks of harm fulfills in part the manufacturer's legal duty to market safe products (not in a defective condition or unsafe to the user or consumer) from product designs minimizing the risk of injury and warning users of remaining risks where foreseeable user behavior might lead to injury. Legal obligations also require safe designs or product safeguards for foreseeable misuse.

Most written warnings found on a 1982 passenger vehicle were located under the hood. These were a battery CAUTION label, a CAUTION-refrigerant label, a CAUTION-fan embossed on the fan shroud and a NEVER OPEN HOT embossed on the radiator cap. In the trunk was a CAUTION-instructions for jacks. Vehicle load limits and tire inflation recommendations were affixed to the car body forward and inside the driver's door.

Other warnings found on the 1982 passenger car were a fasten seat belts backlit legend, coolant temperature light, brake system warning light, oil/choke indicator light, generator indicator light, check engine light, and headlight high-

Table 20-1 Illustrative Automotive Hazards

Loss of vehicle control may be caused by:
- Sudden movement of the driver's seat while the car is in motion.
- Poor braking action due to inadequate size, improper trailering, hitching, wet conditions, or riding and overheating the brakes.
- Removing ignition key while vehicle is in motion.
- Not engaging parking brake when driver leaves the vehicle.
- Descending a steep slope or long grade at high speeds.
- Using cruise controls at set speeds faster than moving traffic, when vehicle cannot be maintained at a set speed, when roads are slippery with ice or snow, and when roads are winding and traffic varies in speed and volume.
- Use of improperly fitting fasteners.
- Use of tires of different construction.
- Improper tire inflation.
- Vehicle overloading.
- Corrosion preventing good metal-to-metal contact at wheel mounting surface causing wheel nuts and wheels to loosen and come off.
- Failure to torque wheel nuts to specification, improperly tightened wheel nuts, and use of oil or grease on studs or nuts.
- Failure to use high-speed capability tires for operation at speeds faster than 85 mph (140 km/h).
- Spinning wheels faster than 35 mph (55 km/h) to free vehicle from sand, mud, or ice.
- Transaxle failure.
- Loss of visibility from use of windshield washer while warming windshield during cold/freezing weather conditions.
- Improper or incomplete servicing.

Loss of vehicle control—being thrown from the vehicle—can result from:
- Failure to lock doors properly.
- Unintentional opening of doors.
- Failure to fasten seat belts properly.

Loss of vehicle control—person/objects being thrown about a moving vehicle—may be related to:
- Improper stowage, uneven positioning of objects in cars.
- Rear cargo covers or passenger compartment panels not fully reattached, securely latched, or stowed, or are moved while vehicle is in motion.
- Improper jack or tire stowage.
- Unrestrained drivers or passengers in an accident.

Crushing can be caused by:
- Improper jacking, getting beneath a vehicle and starting or running an engine while the vehicle is supported by a jack.
- Having an unrestrained child in the vehicle during an accident or using improper child restraints.

Burns may result from:
- Parking, idling, or operating a vehicle over combustible materials.
- Engine overheating in the absence of an alert driver.
- Overheating of engine coolant (ethylene glycol).

(Continued)

Table 20-1 Illustrative Automotive Hazards (*Continued*)

- Spilling antifreeze or coolant on exhaust system or hot engine parts.
- Exposing a battery to open flames, electric sparks, or smoke.
- Using volatile cleaning solvents for cleaning the inside or the outside of the vehicle, failure to follow manufacturer's directions for use.
- Removing the radiator or thermostat housing cap while the engine and radiator are still hot.
- During engine backfire, not having air cleaner element (flame arrester) in place.
- Caustic burns from battery acid contacting eyes, skin, fabrics, or painted surfaces.

Inhalation of dangerous substances may be caused by:
- Exhaust gases entering the passenger compartment or being emitted in close, confined spaces.
- Obstructed air inlet grille.
- Running or idling the engine with vehicle in a parked position more than 10 minutes with the ventilation system control in the OFF position.
- Running or idling the engine with a vehicle in a parked position and the vehicle has a poorly repaired, damaged, or corroded exhaust system or body.
- Certain cleaning solvents used in small, unvented spaces without approved respiratory protection equipment.
- Driving with hatchback windows open.
- Open trailer mounting holes permitting entry of exhaust fumes.
- Use of carbon tetrachloride, gasoline, benzene, naptha, or other dangerous substances for cleaning.

Laceration may result from:
- Battery gases exploding and the failure to use protective devices.
- Hands, tools, or clothing in proximity to engine cooling fan with the ignition key in the RUN position.

Electric shock can be caused by:
- Loose or missing insulation on battery jumper cables.
- Contact of metal tools or other metal with the positive battery terminal (and attached metal) or any metal on either vehicle in jump starting.
- Failure to check battery fluid levels before jump starting.
- Improper grounding or routing of jumper cables.
- Jump starting using vehicles with different voltages or grounds.

Increasing injury severity during an accident may result from:
- Reclining seat to permit sliding under lap belt while vehicle is in motion.
- Improper seat-belt fit.
- More than one person using a seat belt.
- Twisted or damaged seat belts or belt hardware.
- Too much slack in shoulder belt.
- Wearing seat belt under arm.

beam indicator light. Additionally, there were brake light, turn signal, and hazard light indicators, a key-in-ignition buzzer, a horn, headlight-on buzzer, and a seat-belt buzzer reminder. The light switch was also designed (according to the owner's manual) to flicker in the event of electrical overload or other related problems.

Some current passenger vehicles come equipped with electronic diagnostic systems and displays. In these vehicles warnings are displayed as electronic messages with flashing features, buzzers, and indicator lights on the instrument panel or special instrument pods. With the appearance of electronic displays and increased numbers of displays, warnings in vehicle information centers will take on added significance for normal safe operation.

V. BASIC ELEMENTS OF AUTOMOTIVE WARNINGS

A. Printed Warnings

A.1. SIGNAL WORD A signal word alerts a viewer to a hazard. DANGER, WARNING, and CAUTION are signal words used to capture a person's attention and to signify levels of hazard intensity. These are in accordance with the 1979 revised Society of Automotive Engineers (SAE) J115—Recommended Practice.[3] DANGER means an immediate hazard, irreversible, harmful consequences. WARNING connotes hazards or unsafe practices that can result in severe personal injury or death. CAUTION is used for potential hazards or unsafe practices that could result in minor personal injury or property damage.

A.2. HAZARD A hazard is a source of danger to a person on or near a machine (SAE J115). Hazard has also been described as a condition or changing set of circumstances presenting an injury potential.[4] Specific hazards should be designated as to their hazardous properties such as explosive (batteries), poisonous (exhaust gases, cleaning substances), electrical shock (batteries), or laceration (engine cooling fan). Because people are often not familiar with specific hazards or hazardous properties associated with vehicle components, materials, or combined hazards from multiple sources, clear exposition and presentation is necessary.

A.3. RISK Risk is the likelihood of injury potential, sometimes expressed as a percentage.[4] It reflects the frequency and severity of injury that is likely to occur from the hazard, and the magnitude of the danger. Risk is usually determined by risk/benefit analysis or other systematic tools of safety engineering. Studies have shown that people consistently overestimate or underestimate causes related to fatal injuries.[5] Indicators of the degree of risk should be very clear: gas (vapor) reduces oxygen available for breathing when exhaust gases enter the vehicle through open hatchback windows or a badly corroded exhaust system releases heavy gas (vapor) that may cause suffocation when exhaust gases enter the passenger compartment with the vehicle in close, confined spaces. Disclosure should be commensurate with the degree of risk to promote careful and precautionary behaviors.

A.4. PRECAUTIONS The precautionary message should clearly communicate how to avoid harm. It should contain precise instructions as to what should or should not be done. Short, simple sentences with active verbs should be used. Ambiguities should be avoided. Where graphics or symbols are used to overcome language barriers, care should be taken to insure that the meanings are known to a high percentage of viewers, that population stereotypes are communicated as intended. An ISO study of symbols for automotive controls and displays[6] suggests a minimum recognition rate of 75 percent. For most purposes, symbols will require added words for clarity and emphasis. In addition, precautions should be complete; comprehension is degraded by vague or ill-defined terms, highly technical words, and complex or lengthy phrases. "Use eye or face guards when servicing" (battery explosion, corrosive burns), "do not open if engine is hot" (burns from radiator or thermostat housing cap), or "fasten seat belts securely" (increasing injury severity in accident) are sample precautionary messages.

A.5. PROTECTIVE MEASURES If special protection is needed or required by protective equipment or apparel, the item or items should be specified. For example, eye guards, such as goggles or shields, should be used during battery servicing.

B. Customizing Warnings

A warning should fit the circumstances or conditions that require that a person be warned. General requirements for a warning should be adapted for specific hazards or risks, vehicle characteristics or functional operations. They may necessitate additional information as brief explanatory notes, diagrams, and combined warnings and instructions, as may be found with vehicle jacks.

The warning should be placed where it is *needed*. Care should be taken to prevent obscuration or blockage under ordinary and even unusual circumstances, such as low illumination or night conditions. Consideration should be given to when in a series of events it is needed to give sufficient time for avoidance behavior or appropriate corrective action to take place. Placement of the warning should take into account vehicle performance or interactions that might degrade the warning for the effective life of the vehicle. It should be durable and easily read for the life of the vehicle. For warnings under the hood, this may require special efforts to protect embossed or molded lettering from engine fluid and lubricant buildup that may cover the warning message. Chemically resistant labels are often needed to prevent degrading reactions that might affect the readability of the warning when needed.

Customizing the language of warnings requires that special attention be given to colors used. As evolved, specific colors have come to reflect conscious and subconscious meaning, with red denoting danger, green suggesting safety, and yellow relating caution. The use of appropriate color in a warning can signal hazards immediately to a universal population where language might present communication barriers.

Warning size, layout, composition, type size for lettering, emphasis by contrast, capitalization, blocking, underlining, or other means should together enhance the warning message. Specifications may be required by law, industry, or government standards or industry practice such as ISO or DOT symbols, identification codes, and diagrams.

Customizing warnings must take into account what is known about human behavior and integrate this information into the warning design process. Especially important is knowledge about what shapes safe behaviors or causes people to behave unsafely in the presence of hazards and what triggers the modification of behavior. Human factors research has provided valuable data on human information processing such as what attracts the operator's attention, what distracts or overloads the operator, and what information or way of presentation goes beyond normal human capabilities.[7] McFarland[8] has examined in depth the psychological and behavioral correlates of automobile accidents and provides an instructive view of the interrelationships among driver, vehicle, and the environment.

C. Other Warnings

Automotive warnings include static and flashing lights of various colors and configurations and auditory signals such as buzzers, horns, bells, chimes, tones, and sirens. Such warnings should meet the general requirements for warnings with additional care to such considerations as attention-gaining features in the presence of specific backgrounds, brightness, contrast, audibility, reliability, annoyance, overload, understandability, and standardization.

D. Other Information

Legal requirements and government or industry standards and practices may require special information. Symbols and identifications for controls and displays for passenger vehicles, trucks and buses are listed in U.S. Federal Motor Vehicle Safety Standard (FMVSS) No. 101 (43 FR 27542 6-26-78). New vehicle requirements can also be found in FMVSS No. 100 series for accident prevention, FMVSS No. 200 series for injury protection, and FMVSS No. 300 series for post accident protection.

Other government regulations or stipulations that may require labeling or tagging, record disclosure, defect notice, or recall are:

- National Traffic and Motor Vehicle Safety Act of 1966 administered by the Department of Transportation (DOT) and the National Highway Traffic Safety Administration (NHTSA).
- Clean Air Act with 1977 amendments administered by the Environmental Protection Agency (EPA).
- Motor Vehicle Information and Cost Saving Act of 1972 administered by DOT and NHTSA.
- Consumer Product Safety Act (1972) administered by the Consumer Product Safety Commission (CPSC).

- Energy Policy and Conservation Act of 1975 administered by various agencies, such as the Federal Trade Commission (FTC) for labeling, DOT, NHTSA, and EPA.
- Federal Hazardous Substances Act (1980).
- Poison Prevention Packaging Act (1971) administered by the CPSC.
- Lead-Based Poison Prevention Act (1971) administered by the CPSC.
- Toxic Substance Control Act (1976) administered by the Environmental Protection Office of Toxic Substances.
- Flammable Fabrics Act (1953) administered by CPSC.
- Radiation Control for Health and Safety Act (1968) administered by the federal Public Health Service.
- Federal Boat Safety Act of 1971 administered by the Coast Guard.

The Department of Defense (DOD) issues standards for automotive warnings such as backup lights (FED-STD-515/16), four-way flashers (FED-STD-515/7), instrument panel instruments and control devices (FED/STD-515/3A), and standard safety devices (FED-STD-515A). Guidelines and safety standards for warnings appear in military publications such as the 1975 military handbook *Human Factors Engineering Design for Army Material* (MIL-HDBK-759).

Where automotive products are produced and marketed internationally, as in Canada for United States manufacturers, additional laws may apply. For example, the Canada Motor Vehicle Tire Safety Act (1976), administered by the Ministry of Transport (MOT), specifies minimum safety standards for tires and the use of the National Safety Mark.

The Society of Automotive Engineers (SAE) publishes annual SAE handbooks with standards and recommended practices reflecting broadly accepted engineering practices or requirements. Standards and recommended practices are periodically updated. SAE J115, for example, is a recommended practice for safety signs to promote the safety of persons associated with off-highway work machines and may be applied to specified tools, machines and machinery. SAE J115 designates signal words, color combinations, letter sizes, and durability for both permanent and temporary safety signs.[3] The SAE standard for symbols for motor vehicle controls, indicators, and tell-tales is SAE J1048. Universal symbols for operator controls on industrial equipment, a recommended practice, is SAE J298.

SAE standards also address visual and auditory alarm systems. Vehicle warning lamps and hazard warning signal flashers standards appear in SAE J595b, J887, J910b, J1054, J1056, and J1104. A backup lamp standard is J593e. Turn signal lamps, switches, and flasher standards are found in SAE J588e, J589b, and J590a. Standards for flashing warning lamps for authorized emergency, maintenance, and service vehicles can be located in SAE J575, J595b, and J845. Flashing warning device standards for agricultural and industrial wheeled equipment are detailed in SAE J96 and J974. Standards for school bus red-signal lamps and stop arms appear in SAE J887a and J1133. A recommended practice for emergency roadway warning devices is SAE J774c. The safety alert symbol for agricultural equipment is described in SAE J284a. An SAE standard for vehicle traffic horns is J377. A mobile construction machinery forward warning horn recommended practice is SAE J1105.

Other organizations promulgating standards for vehicle warnings are the International Organization for Standardization (ISO), the American National Standards Institute (ANSI), and the American Society for Testing and Materials (ASTM).

It should be noted that mere conformance to government regulations and trade standards does not meet all legal and moral obligations for warnings.

VI. THE PROCESS OF PREPARING WARNINGS

Preparing effective warnings is part of the system safety effort of responsible manufacturers. When automotive products have residual hazards despite efforts to eliminate or minimize them, manufacturers have the duty to safeguard prospective purchasers and users. Warnings are part of the manufacturer's safeguarding system.

Sufficient and adequate warnings are often the result of systematic procedures involving management, designers, engineers, safety and human factors specialists, graphic artists, and production, legal, and marketing personnel. The process is a cooperative effort requiring clear guidelines from initiation through development to final approval. Good communications foster the exchange of information about all possible hazards, risks, and safeguarding remedies in light of human behavioral responses from the product design stage to production releases. Feedback from consumers, sales and marketing groups, government agencies, and litigation is effectively used as a basis for further refinements and improvements.

Manufacturers' guidelines for generating warnings often include management policy, how the warning design process is initiated, how warnings are developed, and the requirements for approval and production of warnings. In the 1970 *John Deere Design Data Manual*[9] management policy clearly indicates that safety signs are an integral part of machine design of the company and that signs are designed to alert the operator to possible personal injury hazards. Exact specifications for design, color, material, style, and size of type, copy, symbols, layout, artwork, and overseas languages are given. The procedures for ordering signs and for obtaining approval are detailed. Another manufacturer of special-purpose vehicles, FMC Corporation, has developed a product safety sign and label system for the purpose of combining written and pictorial information into safety signing and labeling communications and the minimizing of accidents due to latent product hazards.[10] The FMC manual details label formats, the determination of hazard intensity level, instructional messages, pictorial selection and design, safety instructions, multi-language labels, colors, and label development procedures. Drawing guides, safety color swatches, and master art are included. Selected warnings are shown in Figure 20-1.

A typical procedure in the design of warnings is the evaluation of the following considerations:

1. Does this product present a hazard and risk that cannot be eliminated or reduced by reasonable accident prevention methods and that require safeguarding and warnings?
2. What is the nature of the hazard? Is an ordinary person likely to know about this hazard? What will communicate the seriousness of the hazard?
3. What is the hazard level intensity: danger, warning, caution? What will emphasize the level chosen?
4. What instructions are needed for harm avoidance? How can these best be communicated to emphasize the gravity of the risk?
5. What consequences are likely to result if the warning is not heeded? How can this be communicated effectively, that is, by pictorials, symbols, inverted sentences, graphic emphasis?
6. Where should the warning be placed for the success-

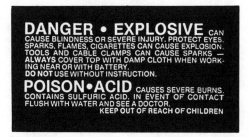

CAUTION: (1) WHEN USING JUMPER CABLES BETWEEN NEGATIVE GROUNDED BATTERIES, CONNECT ENDS OF ONE CABLE TO POSITIVE (+) TERMINAL OF EACH BATTERY. (2) CONNECT ONE END OF OTHER CABLE TO NEGATIVE (–) TERMINAL OF "GOOD" BATTERY. (3) CONNECT OTHER END OF CABLE TO ENGINE BLOCK ON VEHICLE BEING STARTED (NOT TO NEGATIVE (–) TERMINAL OF BATTERY). (4) REVERSE PROCEDURE WHEN DISCONNECTING. **NOTE:** IF EITHER OR BOTH BATTERIES ARE POSITIVE (+) GROUNDED, SEE VEHICLE OWNER'S MANUAL FOR INSTRUCTIONS OR SEEK SERVICE ASSISTANCE.

A

| (DANGER) Follow Instructions. Moving Fan Blade. | Keep hands and clothing clear of moving fan blade. Blades are exposed and can cause personal injury. | CAUTION Removing Fan Cover Exposes Moving Blades. | Do not remove this cover with engine running. Moving fan blade will be exposed which could cause personal injury. |

CAUTION-FAN

B

CAUTION: CONTAINS ASBESTOS FIBERS. AVOID CREATING DUST. BREATHING ASBESTOS DUST MAY CAUSE SERIOUS BODILY HARM.
When servicing this brake lining or any component related to it or located near it, prevent asbestos dust from becoming airborne by vacuuming the assembly with an industrial type vacuum cleaner equipped with a high efficiency filter system and by washing the assembly with an appropriate brake parts washer if necessary. Never remove dust or dirt from this assembly by blowing with compressed air.

C   **D**

Figure 20-1 Automotive warning labels: (A) Battery warning labels, (B) Fan warning labels, (C) Tire warning label, (D) Chemical warning label, and (E) Multi-language warning label for child restraint.

INFANT CARRIER

Always . . . Secure the Baby in the Infant Carrier with the Built-In Harness.

Place a shoulder strap over each shoulder, and adjust for a comfortable fit. Slide the retainer strap up near the chin.

To keep very small infants centered in the Infant Carrier, receiving blankets should be rolled up and placed on each side of the baby.

In the Car, the Infant Carrier Rides Backwards and Must Face the Seatback. The Infant Carrier Must be Secured with the Car Lap Belt.

Extend the car lap belt across the Infant Carrier and insert the belt through the slots to the retainer opening and buckle securely. If the lap belt is adjustable, extend it fully from any windup device and remove all slack.

If the car shoulder belt is permanently attached to the lap belt, tuck the shoulder belt between the Infant Carrier and seatback as shown.

CAUTION: Do not use this Infant Carrier with any lap-shoulder belt system which allows the webbing to slide freely thru the latch plate in both directions when the belt system is fastened unless a locking clip is used. Excessive slack in the Vehicle Restraint System could reduce the amount of protection because it would not be able to properly restrain the carrier and child in an accident.

- For babies up to 20 pounds.

- For use in 1968 and later passenger cars, vans and trucks that are equipped with lap belts.

- May be used with folding seatbacks only if latches are provided to hold the seatback upright.

- The seatback facing the Infant Carrier should be padded to its full height and free of any hard objects such as a radio speaker grille. The right front passenger seat is recommended. (Head restraint should be in down position.)

- Avoid using the center seat belt position if the seat has a built in centre arm rest or if the infant would be facing a gap between seats or seats are not in alignment.

- Remember, the Infant Carrier can get very hot if left in the sun.

- May be washed in mild soap and water or vinyl cleaner. Any raw edges that may be present can be easily removed with an emery board or sandpaper.

- If the baby would be more comfortable, the bottom of the carrier can be levelled by using a pillow or rolled up blanket, as shown. Do not put leveling devices inside the Infant Carrier.

Retainer Strap
Courroie de retenue

Shoulder Belt
Baudrier

Adjustment
Ajustement

Slot
Enoocha

Lap Belt
Ceinture sous abdominale

Car Seatback
Dossier du siege de voiture

Blanket Roll
Couverture roulée

Level
Niveau

PORTE BÉ BÉ

Attachez . . . toujours le bébé dans le porte-bébé avec la courroie incorporée.

Placez une bretelle par-dessus chaque épaule et l'ajuster de façon à ce qu'elle soit confortable. Glissez la courroie de retenue vers le haut à proximité du menton.

Afin de garder les très petits bébés centrés dans le porte-bébé, il faut rouler des couvertures et les placer de chaque côpé du bébé.

Dans la voiture le bébé fait face à l'arrière. Attachez le porte-bébé avec la ceinture abdominale de la voiture.

Passez la ceinture sous-abdominale de la voiture par-dessus le porte-bébé et insérez-la à travers les encoches à l'ouverture de retenue et bouclez fermement. Si la ceinture sous-abdominale est réglable, étendez-la entièrement à partir de n'importe quel dispositif d'enroulement et enlevez tout jeu possible.

Si le baudrier de la voiture est attaché d'une façon permanente à la ceinture sous-abdominale, rentrez la ceinture entre le porte-bébé et le dossier tel qu'indiqué.

MISE EN GARDE: Ne pas utiliser ce porte-bébé avec un système à ceinture-baudrier permettant aux sangles de glisser librement à travers la plaquette de verrouillage dans les deux sens quand le système de ceinture est attaché à moins d'utiliser une pince de blocage. Si le dispositif de protection a un jeu excessif ceci pourrait réduire l'effet de protection vu que dans un accident il ne pourrait pas retenir adéquatement le porte-bébé et l'enfant.

- Pour bébés pesant jusqu'à 20 livres.

- À utiliser dans les voitures de tourisme, fourgonnettes et camions 1968 et plus récents qui sont équipés de ceintures sous-abdominales.

- S'utilise avec dossiers rabattables seulement si des loquets sont fournis pour tenir le dossier droit.

- Le dossier faisant face au porte-bébé doit être rembourré jusqu'à sa pleine hauteur et être dénué de tout objet qui une grille de haut-parleur de radio. On recommande le siège du passager avant droit. (L'appuiête doit se trouver dans la position abaissée.)

- Éviter d'utiliser la place de la ceinture de sécurité centrale si le siège a un appui-brasincorporé ou si le bébé fait face à un vide entre les sièges ou si les sièges ne sont pas alignés.

- N'oubliez pas que porte-bebe devient tres chaud si on le laisse au soleil.

- Se lave avec du savon doux et de l'eau ou du nettoyant pour vinyle. On peut éliminer facilement avec une lime émerit ou un papier sablé tout bord irrégulier.

- Pour donner plus de confort au bébé on peut niveler le bas du siège avec un coussin ou une couverture roulée tel que montré. Pour niveler le bas du siège, ne rien ajouter à l'intérieur du porte-bébé.

Date

E

Figure 20-1 (*Continued*)

ful promotion of safe behaviors or the avoidance of unsafe behaviors? When in the process of using the product will the warning serve its purposes most effectively? How can interferences with the warning message be removed?

7. Do the elements of the warning—layout, color, size, attention-gaining properties, etc.—serve the purpose?

8. What are the results of reliable testing with representative groups of potential users and purchasers? Will the warning serve the needs of those handicapped by language differences, educational level, activity overload or distraction, permanent or temporary condition?

9. Have the results of testing been used to reasonably improve the warning?

10. Does the warning meet the approval criteria of management, government, and industry? Is additional standardization required?

Ultimately, the success of the warning design process is judged by warning adequacy as part of the safeguarding system, that is, if risk/benefit assessments indicate an effective reduction in personal injury.

VII. AUTOMOTIVE WARNING TESTING AND EVALUATION

The effectiveness of an automotive warning (whether in written, visual, auditory, or other form) or instructions for safe use should be systematically evaluated before being put into place for general use. Dorris and Purswell[11] note that formal evaluations of warnings either are not conducted or are kept proprietary to the disadvantage of both researchers and those who could benefit from effective warnings.

The evaluation process, which includes formal testing, should be part of product design and development beginning with the identification of potential hazards and risks in the foreseeable use and misuse environment. Once these are identified, alternate designs for specific hazard-alerting purposes can be generated and initially screened or checked for adequacy against legal, governmental, organizational, and professional criteria. The target population can also be identified in detail as to age, educational level, gender, physical health, handicaps and related descriptors. Behavioral goals should be determined as to desirable responses in the hazardous conditions or changing set of circumstances such as observable avoidance reactions, reported awareness, recorded intent to alter habituated usage, or influence others, such as children.

Before formal testing procedures are drawn up, consideration should be given to professional, ethical, and legal principles for the conduct of research with human participants such as those published by the American Psychological Association.[12] The APA ethical principles, for example, call for initial judgments of the best ways to satisfy scientific and human welfare goals, including the weighing of scientific and humane values; acceptable ethical practice and treatment of research participants by those conducting research; making full disclosure of elements of the research that might influence willingness to participate, openness, and honesty; respecting individual freedom of choice in participating; the clarification of the roles of the investigator and participant; confidentiality of information (especially as to individual identities); and protection from physical and mental discomfort, harm, and danger.

In the study of warnings it is often not possible to put participants in the identical dangerous or hazardous situation where a "realistic assessment" or where actual behaviors in response to situational warnings can be made. For humane and ethical reasons, studies should be drawn to make study simulations as close to the defined situation as possible. Relatively high-fidelity studies can give good assessments without violating humane considerations.

In implementing warning study goals, good experimental design should be used in drafting questions to be answered by the study, in defining and selecting the study population so results can have practical applicability, in conducting actual study sessions or getting questionnaire or interview responses, and in the analysis and reporting of the findings.

The effectiveness of warnings can be determined by appropriate testing.[13] The results of reliable testing can be used to increase warning effectiveness and to meet, in behavioral terms, the assertion of 402 A Restatement of Torts, section j, that "where warning is given, the seller may reasonably assume that it will be read and heeded."[14] Clearly, if adequate automotive warnings and instructions are to serve their function effectively in system safety, considerably more information than is presently available will have to be provided by valid, reliable, and regular testing and evaluation.

VIII. THE DUTY TO WARN IN LITIGATION

Illustrative cases involving the duty to warn are *Gherna* v. *Ford Motor Co.*, 246 Cal. App. 2d 639, at page 651 (55 Cal. Rptr 94); *Comstock* v. *General Motors Corp.*, 358 Mich 163, 99 NW 2d 627, 78 ALR 2d 449 (1959); *Hiigel* v. *General Motors Corp.*, 544 P.2d 983 (Colo, 1975); *Barth* v. *B.F. Goodrich Tire Co.*, 265 Cal. App. 2d 228, 71 Cal Rptr 306 (1968); and *Technical Chemical* v. *Jacobs*, 480 SW 2d 602 (Texas, 1972). These cases are noted to illustrate issues concerning the special communications that warnings and instructions represent and evolving concepts of the adequacy of warnings.

CITATIONS

[1] U.S. Congress, Committee reports of the U.S. House of Representatives and the U.S. Senate: *Senate Report S 3005* (June 23, 1966) and *House of Representatives Report HR 13228* (July 28, 1966) for *U.S. National Traffic and Motor Vehicle Safety Act, 1966.*

[2] R. Cunitz, "Psychologically Effective Warnings." *Hazard Prevention*, May/June 1981, pp. 5-7.

[3] *SAE Handbook 1982.* Warrendale, PA.: Society of Automotive Engineers, 1982.

[4] H. Philo, "New Dimensions in the Tortious Failure to Warn." *Trial*, November 1981, pp. 40-45.

[5] S. Lichtenstein, P. Slovic, B. Fischoff et al., *Perceived Frequency of Low Probability, Lethal Events.* Report 76-2. Eugene, OR.: Decision Research. (Decision Research is a branch of Perceptronics.)

[6] *Symbol Study—1972.* Geneva, Switz.: International Organization for Standardization, Technical Committee 22, Subcommittee 13, Working Group 5, June 1973, p. 17.

[7] W. Woodson, *Human Factors Design Handbook: Information and Guidelines for the Design of Systems, Facilities, Equipment and Products for Human Use.* New York: McGraw-Hill, 1981, pp. 520-523, 559-560.

[8] R. McFarland, "Psychological and Behavioral Aspects of Automobile Accidents." *Traffic Safety Research Review*, September 1968, pp. 71-79.

[9] *John Deere Design Data Manual*, No. 4, 1970 revision. Moline, IL.: John Deere Company, October 1970.

[10] *Product Safety Sign and Label System.* Santa Clara, CA.: FMC Corporation, 1980.

[11] A. L. Dorris and J. L. Purswell, "Human Factors in the Design of Effective Product Warnings." *Proceedings of the Human Factors Society, 22nd Annual Meeting*, Detroit. Santa Monica, CA.: Human Factors Society, 1978, pp. 343-346.

[12]*Ethical Principles in the Conduct of Research with Human Participants.* Washington, D.C.: American Psychological Association, 1973.

[13]*Market Facts: Evaluation of the Impact of the Communications Antenna Labeling Rule.* Report No. CPSC-C-79-116J. Final report to the Consumer Products Safety Commission. Washington, D.C.: U.S. Government Printing Office, November 21, 1980.

[14]Restatement (Second) of Torts, 402 A, 1965, pp. 347–358.

21

Product Recall and Recall Prevention

JOHN J. WARGO
Manager, Reliability and Quality Assurance
The Jacobs Manufacturing Company
Bloomfield, Connecticut

John J. Wargo, who received a B.A. in Statistics from Rutgers University, is a Certified Quality Engineer. He has more than 30 years experience in Quality Assurance and Reliability Management with General Motors, U.S. Gauge Division of AMETEK, Colt Firearms, and The Jacobs Manufacturing Company. His professional memberships include the American Society for Quality Control (ASQC) and the Systems Safety Society. He performed a co-editorial review of the ASQC Product Recall Planning Guide *and has delivered numerous papers on product quality, product recall, and product liability prevention. The author may be reached at 57 Woodhaven Road, Glastonbury, Connecticut 06033 (203-243-7644).*

I. INTRODUCTION

This section briefly considers some of the automotive history in the United States leading to federal legislation to regulate manufacture to minimum standards. Also, discussed are the steps leading to a product recall, the action that must be taken to assure that product is returned or corrected, and a preventive program to minimize exposure to product liability and recall.

II. HISTORICAL PERSPECTIVE OF AUTOMOTIVE RECALL

The automotive industry in the United States historically was one of change and improvement both functionally and cosmetically, as is evidenced by the yearly model changes that predominated the industry's competitive growth. Through a combination of improved highway conditions, more vehicles capable of greater speed, plus a dramatic increase in the number of drivers and miles traveled per year, the number of highway fatalities escalated at an alarming yearly rate. Although many concerned groups, through training programs, voluntary standards, etc., had succeeded in reducing the number of fatalities per 100 million miles of travel from 40 early in the century to 5.7 in 1966,[1] the total fatalities exceeded 49,000 in 1965. Many of the fatalities were not vehicle caused, as in drunken driving fatalities, but public concern, aroused by Ralph Nader in 1965, became directed at the automobile.

This public concern led to the enactment of legislation, in 1966, of two Congressional acts regarding motor vehicle safety: the Highway Safety Act and the National Traffic and Motor Vehicle Safety Act (NTMVSA). The purpose was "to provide for a coordinated safety program and establishment of safety standards for motor vehicles in interstate commerce to reduce deaths and injuries occurring in such accidents."[3] The National Highway Traffic and Safety Administration (NHTSA), established in 1970, is the federal agency responsible for reducing the number of accidents and with the assistance of the National Motor Vehicle Advisory Council is empowered to recommend motor vehicle safety standards. By December 31, 1974, NHTSA had promulgated 58 motor vehicle safety standards, 52 of which were in effect. As of May

1983, there are 201 NHTSA motor vehicle safety standards in effect, plus 26 additional standards relating to motor vehicle parts.

In addition, the NTMVSA gave the Secretary of Transportation the power to enforce compliance to the specifications as written. This act and the safety provisions contained therein provide the basis for and the requirement to correct or recall an automotive product that fails to meet the safety provisions as outlined.

In the period from 1966 to 1973 the number of fatalities per 100 million miles traveled continued downward to 4.3 in 1973. Although 56,000 Americans died in traffic crashes in 1973,[2] had the 1966 rate of 5.7 continued, 72,000 citizens would have perished on the highways that year. In other words, 16,000 lives were saved in one year. Both public arousal and the federal legislation have been successful in their effort to save lives.

In more recent history, the rate of fatalities per 100 million miles traveled has maintained a downward trend as the number of vehicles and vehicle miles traveled has increased steadily (Table 21-1). Again, using the 1966 rate of 5.7 as a base, 252,144 additional citizens would have perished in the 7 years from 1975 to 1981 had not some action been taken. It can be argued that the federal legislation was not the sole reason for the reduction in fatalities, but it did bring about a public awareness that resulted in action on several fronts.

III. LEGAL REQUIREMENTS IN RECALL

The National Traffic and Motor Vehicle Safety Act (NTMVSA)[3] provided the legal basis as well as the enforcement to recall items not in compliance with minimum safety standards. This act, although a major contributor to enforced product recall, was not alone in requiring automotive products to be recalled. The Magnuson–Moss Warranty Act, the Environmental Protection Agency (EPA), the Uniform Commercial Code, the Society of Automotive Engineers (SAE), and the American National Standards Institute (ANSI), to name a few, can cause, directly or indirectly, a product recall if minimum standards are not met, particularly when safety is involved.

The discussion that follows is a very brief highlight of recall-related portions of the NTMVSA.

Table 21-1 Motor Vehicle Fatality Rate in the United States (1975–1981)

YEAR	NUMBER OF MOTOR VEHICLE FATALITIES	ESTIMATED NUMBER OF VEHICLE MILES TRAVELED (100 MILLION MILES)	NUMBER OF FATALITIES PER 100 MILLION MILES TRAVELED	NUMBER OF REGISTERED MOTOR VEHICLES (AUTO–TRUCK–BUS)
1975	44,525	13,276.64	3.53	132,948,709
1976	45,523	14,023.80	3.35	138,542,904
1977	45,878	14,670.27	3.25	142,092,568
1978	50,331	15,447.04	3.26	148,414,612
1979	51,093	15,291.33	3.34	151,869,299
1980	51,091	15,278.78	3.34	155,796,219
1981	49,301	15,502.71	3.18	158,456,511

A. National Traffic and Motor Vehicle Safety Act of 1966

A.1. AUTHORITY The act granted the authority to the Department of Transportation, through the National Highway Traffic Safety Administration (NHTSA), to enact federal motor vehicle safety standards (FMVSS). These standards apply not only to motor vehicles, but also to motor vehicle equipment including replacement parts.

The authority granted to enforce the NTMVSA is explicitly detailed in Section 112 (a):

(1) The Secretary is authorized to conduct any inspection or investigation—

    (A) which may be necessary to enforce this title or any rules, regulations or orders issued thereunder, or

    (B) which relates to the facts, circumstances, conditions, and causes of any motor vehicle accident and which is for the purposes of carrying out his functions under this Act.

(2) For purposes of carrying out paragraph (1), officers or employees duly designated by the Secretary, upon presenting appropriate credentials and written notice to the owner, operator, or agent in charge, are authorized at reasonable times and in a reasonable manner—

    (A) to enter (i) any factory, warehouse, or establishment in which motor vehicles or items of motor vehicle equipment are manufactured, or held for introduction into interstate commerce or are held for sale after such introduction, or (ii) any premises where a motor vehicle or item of motor vehicle equipment involved in a motor vehicle accident is located;

    (B) to impound for a period not to exceed 72 hours, any motor vehicle or item of motor vehicle equipment involved in a motor vehicle accident, and

    (C) to inspect any factory, warehouse, establishment, vehicle, or equipment referred to in subparagraph (A) or (B).

        (1) For the purposes of carrying out the provisions of this title, the Secretary, or on the authorization of the Secretary, any officer or employee of the Department of Transportation may hold such hearings, take such testimony, sit and act at such times and places, administer such

oaths, and require, by subpoena or otherwise, the attendance and testimony of such witnesses and the production of such books, papers, correspondence, memorandums, contracts, agreements, or other records as the Secretary, or such officer or employee, deems advisable.

(2) In order to carry out the provisions of this title, the Secretary or his duly authorized agent shall at all reasonable times have access to, and for the purpose of examination the right to copy, any documentary evidence or any person having materials or information relevant to any function of the Secretary under his title.[3]

A.2. DISCOVERY, NOTIFICATION, AND REMEDY OF MOTOR VEHICLE DEFECTS Section 151 of the NTMVSA characterizes the discovery of motor vehicle defects and stipulates the procedure for subsequent notification and remedy:

Section 151. If a manufacturer—

(1) obtains knowledge that any motor vehicle or item or replacement equipment manufactured by him contains a defect and determines in good faith that such defect relates to safety; or

(2) determines in good faith that such vehicle or item of replacement equipment does not comply with an applicable Federal Motor Vehicle Safety Standard prescribed pursuant to Section 103 of this Act; he shall furnish notification to the Secretary and to owners, purchasers, and dealers, in accordance with Section 153, and he shall remedy the defect or failure to comply in accordance with Section 154.[3]

A.3. THE TYPE AND CONTENTS OF NOTIFICATION In Section 153 the type of notification to be made is specified as follows:

a) The notification required by Section 151 or 152 respecting a defect in or failure to comply of a motor vehicle or item of replacement equipment shall contain in addition to such other matters as the Secretary may prescribe by regulation—

(1) a clear description of such defect or failure to comply;

(2) an evaluation of the risk to motor vehicle safety reasonably related to such defect or failure to comply;

(3) a statement of the measures to be taken to obtain remedy of such defect or failure to comply;

(4) a statement that the manufacturer furnishing the notification will cause such defect or failure to comply to be

(5) the earliest date (specified in accordance with the second and third sentences of section 154 (b) (2) on which such defect or failure to comply will be remedied without charge and, in the case of tires, the period during which such defect or failure to comply will be remedied without charge pursuant to Section 154; and

(6) a description of the procedure to be followed by the recipient of the notification in informing the Secretary whenever a manufacturer, distributor, or dealer fails or is unable to remedy without charge such defect or failure to comply.

b) The notification required by Section 152 or 152 shall be furnished—

(1) within a reasonable time after the manufacturer first makes a determination with respect to a defect or failure to comply under section 151; or

(2) within a reasonable time (prescribed by the Secretary) after the manufacturer's receipt of notice of the Secretary's determination pursuant to Section 152 that there is a defect or failure to comply.

c) The notification required by Section 151 or 152 with respect to a motor vehicle or time of replacement equipment shall be accomplished—

(1) in the case of a motor vehicle, by first class mail to each person who is registered under State Law as the owner of such vehicle and whose name and address is reasonably ascertainable by the manufacturer through State records or other sources available to him;[3]

In addition to the main body of the NTMVSA, many parts provide details pertaining to particular aspects such as Certification of Inspection Standards, Vehicle Manufactured in

Two or More Stages, Manufacturers Identification, and Defect Reports and Record Retention.

B. The Environmental Protection Agency

The EPA has the authority to order the recall of automobiles for environmental reasons. Each year the EPA issues minimum standards for automobiles on four types of pollutants: hydrocarbons, carbon monoxide, oxides of nitrogen, and particulate matter.

The EPA began to exercise its recall authority in 1972. In 1976 the EPA asked Chrysler to recall 208,000 cars for maintenance problems producing excessive air pollution.[4] From 1972 through 1983 nineteen million vehicles were recalled for environmental reasons, including voluntary recalls by the manufacturer.

C. The Magnuson–Moss Warranty Act

The Magnuson–Moss Warranty Act (1975), like the NTMVSA, was written in response to consumers' perceived treatment by manufacturers. At the time, Senator Warren G. Magnuson stated:

> [T]hat there are problems with guaranties, warranties, and product servicing seems to be beyond question. For the Commerce Committee, like many individual members of Congress, receives a steady flow of mail complaining:
>
> 1. That recently purchased product is defective and won't be repaired or replaced by the manufacturer.
> 2. That certain defects or failures in a product have not been repaired, despite frequent visits to the repair shop.
> 3. That the prices charged for minor repairs are exorbitant.
> 4. That significant parts of a product's mechanism were not covered by the guaranty, but this was not clear at the time of sale.
> 5. That disputes with the manufacturer as to the coverage of the guaranty and the allocation of costs under it always seem to be resolved in favor of the manufacturer.[5]

The act explicitly includes coverage of motor vehicles and motor vehicle parts. In the case of automotive parts sold to consumers, a manufacturer may not disclaim responsibility for personal injury caused by a defective product. Hence, the relationship to product recall and the NTMVSA.

D. Other Standards

In the case of consensus standards developed by professional groups, such as the American National Standards Institute (ANSI) and the Society of Automotive Engineers (SAE), or other standards that might be commonly accepted by industry, they may be used to determine the defectiveness of a product. Failure to meet these standards would make a finding of defectiveness quite likely. And, as this "defectiveness" related to personal injury, the NTMVSA rules would apply.

IV. ACTION TO BE TAKEN IN A RECALL

In the provisions of the NTMVSA, note that the law pertains to *any* safety-related deficiency that develops in a vehicle. It applies regardless of whether or not the deficiency entailed a violation of a safety standard. The sole criterion is that the deficiency constitutes a *safety hazard.*

It is interesting to note that safety-related defects can be grouped into two categories: design and inadequate quality control. *Quality-control-related defects have been responsible for twice the number of recall campaigns; however, design defects have caused the recall of twice the number of vehicles.*

The discussion in our Subsection III contains excerpts from the NTMVSA that must be observed in an automotive recall. The discussion that follows reemphasizes and elaborates on these provisions, and details how a company should effectively respond to a recall of one of its products to meet the provisions of the NTMVSA.

A. Establish Cause

The discovery, allegation, or example of a safety-related defect may come from any of a number of sources. The largest number generally come from the manufacturer's organization, but the NHTSA and its information sources or users themselves may be the source. Regardless, the facts must be substantiated as quickly as possible to determine if, in fact, the product is at fault and, if so, what component or assembly is responsible. Once the determination has been made that a recall is necessary, the next step is clear.

B. Notification

The law is very specific as to who should be notified once a determination is made that a product has a safety-related defect. "The Secretary, owners, purchasers and dealers" must be notified within a reasonable time after the manufacturer first makes a determination. In the case of motor vehicles, notification must be made by first-class mail to each person who is registered, under state law, as the owner of such vehicle.

The notification to the customer must be very clear, stating the reason for the recall and the method by which repair or replacement will be accomplished. Also, included should be the person or agency that the customer must contact to accomplish the correction.

C. Remedy of Defect

The NTMVSA requires that defects that relate to motor vehicle safety must be remedied without charge by repairing, replacing, or refunding the purchase price. If it has been determined that a defect can be repaired, the manufacturer must outline a precise method to accomplish the correction to ensure that it be done properly. Also, training may be required for field personnel if the repairs are to be done at dealers, distributors, or on site. If a part is to be replaced with a new or modified part, the manufacturer must determine if replacement parts are in stock and must schedule production of replacement parts should insufficient numbers be available.

D. Initial Actions

The manufacturer's first consideration is to evaluate the company's financial exposure and, subsequently, to obtain and/or allocate funds as necessary to carry out the details of the recall. A determination of per vehicle costs should be made, including notification, transportation, repair or replacement, and labor costs, and the magnitude of the recall should be estimated both in numbers and in geographic location. Utilizing its records, the manufacturer should then trace the defect type to the smallest product group that was affected exclusively—as distinguished by serial number, model, or engineering change, for example—in an effort to restrict recall to only those items affected. Lacking good product traceability, a company may be forced to recall many more times the number of products than necessary in order to find all of those that are defective.

E. Subsequent Actions

Once the company's financial exposure is appraised, funds are allocated, and the recall is in progress, a system is needed to determine:

1. How many responded to the notification.
2. How many of those responding actually were defective.
3. What were the actual costs.
4. How recall results can be routed to a central information source.
5. What should be done in cases where no response is obtained.
6. By audit how effective rework has been after recall is accomplished.

V. PREVENTION

The obvious response to "How do you prevent recall of product?" is "Do not make defective product!" This may seem to be a glib response; however, much can be done to prevent defective products through *quality control systems, a product safety committee*, and *design safety reviews*.

A. Quality Control Systems

The basic reason for quality control systems is to assure that product conforms to specification. The quality controls begin with design reviews and include controls of purchased material, in-process manufacture controls, and field-performance evaluations.[6] Product liability prevention and product quality are often considered synonymous in manufacturing since having good product quality is related to good product performance and customer satisfaction. The design-to-user control concept is known as a *total quality control system*.[7]

There are numerous texts and articles that describe good quality systems. Here we shall only list the control areas described in the *American National Standard Generic Guidelines for Quality Systems*, ANSI Z-1.15, 1979:

1. Design Assurance and Design Change Control
2. Control of Purchased Material
3. Production Quality Control
4. User Contact and Field Performance

B. Product Safety Program

In a product safety program the key to success in product liability prevention appears to be a responsible and knowledgeable management coupled with precise definitions of safety objectives, effective record and control systems, and continued checks and balances to minimize risks.[8]

B.1. POLICY Initially, management should have a statement of policy on how to protect the company from product liability losses.[9] This policy should state the company's objectives that concern minimizing potential product hazards. The marketing, engineering, quality assurance, manufacturing, purchasing, and field service departments should be completely versed with this policy and their role in product liability prevention.

B.2. RESPONSIBILITY The responsibility for product safety may be assigned to an individual, to quality assurance, to a product safety committee, or to some other area. But there should be no doubt within an organization where the authority for product safety rests.

B.3. PRODUCT SAFETY COMMITTEE A product safety committee in many companies is responsible for prevention and recall planning. At the minimum, this committee will have personnel from quality assurance, product engineering, marketing, and field service in its membership, with the chairmanship often resting with the department of quality assurance.

To ensure that proper precautions have been taken and that corrective measures are taken when needed, a plant product safety committee is charged with the review of all of the safety aspects of the company's product, including such things as published product-related company literature, warranty statements, new product design reviews, user's instructions, warning labels, accident reports, and customer complaints. The scope of the committee's actions varies from company to company depending on the company's size and structure.

George A. Peters describes one company's effort in product safety by using the following seven elements:

1. Programmatic—Identify the legal requirements for safety and set objectives.
2. Feedback—Establish a means to learn from experience.
3. Emphasis—Early identification of all probable hazards.
4. Analysis, Risk Assessment—Brief analysis of facts relating to frequency and severity of accidents.
5. Scope—Cradle to grave concept.
6. Testing—Demonstrate the absence of risk.
7. Record Keeping—Keep records to prove safety analyses and testing were in fact performed, provide for traceability, maintain lists of standards that apply, etc.[10]

B.4. RECALL PLANNING Obviously a company without a recall plan would experience difficulty in responding to the many requirements of a mandatory recall. In 1981 the American Society for Quality Control published a recall planning guide in which the following objectives in planning are offered as a minimum:

1. Specifically identify the product(s) involved at the time when a problem might be discovered.
2. Trace shipments to obtain access.
3. Stop manufacture and further distribution.
4. Isolate and make disposition of suspect product(s).
5. Be prepared with a plan of how a specific product would be recalled prior to the need to recall a product.
6. Identify who will do what within an organized response to a recall event.
7. Adjust the product development/manufacturing system to preclude a recurrence of the problem, within acceptable economic and technical limitations.[11]

B.5. DESIGN SAFETY REVIEWS One of the most important preventive measures that a manufacturer can take is to have a design safety review, since such a review properly takes place before production quantities are produced. Safety reviews should begin at the concept stage and conclude with a final safety analysis before a product is released for production.

Many analytical methods have been developed to choose from, accommodating a great range of products. One design-safety checklist specifies eleven methods:

1. Gross-Hazard Analysis
2. Classification of Hazards
3. Failure Modes and Effects
4. Hazard-Criticality Ranking
5. Fault-tree Analysis
6. Energy-Transfer Analysis
7. Catastrophe Analysis
8. System/Subsystem Integration
9. Maintenance-Hazard Analysis
10. Human-Error Analysis
11. Transportation-Hazard Analysis[5]

In addition to product safety committee members, design reviews are attended by representatives from all major functions, each with specific objectives in analyzing the design to arrive at a safe, producible, cost-effective product.[11] A chart of product safety responsibilities,[12] prepared by the product safety committee, is helpful in explaining to all concerned the departments to which specific responsibilities apply.

VI. SUMMARY

Product recall can be minimized by carefully planned preventive and control programs that require active support by company management. If it is necessary to have a recall, an advance plan will reduce company financial outlays and provide rapid response to the problem.

Our laws, by their very nature, are a response to society's needs. Therefore, it is incumbent on those whose positions are related to product safety and liability prevention to make themselves aware of the latest changes in the law as well as the latest preventive technology.

CITATIONS

[1]J. M. Juran, "Auto Safety Legislation . . . A Decade Later." *Quality*, Vol. 16, No. 10, pp. 26–31, October 1977.
[2]A. G. Detrick, "The Government's Role in Automotive Quality."

SAE paper 750031. Warrendale, PA.: Society of Automotive Engineers, 1975.

[3]*National Traffic and Motor Vehicle Safety Act of 1966* (Title 15, United States Code, Sections 1391–1431).

[4]"Detroit Stunned by Recall Blitz." *New York Times*, March 12, 1978.

[5]"Special Report—Products Liability." *Machine Design*, pp. 18–44, March 28, 1968.

[6]J. J. Wargo, "Product Liability Prevention in Manufacturing." *10th Annual Product Liability Prevention Conference Proceedings*, New York, 1979.

[7]A. V. Feigenbaum, *Total Quality Control*. New York: McGraw-Hill, 1961.

[8]H. D. Rue, "Who Is Responsible for Defective Product?" *PLP–77 W Proceedings*, Palo Alto, CA., March 16–18, 1977. Newark: New Jersey Institute of Technology, 1977.

[9]L. C. Walsh, *Dartnell's Product Liability Manual*. Chicago: The Dartnell Corporation, 1979. (Includes a good example of a statement of policy as concerns company objectives to minimize potential product hazards.)

[10]G. A. Peters, "What to Do About Product Liability." *Hazard Prevention*, Vol. 16, No. 12, pp. 27–29, November/December 1980.

[11]*Product Recall Planning Guide*. Milwaukee: American Society for Quality Control, 1981.

[12]R. M. Jacobs, P.E., "The Technique of Design Review." *PLP Proceedings*. Newark: New Jersey Institute of Technology, 1979.

[13]Chart of Product Safety Responsibilities, *Product Liability Portfolio*. New York: Man & Manager, Inc., 1975. (A good example of a chart of product safety responsibilities.)

22

System Safety Engineering

REX B. GORDON, P.E., C.S.P.
Safety Consultant
Irvine, California

Rex B. Gordon earned an M.P.H. at the University of California, Berkeley, specializing in Chemistry and Environmental Health Engineering. For over 20 years he has been a leader in the formulation and expansion of the System Safety Concept. During this period he has held responsible positions with several major corporations in system safety engineering, lectured at various universities, and published numerous technical papers on the applications of system safety technology. He is actively affiliated with the System Safety Society as a Fellow, the American Society of Safety Engineers, the Product Safety Management Academy, and the American Management Association. He has served as President of the System Safety Society, as General Chairman of the 2nd International System Safety Conference, and a Director of the Board of Certified Safety Professionals. At present he performs consulting in system and product safety, with offices at 17981 Butler Street, Irvine, California 92715 (714-760-2789).

I. INTRODUCTION

The professional practice of safety engineering and management encompasses three primary elements:

1. Reduction of the extent of personal injury and property damage *subsequent* to the occurrence of an accidental mishap. This is exemplified by such provisions as emergency medical response teams, fire alarms, automatic fire suppression devices, and seat belts.
2. Reduction of those factors that are felt to cause or to contribute to the *increased likelihood* of accidental mishaps. For example, guarding of nip points on machines, local exhaust ventilation where toxic fumes or dusts are generated, driver education and licensing.
3. Reduction in the *vulnerability* of an entity capable of being held liable for injury, suffering, or loss resulting from an accidental mishap. This element includes such factors as hazard risk analysis, intrinsic safety in design, carefully worded operating instructions, and so forth.

While it is generally accepted that the responsibility for implementing the first and second elements defined above are traditionally delegated by upper management to specific functional activities within an organization (often designated as the "safety engineering" or "loss control" unit), there is considerably less agreement within the management community on how the third of these elements should best be implemented. This uncertainty results from a combination of factors. The relatively recent emergence, rapid expansion, and changing nature of the product liability situation has brought new dimensions to the field of risk management. Traditional organization and functional responsibility patterns cannot respond to the product liability prevention challenge in an optimum manner.

The diverse nature of this third element of professional safety engineering and management expands beyond the scope of traditional functional organizational entities and professional disciplines. Therefore, no single professional group has been successful, or even highly motivated, to claim exclusive responsibility for the product liability prevention function within a corporation, business, or governmental activity.

The established safety engineering activities were not always anxious to venture too deep into the unfamiliar territory of product liability prevention. Successful practice in this field requires knowledge, tools, and interfunctional relationships that are not required for the more traditional aspects of loss control; therefore, they are not well understood.

Within most commercial and product-oriented businesses, product liability matters in the past were most often relegated to the legal and insurance areas—"risk management" activities. Engineering, manufacturing, and quality control managers were often asked to provide inputs during litigation procedures to bolster the company's defense against a claimant. In general, such defense tactics were more reactive than preventive in nature.

In contrast with the commercial business trends in this area, the aerospace industry, beginning in the early 1960s, was responding to a new set of contractual requirements being imposed by the U.S. Air Force (and later by the other services and NASA). These were related to a new field of endeavor referred to as *system safety engineering*. The basic purpose of this functional activity was to evaluate within a given project all the various technical aspects pertaining to the potential of foreseeable accidents and to organize this information in a manner allowing higher management to make enlightened decisions that could help minimize future accidents.

The primary motivation on the part of the Department of Defense (DOD) and NASA in implementing system safety activities was that of protection against schedule slippage, cost overruns, and unfavorable publicity, which often resulted from dramatic aerospace accidents. However, a direct spin-off of this aerospace technology can be readily adapted to the field of product liability prevention within any type of commercial venture, including the automotive industry.

It is the intent of this section to highlight some of the more pertinent aspects of the theory and practice of system safety engineering as they relate to product liability prevention. This discussion will also attempt to provide guidance for managerial action by optimizing the organizational responsibilities inherent with implementing the third element of the professional practice of safety engineering—i.e., reducing vulnerability to product liability judgments.

II. THE SYSTEM SAFETY CONCEPT

The genesis of the *system safety concept* was the need envisioned by Air Force project management for gaining a grasp over the extremely complex and hazardous interfaces between the numerous subsystems and elements that comprised the Minuteman Missile System. The U.S. Air Force had learned by costly experience in earlier missile programs that optimum design safety did not automatically come along with the missile subsystems and launch pad facilities. The high cost and single-flight nature of these systems precluded the more familiar fly-fix-fly approach used in aircraft development to find and resolve technical subsystem interface deficiencies.

Since the Air Force provided direct project management control over all Minuteman contractors, formal requirements were written into these contracts requiring that system safety analysis documentation be prepared and submitted for Air Force review and appropriate action. Over the years, since this initial action in the early 1960s, both the specific analytical techniques and the method of managing system safety programs on complex weapon and space programs have been continually upgraded. A new subdiscipline of the safety engineering community called system safety engineering has been developed, and a military standard covering system safety programs established. A professional, nonprofit organization, the System Safety Society, was formed by these specialists for the promotion of the system safety concept.

In its most basic form, the concept postulates an organized effort having the specific objective of minimizing unnecessary risks of accidental mishaps within a defined system, product, or activity by means of:

- Early evaluation of identifiable hazards.
- Incorporation of cost-effective hazard control features during design and operational planning.
- Testing for hazardous characteristics and effectiveness of hazard control provisions.
- Continued surveillance of hazard risks aspects throughout the total life span of the system, product, or activity, including ultimate disposal aspects of any hazardous materials.

In order for the system safety concept to be effectively implemented, at least three critical conditions must coexist within an organization. There must be a top management awareness of and commitment to expending resources for a system-safety-type effort at the very beginning phases of a new endeavor, with the commitment continuing through to its conclusion. This management commitment must be manifested by formal policy statements, appropriate delegation of authority, and specified checkpoints that must be satisfied from a system safety viewpoint prior to the initiation of subsequent key events such as design release, production start, new product marketing, or a hazardous operation. Concurrent with this top management commitment and the implementing of policy directives, there must be present within the organization the technical capability to implement the required, detailed hazard risk analysis, corrective action evaluation, and hazardous-characteristic testing. The third condition that must be satisfied relates to the organizational structure and assignment of functional responsibilities.

It is not difficult to recognize the critical need for incorporating, within an organizational structure, those features that would encourage the flow of product liability prevention information up to top management for evaluation and appropriate action. It is from top management perspective that these decisions can be based on the best interest of the overall organization. Unfortunately, due to lack of foresight, the system safety or product liability prevention activity, once established, is often assigned to a middle-management function. Because of inherent provincial interests, this often restricts the scope of coverage and flow of information upward since findings may often seem critical of that particular function's efforts.

III. ORGANIZATIONAL CONSIDERATIONS

In attempting to define optimum organizational structures and functional responsibilities for system safety activities within a company, the concept of risk management must be explored to provide a conceptual background. Texts on the subject often refer to two basic types of risk about which the executive officers of a business must be concerned:

1. *Speculative Risk.* This type of risk deals with risks related to obtaining a profit from a venture or product line. Expending funds for new product development, product quality, facilities, and advertising are examples of speculative risk expenditures.
2. *Pure Risk.* These are risks that are inherent in operating a company. They include such risk factors as a fire in the manufacturing plant, on-the-job injuries to employees, and product liability lawsuits. Pure risks are normally covered by insurance policies.

Most companies are organized so that a high percentage of management resources are expended to minimize the speculative risk aspects. Comprehensive marketing studies are usually prepared and analyzed prior to introduction of a new product; quality checks and customer service people attempt to promote buyer satisfaction; and engineering studies to reduce manufacturing costs are continually being performed.

On the other hand, pure risk factors often receive a somewhat condescending management attention, and usually only when a problem related to pure risk has surfaced. Traditional risk management theory tends to emphasize the importance and methodology of obtaining cost-effective insurance coverage for the various common pure risk hazards. Pure risk reduction activities are generally given limited resources. They typically are limited to industrial health and safety programs, which may incorporate workers compensation, fire prevention, and industrial hygiene—but probably not product safety engineering. The typical industrial safety engineering efforts have responsibility for postaccident emergency response and enforcement of health and safety standards. They generally report to a personnel services, industrial relations, or corporate medical manager. Individuals performing these typical safety engineering functions are not normally equipped by training, experience, or organizational placement to become effective in the pure risk area of product liability prevention, even though they may be highly motivated to do so.

In consideration of the generally higher potential for losses associated with product liability cases than with workers compensation cases, OSHA violation fines, and many other pure risk factors, it is surprising that formalized product liability prevention functions have not become more established within management theory and practice than they appear to have to date. Perhaps those most commonly relied on by top management for advice in the product liability prevention area—the staff of the corporate legal office—are not always motivated so much toward precluding litigation as top management might expect. After all, the legal office's worth to the company is based to a large extent on the number of lawsuits being handled. An aggressive product liability prevention program implementing the system safety concept approach could conceivably reduce the number and severity of product liability lawsuits or claims.

Since neither the lawyers, industrial relations/safety managers, insurance/risk managers, or management theory professors appear to be ready to champion the case for system safety concept application in commercial companies as a product liability prevention technique, the role of the product safety specialist within an unenlightened company management structure can be somewhat frustrating at times. A number of system safety experts, having moved away from the aerospace industry environment where they have been learning and practicing system safety engineering and management, have been promoting the application of the system safety concept to various related areas of endeavor, including automotive manufacturing, rapid transit, and highway safety. Most of these experts have moved into consulting, lecturing, and related endeavors. Some have moved into responsible corporate positions. Therefore, the process of transferring concepts and technology gained in aerospace to the system safety area, while slow, is gaining momentum and in a few years should gain acceptance as a basic management approach toward a most perplexing and complex problem area.

The basic considerations in evaluating the proper placement of the product liability prevention activity within an organization structure are generally as follows:

1. Upper management cannot effectively delegate responsibility for product safety assurance to a single activity or person within the organization.
2. Management cannot assume that established functional units, such as engineering, manufacturing, quality, or personnel, will properly identify or correct product safety deficiencies in a timely manner as a routine part of their normal activities.
3. Management must accept the fact that it is management that must assume a direct and continuing responsibility for product safety assurance in design, manufacture, and use phases and that they must assign system safety specialists to the critical function of product safety risk evaluation and surveillance to assist in this effort.
4. The system safety specialist or activity thus designated must be organizationally located and specifically authorized to have access to all product design, evaluation, user complaints, and accident/litigation documentation, while at the same time be free from constraints and political pressures of any middle management having vested interests in avoiding at-

tention highlighting possible deficiencies within their spheres of accountability.

5. Implementation decisions for reducing potential product liability risks identified by the system safety specialists should be the designated responsibility of a high-level management committee consisting of those accountable for the design, manufacture, quality, user instruction, and field complaints. Legal staff representation should be assigned to advise the committee on the potential liability risks and avoidance aspects of their determinations, actions/inactions, and related documentation.

IV. SYSTEM SAFETY TECHNIQUES

Effectiveness in avoiding product liability risks is somewhat analogous to successful piloting of a ship through a rocky narrows. In both cases there is a need to be very aware of where the hazards are located, how to avoid them, how to make maximum use of the mistakes of others, and up-to-date knowledge of the techniques that others have found helpful in getting through. There is little glory in gaining knowledge from a catastrophic learning experience firsthand. Prior to an accident, management seems more concerned with the delays and extra costs associated with hazard avoidance than with the potential savings being realized.

As a ship's pilot must be knowledgeable of the waters being traversed, the assigned safety specialist must also be knowledgeable of the specialized techniques and practical applications of the system safety concept. This concept has been expanding in scope, practice, and effectiveness for over 30 years.

Working knowledge of the system safety concept is not yet well understood in many commercial industries. However, there is a growing number of textbooks, documents, and professional and technical publications that deal specifically with the application of system safety techniques and philosophy to nonaerospace endeavors. These publications discuss how to modify proven system safety concepts into cost-effective product liability risk avoidance techniques.

This limited discussion is not intended to serve as a how-to-do-it handbook, but rather as a guidepost providing general information, basic principles, and guidance for finding suitable reference material for performing an in-depth study of this rapidly expanding technical and managerial discipline.

In the book *Loss Control Management* [F. E. Bird and R. G. Loftus (eds.), Loganville, Ga.: International Loss Control Institute, 1976], this author defined, in Chapter 16, the basic principles and techniques associated with the system safety concept. Included in the discussion of system safety analysis was the identification of three basic elements that apply to all such activities irrespective of the specific type of analytical technique or system involved. In brief these are as follows:

1. *Identification.* Clear definition of each of the potential accident-causing factors associated with the product, operation, and/or activity.
2. *Evaluation.* Establishing a finite or relative measure of the serousness of each identified hazard. This is normally a function of two factors:
   a. The severity of consequence should the hazard result in an accident.
   b. The likelihood or potential of the actual occurrence of the accident.
3. *Communication.* Without a ready means to present adequately the key findings and recommendations resulting from system safety analysis to appropriate management decision makers, the effort expended in performing the analysis will have been in vain. Any management system that expends resources for performing hazard analyses, without assuring effective management review and implementation follow-up is not only wasteful, but also is preparing potential added liability risks should the unacted upon analysis/ recommendations be recovered by the plaintiff in a liability lawsuit.

The author has previously defined system safety analysis as follows:

System Safety analysis provides before-the-loss identification, evaluation and communication of those factors and interactions within a given system which could cause inadvertent injury, death or material damage during any phase or activity associated with the given system or product's life span.

To be most effective, system safety analysis documentation should be:

1. *Timely.* It should be conducted prior to design freeze or production if possible.
2. *Concise.* It must be understood by busy managers.
3. *Factual.* Credibility of the analysis must be maintained if it is to be properly received by management.

V. ANALYTICAL TECHNIQUES

A variety of analytical approaches and techniques have evolved within the system safety discipline in response to the differing nature of the various life-span phases of programs, and types of products or operations involved. Although some notable exceptions exist, in general, each of the existing techniques can be grouped under one of the following three categories:

- Preliminary Hazard Analyses (PHA)
- Design Safety Analyses (DA)
- Functional Safety Analyses (FSA)

A. Preliminary Hazard Analyses (PHA)

A.1. WHY PERFORM A PHA? Preliminary hazard analyses are performed to identify those conditions that, from previous related systems and experiences, can be expected to be potential hazards in the system being planned. For example, any contemplated system that may involve high-pressure compressed gases must be considered to have a potential inherent hazard that must be properly safeguarded by design and procedures. The findings and recommendations developed in performing a systematic preliminary hazard analysis (covering all basic components and operational considerations of the contemplated system) become the primary guide for safety-related planning within the program. This would include the determination of those areas where safety requirements must be imposed on design, those safety characteristics that must be verified by development testing and design safety analyses, and those use-phase safety activities (such items as special safety equipment, training, testing, facilities, etc.) that must be planned and budgeted.

A.2. WHEN TO PERFORM A PHA For maximum effectiveness, the preliminary hazard analysis effort should be initiated at the earliest practical time after the start of the program's conceptual phase. It should be treated as a continuing effort, requiring periodic updating and review for compliance implementation status, rather than as a one-time-only task. PHAs can be beneficially performed as the initial system safety effort on any type of system, operation, or product, regardless of the life-span phase involved. Therefore, the PHA should not be omitted just because the system safety program is not instituted during the conceptual phase.

A.3. HOW TO PERFORM A PHA To best assure a systematic, rigorous coverage, the PHA should be conducted in conformance with a preestablished matrix format and/or set of ground rules, tailored to reflect best the nature of the system to be analyzed, the extent of available information about the system, and the planned use of the analysis output data.

A typical safety analysis matrix format, both basic and preliminary, is shown in Figure 22-1. To conduct a PHA using such a format, the analyst should:

1. Survey the overall scope of the system to be analyzed and, on paper, subdivide the system into convenient (1) physical subsystems or elements (items), (2) operations or activities (functions), and (3) life-cycle phases (modes), such as testing, repair, transportation, storage, use, and disposal.
2. Check to see that the entire system being analyzed is encompassed within the items, functions, and modes identified in step 1 and that descriptive terminology is assigned. If certain areas are to be excluded from analysis, they should be specifically noted to avoid possible misunderstanding later.
3. Identify the hazardous aspects associated with each identified item or function for each mode. This is accomplished by first entering an "item" designation in column 1 of the PHA matrix form. Under this item description, enter the various general functions that the item is to perform. Next, consider each life-cycle mode and note any hazardous conditions associated with the specific item, function, and mode being considered. The mode and identified hazardous condition (summarized) are entered in columns 2 and 3 of the matrix. This basic process is then continued until all items and functions have been systematically considered.

SYSTEM:_____ SUBSYSTEM:_____		PRELIMINARY HAZARD ANALYSIS		PREPARED BY:_____ PG __ OF__ ISSUE DATE: _____ REV ____	
1	2	3	4	5	6
ITEM/ FUNCTION	MODE	HAZARDOUS ASPECT	HAZARD CATEGORY	NEEDED SAFETY PROVISIONS	CORRECTIVE ACTION PRIORITY

Figure 22-1 Typical matrix format for a preliminary hazard analysis (PHA). [From F. E. Bird and R. G. Loftus (eds.), *Loss Control Management.* Loganville, GA.: International Loss Control Institute, 1976. Reprinted with copyright permission of the International Loss Control Institute.]

4. Evaluate the potential severity of each hazardous event and assign a relative hazard severity category code in column 4. The category code used should be structured to reflect the nature of the system involved and defined by the analyst in clear terms. Military Standard 882A provides the following generic categories of hazard severity, which have become basic terminology in most DOD- and NASA-related system safety engineering activities:

I. Catastrophic   Death and severe injuries
                    System loss

II. Critical   Severe injuries
                    Major damage

III. Marginal   Minor injuries
                    Minor damage

IV. Negligible   Minimal damage
                    No loss of function

For this step the analyst does not need to be concerned with the expected likelihood of occurrence factors, nor should his or her assignment of the severity category be influenced by potential external hazard control considerations not currently inherent in the system being analyzed, unless specifically noted, or stipulated as a ground rule of the analysis.

5. Designate those safety provisions needed to control or eliminate the severity and probability of each hazardous event noted. Only the key words need to be entered in column 5, with details provided in supplemental sheets or reports as appropriate to assure proper attention and action.

6. Note in column 6 the relative safety priority for initiating/complying with the needed safety provisions described in column 5. The safety priority ranking is a subjective determination on the part of the analyst that is used to highlight those areas within the analysis that should receive priority attention. Factors used to assess criticality ranking include hazard severity, likelihood of occurrence, and the impact on program to institute corrective action (i.e., cost schedule and performance.)

A suggested criticality ranking guideline is as follows:

1. *Routine.* Should be adequately handled through routine channels for obtaining corrective action.

2. *Special.* Requires special follow-up action because of some unique aspect that might prove to be a problem when handled through routine channels.

3. *Critical.* Requires special management attention because of the extent of the program impact.

4. *Critical Priority.* The same as (3) except that a special time constraint exists that dictates immediate management attention.

The status of action taken in response to the findings contained in the analysis should be kept current by the person responsible for safety surveillance. At periodic intervals, the criticality rankings should be reevaluated, adjusted as needed, and properly distributed to the affected persons. The active participation of program and functional management in assuring that all open hazard control concerns are properly evaluated and resolved is essential to a successful system safety analysis effort.

B. Design Safety Analyses (DSA)

B.1. WHAT IS A DSA? There are two basic types of design safety analyses: inductive and deductive. The inductive approach involves the systematic evaluation of the effect each system component or element would have on the safety of the system should it fail to operate in the prescribed manner and time; it is the "what happens if . . ." approach. The deductive approach starts with a given identified hazardous event and systematically evaluates all predictable events, conditions, and influences that could cause the event to occur—a "how could it happen" approach. Both approaches are basically oriented to obtain the following set of objectives:

1. Verification that the design satisfies the established safety-related criteria.
2. Identification of specific design features that, if modified, would provide effective improvement in inherent safety, and the identification of the relative benefits in initiating such changes.
3. Documentation of objective base-line data that can be used in: (1) evaluating safety aspects of contemplated design changes, (2) interfacing safety considerations with other subsystems, and (3) compliance with legal or contractual obligations in the area of safety assurance.

B.2. WHEN TO PERFORM A DSA In the idealized system development program, the basic design safety requirements and criteria will be established during the concept phase, based on data provided from the preliminary hazard analysis effort. These requirements (e.g., pneumatic pressure vessels and system components shall be designed with a 4 to 1 safety factor above maximum operating pressure, a pressure relief valve shall be installed so as to relieve any pressure within the system greater than 110 percent of maximum operating pressure, etc.) are factored into detailed equipment specifications and then into the design during the initial part of the engineering phase. Following testing and evaluation, the design is approved as meeting all specified requirements, and it is released for production.

In such a system development approach, the optimum time to perform the DSA is prior to the final design approval and as soon as sufficient design detail is available to permit a thorough analysis. Acceptable findings by the DSA should be a prerequisite to final design approval.

In situations where the above conditions are not present, the DSA can be performed and utilized at any time a design safety assessment is wanted, provided sufficient design and operational details are available.

As previously indicated, two basic types of DSAs exist, inductive and deductive. In most situations, the inductive analysis should be conducted first. The data contained in the inductive analysis normally provide essential inputs and guidance for planning and performing the deductive analysis. The following discussion will illustrate the unique features of each DSA approach and how each can be oriented to provide complementary functions.

B.3. INDUCTIVE METHODS As with the PHA, inductive design safety analyses are most effectively and systematically performed with the use of a matrix form. The primary difference between the PHA and DSA format and approach is that the DSA is considerably more detailed in terms of specific design features, failure modes, and design improvements needed. The DSA matrix is also oriented toward organizing certain data helpful in performing deductive analyses (logic modeling) on critical hazardous situations.

The basic advantages of the matrix format approach are:

1. It encourages the analyst to ask (and answer) certain key questions on each item under study.
2. By locating the data entered in prescribed locations on the sheets, it makes review and recovery of wanted information easier.
3. It promotes a more systematic and comprehensive investigation.

Although the specific titles of the vertical columns used can be altered to best suit the situation pertaining to a given program or system, all matrix forms used for the inductive DSA on the same program should be similar.

A typical DSA matrix format is shown in Figure 22-2. This matrix is oriented for a qualitative safety evaluation on either a total system or a subsystem (should the analyst's concern be limited to specific subsystems only, due to assigned responsibilities or contractual obligations). For situations where a quantitative safety analysis is to be performed, a supplemental sheet, attached to the basic matrix and cross-referenced by the item number (column 1), should be used (see Figure 22-3).

1	2	3	4	5	6	7	8	9	10
				EFFECT OF	HAZARD CATEGORY	ITEM NUMBER	ENTRY IN QSS		
COMPO-NENT NAME	PART NO.	FAILURE MODE	LIFE CYCLE OR OPERA-TING MODE	FAILURE ON SYSTEM/SUB-SYSTEM				REMARKS/ NEEDED ACTION	CORRECTIVE ACTION PRIORITY

(header: SYSTEM: ____ SUBSYSTEM: ____ DESIGN SAFETY MATRIX ANALYSIS PREPARED BY: ____ Pg. __ OF __ ISSUE DATE: ____ REV. ____)

Figure 22-2 Typical design safety analysis (DSA) matrix format. [From F. E. Bird and R. G. Loftus (eds.), *Loss Control Management*. Loganville, GA.: International Loss Control Institute, 1976. Reprinted with copyright permission of the International Loss Control Institute.]

B.4. DEDUCTIVE METHODS The deductive safety analysis techniques provide one of the most effective and versatile approaches to predictive safety analyses available to the safety professional. The basic concepts involved can be used to perform simple qualitative evaluations (requiring no special training other than basic instructions and knowledge of the system to be analyzed) or very complex quantitative studies (requiring specialized training, computer programs, and experience). The expense of performing such studies increases proportionally to the complexity and scope of the effort. There-

8a	8b	8c	8d	8e	8f	8g	8h	8i
ITEM NO.	HAZARD FAILURE MECHAN-ISM	PRIMARY FAILURE RATE	DATA SOURCE	HAZARD DURA-TION PERIOD	SECONDARY FAILURE CAUSES	COMMAND INPUTS	LIKELIHOOD OF OCCURRANCE ESTIMATE	REMARKS

(header: SYSTEM: ____ SUBSYSTEM: ____ DESIGN SAFETY ANALYSIS MATRIX QUANTITATIVE SUPPLEMENT SHEET PREPARED BY: ____ Pg. __ OF __ ISSUE DATE: ____ REV. ____)

Figure 22-3 Quantitative supplemental sheet (QSS) to a DSA matrix format. [From F. E. Bird and R. G. Loftus (eds.), *Loss Control Management*. Loganville, GA.: International Loss Control Institute, 1976. Reprinted with copyright permission of the International Loss Control Institute.]

fore, selective judgment is needed in planning the analytical effort to be initiated to assure that its cost is justified by the hazard risk being evaluated.

The deductive approach begins with a defined undesired event, usually a postulated accident condition, and systematically organizes in a graphic form all known events, faults, and occurrences (within the context of the system mode established) that could cause or contribute to the occurrence of the undesired event. The data organized within the inductive PHA and DSA matrix formats described above provide both the basis for selecting the undesired event to be evaluated and the causative factors needed to complete the analysis.

To illustrate in a very elemental manner the basic application of these techniques, a hypothetical "System AZ," as diagrammed in Figure 22-4, will be used as an example aid throughout the remainder of this discussion. As may be noted, this system consists of two subsystems, Sub-A and Sub-Z. Sub-A has two operating modes of interet, i.e., "Stand-by" for

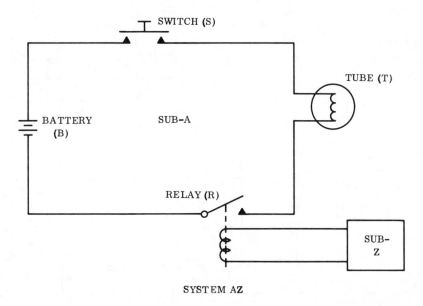

SYSTEM AZ

Figure 22-4 Example System AZ illustrating application of DSA techniques. [From F. E. Bird and R. G. Loftus (eds.), *Loss Control Management.* Loganville, GA.: International Loss Control Institute, 1976. Reprinted with copyright permission of the International Loss Control Institute.]

23 hours a day and "Ready" for the remaining 1 hour each day. It is given that inadvertent operation of tube (T) is a catastrophic hazard for the purpose of this illustration.

The analyst has performed the DSA matrix analysis on System AZ as illustrated in Figures 22-5 and 22-6.

C. Fault Tree Analysis (FTA)

The most commonly used safety logic model technique within the system safety discipline is the fault tree analysis (FTA). The basic concept and ground rules for the FTA were originated by Bell Telephone Laboratory engineers in the early

| SYSTEM: AZ | | | DESIGN SAFETY ANALYSIS MATRIX | | | PREPARED BY: J. Jones | | Pg. 1 OF 1 | |
| SUBSYSTEM: A | | | | | | ISSUE DATE: 3 May 71 REV. 0 | | | |
1	2	3	4	5	6	7	8	9	10
COMPO-NENT NAME	PART NO.	FAILURE MODE	LIFE CYCLE OR OPERA-TING MODE	EFFECT OF FAILURE ON SYSTEM/SUB-SYSTEM	HAZARD CATEGORY	ITEM NUMBER	ENTRY IN QSS	REMARKS/NEEDED ACTION	SAFETY CRITICAL-ITY
Battery	(B)	Insufficient Voltage Output	Stand-By	N/A in this mode	I	A1a	No	-	-
			Ready	Tube (T) will not operate	I	A1b	No	-	-
Switch	(S)	Closes Inadvertently	Stand-By	Partially Enables Circuit	II	A2a	Yes	-	I
			Ready	N/A in this mode	-	A2b	No	-	-
		Fails to Close	Stand-By	N/A in this mode	-	A2c	No	-	-
			Ready	Tube (T) will not operate	I	A2d	No	-	-
Tube	(T)	Premature or Delayed Operation	Stand-By	Major System Damage will occur	III	A3a	Yes	FTA should be Developed	III
			Ready	Damage will occur	III	A3a	Yes		
		Fails to Operate	Stand-By	N/A in this mode	-	A3b	No	-	-
			Ready	Sub-A will perform intended function	I	A3c	No	-	-
Relay	(R)	Closes In-advertently	Stand-By	Partially Enables Circuit	II	A4a	Yes	-	-
			Ready	Tube (T) will operate in-advertently	III	A4b	Yes	FTA Evaluation with Item No. A3a	II
		Fails to Open	Stand-By	N/A in this mode	N/A	A4c	No	-	-
			Ready	Tube (T) will remain operating past intended time	III	A4d	Yes	FTA Evaluation with Item No. A3a	II

Figure 22-5 Completed DSA matrix sheet for Subsystem AZ. [From F. E. Bird and R. G. Loftus (eds.), *Loss Control Management*. Loganville, GA.: International Loss Control Institute, 1976. Reprinted with copyright permission of the International Loss Control Institute.]

1960s, and they have been undergoing continuous refinement, particularly in the mathematical evaluation area. For the purpose of this discussion, all illustrations used will be based on the current FTA techniques as typically used by DOD contractors. Other methods and techniques are being developed and used for specific applications, which are also deductive safety analyses even though they may not conform to the FTA technique methodology as herein described.

In essence, the following five basic steps are typically involved in performing any depth of FTA from qualitative approximation to a rigorous mathematical treatment:

1. Select the undesired event to be evaluated, and define the system configuration life-cycle mode and environment for the purpose of the study.
2. Obtain data, drawings, and functional information available to obtain a thorough understanding of the system to be analyzed.
3. Construct the fault tree logic diagram (see the description of technique below).
4. Evaluate the logic diagram (using either the subjective or objective approaches as discussed below).
5. Prepare a summary conclusion of the FTA findings for management review and appropriate action.

C.1. FAULT TREE LOGIC DIAGRAM CONSTRUCTION Although sufficient for many applications, the following discussion of fault tree logic diagram construction must be recognized as being very elementary in nature. Many refinements and tricks-of-the-trade needed for moderate to highly complex systems may be obtained from careful study of applicable references. Although our example is based on a simple logic diagram, complex fault trees are normally prepared using computer programming both to draw diagram layouts and to solve probability calculations.

The diagram is started by drawing a rectangle at the top-center of a blank sheet, into which is written the concise statement of the undesired event ("top event") to be evaluated. At the next lower level, note in separate rectangles the various independent life-cycle and/or time phases to be evaluated. Below each of these events are placed the input factors that (either unassisted or in combination) are necessary and sufficient to cause that event to occur. This is done using specific symbols and ground rules.

SYSTEM: AZ			DESIGN SAFETY ANALYSIS MATRIX			PREPARED BY: J. Jones Pg. 1 OF 1		
SUBSYSTEM: A			QUANTITATIVE SUPPLEMENT SHEET			ISSUE DATE: 3 May 71 REV. 0		
8a	8b	8c	8d	8e	8f	8g	8h	8i
ITEM NO.	HAZARD FAILURE MECHAN-ISM	PRIMARY FAILURE RATE	DATA SOURCE	HAZARD DURA-TION PERIOD	SECONDARY FAILURE CAUSES	COMMAND INPUTS	LIKELIHOOD OF OCCURRANCE ESTIMATE	REMARKS
A2a	Switch(s) closes dur-ing "stand-by"	1×10^{-9}/hr	FARADA	23 hrs per day	Vibration or Shock > 5g	Operator closes switch manually	Primary: 2.3×10^{-8}/day Secondary: 1×10^{-3}/day Command: 1×10^{-2}/day	Secondary likelihood - based on con-sideration of transport ac-cident. Com-mand-Human error estimate.
A3a	Tube(T) op-erates in-advertently	No known means of primary failure in this manner		24 hrs per day	Non-known	Early in-put signal, or delayed removal	Primary: Negligible	Command in-put likelihood needs evalua-tion
A4a	Relay(R) closes during "stand-by"	1×10^{-11}/hr	Vendor's Report	23 hrs per day	Vibration or Shock > 5g	Current (> 200 mA) on relay coil	Primary: 2.3×10^{-10}/day Secondary: 1×10^{-3}/day	Command in-put needs evaluation.
A4b	Relay(R) closes during "ready"	1×10^{-11}/hr	Vendor's Report	1 hr/day	Vibration or Shock > 5g	Current (> 200 mA) on relay coil	Primary: 1×10^{-11}/day Secondary: 4×10^{-5}/day	Command needs evalua-tion.
A4d	Relay(R) fails to open following intended closure during ready	1×10^{-6}/hr	Engineer-ing esti-mate based on contacts sticking	1 hr/day	High Temp (> 1000°F) Shock (> 10g)	Coil re-mains energized	Primary: 1×10^{-6}/day Secondary: 1×10^{-5}/day	Command mode needs evaluation.

Figure 22-6 Completed DSA matrix quantitative supple-mental sheet for System AZ. [From F. E. Bird and R. G. Loftus (eds.), *Loss Control Management*. Loganville, GA.: In-ternational Loss Control Institute, 1976. Reprinted with copy-right permission of the International Loss Control Institute.]

For the purpose of this example, refer to Figure 22-5 to note that for Subsystem A three safety-critical (HAZARD CATEGORY III) failure modes were identified by the DSA. These all related to the same basic fault as described in Item No. A3a. Therefore, this fault condition will be designated as the undesired event to be evaluated by FTA in this illustration.

The DSA matrix quantitative supplement sheet (Fig-ure 22-6) has been completed for all item numbers assigned a Hazard Category of II or greater. Upon completion of this sheet, the analyst would next begin construction of the FTA logic diagram (illustrated in Figure 22-7). This diagram consists of various shaped symbols, in or around which are placed words and/or numbers. To the experienced FTA ana-

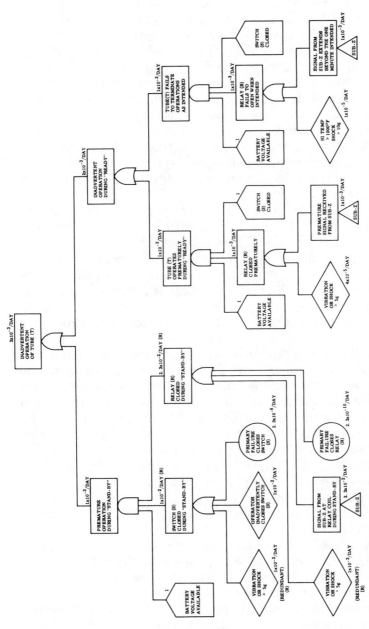

Figure 22-7 Sample fault tree diagram (for System AZ). [From F. E. Bird and R. G. Loftus (eds.), *Loss Control Management.* Loganville GA.: International Loss Control Institute, 1976. Reprinted with copyright permission of the International Loss Control Institute.]

lyst, it provides a graphic description of all the ways the top event can occur, its probability of occurring, the critical path by which it most likely can occur, how the probability of hazard can best be reduced, and the various possible solutions that would *not* effectively reduce the probability of hazard.

The diagram illustrated is the most elementary form that can be used and is shown here for concept description only. For almost any system requiring a quantitative FTA or other inductive technique, many other specialized symbols and mathematical refinements must be used to obtain full benefit of this analytical approach.

The key to preparing and evaluating an FTA logic diagram is an understanding of the logic symbols used. The basic symbols used in this illustrative example are defined in Figure 22-8.

In the typical form, probabilities are added when passing up through an "OR" gate, and multiplied when passing through an "AND" gate. This provides a reasonable mathematical approximation only if the probabilities are small and redundant events are noted and accounted for in the mathematical treatment. The use of Boolean algebra reduction, or simulation techniques, is needed for more complex and involved FTAs and where more than numeric approximation is desired.

With this basic background, the method by which this simple logic diagram (Figure 22-7) was constructed can now be explained. Note that the undesired (top) event selected did not specify the operational mode. Therefore, the initial step was to identify all the various system modes that must be considered. In this case there are two: standby and ready. These were drawn so as to be connected to the top event through an "OR" gate, since the top event could occur in either mode. Next the left-hand placed event was developed (as a general rule, the various modes are placed left to right on the sheet in relation to the sequence of their normal occurrence in the system life span).

Operation of tube (T) during stand-by mode requires three conditions to coexist: voltage available from battery (B), switch (S) closed, and relay (R) closed. These three conditions are therefore entered into the appropriate event symbols on the diagram and connected through an "AND" gate to the previously defined event rectangle. (*Note:* For the sake of simplicity of this illustration, potential short circuits, externally induced currents, bent pins, and similar fault modes

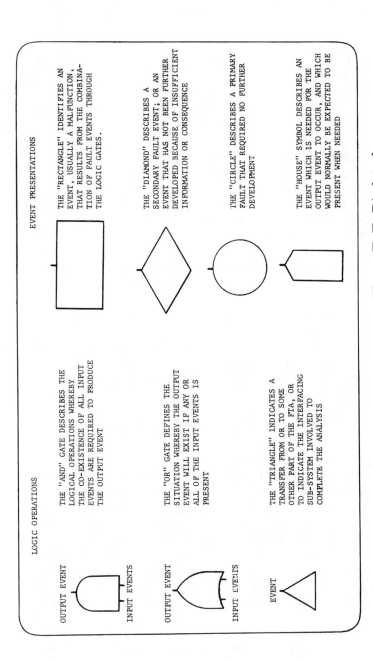

Figure 22-8 Basic fault tree symbols. [From F. E. Bird and R. G. Loftus (eds.), *Loss Control Management*. Loganville, GA.: International Loss Control Institute, 1976. Reprinted with copyright permission of the International Loss Control Institute, 1976. Reprinted with copyright permission of the International Loss Control Institute.]

that should be considered in detailed quantitative DSAs of safety critical electronic equipment are excluded in this example.)

In completing the various branches of the diagram, events placed in rectangles are subsequently developed, revealing the logical interrelationship of system fault events that can cause them. The branch is completed with all input fault events either placed in a circle (indicating primary basic fault), a diamond (indicating a secondary fault or condition that is not to be developed further), or a rectangle to which has been assigned a transfer or reference symbol. In general, it is helpful to consider each fault as the possible result of primary, secondary, and commanded failures. These causative faults are placed in appropriate symbols and connected to the event block through an "OR" gate, since any of the three fault conditions by itself could cause relay to close. Since the faults that would cause the relay coil to become energized must be determined from an analysis of the interfacing subsystem (Sub-Z), a transfer symbol was attached to this rectangled event.

In actual practice, this transfer symbol would initiate an effort to conduct an FTA on Sub-Z, with the top undesired event being the situation described in the event rectangle having the transfer symbol attached. In complex systems the FTA will comprise many pages of diagrams, interrelated by appropriate use of some transfer coding system established in advance. For the purpose of this example, only the assumed numeric probability that resulted from the FTA of Sub-Z is indicated.

The right-hand branch of this diagram or "tree" was developed in a similar manner, with the basic differences being that during the "ready" mode, switch (S) is normally closed and the inadvertent operation of tube (T) could occur either because of improper initiation or failure to terminate operation after the intended one minute had elapsed.

Note that the data collected and organized in the quantitative supplemental sheet to the DSA matrix are specifically oriented to support the preparation of the logic diagram, and the numeric evaluation that follows the construction of the diagram.

C.2. FAULT TREE EVALUATION In many instances, the mere process of developing and/or subjectively reviewing the logic diagram provides important insights relative to weak points in the system design. Fault conditions not previously considered important may be shown to be critical factors; conversely, other aspects often receiving much more attention are revealed not to be as significant as a result of controlling factors provided in the design. The number of independent faults/conditions needed to cause some undesired event, as revealed in the diagram, is a gross means of evaluating the relative safety of alternate paths or design approaches. However, whenever feasible, the evaluation process should be as objective as practicable, utilizing the best available probability estimates for the various individual fault conditions identified. There are two basic approaches used to solve top event probabilities. These are (1) calculation and (2) simulation. In both methods, the key factor is the assignment of the most realistic estimates of failure probability possible to the final failure mechanisms/conditions identified within each branch of the diagram.

The *calculation* approach can be used for fault trees that do not involve reparable faults (i.e., fault conditions that may be detected and corrected during the time covered by the analysis) or other time-related dynamic conditions that cannot be adequately accounted for by the logic diagram. For these more sophisticated evaluation requirements, the simulation approach is suggested.

For logic diagrams suitable for calculation or deterministic evaluation, the classical probability approach may be used, where each logic gate indicates the operation to be performed on the probability estimate inputs (i.e., union for "OR" gates and intersection for "AND" gates). Figure 22-9 provides the elementary Boolean simplification.

Calculation errors will result if the failure rate data inputs are not all based on the same time period (e.g., failures per 1000 operating hours, failures per million cycles, etc.). A second consideration is the proper handling of redundancies. *Redundancies*, in FTA terminology, refer to events, faults, conditions, etc., that are similar enough in time and nature that if they were to occur in real life, they would satisfy or significantly alter the likelihood of satisfying more than one entry within a given fault tree diagram. In situations where two or more redundant events exist within a fault tree in a logical relationship such that they must pass through an "AND" gate before reaching the top event, a serious error could result in calculation of the top event probability unless the redundancy is removed or treated.

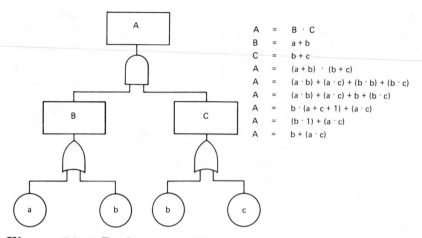

Figure 22-9 Boolean simplification. [From F. E. Bird and R. G. Loftus (eds.), *Loss Control Management.* Loganville, GA.: International Loss Control Institute, 1976. Reprinted with copyright permission of the International Loss Control Institute.]

Multiplying the probabilities of the same occurrence will give an unrealistic low estimate of hazard probability. To avoid this error, the analyst must identify and remove redundant probabilities before performing his calculation. This can be done by direct observation of the logic diagram or by reducing the fault tree to an algebraic expression (by assigning a code system to each noted event and cause) and then operating on this expression by Boolean algebraic theorems to remove redundances.

In the *simulation* approach, fault tree logic is programmed together with the assigned failure and repair rate data. A large number of trials are run with the various events occurring the designated times in a random manner. The frequencies at which various logic gates are operated and "top event" conditions occur is noted. The occurrences are counted, and reported in a suitable manner. The simulation approach has all the advantages of the calculation approach except for the greater amount of computer time needed to simulate fault trees with small probabilities. Simulation offers several additional advantages, i.e., the critical paths are listed and the computer can solve larger fault trees (often as much as 10 times larger). Simulation has gone through many stages of development; in its early stages, the amount of computer time required became prohibitive. However, special techniques such as importance sampling have reduced greatly the computer time needed.

In addition to the design-oriented analytical procedures described above, other applications of system safety analysis techniques indicate methods that can be used to provide before-the-fact hazard evaluation of various types of industrial process operations. One of the more frequently used techniques is the *operational safety analysis*. This attempts to identify and evaluate potential hazards that could exist during anticipated operation/use and repair and disposal activities associated with a given system. A basic matrix sheet used for this type of effort is shown in Figure 22-10.

Further refinements of these concepts and techniques should prove invaluable for effective before-the-accident controls in all forms of industrial operations.

TASK/FUNCTION	REF CODE	HAZARDOUS CONSIDERATIONS	HAZARD CATEGORY	EXISTING SAFETY PROVISIONS	NEEDED SAFETY PROVISIONS/ REQUIREMENTS	PRIORITY

SYSTEM: _____
SUBSYSTEM: _____
OPERATING SAFETY MATRIX ANALYSIS
PREPARED BY: _____ PG ___ OF ___
ISSUE DATE: _____ REV _____

Figure 22-10 Typical matrix format for operational safety analysis. [From F. E. Bird and R. G. Loftus (eds.), *Loss Control Management*. Loganville, GA.: International Loss Control Institute, 1976. Reprinted with copyright permission of the International Loss Control Institute.]

RESOURCES

For those wishing to increase their understanding of the theory and/or practice of the system safety concept beyond that briefly covered in this section, the following selected references are suggested:

Publications of the System Safety Society

The System Safety Society publishes a technical journal, *Hazard Prevention*. This bimonthly journal contains articles and features dealing with current concepts and advances in the system safety area. Bound *Proceedings* covering papers presented at the biennial International System Safety Conference are also available for purchase from the society. Membership information and order forms for their publications can be obtained by writing to the System Safety Society, 4502 Parkglen Circle, Irvine, CA. 92714 (714-551-2463).

Reference Books

Current publications covering various aspects of System Safety include:

1. D. B. Brown, *Systems Analysis and Design for Safety.* Englewood Cliffs, N.J.: Prentice-Hall, 1976.
2. S. W. Malasky, *System Safety: Technology and Application.* New York: Garland STPM Press, 1982.
3. H. E. Roland and B. Moriarty, *System Safety Engineering and Management.* New York: Wiley, 1983.
4. C. O. Smith, *Products Liability: Are You Vulnerable?* Englewood Cliffs, N.J.: Prentice-Hall, 1981.
5. Military Standard 882A, System Safety Program Requirements. Washington, D.C.: U.S. Government Printing Office, 1977.

VI

DISCOVERY AND SETTLEMENT

The trial lawyer must be skilled, proficient, and aggressive in terms of investigating and otherwise uncovering all of the pertinent facts and circumstances of any accident involving a potentially major claim or lawsuit. His (or her) legal analysis should be formulated on the broad base of relevant and seemingly collateral information that can be accumulated by the diligent efforts of all those assisting in the preparation of the case for settlement or trial. His decisions and actions will be only as good as the completeness, accuracy, validity, and reliability of the information upon which he must rely.

The automotive engineer may become involved in a claim or lawsuit in many ways. He (or she) may perform an initial on-site accident investigation on behalf of any one of the possible claimants or litigants. He may collate and review all of the available technical information on a case in order to advise the claims or legal staff. He might serve as a coordinator to obtain draft answers to written interrogatories propounded by another party. He might assist defense counsel by explaining the design and function of a product, providing the appropriate documents and knowledge of past experience with the product and product litigation, and conducting demonstrative tours of certain design, manufacturing, or test facilities for the trial attorneys. He may be asked to sign affidavits or declarations pertaining to technical, corporate, or industry matters. He might serve as a technical adviser to local trial counsel or act as the company representative in the courtroom during the trial of a lawsuit.

Almost any engineer, at some stage of his career, should expect to be deposed as a witness or to act as an expert witness at time of trial. The plaintiff attorney may seek the advice of engineers to help reconstruct an accident, render opinions of whether the case has any merit or where the "weak spots" might be, perform tests or experiments on relevant issues, help to frame questions for interrogatories, suggest items for motions to produce, and recommend areas of questioning for scheduled deponents. Some engineers serve merely as advisers, but most engineers who get involved in a lawsuit are expected to become ready to express ultimate conclusions in the role and status of an expert witness both for oral deposition and at trial. Regardless of how the engineer might become involved in a lawsuit, he should understand something about the anatomy of a lawsuit and its dynamic processes, the language of the participants and their roles, and the basic rules of the advocacy process. He should be prepared for such experiences long before they suddenly happen to him, since the necessary understanding does not come in the form of an overnight revelation to most engineers.

Section 23, Research Materials, suggests how the lawyer or engineer can gain initial access to the enormous information resources available in libraries or other technical information respositories. As other sections in this book on automotive engineering and litigation illustrate, there is a vast amount of information available on almost any technical topic or legal aspect of litigation involving automotive vehicles. Finding what is needed and properly evaluating it may be time-consuming, but it is a vital part of any lawyer's case evaluation or preparation for trial.

Product liability lawsuits usually involve two major phases: liability and damages. The liability phase generally revolves around engineering opinions as to fault based upon all of the facts and circumstances of the particular case. The damages phase usually revolves around medical opinions as to the nature and extent of injuries. Increasingly, economics experts have become involved in evaluating personal injuries, business losses, and punitive damages in economic terms. The economics expert assists the jury in reaching a verdict that must be expressed and rendered in the form of monetary value (dollars). The economics expert is often needed, where the potential damage award is high, to provide the kind of special knowledge that may be beyond the normal understanding and experience of most jurors in order to avoid speculative, excessive, undervalued, or unreasoned judgments. In Section 24, The Economics Expert, the author clearly shows how such an expert evaluates and calculates the present value of monetary losses suffered from the legal wrongs of others. The section provides important guidance to the trial attorney in dealing with and examining an economics expert. By reading this section, the automotive engineer will understand that jury verdicts may not be wild guesses, emotionally tainted, or unjustified in terms of actual damages. The amount is based upon the judge's jury instructions and guidance, the economist's presentation of specified quantitative information as permitted by the judge and the law, and the jurors' perception and reaction to the evidence, which is admitted only after the judge determines its probative value, reliability, and lack of undue prejudicial effect.

Since most lawsuits are settled prior to trial, most lawyers need to know something about how claims are handled, evaluated, and settled by insurance companies. This is a topic not usually taught in law schools. Learning only by experience may be costly, and unfair misperceptions and antagonisms can be created. Wide differences in settlement tactics, procedures, and opinions may exist because of the wide variety among numerous insurers, conflicts of interest between insurers on the same case, the changing insurance company policies as implemented through various regional offices, the personalities of the individual claims adjustors, the conflicts between in-house or local defense counsel recommendations, and each participant's recent experiences in claims negotiation and trial results. Swift resolution of claims may be achieved by better overall understanding, as well as by the forcing function of bad faith causes of action and prejudgment interest. Section 25, Effective Claims Handling, describes how to process the typical automobile accident claim, from the viewpoint of an experienced claims handler, in order to facilitate the proper evaluation and settlement prior to the possible filing of a lawsuit. If the lawyer and the engineer develop a better comprehension of the role, function, and procedures of the insurance carriers, many settlement delays, misunderstandings, and costly problems could be avoided.

The concluding section of Part VI, Structured Settlements (Periodic Payments), covers an area that has grown rapidly both in its importance and in its implications for the lawyer, insurer, and corporate enterprise. Any case with "big damages" should be carefully evaluated as to the merits of various periodic payment schemes, but this should be done well before trial to avoid costly errors and possible legal malpractice. It is essential that trial lawyers adequately understand all of the considerations and ramifications of structured settlements prior to any negotiation that may involve offers or demands that may seem enticingly structured. Rigorous discovery will narrow and illuminate the issues for all parties, and an appropriate structured settlement may provide an early and palatable resolution of a conflict situation.

23

Research Materials

PAMELA A. HOEFT, M.A.
President, Hoeft Associates
Arlington, Virginia

*Pamela A. Hoeft was educated at the University of
Michigan (M.A. in Instructional Technology in 1975),
Eastern Michigan University (B.S. in Library Science and
Chemistry in 1968), and Central Michigan University
(1964–1966). She was elected to Alpha Beta Alpha, the
national Library Science honor society. Currently, she
heads Hoeft Associates, an information brokerage firm that
provides information services and documents to domestic
and foreign clients. Her knowledge of the more than 500
libraries in the District of Columbia area and of computer
literature search sources, along with her chemical, public,
and academic library experience, allows research and
retrieval of information that is valuable in such areas as
research and development, product liability, litigation
support, "state-of-the-art studies," patentability, and market
planning. She had done pro bono work for the Petosky
Public Library, Michigan, and for the Michigan
Department of Education. Her professional affiliations
include the American Library Association, the American
Society of Information Science, the American Chemical
Society, the Association for Educational Communications
and Technology, the National Education Association, the
American Business Women's Association, and the Small*

Business Advisory Council of the Arlington, Virginia, Chamber of Commerce. The author may be contacted at Hoeft Associates, Arlington Virginia 22202 (mailing address: P.O. Box 2323; office address: 2001 Jefferson Davis Highway) and by phone (703-920-2216).

I. INTRODUCTION

Research materials for use in automotive engineering and litigation perform several functions. They can provide background information for use during the discovery process to familiarize one with a general concept or specific features of an area of automotive engineering. Questions for interrogatories can include more specific inquiries into the opposition's knowledge of known technology. Collections of material indicating knowledge of an individual or corporate entity and/or certified copies of documents such as patents may supply supporting evidence.

Research material of new information takes the form of periodicals, patents, dissertations, government or institutional bulletins, industrial technical publications, etc. These materials provide the most recently published information dealing with a topic. The topic may be altogetherly new or it may be another method of dealing with known information. These materials may be accessed by manual or computerized searching through a variety of indices, bibliographies, or data bases.

II. INDICES AND BIBLIOGRAPHIES

Indices particularly useful in the automotive engineering field include the following:

- *Engineering Index*
- *Applied Science & Technology Index*
- *Science Citation Index*
- *Electrical and Electronics Abstracts*
- *Applied Mechanics Reviews*
- *Safety Science Abstracts*
- *Cumulative Index: Society of Automotive Engineers Technical Papers*

Bibliographies dealing with specific topics within areas of automotive engineering are also available. Congresses dealing with specific areas of interest within the automotive field frequently publish speeches and materials that were presented. Examples of some of these titles follow:

- 1st International Congress on Automotive Safety. *Standardization of Automotive Diagnostic Systems*. Washington, D.C.: U.S. National Motor Vehicle Safety Advisory Council, 1972.

- National Safety Belt Usage Conference. *Proceedings.* Washington, D.C.: National Highway Traffic Safety Administration, U.S. Department of Transportation, 1974.
- *Third International Conference on Occupant Protection.* Warrendale, PA.: Society of Automotive Engineers, 1974.
- International Symposium on Automotive Technology & Automation. *ISATA 77.* Croydon, Eng.: Automotive Automation Ltd., 1977.
- *ASTM–SAE Symposium on Viscometry and its Application to Automotive Lubricants.* Warrendale, PA.: Society of Automotive Engineers, 1973.

III. DATA BASES

Data bases provide one of the most rapid means to search a multitude of materials for a specific topic. With the information explosion, there are a multitude of data bases readily available from several vendors. Due to the volume of data bases (over 1500) available to the general public, it is sometimes necessary to use some basic reference materials dealing with data bases and their content in order to determine the applicability of a data base to the specific content area. Some of the more extensive references follow:

- *Encyclopedia of Information Systems and Services,* 4th ed. Detroit: Gale Research Company, 1980.
- *Computer-Readable Data Bases: A Directory and Data Source Book.* White Plains, N.Y.: Knowledge Industry Publications, 1979.
- *Datapro Directory of On-Line Services.* New York: McGraw-Hill (published annually).

Major vendors such as Dialog Information Services (Dialog), BRS, Inc., and SDC Search Systems (Orbit) provide catalogs with a description of the types of materials within the data base. Frequently they have the data bases categorized in a subject index to aid researchers in determining a source for searching. The data base vendors also demonstrate a concern for research budgets by providing inexpensive searching through their indices of some data bases. This searching will indicate the number of "hits" that you would locate within a particular data base you may choose for your topic. This allows you to determine the practicality and expense of using that data base, in relation to your topic, prior to spending money on searching the data base itself.

IV. OTHER RESOURCE PUBLICATIONS

Other reference works, such as dictionaries, encyclopedias, textbooks, monographs, tables, and formularies, compile useful bits of scattered information and put them in a more useful format. These materials are updated frequently, with the most recent publication generally available in the reference collections of most technical libraries.

Periodicals, another source of valuable information, are published by associations, societies, universities, companies, commercial publishers, and individuals.

Dissertations provide a tremendous amount of material; they are searchable through sources such as *Dissertation Abstracts* and are machine searchable from 1861 to the present on the *Comprehensive Dissertation Abstracts* data base available through Dialog. Although retrieving the actual dissertation is sometimes challenging, this process is becoming easier thanks to University Microfilms in Ann Arbor, Michigan. Here, microfilm or paper copies may be purchased of research material that is on file.

V. INFORMATION CENTERS

The National Technical Information Service, 5285 Port Royal Road, Springfield, Virginia 22161, provides access to information involving government-sponsored research or analyses. Materials since 1964 are searchable by an on-line computer search service. The service and publication can be obtained for a fee.

The National Referral Center is operated by the Science and Technology Division of the Library of Congress, Washington, D.C. 20540. This service will direct an individual with a specialized question to a potential source of information, usually an organization with a known specialty in the particular field. The data base containing this information at the National Referral Center is subject indexed and available free to users of the Library of Congress. The center does accept telephone and written requests and will generally respond within a few days.

An excellent source of information for the researcher in the motor vehicle field is the United States Patent and Trademark Office Patent Search Room at 2021 Jefferson Davis Highway, Arlington, Virginia 22202. The Patent Search Room contains over 4 million patents. The Scienfific Library of the Patent Office, at the same location, contains scientific and technical literature and periodicals along with an extensive collection of foreign patents.

The Attorney's Record Room at the Patent Office allows the public to have access to the files for the prosecution of a patent. These file histories contain various documents detailing what transpired in processing the patent application, the issuance of the patent, and subsequent actions (e.g., notice of suit). Occasionally one will find development and testing reports, mention of problems encountered and their solutions, and production information that the patent attorney or inventor has disclosed in the course of securing the patent.

There are depository libraries for patents throughout the country (as listed in Table 23–1). It is helpful to note that their collections are most useful if you have the patent number (most of these collections are arranged by patent number, thus making searching by subject matter very difficult).

In determining the nature of a patent search, one can decide whether the search should be a manual one through the records available at public facilities or should be by computer through one of the many data bases that deal with patents and that are available through vendors such as BRS, Inc., Dialog Information Services, SDC Search Systems, and Pergamon Infoline Questel, Inc. Often a combination of manual and computer searching is required.

An analysis of an automotive company or a company whose products relate to the automotive industry is possible by preparing a computer-generated organizational profile. This organizational profile shows, by patent classification, the patent activity for that corporation or company. Such material is useful for studying a competitor's activity, market research, and product development and determining the knowledge of a corporation in a specific area.

VI. SPECIAL LIBRARIES

Special libraries dealing with the automobile and its components are scattered throughout the country. They include libraries of associations, corporations, and private individuals. An extensive listing of these libraries is available by library name, subject, and state listings in the *Directory of Special*

Libraries and Information Centers, which is published by Gale Research Company in Detroit, Michigan. Some restrict the use of their facilities; others are open to the public. Some of the libraries charge a fee, while others are free.

VII. TRADE ASSOCIATIONS

Generally, trade associations provide a tremendous amount of material relative to their industry. An association of particular note in the automotive field is the Motor Vehicle Manufacturers Association of the United States, Inc., 300 New Center Building, Detroit, Michigan 48202. It has five library divisions:

1. *State Regulations*—all state codes; materials on state automotive legislation.
2. *Communications*—clippings by subject relative to motor vehicles; pertinent speeches; world's largest collection of automotive photographs. (This is the public affairs branch of the association.)
3. *Technical*—motor vehicle reports and studies; world's largest collection of accident reports; complete collection of government codes. (The government codes and accident reports have been computerized by Wayne State University and may be retrieved through it.)
4. *Patents Library*—world's largest collection of automotive or vehicle patents; also includes repair manuals, and promotional brochures.
5. *Statistics*—data on production, sales, and world motor vehicles.

These collections are strictly for members. Others may request permission to use them and are usually granted an appointment. But restrictions may apply, and a statement of purpose is required.

A sampling of other associations or industry-related sources of information in the United States and Europe include the following. Restrictions as to the collection's use and fees may be applicable.

American National Standards Institute (ANSI)
1430 Broadway
New York, New York 10018

American Society for Quality Control, Inc.
230 West Wells Street
Milwaukee, Wisconsin 53203

Table 23-1 Reference Collections of U.S. Patents Available for Public Use in Patent Depository Libraires[a,b]

STATE	NAME OF LIBRARY	TELEPHONE CONTACT
Alabama	Birmingham Public Library	(205) 254-2555
Arizona	Tempe: Science Library, Arizona State University	(602) 965-7607
California	Los Angeles Public Library	(213) 626-7555 (ext. 273)
	Sacramento: California State Library	(916) 322-4572
	Sunnyvale: Patent Information Clearinghouse[c]	(408) 738-5580
Colorado	Denver Public Library	(303) 571-2122
Delaware	Newark: University of Delaware	(302) 738-2238
Georgia	Atlanta: Price Gilbert Memorial Library, Georgia Institute of Technology	(404) 894-4519
Illinois	Chicago Public Library	(312) 269-2865
Louisiana	Baton Rouge: Troy H. Middleton Library, Louisiana State University	(504) 388-2570
Massachusetts	Boston Public Library	(617) 536-5400 (ext. 265)
Michigan	Detroit Public Library	(313) 833-1450
Minnesota	Minneapolis Public Library & Information Center	(612) 372-6552
Missouri	Kansas City: Linda Hall Library	(816) 363-4600
	St. Louis Public Library	(314) 241-2288 (ext. 214, 215)
Nebraska	Lincoln: University of Nebraska-Lincoln, Engineering Library	(402) 472-3411
New Hampshire	Durham: University of New Hampshire Library	(603) 862-1777
New Jersey	Newark Public Library	(201) 733-7814
New York	Albany: New York State Library	(518) 474-5125
	Buffalo and Erie County Public Library	(716) 856-7525 (ext. 267)
	New York Public Library (The Research Libraries)	(212) 930-0850
North Carolina	Raleigh: D. H. Hill Library, N.C. State University	(919) 737-3280
Ohio	Cincinnati & Hamilton County, Public Library of	(513) 369-6936
	Cleveland Public Library	(216) 623-2870
	Columbus: Ohio State University Libraries	(614) 422-6286
	Toledo/Lucas County Public Library	(419) 255-7055 (ext. 212)

(*Continued*)

Table 23-1 (*Continued*)

STATE	NAME OF LIBRARY	TELEPHONE CONTACT
Oklahoma	Stillwater: Oklahoma State University Library	(405) 624-6546
Pennsylvania	Philadelphia: Franklin Institute Library	(215) 448-1321[d]
	Pittsburgh: Carnegie Library of Pittsburgh	(412) 622-3138
	University Park: Pattee Library, Pennsylvania State University	(814) 865-4861
Rhode Island	Providence Public Library	(401) 521-7722 (ext. 226)
South Carolina	Charleston: Medical University of South Carolina	(803) 792-2372
Tennessee	Memphis & Shelby County Public Library and Information Center	(901) 528-2957
Texas	Dallas Public Library	(214) 748-9071
	Houston: The Fondren Library, Rice University	(713) 527-8101 (ext. 2587)
Washington	Seattle: Engineering Library, University of Washington	(206) 543-0740
Wisconsin	Madison: Kurt F. Wendt Engineering Library, University of Wisconsin	(608) 262-6845
	Milwaukee Public Library	(414) 278-3043

[a]The libraries listed herein, designated as patent depository libraries, receive current issues of U.S. Patents and maintain collections of earlier issued patents. The scope of these collections varies from library to library, ranging from patents of only recent months or years in some libraries to all or most of the patents issued since 1870, or earlier, in other libraries.

These patent collections are open to public use and each of the patent depository libraries, in addition, offers the publications of the patent classification system (e.g., *The Manual of Classification, Index to the U.S. Patent Classification, Classification Definitions*, etc.) and provides technical staff assistance in their use to aid the public in gaining effective access to information contained in patents. With one exception, as noted in the above table, the collections are organized in patent number sequence.

Depending upon the library, the patents may be available in microfilm, in bound volumes of paper copies, or in some combination of both. Facilities for making paper copies from either microfilm in reader-printers or from the bound volumes in paper-to-paper copies are generally provided for a fee.

Owing to variations in the scope of patent collections among the patent depository libraries and in their hours of service to the public, anyone contemplating use of the patents at a particular library is advised to contact that library, in advance, about its collection and hours, so as to avert possible inconvenience.

[b]Table reprinted from *Official Gazette of the United States Patent and Trademark Office*, Vol. 1020, No. 4. Washington, D.C.: U.S. Department of Commerce, July 27, 1982.

[c]Collection organized by subject matter.

[d]Call only between the hours of 10:00 A.M. and 5:00 P.M.

American Trucking Association, Inc.
1616 P Street N.W.
Washington, D.C. 20036

Center for Auto Safety
1346 Connecticut Avenue N.W.
Washington, D.C. 20036

Environmental Protection Agency
Office of Air, Noise, and Radiation
Office of Mobile Source Air Pollution Control
Emission Control Technology Division (Ann Arbor)
Motor Vehicle Emission Laboratory
Environmental Protection Agency
c/o Library
2565 Plymouth Road
Ann Arbor, Michigan 48105

European Organization for Quality Control (EOQC)
Barenplatz 2
P.O. Box 2613
CH-3001 Berne, Switzerland

Motor and Equipment Manufacturers Association (MEMA)
222 Cedar Lane
P.O. Box 439
Teaneck, New Jersey 07666

Motor Industry Research Association (MIRA)
Information Section
Motor Industry Research Section
Watling Street
Nuneaton CV10 0TU, Warwics, England

National Road and Traffic Research Institute
Information and Documentation Section
Statens Vag-och Trafikinstitut
Biblioteket
S-581 01 Linkoping, Sweden

Recreation Vehicle Industry Association (RIVA)
14650 Lee Road
P.O. Box 204
Chantilly, Virginia 22021

Society of Automotive Engineers, Inc. (SAE)
400 Commonwealth Drive
Warrendale, Pennsylvania 15096

Southwest Research Institute
Library
6220 Culebra Road
P.O. Drawer 28510
San Antonio, Texas 78284

Union of Automobile, Motorcycle and Cycle Technology
157–159, rue Lecourbe
75015, Paris, France

United Automobile, Aerospace and Agricultural Implement
  Workers of America (UAW)
Research Department
8000 East Jefferson Avenue
Detroit, Michigan 48214

University of Arizona
Engineering Experiment Station
Tucson, Arizona 85721

University of Michigan
Engineering-Transportation Library
Undergraduate Library Building
Ann Arbor, Michigan 48109

VIII. INDIVIDUAL EXPERTS

Literature searches frequently reveal experts in a particular field or technology: they can be used to determine potential problem solvers and, possibly, to help find expert witnesses for a case. A tactic employed by some attorneys in preparing for cross-examining an expert witness is to secure copies of all of his or her published material. This published material may be in the form of books, periodical articles, patents, monographs, papers presented at conferences, etc. In most searches involving technological fields, it is possible to determine the number of times an expert's publication has been cited as a reference by other authors by consulting the *Science Citation Index*. This can indicate the acceptance of an individual as an expert in a field by others in the scientific community.

IX. CERTIFICATION

There are certification departments at the Library of Congress, the United States Patent and Trademark Office, and other government agencies. These departments are useful for certifying materials to be used as evidence. However, it is not always possible to certify every document.

X. LAW LIBRARIES

Legal research through traditional law library materials should be standard practice in any case of automotive litigation. Computerized legal research sources can often assist the researcher in determining which of these materials to access. LEXIS (Mead Data Central) and WESTLAW (West Publishing Company) are the two main computerized legal research systems in use today. Each system has its advantages and disadvantages. An excellent comparison of these systems and other computer-assisted forms of legal research may be found in the fourth edition of *Effective Legal Research* by Miles O. Price, Harry Bitner, and Shirley R. Bysiewicz (Boston: Little, Brown, 1979, pp. 459–468).

24

The Economics Expert

ERNEST T. KENDALL, Ph.D.
President, Commonwealth Research Group, Inc.
Boston, Massachusetts

Dr. Ernest T. Kendall is a consulting economist who has studied the automobile industry for the past eight years. He has analyzed the economic effects of federally mandated safety, fuel economy, and emissions standards for new automobiles for the National Highway Traffic Safety Administration; has evaluated the economic, insurance, and safety aspects of on-the-road electric vehicle use for the U.S. Department of Energy; and has presented expert economic testimony regarding the economic loss resulting from automobile-related incidents in a number of cases in both federal and state courts. Dr. Kendall is the president of Commonwealth Research Group, Inc., a Boston-based economic research and consulting firm, located at 230 Beacon Street, Boston, Massachusetts 02116 (617-536-3146).

I. INTRODUCTION

In automotive litigation, an expert economic witness is required for several reasons. First, the economic expert's role is to determine and testify to the value of any economic loss by the injured parties. Second, an expert economist is needed, in product liability cases, to derive and present information that will help the trier of fact to determine whether or not a product is unreasonably dangerous and, if so, what dollar amount of punitive damages might be appropriate.

An economist is uniquely qualified for such purposes. In many cases, even temporarily disabling injuries can result in long-term economic losses due to the setback of jobs and professional careers, requiring knowledgeable projections of previously expected and now probable future earnings. Cases involving claims of wrongful death also require similar projections of future events. While an economist cannot predict the future earnings of any one individual with complete certainty, a skilled labor economist can predict the statistically most likely ("expected") future compensation of an average individual in a given type of work and can knowledgeably reduce it to its present value. In determining the reasonableness of product liability cases, a skilled microeconomist can determine those costs that are appropriately allocated to the cause of a claimed product defect and can estimate the market response to the increased costs and prices resulting from its correction. Since increased costs frequently cause increased prices and, therefore, a decline in the level of sales, the economist's professional knowledge is needed to define that cost increase that would be "reasonable."

An economist can accomplish these things because of the nature of professional inquiry in this field of study. In primarily capitalist economies such as those existing in the United States, the United Kingdom, and a number of other countries, economic research is concerned with the study of markets. "Product" markets are studied to determine the factors that affect the costs of production, prices of goods, market risks, and profits. "Input" markets—the markets for inputs to production (labor, land, capital, and entrepreneurship)—are studied to determine the factors affecting employee compensation and employment levels, interest rates, capital value, and the return on investment required to attract capital funds. This research gives the economist a body of knowledge upon which to draw conclusions regarding past, present, and future economic events. A good economic expert witness is one who can explain the methodology used in—and results obtained from—complex and sophisticated analyses, based on this research, doing so in plain and simple language that is readily understood by judge and jury alike.

Expert economic testimony is beneficial to both defense and plaintiff attorneys, as well as to the court. Without such expert evaluation of economic loss, settlements must be made arbitrarily, without knowledge of the facts. Such settlements may be unfair to either side in a dispute. Thus, the economic witness can help defense attorneys to minimize the possible maximum loss and can be used by plaintiff attorneys to help maximize the minimum amount of recovery.

The economic witness is usually called upon to evaluate any or all of three categories of loss:

1. *Personal Loss.* Loss to an injured party or a decedent's dependents.
2. *Business Loss.* Loss to business firms as a result of the defendant's actions.
3. *Punitive Damages.* Damages imposed to prevent a continuation or recurrence of wrongful behavior.

The first two of these categories require projections of future events, including future employee compensation and household contributions, and future market share and profitability of affected business firms. The third category, when applied in product liability cases, requires a knowledge of the capital structure, production costs, and profitability of the product's manufacturer.

A considerable amount of data and information are required in order for the economist to perform such analyses. Therefore, it is best for the lawyer to call upon the economist at an early stage of litigation. Working closely with the lawyer, the automotive engineering expert, and, when appropriate, the accountant, the economist can advise as to what information should be obtained in discovery, can provide assistance in pretrial preparation, can provide expert testimony, and can evaluate offers of structured settlements.

II. EVALUATION OF PERSONAL LOSS

Personal economic loss resulting from automobile-related incidents can be experienced by an injured party and by his or her dependents, and by the dependents of a decedent in cases involving wrongful death. For individuals who are not self-employed, this economic loss is normally comprised of the following elements:

1. Lost future wages, commissions, and bonuses.
2. Lost future employer-paid benefits (including retirement benefits).
3. The dollar value of lost household contributions.

It is not necessary for an injury to prevent a return to a former occupation for the injured person to incur an economic loss whose effect will be felt for a number of years into the future. Persons in many skilled, professional, and business occupations will have a *growth in responsibility and earnings* with increased experience, especially during the first two decades of an individual's working life. A serious injury can set back this growth of earnings, resulting in an economic loss extending for a number of years.

This concept is illustrated in Figure 24-1. There, earnings are presented in constant dollars in order to show their growth due to increased experience alone and to avoid the complications presented by inflation. Earnings usually increase rapidly during the first few years of an individual's career. This rate of growth then declines over time until, finally, the individual reaches his or her maximum level of real earnings. This is indicated by point A on the graph in Figure 24-1.

The time required to reach this point varies with each different occupation. *Skilled craftsmen* in union jobs may typically undergo a four-year apprenticeship during which time their hourly wage increases at a rapid rate and after which they receive the union-negotiated wage rate for journeymen, finally achieving their last major increase in real wage if and when they obtain a master's license.

Growth in the *earnings of professionals* may continue for a longer period of time. Lawyers in large law firms often wait 5 years before learning whether or not they will be accepted as partners, and then can wait another 5 years before that actually happens. Economists and college professors may take 10 to 15 years to reach their maximum level of real earnings. Engineers, on the other hand, may start at a relatively high initial salary and get sizable increases for the first 5 to 10 years of their careers, but then receive only inflationary increases after that time. Their later increases in real earnings depend upon their ability to win promotions into management and supervisory positions.

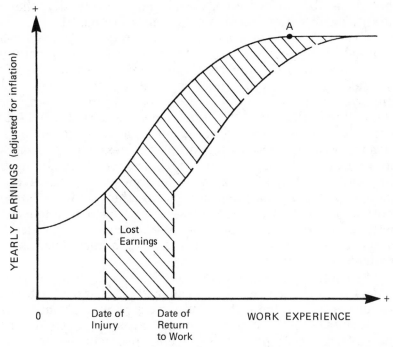

Figure 24-1 Loss of earnings to professionals, managers, and skilled workers due to personal injury can extend over a considerable period of time after the person returns to work.

Wages for unskilled workers are usually determined by the existing wage rates in manufacturing jobs in local geographical area. Jobs that require few, if any, entry-level skills must compete with production-line jobs in order to attract workers. Thus, the growth rate in wages for unskilled jobs is determined by labor union agreements, which are normally based on recent increases in both worker productivity and consumer prices. Until the late 1970s, worker productivity generally increased at a rate of 3 percent per year, while inflation increased at about 6 percent per year on average. More recently, however, little if any increase has occurred in worker productivity, while inflation rates have risen considerably. It therefore becomes a matter of expert economic opinion today to forecast wage rate increases throughout the remainder of the 1980s and beyond. Such opinion is not unanimous and may be argumentative, so the economic expert should be able to describe, clearly and specifically, the assumptions on which his or her forecasts are based.

Earnings of *self-employed persons* and *employee–owners* of closely held companies are the most difficult to evaluate and project into the future. Since "employer-paid" benefits are not taxed except under special circumstances, self-employed persons tend to take as much of their compensation as possible in this form. The question arises as to the extent to which a "company-owned" car, boat, vacation house, or insurance policy represents a genuine business expense and not personal compensation. Similarly, are club memberships, directors' meetings in vacation locations, and travel costs actually for business purposes, or are they really a part of individual compensation? Unless the division of such costs between personal and business use is clearly specified in employee agreements, the answers to such questions may be difficult to ascertain.

Projection of future compensation of self-employed persons is complicated by two considerations. First, when such persons employ others, their employees represent both a cost and a source of profit to the owner–employee. Second, when the self-employed person is an entrepreneur in the initial stages of establishing a business, current compensation may be quite low and may not be indicative of long-term earnings. A recent case illustrates the first type of complication: A consulting structural engineer was injured, receiving leg injuries that now prevent him from climbing buildings to inspect work in progress and that also prevent him from standing at a drafting table for any length of time. His income after recovering from his injuries has been greater than before his accident; however, his loss of clients while he was recovering and his present need to hire draftsmen and inspectors have caused him a real and rather sizable loss of lifetime income.

The effects of personal injury on the *lifetime income of entrepreneurs* is illustrated by another recent case: A scrimshaw artist of extraordinary talent set up her own business in her home. She developed outlets for her products and established a growing sales force to represent them throughout New England. Nevertheless, her yearly income during her first two years of this activity was only around $4000. Injured by falling in a store's parking lot, she sprained her wrist and forefinger, incurring a 10 percent loss of their use. Unable to produce the same high-quality work after this accident, she went to work for a mass-producer of scrimshaw items. Her earnings in the first year after her accident amounted to $23,000. Nevertheless, her loss in lifetime income shall have been very high—and this fact was acknowledged in the jury's award.

A third case, involving the death in an airplane crash of a 34-year-old chief executive officer (CEO) of a publishing business, illustrates the complexity of economic issues that surround entrepreneurs and owners of closely held businesses. This executive was credited with the invention of a new product that served as the basis for creating his new company. At the time of his death his yearly earnings were approximately $250,000, and the claim by his estate for economic loss alone amounted to well over $10 million, as documented and determined by the plaintiff's economist. The economist consulted by the defense attorneys pointed out that the financing for the new company had been provided by an existing business firm owned by the decedent's family and of which the decedent was also the president at the time of his death; that both companies produced similar products and sold them to the same customers; and that average earnings of CEOs of companies having comparable sales revenues were only about $47,000 per year at the time of the accidental death. Thus, almost $200,000 of the decedent's yearly income was probably *a return to capital*, rather than earned income, and should not be used as a basis for projecting lost future income.

The loss of earned compensation caused by injury or death resulting from an automobile accident is frequently accompanied by a concomitant *loss of household services*. An individual's work contribution to his or her household has value even though it is normally not paid for with money. The monetary value of household production is somewhat difficult to determine, however. It is now a standard practice to impute market wage rates to the various jobs performed around the house and simply to multiply those wage rates by the average number of hours per week spent in each type of job. The choice of appropriate market wage is made based on the stated level of skill of the individual in performing such tasks.

This method of valuing household services is subject to some inaccuracy. A person unskilled in plumbing may take much longer to change a faucet washer than would even a new plumber's apprentice. Still, the household would not have to pay the travel time of the plumber's apprentice, so the imputation of that wage rate could be fair and reasonable. Similarly, a person washing clothes in a household's washing machine does not wash as many clothes in an hour as does a washing machine attendant in a commercial laundry. Since the efficient household worker normally does other tasks at the same time, the number of work hours allocated to clothes washing should be limited to their actual value. If this is done, a market wage may be closely representative of the actual market value of such a task. In any event, the value of lost household services should not be overlooked since it represents a real—and frequently sizable—loss to the household.

Economists can evaluate the future stream of expected earnings, benefits, and household services in one of several accepted ways. Average total life expectancy may be determined using tables published by the U.S. Department of Health and Human Services, and loss projections may be made for all or part of the "expected" remaining lifetime. Alternatively, the loss projected for each future year may be weighted by the probability of life in that year. Either method produces similar results.

Determination of the present value of future loss is highly dependent upon the wage growth rates and discount rates used by the economist. Some economists tend to simplify these calculations by assuming a "real" growth in income that is based on the national average growth of productivity and by assuming a "real" interest rate of roughly 3 percent in discounting future values back to their present value.* While this method is accepted by many professional economists, *it can be successfully challenged in cross-examination.* The wages of workers and earnings of professionals depend on local market conditions of supply and demand for their labor. Wage growth rates vary widely over the various occupations and, as described above, over the occupational life span of each individual. Real interest rates did range between 2.0 and 3.5 percent for many years, but they have been much higher than that since the late 1970s due to restrictive monetary policies by the Federal Reserve Board. *Thus, an economic analysis based on actual recent occupation-specific wage growth rates and interest rates is less likely to be successfully attacked.*

---

*The term "real" growth in economics refers to a rate of growth that does not include inflation, i.e., the appropriate inflation rate each year is subtracted from the actual wage growth rate or interest rate.

Expected work life spans are usually based on statistics published by the U.S. Department of Labor. In the past, these statistics accounted for unemployment and voluntary withdrawals from the labor force by subtracting such nonworking time from the average age at retirement of working men and women. More sophisticated analyses have now been performed by this federal agency using 1977 population data, and economists will soon be able to adjust future years' projections of earnings by the probability that they will actually be received.

III. EVALUATING BUSINESS LOSS

When automobile accidents result in injury to—or death of—a key person in a business, the business itself may suffer a wrongful loss. This is particularly true when the person directly harmed in the accident is an owner in a small, closely held business. In some such cases the business may be irretrievably harmed so that an injured plaintiff or a decedent's estate has lost all of their share of the future profits of the company, as well as their direct compensation.

Evaluations of the *economic loss of an ongoing business* are made in a manner similar to that used in evaluating the loss resulting from personal injury: the economist analyzes the probable future market share and profitability of the firm, assuming the continued availability of the key person, and then determines these factors under now existing circumstances. To do so, the economist may work with the firm's accountant, lawyers, and managers and owners. The economist's unique contribution is a knowledge of the particular market forces acting in the market in which the firm is involved and a grasp of the macroeconomic events that can affect that market. Using this knowledge and combining it with an analysis of the cost, production, and sales processes of the firm, the economist determines the firm's probable future market share and size and its expected profitability.

When the loss of the services of a *key person* causes the firm to terminate its business, the economic loss that results is its fair-market value prior to the accident, less the monies received from the sale of its remaining assets. A number of economic factors have been specified by the Internal Revenue

Service (IRS) for consideration in evaluating closely held businesses. In its Rev. Rul. 59-60, these factors are described as:*

1. The nature and history of the business.
2. The economic outlook in general and the condition of the business.
3. The book value of stock and financial condition of the business.
4. The earning capacity of the company.
5. The dividend-paying capacity of the company.
6. Goodwill and other intangible assets of the firm.
7. Stock sales and amount of stock to be valued.
8. The market price of stock of similar corporations.

The relative weight given to each of these factors is a matter of subjective judgment and should be based on common sense. In this area alone, the economic expert is permitted an *advocacy role*; therefore, it is to be expected that the economist's evaluation will be contested in court. This is appropriate for it permits the trier of fact to examine the assumptions used in making the evaluation, on both sides, and thus to arrive at a fair determination of economic loss.

IV. THE ECONOMIST'S ROLE IN PRODUCT LIABILITY

The economist can serve two purposes in product liability cases. First, economic analysis can provide information that can help to determine whether or not a purported act of negligence in design, manufacture, or quality control and product assurance was *economically unreasonable*—or if the manufacturer could have reasonably been expected to act otherwise. Frequently, an economic *cost-benefit analysis* is needed to determine whether design, production, or product-testing procedures could have been improved to yield greater safety assurance at a reasonable cost. (The most important recent issue here involves the installation of air bags and other passive restraints. Unless such restraints are mandated by federal regulations, the reasonableness of automobile manu-

---

*Much of this material is based on a comprehensive discussion by H. Calvin Coolidge, "Valuation of Closely Held Businesses," as published in Irving L. Blackman, *The Book of Tax Knowledge*. New York: Boardroom Books, 1981.

facturers' failure to install them may well be tested in the courts.)

The second purpose that economists can serve in product liability cases is to provide information that will help the trier of fact to establish a *fair value for punitive damages.* If punitive damages are to be used as a deterrence of future misconduct, they should be at least equal to the manufacturer's cost savings derived from the negligent act. However, the question arises as to whether marginal or average costs should be used as this measure. The economist, through analyses of the production and cost functions of the firm, can derive both of these measures and make recommendations as to which is more appropriate.

A manufacturer may be charged with negligence as a result of economic considerations in the design, production, and testing of a product. Inferior materials may be specified for use in components in order to reduce those components' costs. Production procedures may result in an unsafe assembly as a result of efforts to reduce labor costs. Testing to ensure that components meet design specifications may be performed on only a limited scale in order to reduce testing costs. In each case, the probability of a component failure, resulting in a threat to safety, must be balanced against the increased cost incurred in reducing that probability. Testing of every component received from an automobile supplier, for example, would detect all faulty units before they are installed in a new car. Yet, such complete testing could be prohibitively expensive—and would be impossible where destructive testing is required.

Thus, small samples of each lot of received parts are usually tested. It is then necessary to determine the statistical reliability of such test results. This statistic depends on more than just the sample size: both the safety factor incorporated into the component's design and the strength and homogeneity of the materials used in the component affect the reliability with which product assurance is determined by small sample tests. The reasonableness of the manufacturer's achieved test reliability must include considerations of these additional factors. The *economic test for reasonable behavior* involves the equating of marginal benefit to marginal cost: assuming correct engineering, testing should continue to the point where the cost of one additional test becomes greater than the value (however defined) of the improved reliability of test results that will be achieved.

The reasonableness of a manufacturer's *failure to incorporate newly developed safety innovations* into its new automobiles is also determined by a comparison of marginal costs and benefits. The dispute surrounding the installation of air bags and other passive restraints is an example of this situation. Here, the industry's refusal to install such equipment has been based on economics: the additional cost of such equipment would increase new-car prices and thereby reduce new-car sales and manufacturers' revenues and profits. Until they were rescinded on October 23, 1981, by the Administrator of the National Highway Traffic Safety Administration (NHTSA), federal rules required the installation of passive restraints (air bags or passive seat belts) in 1983 and subsequent years' new models. The rescission of this rule was prompted by manufacturers' objections made on economic grounds. However, since it takes five years to design a given year's new line, the fixed costs for design, tooling and dies, and assembly have been met and are now sunk costs. The only costs remaining for their implementation are the costs of the passive restraints themselves. Thus, the economic arguments of the manufacturers are subject to rebuttal. Further, the liability of the government itself is now at question. The rescission was successfully challenged by insurers, and the right of a federal agency to rescind a rule that it previously promulgated is, at the time of this writing, being considered by the Supreme Court.

When punitive damages appear to be warranted, the economist can determine the various values that might be appropriate. To an economist, the *minimum* such value is that which *would remove the profitability of negligent behavior*. Since punitive damages are, by their nature, intended to deter manufacturers from engaging in future wrongdoing, actual awards may be sought that are greater than that minimum. The sum total of such awards may be based on the size of the manufacturer's annual sales revenues, capital value, or profits. Since profits of automobile manufacturers in any given year will depend on market conditions, profitability might not be the best standard against which to determine the size of punitive damages. Such profits may be low in any given year simply because of poor management or failure to anticipate the nature of market demand. Such poor performance is usually corrected over time, or the manufacturer goes out of business. In other years, poor profits may result from macroeconomic conditions. High unemployment rates and/or high interest rates reduce the demand for new cars, reducing sales revenues and profits and even causing losses for a while. However, all these factors are irrelevant to product liability litigation, and punitive damages sufficient to punish the manufacturer for proven wrongdoing should usually be based on other factors.

V. EXAMINING THE EXPERT ECONOMIC WITNESS

An economist may be used as an expert witness if his or her specialized knowledge will assist the trier of fact in understanding the evidence or in determining a fact in issue. Thus, the first hurdle for admissibility is the existence of an issue related to the cause of action, the understanding of which requires more than common sense or the range of knowledge and experience possessed by the average person. The proponent need not establish that the judge or jury is totally unable to comprehend stated facts but only that the economist's opinion, as a result of his special training, knowledge, and experience, would be more accurate and less conjectural than an opinion arrived at in the absence of such skills.

Where an adequate understanding of the financial or monetary facts in evidence is beyond the capability of lay jurors, an economist's testimony may be admitted for two different purposes: (1) to *explain* the significance of specific data, figures, or terminology that the court has already found to be material or relevant and (2) to provide an *opinion* as to economic value, contribution, share, loss, impairment, or potential.

When an economist is used to express an opinion as to value, the proponent's direct examination of the expert should take place after all of the essential facts have been put into evidence. The reason for such timing is that the expert is not competent to testify as to the facts about which he has no personal knowledge, although he is competent to draw inferences from them. Counsel's examination should then proceed in the following manner: (1) a review of the expert's qualifications, (2) a justification for expert opinion in the case at hand, (3) a review of the bases for the expert's understanding of the particular facts in issue, (4) the solicitation of an expert opinion, and (5) an inquiry into the details, certainty, and significance of the opinions.

In *qualifying the expert*, the economist is introduced to the court, sworn in, and asked to properly identify himself for the record. The proponent then elicits the following information as to the witness's qualifications as an economist: (1) degree and university; (2) postdoctoral academic study; (3) informant history as a practicing economist: (a) corporate, (b) governmental, (c) academic; (4) major projects or studies; (5) publications: (a) books, (b) articles; (6) professional memberships; (7) honors or citations; and (8) previous testimony: (a) legislative (federal, state, or local), (b) administrative (federal, state, or local), (c) judicial (federal, state, or local). The qualification of the witness should be carried out with two objectives in mind: (1) impressing the jury and judge and (2) establishing that the expert possesses the requisites of knowledge, training, and skill that the layman lacks.

Once qualified, the bases for the expert's opinion must be established. The federal rules for evidence—which are similar to the rules followed in state courts—are as follows with regard to expert testimony:

Federal Rules of Evidence, Rule 702 states that if scientific, technical, or other specialized knowledge will assist the trier of fact in understanding the evidence or in determining a fact in issue, a witness qualified as an expert by knowledge, skill, experience, training, or education may testify thereto in the form of an opinion or otherwise.

Federal Rules of Evidence, Rule 703 states that the facts or data in the particular case upon which an expert bases an opinion or inference may be those perceived by or made known to him at or before the hearing. If those facts or data are of a general type reasonably relied upon by experts in the particular field in forming opinions or inferences upon the subject, those facts or data need not be admissible in evidence.

After qualifying the witness as an expert economist, the lawyer offering the expert's opinion as evidence must *lay the foundation* for the admissibility of that opinion. The foundation is composed of four elements: (1) establishing the need for expert evaluation, (2) establishing the accepted methodology for economic analysis of this type, (3) establishing factual assumptions, comprised of the previously admitted evidence in the case, and facts personally known to the expert, and (4) establishing the steps actually performed by the economist in evaluating the facts.

Examination of the witness should be conducted with the following objectives in mind: (1) impressing the judge and jury as to the need for an economist's expertise in the analysis of certain facts and the drawing of inferences therefrom, owing to the complexity of the issue and the existence of a valid scientific methodology for reaching opinions on such issues, and (2) establishing that the expert before the court did in fact perform an analysis by application of accepted methodology.

The economist cannot predict the future of any particular individual but can only determine statistically expected average life span, work life expectancy, and earnings and earnings growth in the particular occupational category and age group of the individual concerned. Thus, the opinion of the economist regarding the value of future personal loss must be obtained through use of a properly phrased hypothetical question. This hypothetical question must contain the facts in evidence and must permit the economist to make a general conclusion regarding the particular category into which the wronged individual falls.

The economist's opinion will be based on national and regional statistics. It must be shown on direct examination that these statistics are evaluated and accepted by professional economists in their performance of economic analyses. Otherwise, their use may be successfully objected to as being hearsay evidence. Similarly, the methodology used by the economist in arriving at an opinion should be described and validated as one accepted in common or preferred use by the economics profession.

Similar descriptions should be made of the methodology used in determining an opinion regarding business loss, the reasonableness of a manufacturer's behavior in product liability cases, and information regarding the value of possible punitive damages. In these cases, however, a hypothetical question is not appropriate. The economist's opinion should be based on personal examination of the relevant data pertaining to the firm and its industry.

Cross-examination of an expert economic witness should be made with care since it may result in additional opinions that are not favorable to the examiner's case. Still, economic analyses may be challenged on the bases of their assumptions and, on occasion, of the subject matter of the analysis itself. In such situations, when the size of the exposure warrants the expense, defense attorneys will frequently retain economists to assist them in the preparation of a knowledgeable cross-examination.

ACKNOWLEDGMENTS

The author wishes to acknowledge Serena Domolky, a Boston attorney in private practice and a consulting staff member of Commonwealth Research Group, Inc., for her contribution of the fifth and final subsection of this article—Examining the Expert Economic Witness.

25

Effective Claims Handling

JOSEPH O. KERN
Claims Consultant
Los Angeles, California

The author joined the claims department of a well-known casualty carrier upon his graduation from UCLA in 1948 and worked in various functions, ranging from field claims representative to claims supervisor. During that 18 years of employment, his claims work brought him in constant contact with lawyers. Out of this contact, it became apparent that it would be helpful for lawyers (particularly those representing claimants) to understand the claims man's distinctive attitude and viewpoint on the handling of soft-tissue injury claims. With such an understanding, the plaintiff's advocates would be in a much better position to present claims for their clients that could be resolved through a discussion on a basis of merit rather than through litigation. For the subsequent 17 years, Kern has been working in the capacity of "claims consultant" to attorneys handling personal injury cases. He is a frequent lecturer to numerous bar groups, speaking from experience acquired in 35 years of claims handling. He is presently a Claims Consultant and can be contacted at 2619 Wilshire Boulevard, Suite 912, Los Angeles, California 90057 (213-382-4262).

I. INTRODUCTION

Too few people have given sufficient thought to the preparation and management of the soft-tissue injury case with a view toward its acceptance by the claims person who will ultimately evaluate and settle it. Rather, many plaintiffs' advocates gather their clients' medical reports and specials in a haphazard, disorganized manner, failing in many instances to read carefully the reports and to check the bills that the adjuster will scrutinize for flaws. These flaws become the adjuster's weapons for argument to mitigate damages. At the time the claims person takes exception to some item of liability or damages, his adversary may become disillusioned about casualty carriers in general and will "file, serve, and talk later."

This kind of impasse leads to a plethora of unnecessary litigation and expense for both sides, not to mention the long-term effects of higher insurance premiums and costs for public services rendered in the courts. Without exception, every casualty carrier is literally in the business of settling claims. Most carriers will make an honest effort to settle equitably the vast majority of cases presented to them.

The author has had 18 years of experience with an insurance carrier and 17 years of experience as a claims consultant for plaintiffs' lawyers. His total experience supports the contention that if a claim is presented in CREDIBLE form, it is likely to elicit an equitable settlement offer.

The purpose of this section is to provide guidelines to help plaintiffs' lawyers avoid the most common pitfalls of a personal injury practice. Such an improved approach to claims handling would benefit defense attorneys and insurance claims personnel by promoting a more efficient, equitable, and professional approach to the resolution of meritorious claims. Though we will be dealing primarily with the so-called "bread-and-butter" soft-tissue injury, some attention will be devoted to more substantial cases.

II. ORGANIZATION AND MAINTENANCE OF THE PERSONAL INJURY FILE

Personal injury cases involve voluminous paper work, with a resultant deluge of different kinds of correspondence becoming a part of the same file. Investigation reports, medical reports, medical bills, other documentation of special damages, pleadings, and general correspondence all become a part of the file in an ongoing fashion. If these materials are individually accessible for review, much valuable time will be saved.

A segregated, legal-size file folder is purchasable but expensive. A simple inexpensive solution is to place an open letter-size manila folder within an open legal-size manila folder. At the top left side, fasten the left side of the letter-size folder to the left side of the legal-size folder. At the top of the right side of the letter-size folder, place an Acco-base through the front. Immediately below, place an Acco-base through the rear so that materials may be affixed to both sides. Finally, place an Acco-base at the top of the right side of the legal-size folder. Having accomplished the above, you will have four separate Acco-based areas to which designated materials may be affixed:

- *Acco-base One.* Summary sheet: type of case, retainer agreement, interview sheet, authorization forms, investigation, general correspondence.
- *Acco-base Two.* Yellow legal log sheet on which to note secretarial instructions, conversations with claims people, offers, demands, and the like.
- *Acco-base Three.* All items of special damages.
- *Acco-base Four.* Pleadings and discovery materials.

A. Diary Review

Regular reviews of files on a 30- to 60-day diary basis are essential to the efficient and timely settlement of cases. Make regular checks with clients and their doctors as to the completion of treatment and the obtainment of medical reports.

On the day the client signs a retainer agreement, the file should be diaried for review and noted in a Statute of Limitations log. If you do not keep logs or formal diary systems, impending statutes may be entered in your appointment calendar. Be sure to familiarize yourself with the statutes of limitations affecting governmental agencies, such as municipal transportation systems, that may be owned and operated by the city in which you practice.

Uninsured motorist cases may also be an exception to the general rule that being under the age of majority tolls the statute of limitations. For example, in California a minor's tender years do not protect him from the one-year statute of limitations in which to make a claim for his injuries. Note the exceptions in your state.

III. COLLATERAL SOURCES

Some casualty insurance carriers insert reimbursement clauses in their medical payments coverage contracts. Their insureds are obliged to sign an agreement to reimburse the carrier out of an anticipated third-party case recovery as a condition to qualify for the benefits of their medical payments coverage. In California and in some other states, the statutes provide that a carrier may take credit for all payments made under the medical payments coverage as an offset against whatever benefits may become due under the uninsured motorist portion of the case. Hence it becomes important to unearth all other available benefits, such as group medical insurance, through the client's or spouse's employers.

The great advantage of handling every aspect of the personal injury case is that you will always be in a position to advise your clients exactly what they will net from a settlement offer. In the event their cases present liability or other problems, their cases will be easier to compromise if medical bills can be paid by collateral sources rather than having to come out of the third-party settlement figure.

IV. NECESSARY AGREEMENTS AND FORMS

A. Retainer Agreements

Generally, personal injury retainer agreements are based on a contingency fee equal to one-third of the gross recovery if the case is settled before suit is filed, and 40 percent after litigation commences. If the case is settled immediately after the suit is served upon the defendant and before the expense of extensive discovery has been undertaken, counsel is afforded the flexibility of retaining the one-third contingency if it is advantageous to do so. On the other hand, retainer agreements that do not increase to 40 percent until 30 days before trial may prove to be burdensome.

The bulk of the work may have been completed long before the setting of a trial date. Since over 90 percent of the personal injury cases are settled before trial, the contingency agreement must take these factors into account.

Most retainer agreements provide that counsel will advance costs. These costs are reimbursed after the contingency fee is taken off the top of the gross settlement figure. Some law firms require their clients to advance costs. Many potential clients will balk when this arrangement is proposed; consequently, many substantial cases may find their way to another law office.

It is wise to include a Power of Attorney agreement in the retainer. Clients may be out of the country when it is necessary to act on their behalf. It is very important that the retainer reserve counsel's right to associate other counsel or experts for trial or for other purposes where outside expertise is required.

B. Authorization Forms

The authorization forms require the client's signature. They authorize counsel to secure necessary information regarding police reports, medical reports, and the like.

C. Information (Interview) Sheets

The initial procurement of detailed information from the client makes for the more efficient and convenient handling of the case.

V. CLIENT ORIENTATION

Cases will proceed more smoothly if clients are carefully advised at the outset, of the general stages through which the average case proceeds to settlement. They should be instructed to discuss their cases with no one. They may give no statements, oral or written, to any investigator or claims representative.

If medical treatment is in progress, clients should be encouraged to keep their appointments faithfully for as long as the attending physician deems it necessary. Any prolonged interruption of medical treatment does grave harm to the credibility of personal injury cases.

If medical treatment has not begun, it should be instituted immediately. An insurance adjuster will always question the authenticity of an injury for which delayed medical treatment is administered.

It is unwise to impart to clients an expectation of what their actual settlement figure may be. It is impossible to evaluate properly any case until such time as all of the pertinent parts of the case are available for evaluation. Providing that liability is clear, it is safe to advise clients that they are entitled to recover all tangible verifiable items of expense that they have incurred as a direct result of their injuries (Special Damages) plus compensation for pain and suffering and any permanent disability or residuals (General Damages).

VI. THE NEED AND METHODS FOR PRESERVING EVIDENCE

It has been found, from over 30 years of experience, that extensive investigation is not necessary for the vast majority of soft-tissue cases in which liability is not in dispute. However, a thorough investigation should be conducted in any major injury case—no matter how obvious the defendant's liability may appear at first blush.

Adjusters lay considerable emphasis on the magnitude of an impact as an indicator of the probability of resulting injury. Hence pictures of all vehicles become important if the damage is extensive. Often an accident site may subsequently be altered by construction or other means, following an accident. Pictures of the original site may prove crucial to the proof of a disputed liability case.

A resourceful investigator may be able to secure a statement from an adverse witness; hold off on the representation letter to a defendant until your investigator has completed his investigation.

Always check on the disposition of the defendant's motor vehicle citations. Many times insured defendants may not receive timely instructions and plead guilty to a traffic violation. A plea of guilty to a criminal charge is admissible in California in a civil suit for damages.

A. How to Select an Investigator

There are many licensed investigators whose statements are not worth the price of the ball-point pen with which they took them.

If possible, select an investigator who worked as a claims adjuster for a casualty company. Insurance adjusters receive formal "school" training as well as practical field experience. They generally are better informed in the areas of insurance coverages and procedures and may be able to assist you with additional problems encountered in some of your more difficult cases.

Never leave any investigator to his own devices. You must either tell him *exactly* what you expect.

Obtain a police report. If possible, take your client or witness to the scene of the accident.

B. Investigation

Formulate from the limited information on hand exactly how you wish to plot the course of the investigation. For example, if the police report indicates that your defendant was driving an out-of-state car in a residential area and, in the process, "wiped out" your minor client, who darted out into the street, there is always the possibility that this stranger to the neighborhood may have been looking for an address.

If an accident occurred at a blind, uncontrolled intersection, check the speed limit in the Vehicle Code to see if there may be an opportunity to develop the defendant's fault either through a statement by your investigator or through the taking of the defendant's deposition. In other words, hypothesize a theory of liability and proceed to develop it.

VII. WITNESSES

Whenever the testimony of a witness appears to be crucial to the successful conduct of a serious personal injury case, a deposition of the witness should be taken immediately to preserve his testimony. Here again, the witness should be taken to the scene of the accident. The witness should be permitted to review the police report and any other portion of your investigation that may help him to recall all that has transpired prior to his deposition. This same care and preparation should be taken prior to the taking of anyone's deposition.

Counsel will always find it advantageous to take an independent witness or principal to the scene of an accident so that both may become thoroughly familiar with the conditions at the scene prior to the taking of statements and/or depositions.

VIII. THE IMPLICATIONS OF "COMPARATIVE NEGLIGENCE"

Specific forms of "comparative negligence" prevail in many states (such as California).

Before embarking upon any personal injury cases, the practitioner should consider the possible implications of his immediate situation. For example, your clients may include a number of persons whose legal status with reference to liability is quite different. You may be representing a drunk driver who, although he entered the intersection on a green light and was struck by the cold sober defendant entering on a red light, might later be charged with some "comparative negligence" based on the fact that he may have been able to avoid the accident had he been sober.

Complicate this situation with a severely injured guest in your driver's car who also was sober, escaping completely the onus of any "comparative negligence." A conflict of interest arises out of the joint representation of your driver and his guest, by virtue of the fact that the guest has a "dead-bang" case against the red-light runner, and he may have something going against his drunk host. Obviously, you keep the innocent guest as your client, explaining to the driver that his interest will be well protected by one of your colleagues in another law office. It is advisable to make note of any possible conflict of interest situation on the interview sheet.

Resolving a case involving "comparative negligence" in California requires evaluating the case on the basis of damages and first arriving at a value assuming clear liability. The plaintiff's potential settlement may consist of his comparative share of what the case would have settled for had the defendant's liability been clearly established. For example, a case is worth $10,000 from the standpoint of damages. Your client contributed 25 percent of the negligence. Your client takes 75 percent, or $7,500, as his comparative share of the full value.

IX. GUEST CASES

The law varies from state to state for guest cases; in California, for example, guests may have claims against another driver, against their host driver, and even against another guest in the same car or another car, providing that the other guest commits a negligent act contributing to the accident. The other guest might call his driver–host's attention to an attractive person on the sidewalk, resulting in a rear-end accident with the car ahead.

The resolution of guest cases may also be complicated by the fact that a partially negligent driver–host may collide with a partially negligent uninsured motorist. In that case, two different coverages of the host's insurance policy come into play. The portion of the claim against the host might have to be resolved in the courts, whereas the insurance policy provides that the claim against the uninsured motorist may not be resolved in the courts but in one of the many arbitration procedures prescribed in its policy. Hence, it becomes important to make a clear evaluation of the exact status of your client with reference to the maximum insurance benefits to which he may become entitled, and then proceed accordingly.

X. MEDICAL REPORTS

A. Attending Medical Reports

In the parlance of a claims man's vernacular, Attending Medical Reports refer specifically to claimants' or plaintiffs' medical reports that are prepared by the treating physicians.

Casualty companies sometimes request medical information on their own short-form reports directly from the attending physician in such cases where the company representative is dealing directly with an insured or with a claimant not represented by counsel. For the most part, a narrative report is required to permit the physician to spell out in detail all of the medical information necessary to facilitate a proper evaluation of the patient's injuries.

Many so-called "family doctors" disdain a personal injury-type practice because of the extra demands on their time and the extra clerical overhead required to accomplish the voluminous paperwork. Family doctors may be hesitant to treat on a "lien basis" because it may not be financially feasible for them to wait until the patient's case is settled to be paid for their services.

Some physicians do treat on a "lien basis," and they may specialize in the treatment of traumatic injuries, offering treatment to cover orthopedic, neurological, cosmetic, and every other variety of traumatic injury. Among these medical specialists there may be some who acquire notorious reputations among the casualty carriers because of the ongoing similarity of their medical reports and their exorbitant charges for the treatment of soft-tissue injuries. Eventually, every report from such a physician becomes a candidate for careful scrutiny by the "jaundiced eye" of the claims representative with whom you may be dealing.

Although this may be the very first report of this kind that you have submitted to a claims person, he or she may have reviewed a hundred just like it. That same report might appear to you, and indeed it could actually be, a true and accurate account of the soft-tissue injuries sustained by your client; however, its credibility may be tainted in the eyes of the beholding claims representative who is called upon to translate its contents into settlement dollars for your client.

From the claims handling viewpoint, the preparation of any soft-tissue injury case must have as its goal an ultimate discussion of its value on the basis of its individual merit; hence, you must select a physician who does not overtreat or overcharge and who has the experience and capacity to prepare a credible report. The credibility factor of your case is the key to a successful personal injury practice.

Attending medical reports should, at the very minimum, contain the following information (as well as exclude particular information as indicated here):

- *HISTORY*: Should not go into any of the details of the accident other than auto vs. auto or auto vs. pedestrian, etc. Should not volunteer any extraneous medical history unless directly related to the injuries received in the instant accident.

- *COMPLAINTS*: Should contain a complete description of every area of complaint with the physician's supporting observations of bruises, limitations of movement, and the like.
- *X-RAYS*: Should have a coinciding area of complaint for every x-ray taken.
- *DISABILITY*: Should contain positive statements regarding temporary and/or permanent disability that go hand in hand with a loss of earnings claim: "The patient was totally disabled from performing the tasks required by his occupation from January 29 through March 1."
- *PROGNOSIS*: Should always be "guarded" to leave the door open for recurring symptoms that often reappear in severe soft-tissue injuries.

The visible evidences of soft-tissue injuries may disappear completely within several days after an accident. From that time on, a physician may be dealing with more subjective complaints than objective findings. The longer the subjective complaints continue beyond a time that the claims person believes to be a reasonable period, the more suspect the complaints become to the claims person evaluating the claim for settlement.

In this regard, it is noteworthy to comment upon a November 1979 report in *The Journal of Neurological and Orthopedic Surgery* prepared by Charles E. Wexler, M.D., a physician in Encino, California. The abstract of the report follows:

51 consecutive patients having cervical, and/or thoracic and/or lumbar thermograms were reviewed. 90 thermograms were performed in the 51 patients. In the 37 cases that had EMG studies, there was a direct correlation, positive or negative, between the EMG and the thermograms of 78%. The EMG correlated with the objective clinical findings in 86% of the cases; the thermograms in 92% of the cases.

Wexler concluded:

The thermograms provide a graphic complementary perspective to the EMG and to the myelographic evaluation of pain and/or herniated discs. Its statistical accuracy is comparable with these procedures, and it provides a perspective not obtainable by them. The thermogram is a picture of physiology and can evaluate and demonstrate sensory nerve damage thereby providing unique information unobtainable by other diagnostic tests.

Therefore, from a claims evaluation standpoint, the objective evidence produced by a thermogram could carry great weight in evaluating a claim, as much weight as any other objective evidence of injury.

B. Defense Medicals

The overwhelming majority of soft-tissue injury cases are settled without the benefit of a Defense Medical Report, which is prepared by a physician sometimes referred to as an Independent Medical Examiner and whose report has come to be identified as an IME or Independent Medical Examination.

Since the services of these examiners are procured to protect the interests of casualty carriers and their insureds, their reports are not as objectively independent as their title implies.

Many defense doctors fall into the same conservative pattern of understatement in report after report, just as some of their plaintiff-oriented colleagues may habitually exaggerate the medical aspects of their patients' cases. Oftentimes, one is led to marvel at the dissimilarity of two reports, both purportedly describing the injuries of the same patient.

The importance of the IME generally comes into play in conjunction with severe soft-tissue injuries and more often where there is the probability of permanent or partial disability evidenced by problems of a functional or cosmetic nature resulting from serious objective injuries. The defendant customarily is entitled to one IME of the plaintiff. Usually, this examination is performed after the plaintiff's case is in litigation.

In order to make the most of the defendant's one opportunity to examine the plaintiff, the defendant's carrier will first obtain every item of medical information available on the plaintiff. Then all of this information is sent to the independent medical examiner well in advance of the scheduled IME.

The independent medical examiner is thereby accorded the advantage of having on hand all attending medical information to use as a reference for his examination. Unless one is dealing with a serious objective-type injury, it is generally unwise to supply the defendant's carrier with so much medical ammunition in advance of the IME.

A client should always be accompanied by his lawyer to an IME. Some physicians habitually ask irrelevant questions regarding the facts of the accident. A plaintiff requires the same legal protection at an IME as he or she does at a deposition. There is a distinct advantage in attending an IME for the information gained for the purposes of cross-examining the defense doctor at trial.

In terms of claims handling for soft-tissue injuries, the defense medical examination occurs in a minority of cases, usually when there is a serious dispute as to the validity of the claim. Therefore, once such an examination has been conducted, the person handling the file on the part of the claimant should reevaluate the entire file and update it accordingly.

XI. AUTOMOBILE INSURANCE POLICIES

Automobile insurance carriers constantly are adding benefits to their insureds' policies. Since the most accessible assets of defendant drivers are their liability coverages, it becomes a rewarding task to acquire an in-depth knowledge of the possible benefits accruing to a client through the insurance policies of a defendant driver and through the client's own policies as well. The following guidelines hopefully will serve to ring that necessary bell leading to the recognition of first-party and third-party benefits that are not initially apparent.

Since the coverages and conditions of auto insurance policies vary among our United States—and, indeed, within the individual states themselves—it becomes necessary to scrutinize clients' possible insurance benefits on a case-to-case basis. It is not possible to rely on one's general knowledge of what one understands a standard auto policy to contain. It may also prove advisable to obtain a copy of the defendant's auto policy if some question of coverage is in doubt. Clients' collateral benefits, such as group disability or health plans, should also be identified.

A. Defendants' Auto Coverages

"*Primary coverage*" is the liability coverage that applies to the *involved* vehicle. "*Excess coverage*" is the liability coverage that applies to the involved vehicle after the "primary coverage" has been exhausted. Liability auto coverages are referred to interchangeably as PL for "personal liability", as PI for "personal injury", and as BI for "bodily injury."

Liability risks are underwritten generally in denominations of 15,000/30,000, 25,000/50,000, and up, the lowest offered coverage conforming generally to the statutory requirements of the state in which it is written. The first figure represents the limit of the amount that may be paid to one person; the second, the maximum amount that may be paid to any number of persons in the same accident.

"*Excess coverage*" exists when an *insured* driver is driving a *nonowned* vehicle or when an insured driver may have his primary coverage with one carrier and his excess coverage with another. Liability coverages may also be written in single-limit denominations wherein any portion or all of the limit may be paid to one or any number of individuals in the same accident.

"Property damage" coverages are single limit and are represented by a third figure, italicized in the following example: 25,000/50,000/*10,000*.

Deeper pockets may be reached when a defendant driver is in the course of his employment or acting as another's agent in some other capacity.

B. Plaintiffs' Coverages

"*Uninsured motorist coverage*" in insurance parlance refers to a first-party coverage providing third-party benefits to an insured who is injured by a negligent uninsured motorist. The insured need not be in an automobile to qualify for the benefits of this coverage.

Uninsured motorist coverage may be written in limits equal to the statutory limits of a particular state, or it may be offered in limits as high as the selected liability limits. Numerous casualty companies include the additional benefit of extending to an insured the limits of his uninsured motorist coverage in instances where the defendant may be *underinsured*. Still other insurance companies write underinsured motorist coverage as a separate coverage within the auto policy.

"*Medical payments coverage*" provides for first-party coverage wherein an insurer agrees to reimburse an insured for reasonable medical expenses incurred as the result of an accident within a prescribed period for prescribed amounts regardless of fault. Medical payments are generally written in amounts from $1,000 to $100,000 PER PERSON for each accident and are usable for periods ranging from one to five years from the date of the accident.

The benefits derived from this expansive coverage add a new dimension to the conduct and management of personal injury cases wherein considerations for future medical care may deter a cautious plaintiff's advocate from consummating a timely third-party settlement. This coverage is of particular value to minors who may have sustained injuries to growth plate areas, or to teeth, or to the face, or to any part of the body where there exists the possibility of permanent cosmetic or functional residuals that cannot be resolved through treatment or prognosis on a short-term basis. This coverage extends to cover insureds in the capacity of pedestrians as well.

XII. AUTOMOBILE POLICY DEFINITIONS

Every auto policy contains a section devoted to definitions. It is important to refer to this section whenever there is a doubt in the reader's mind as to, for example:

- Who is an insured?
- What is an automobile?
- What is an occurrence?
- What is an accident?

A. Key Phrases and Definitions in the Policy

1. "Arising out of the use thereof."
2. "The loading and unloading thereof."
3. "Temporary substitute automobile."
4. "Newly acquired automobile."
5. "In or upon, entering or alighting therefrom."

XIII. CASE EXAMPLES

For the purpose of the following case examples, these abbreviations shall be employed:

- UM—for uninsured motorist coverage
- PI—for personal injury
- Med. Pay.—for medical payments

"Full coverage" shall mean 100,000/300,000 for PI and UM, 100,000 per person for Med. Pay., and no-deductible Collision.

Mary Jones Goes to the Market

Mary Jones drives her fully covered station wagon to the market, accompanied by Henry Jones, Jr., her 10-year-old son, who occupies the front passenger seat. While she is completely stopped in a parking space, another motorist backs into her, causing extensive damage to her car and moderate injury to her and Henry Jr. The other motorist commences to leave the scene. In her haste to alight from her own car, Mary trips and falls to the pavement, severely injuring her right knee. The would-be-hit-and-run motorist sees that Mary is making note of his license number. He returns to the scene. In the course of attempting to wrest her notebook from her, he accidentally causes her to fall to pavement, causing a back injury requiring subsequent hospitalization. While Mary was scuffling with the other motorist, Henry Jr. throws a Coke bottle from within the wagon aimed at his mother's antagonist. The Coke bottle misses its intended target and accidentally strikes an innocent bystander, inflicting facial injuries. The other motorist is uninsured.

All of the above-described incidents "arose out of the use of" Mary Jones' station wagon. Hence all of her claims as well as her son's claims for injuries would be covered under the UM and Med. Pay. coverages. The damage to her car would be covered under her Collision as UM does not pay for property damage. The innocent bystander was compensated under the PI portion of Mary's policy.

Henry Jones, Sr., Picks Up a New TV Set

Henry enlists the help of "Neighbor Joe" to pick up a new TV. On the way to the TV store, they have a flat tire. While extracting the spare, Henry bumps his head on the inside of the wagon, sustaining a mild concussion. They pick up the cartoned TV set and return to Henry's driveway where they proceed to unload it. Henry faints, losing his grip on the TV set, thereby suddenly transferring the full weight of it to Neighbor Joe. Caught off balance, Joe falls backward on the driveway, injuring his back. A neighborhood child who has been watching the proceedings at close range suffers a broken leg when the TV set falls on him.

Henry's initial bump on the head is covered under Med. Pay. ("in or upon"). His subsequent fainting spell is also covered as it is a continuation of the initial event. Neighbor Joe's and Neighbor Child's injuries are covered under Henry's PI because the wagon was being "unloaded" at the time the injuries were incurred. Since the accident occurred on Henry's premises, his Homeowner's Policy would also be applicable.

Mary Jones Takes Kids to School

Mary Jones borrows Neighbor Joe's fully covered station wagon to car-pool kids to school. Riding in the front passenger seat is Nervous Nellie, one of the teachers, whose fully covered vehicle is in the repair shop. The eight other passengers are school children. While traversing a busy thoroughfare, Mary sees a dog running on a collision course with the wagon. Mary feels she has the situation under control, but Nervous Nellie grabs the steering wheel, causing the vehicle to go out of control, climb a sidewalk curbing, and strike a bus-stop bench, killing three persons seated thereon. Mary's seat belt fails to restrain her, and she is catapulted through the windshield, fracturing her skull. The gas tank explodes, and all eight children receive third-degree burns.

Three automobile liability coverages are involved. Neighbor Joe's primary coverage on the *involved* vehicle: 100,000/300,000; Mary Jones' secondary coverage by virtue of her non-owner–driver position: 100,000/300,000; Nervous Nellie's tertiary coverage, since she momentarily exercised control of the car, causing the accident: 100,000/300,000. Hence, there is available a total of $900,000 in auto liability coverages for the third-party claims arising out of this accident. Since each of the three insureds carries $100,000 Med. Pay. per person, there is a total of $3 million coverage available to the 10 injured persons riding in Neighbor Joe's wagon, payable by way of reimbursement in the total amount of $300,000 per person for medical expenses incurred within five years from the date of the accident for injuries received in the accident.

Since laboratory tests proved the seat belts to be defective, and there was a serious flaw in the design of the exploding gas tank, deeper pockets were reached to compensate Mary Jones and the eight children.

Henry Jones, Sr., Buys a New Sports Car

On September 1, 1982, Henry Jones, Sr., buys a new sports car. Knowledgeable Nolan, Henry's insurance agent for the fully covered wagon, gives Henry a quote that prompts Henry to look elsewhere for insurance. Henry forgets to attend to the insurance, and on September 28, 1982, rear-ends a stopped vehicle, totaling two cars and causing severe injury to himself and the other driver. Henry ends up in the hospital, leaving it to Mary to report the accident to Knowledgeable Nolan, whom she believes to have handled the insurance on Henry's sports car. Nolan then advises her that he did not underwrite the risk, "but there is no need to worry because the sports car is a 'newly acquired vehicle,' which is covered automatically for 30 days following the date of its acquisition under the same policy covering your fully covered station wagon."

Mary Jones Has Her Fully Covered Wagon Overhauled

Mary Jones takes her wagon to a local garage. The mechanic tells her the work will take a week. The garage owner lends her an uninsured clunker for transportation, and she rear-ends another motorist on the fourth day of use. Knowledgeable Nolan advises her: "Don't worry—that clunker qualifies as a 'temporary substitute automobile,' and you are fully covered under the same policy that covers your fully covered wagon."

Henry Jones, Jr., Practices on His Pogo Stick

Henry Jones, Jr., is practicing on his pogo stick around the family swimming pool when a drunk, uninsured motorist crashes through the backyard wall, knocking Henry, Jr., into the pool. Henry Jr. receives two broken legs and almost drowns as a result of the mishap. Knowledgeable Nolan tells Henry Sr. and Mary that "it doesn't matter what

Henry was doing or where he was, *so long as he was injured by a negligent, uninsured motorist*: case covered for $100,000 UM and $100,000 Med. Pay."

Henry Jones, Jr., Plays King of the Mountain on Dad's Sports Car

Henry Sr. parks his sports car on his inclined driveway. Henry Jr. is on the roof of the car roughhousing with two neighbor kids who are trying to pull him off from either side. A faulty emergency brake releases, and the car rolls backward down the incline. Before the car reaches the street, all three kids are knocked to the cement driveway, receiving injuries. The sports car continues backward across the street, pinning Neighbor Joe to the side of his station wagon, from which he was alighting.

All three kids were either "in or upon, entering or alighting" from the sports car. Hence, $100,000 Med. Pay. for each. In addition, any benefits available under Henry Sr.'s Homeowner's Policy would apply for injuries sustained on the *premises*. Neighbor Joe made claim against Henry's PI auto coverage and against his own Med. Pay. coverage since he was alighting from his own vehicle. Later, all involved made claim against the manufacturer of the sports car when laboratory tests proved the emergency brake malfunctioned.

Henry Jones, Jr., Is Hit in a Pedestrian Crosswalk

Two westbound drag racers are contesting for honors near Henry Jr.'s school. Henry is crossing from south to north in the west crosswalk. When he reaches the center of the street, he sees the two dragsters bearing down upon him. Drag racer one attempts to go around Henry on the south side and, in so doing, hits Henry with his right front fender, knocking Henry directly into the path of drag racer two. Drag racer one is fully covered; drag racer two is an uninsured motorist.

Since Henry Sr.'s UM and Med. Pay. coverage extends to Henry Jr. as a resident family member and as a pedestrian, Henry Jr. falls heir to the benefit of $100,000 Med. Pay. and

$100,000 UM. A dispute arises between the drag racer's and Henry Sr.'s carrier as to which drag racer is responsible for Junior's damages. The family lawyer files a lawsuit naming both drag-racers as defendants. The adjuster for Henry Sr.'s company advises the lawyer that if he takes his case to judgment, he will automatically invalidate the UM coverage, and that the UM portion of the claim must be handled through an arbitration procedure described under the "Conditions" portion of Henry Sr.'s policy.

Because of the aggravated liability aspects of the case, both carriers tender their $100,000 limits. Henry Jr. will be availing himself of the unused portion of the $100,000 Med. Pay. for the next three or four years for dental work and plastic surgery that cannot be performed at this time.

XIV.   EVALUATION AND NEGOTIATION

"There are many truths of which the full meaning cannot be realized until personal experience has brought it home" (John Stuart Mill, 1806–1873). Such is the case with the evaluation and negotiation of the "run-of-the-mill soft-tissue injury cases" that comprise the bulk of the average PI practice. The only general guideline that I have found to be reasonably accurate over a 35-year period is "If the client nets as much or more than his lawyer and his doctor, he is generally satisfied with the handling of his case."

Formulating demands based on a *multiplication of special damages* is probably the most widespread and unproductive practice in the marketplace of claims today; this can be demonstrated by considering two hypothetical cases and by keeping in mind what already has been said about the importance of CREDIBILITY. There would be absolutely no problem in negotiating a settlement in the range of $1500 to $2000, or three or four times the medical bill of $500, assuming no liability problems and timely medical treatment. Consider another soft-tissue case where treatment may have been commenced two weeks following the accident, where impact was relatively minimal and medical bills totaled $5000. This kind of case is more liable to elicit an offer of one-half the specials than it is likely to be consummated by a settlement in the $15,000 to $20,000 range. Here again, the importance of collateral sources should be reemphasized as Med. Pay., group health coverages, and the like make it possible to compromise problem cases, which may otherwise become litigated.

The point of diminishing returns in the vast majority of soft-tissue injury cases is reached the moment the case goes into litigation: if a case with a settlement range of $3000 to $3500 elicits an offer of $2750, and counsel and client refuse to settle for less than $3500, consider the amount of legal work that must be accomplished to obtain that additional $750 of which counsel will recover a percentage portion for fees. Time is money, and answering interrogatories and taking depositions takes time. Also, clients' interests may be better served by settlement than by litigation because of increased fees and costs.

Very often, when a claims representative asks me for a demand on a soft-tissue case, I may reply, "Whatever is fair." The purpose of this reply is to produce an offer before a demand is made. This gives the "demander" a distinct advantage at the outset of negotiations because he will know more than his adversary from the start. One may be either pleasantly surprised or sorely disappointed by some claims representative's idea of "whatever is fair," depending upon the experience and sagacity of the person making the offer. Suffice it to say, one is always better off in any negotiating situation if one is able to get an inkling of what the other fellow is thinking before committing to a demand.

XV. MAJOR INJURY CASES

In the vast majority of major injury cases, it is wise to litigate as soon as all possible defendants can be identified and a proper complaint be drawn. Major injury cases bring major hardships to the injured and to their families, and time always runs in favor of defendants for a number of reasons: backlog of available trial dates, future availability of witnesses, drain of financial reserves through prolonged medical expenses, and the like.

The one possible exception to the above exists when it can be determined at the outset that the plaintiff's case has a value clearly in excess of the value of the defendant's total assets. If, for example, it is ascertained that the defendant's only asset is his $100,000 PI coverage and the plaintiff lost a leg as a result of the defendant's negligence, litigation may not ensue. Counsel may need only to write a demand letter to the defendant's casualty carrier requesting that the policy limits be surrendered within a reasonable time (30 days would be more than reasonable in this situation). In such states as it is permitted, such a demand letter would set up the carrier for a Bad Faith Action in the event the carrier was inclined to procrastinate about surrendering the policy limits.

XVI. CLAIMS HANDLING SPECIALISTS

Many attorneys are quite effective in handling claims involving soft-tissue injuries, but lawyers have other obligations, such as trial practice, that may distract them, limit their time, or prevent them from keeping up-to-date on the details of claims handling. As with other areas of legal and paralegal practice, specialists or experts in a particular area have evolved due to their special training, unique talents, and special experiences. For example, individuals who have many years of experience in handling claims for insurance carriers and who have subsequently consulted with plaintiff attorneys may have a unique understanding of "both sides" of claims processing. The volume of claims and litigation in any particular office may justify retaining specialists in claims handling as a good business and professional practice.

26

Structured Settlements
(Periodic Payments)

EDMUND A. McGINN, J.D.
McGinn & McGinn
Council Bluffs, Iowa

Edmund A. McGinn is a member of the law firm of McGinn & McGinn, which is involved in the general practice of law. Mr. McGinn received his Juris Doctor from Creighton University College of Law in Nebraska. He negotiated the first million-dollar settlement in Iowa, with a structured value in excess of $2.7 million. He has lectured extensively on the topic of structured settlements at various national, regional, and local bar conferences. His articles on structured settlements have been published in Trial (*June 1982*), Modern Trials II (*July 1982*), *and publications of the Colorado Bar Association and the Florida Academy of Trial Lawyers. The law firm of McGinn & McGinn is located at 222 Council Bluffs Savings Bank Building, Council Bluffs, Iowa 51501 (712-328-1566).*

I. INTRODUCTION

Congratulations, you have just negotiated the periodic payment of your settlement, otherwise known as structuring a settlement. However, the recent popularity of such settlements has created situations in which many attorneys have only had a superficial understanding of the advantages and complexities of the concept of structured settlements.

As with the older concepts of workmen's compensation, small claims, and no-fault legislation—all of which provide periodic payment throughout a period of disability or provide for the periodic payment of judgments—the periodic payment of a settlement usually provides for monthly or determined payment of damages for the lifetime of the injured plaintiff. The payment is only one part of a four-part settlement: (1) cash equal to all special damages, (2) additional cash in a significant sum to provide the victim with a "nest egg," (3) the attorney fee paid in a lump sum or on a periodic or deferred basis, and (4) payment to the victim and/or his family, usually monthly, of a sum sufficient to provide for all support, future medical needs, and general maintenance expenses.

II. A BOOMING BUSINESS SINCE 1979

Since 1979 there have been several thousand structured settlements worth millions of dollars. Lawyers must recognize that the common law theory of lump-sum verdict and lump-sum settlements now has a viable alternative.

With the number of million-dollar-plus verdicts increasing, laws are proposed to limit recoveries, to provide for periodic payments of judgments, and to limit trial by jury.

In February 1981, Jury Verdict Research reported 407 verdicts or settlements exceeding $1 million or more since it began compiling records in 1962. Of these verdicts, 79 were rendered in 1980.

Million-dollar verdicts or settlements will continue because of the following circumstances: the skill, exactness, and efforts of plaintiffs–attorneys in presenting a total comprehensive picture of the actual loss suffered by claimants; inflation and the threat of future inflation; severe injuries suffered by the victim, i.e., paralysis, severe brain damage, etc.; the constant escalation of medical care; escalating wages; and specialized but expensive rehabilitation clinics. We can plainly see that jury verdicts will continue to increase and that periodic payment settlement will more often be proposed as an alternative. Major insurance companies now routinely propose periodic payment settlements in many tort claims.

A periodic settlement may be attractive because it is often assumed that the plaintiff is unable to handle a large sum of money in such a way that future needs are provided for; in addition, the primary benefit is that the invested return of the purported lump sum value is received tax free to the plaintiff throughout the years of periodic payments.

Funding of the periodic payment may be by annuities, purchase of a stock–bond portfolio, or trusts. The stated benefits or problems discussed herein can equally apply no matter which method of funding is used.

III. PARTIES TO AN ANNUITY SETTLEMENT

1. The casualty company is usually the purchaser of the annuity.
2. The casualty company, if not the defendant, is usually the owner.
3. The victim for whom the annuity is written is the annuitant or plaintiff.
4. The victim or his/her family is the beneficiary or the plaintiff.
5. The life insurance company is the recipient of a lump-sum premium.

The purchaser (casualty company) as owner of a life insurance contract (life company) pays a single premium to the life company, and the life company promises to pay periodic payments, usually monthly, to the beneficiary/annuitant for life or a term of years.

The beneficiary is designated by the owner and could be the plaintiff, his family, or a trust. The annuity concept offers many and varied options as to time of payment, guarantees, beneficiaries, as well as other conditions.

IV. AVAILABLE ANNUITIES

Here's how the annuity works. It can be a settlement including one or a combination of the following: straight life; annuity for term certain (5-10-20 years); life with term certain, joint and last survivor; annuity with escalating payments; annuity with deferred payments.

V. CLAIMS FOR CONSIDERATION

A wide variety of claims can be considered for a structured settlement. These could include all personal injury cases, product liability, malpractice, workmen's compensation, and general tort claims.

VI. VALUE OF CLAIM TO WARRANT STRUCTURE

Many economists and insurance companies feel that the claim should be worth $100,000 to warrant structuring. Several leading insurance companies will structure practically all and any claims, regardless of the amount. One major company structured a settlement as low as $1400.

VII. YOUR CLIENT'S CHARACTERISTICS

Characteristics of a client who might warrant structure include lack of education, incompetence, prodigality, alcoholism, etc. Widows, minors (to receive at legal age, etc.), and the brain damaged may also warrant structure. Predictable medical costs are easy to structure; however, where there are uneven or unpredictable medical costs the future payments are more difficult to determine. The monthly payments should equal or exceed the lost wages, rehabilitation expenses, living expenses, etc., and can be a combination of two or three or more annuities to cover specific beneficiaries.

VIII. EXAMPLES OF SETTLEMENTS

The following are a couple of structured settlements experienced by this writer:

Case A

A 51-year-old salesman earning approximately $26,000 annually; rear-end collision; six-month hospitalization; limited quadriplegic; resides at home. All medical equipment is available, house was ramped, outdoor deck added to home, mobile van purchased, etc.

The settlement provided: $454,880 cash received up front; $780,000 paid for annuity; claimant to receive $94,521 annually ($7,876.75 monthly) for life, with five years guaranteed; $20,000 to spouse annually upon death of husband or to commence at 61st month should husband die within first 60 months.

The million-dollar casualty limits were recovered, with additional contribution and waiver of subrogation totaling $234,800, and the case was settled without suit within 19 months of accident. Anticipated benefits are in excess of $2.7 million.

Detailed documentations were made to determine the monthly needs of the claimant. A detailed outline of the life of the plaintiff for 24 hours was recorded and in effect was the script to have been used in a "day-of-the-life" film. Following consideration of the outline, the settlement was expedited and the actual filming not needed. Case reported—23 A.T.L.A. L.Rep III (April, 1980).

Case B

A 24-year-old wife in coma with monthly costs of rest home care at $1346, and approximately $47,000 in medical expenses at time of settlement.

The settlement provided: $456,000 cash up front; $2,500 per month payable to the wife for life, with five years guaranteed; $1000 per month for the husband, with 20 years guaranteed; $750 per month for minor daughter (age 4) for 10 years commencing at age 18, plus an additional $12,000 annually on her 18th thru 22nd birthdays (both guaranteed).

IX. BENEFITS

Benefits to the plaintiff include regular monthly payments sufficient for all needs, periodic (monthly) payments that protect the plaintiff from misuse or squandering, payments guaranteed for life and/or term of years, and relief from expense and worry of investment policy. Management-free income shifts the burden of providing the costs of lifetime care back to the responsible party since the annuity insurance company is supposed to have investment and management expertise, especially in regard to long-range investments. In addition, there are significant tax advantages in that the principal settlement funds and invested earnings thereon are received exempt from income tax.

Rev. Rule 75-232 (1975, 1 CB 94) required that a recovery allocated to medical expenses be completely used up before medical deductions (§213) are allowed. Also, double exclusion based on interaction of medical expenses deduction of §213 and §104(a) exemption for recoveries to reimburse personal injury are prohibited. See IRS §104(a)(2) and Reg. §1 1:04-1(a).

Benefits to the casualty company include the following: A periodic payment of a settlement generally reduces actual costs of verdict or settlement. Reversionary benefits may be payable to the casualty company in the event of early demise of beneficiaries. It becomes a negotiating tool as the company can provide for large future payment without disbursing a larger present value sum. It may help effect an early settlement as the company has said it will pay all present bills, pay the lawyer, and pay enough each month for a lifetime to place the plaintiff in the same or a better financial position than before the accident. It should reduce investigation, legal, and trial costs. It allows assets to stay in the insurance industry. Files can be closed and required reserve terminated. The present value costs (usually lower) reduce the claim experience of the casualty company and therefore should have a direct relation to lowering future customer premium costs. The casualty company avoids future administrative costs of payment as these are assumed by a life company.

Benefits to the attorney may exist as the attorney may choose to receive his fee via annuity over a period of years. This allows balance and continuity in annual income that could result in some tax benefit. However, the fee should be based on the present worth of the settlement rather than on the total sum of future payments.

It would be wise to include an option to structure in the present contingent fee contract. The attorney probably cannot structure a fee if the plaintiff accepts a lump sum. The problem can be avoided by an option in the original contingent fee contract.

If the plaintiff is incompetent, it would be wise to get the fee contract approved by the court prior to the final settlement since a contract with spouse or family is not sufficient. Also, a similar court order on an estate proceeding for a deceased plaintiff should be obtained.

An annuity application will have to be executed by the attorney.

The public benefits because if the plaintiff has dissipated or squandered funds, it is the public who will pay the bills and the expenses of future care. Recipients of large-sum awards are presumed by statistical studies to be victims of unscrupulous advisers, victims of well-meaning friends, or lacking in long-range investment knowledge that would guarantee future income. A structured settlement will provide monthly payments to a plaintiff that are tax free; in addition, payments can continue to a spouse or an heir, free of estate proceeding.

X. ANNUITY

Historically, the annuity may not be the highest or most attractive investment, but when consideration is given to the guarantees, the social advantages of managed money, the beneficial effects on negotiations, plus the tax benefits allowed, very often the result is an attractive package.

A broker's fee is paid for the placement of the annuity—usually 3 to 4 percent on the initial $100,000 (the lower the annuity, the higher the fee).

Many states also charge an "annuity premium tax" that varies from 1/2 to 2 percent. Costs of an annuity vary with all the companies due to their investment patterns. Therefore, the best approach is to settle a case for X dollars and then "go shopping" to see what company will offer the highest return. If the casualty company will not disclose the actual cost of its package, you and your economist should determine the costs as nearly as possible.

The use of the annuity settlement is approved in Rev. Rule 79.220.

XI. TRUST

If you are structuring through a trust and using a third-party specialist company, the following documents must be prepared and executed: settlement agreement, an assignment and assumption agreement, a guarantee of payment performance, and the trust agreement.

The trust will be nondiscretionary, irrevocable (except in the case of death), and can run as long as 30 years.

Payments are usually made to the plaintiff or other heirs, etc., semiannually as interest is received. Fees are usually deducted from the first semiannual payment; thus, all of the money is invested throughout the terms of the trust.

Utilization of a trust method of structuring is approved in Rev. Rule 77-230.

XII. FACTORS TO CONSIDER

We suggest the following steps of procedure in negotiating a structured settlement.

Determine the value of the total case first. Get a sufficient amount in cash to pay all bills, recoup wages, liens, and rehabilitation expenses, and get sufficient additional cash to provide a "nest egg." Determine the per-month future costs and needs of the plaintiff; assure that the monthly payment is inflation-proof.

Have your economist determine true benefits, present worth, and cost of the total settlement. Contact other insurance companies, asking costs of the same benefits; do not dismiss early attempts at rejection of your proposal since it may be the first time the casualty company has ever considered a structured settlement. Consider the structured settlement in cases of catastrophic injuries, especially when the plaintiff has long-term future disability or incapacity. Set as the minimum goal a guaranteed monthly payment to provide lifetime care and support at an income level that allows a person to retain or exceed his or her status prior to injury. Consider education funds for minor dependents as additional annuities. Become acquainted with insurance law and insurance terms or, better yet, contact a specialist.

Specialists in assisting the settlement usually have no fee to the plaintiff or the casualty company because they will be paid by the life insurance company (usually 2 to 4 percent). Some specialist companies represent defendants or the casualty companies only; some companies will work for either the plaintiff or the defendant or will advise and structure for both at the same time. With approximately 1800 life insurance companies in this country, about a dozen can or will write special annuity contracts required by the structure.

XIII. OTHER CONSIDERATIONS

Carefully review all figures with your client. Your fiduciary relationship requires your understanding of and a full disclosure to your client concerning benefits, present worth, discount factors, tax benefits, guarantees, etc., of the structure versus the lump sum. Also, your fiduciary relationship probably obliges you to seek a structured settlement with the same integrity as a lump sum. After a comparison of the two, the final decision is made. One law school professor has indicated that the failure to consider the option of structured settlement is a basis for legal malpractice. Similarly, a casualty company that refuses to consider a proposed structure would be acting in bad faith.

With your economic expert, you can accurately estimate the present value and the rate of return. You and your client do not own the annuity policies, for if you do own them, you have constructively received the funds, and all future income incident to the annuity is taxable as ordinary income. Check the financial strength of your life insurance company, and obtain a Best Report Rating on the company. Insurance companies are rated A+ to C; of the 1800 life companies in the United States, more than 250 are rated A+. Obtain the best possible return by having your specialist shop around.

XIV. NONSTRUCTURABLE CASES

Section 104(a)(2) of the IRS Code exempts from gross income any money received as damages suit settlement or verdict on account of personal injury or sickness. Therefore, if your case is not a recovery for personal injury or sickness, the proceeds of the recovery are NOT exempt under 104(a)(2).

Types of cases not subject to a tax-free structured settlement include lost income, invasion of privacy recovery, payment for services, wages and employment rights, etc.

XV. CREDITOR POSITION

IRS Code Sec. 104(a)(2) states that damages received from personal injury are excluded from gross income of the recipient. Annuity contract or trust, therefore, cannot, should not, and must not convey actual or constructive receipt of the settlement premium. Therefore, the defendant or defendant's liability insurance carrier has all rights of ownership in the annuity or trust, including the right to change beneficiary (Rev. Rule 77-220), and the company is not required to set aside specific assets to secure any part of its obligation (Rev. Rule 79-313).

If the owner and insuror (defendant, casualty company, life company) take bankruptcy, the plaintiff is considered a general creditor. Presumably, however, the bankruptcy court could exempt the annuity from the bankruptcy estate or impose a constructive trust upon it under Sec. 514a(1) of the Bankruptcy Reform Act.

The plaintiff has apparently no assistance in collecting the annuity under the Uniform Commercial Code. This code does not consider the matter of periodic payments and Article Nine excludes judgments; thus, the plaintiff is deemed to have only the rights of an unsecured creditor.

XVI. PERTINENT IRS REGULATIONS

Sec. IRC 104(a)(2) excludes all damages from gross income. With the passage of the Periodic Payment Settlement Act of 1982 (signed into law January 14, 1983), Section 104 has been amended and a new Section 130 added. The act has codified the following revenue rulings.

Punitive damages for personal injury possibly may be received as damages within the meaning of 104(a)(2) [Rev. Rule 75-45, 1975, 1-CB 47].

Trust distributions made from income or corpus of the trust involved are received as damages within the meaning of 104(a)(2) [Rev. Rule 77-230, 1977, 2-CB 214].

Annuity payments from a policy owned by defendant's liability company are received as damages within the meaning of 104(a)(2), subject to limitations of Rev. Rule 65-20 [Rev. Rule 79-313, 1979, 41 IRB. 8].

Congress, for no sound reason, continues to exclude damages from gross income. It appears that congressional tax committees continue to believe that damage awards do not constitute income within the meaning of the Sixteenth Amendment [H.F. Rep. No. 767-6th Cong. 2nd Sess. 9-10 (1917); also LA. L. REV. 672 (1970)].

The court, however, in the 1955 case of *Commission* v. *Glenshaw Glass Co.* [343 U.S. 425, 431 (1955)] stated that personal injury damages representing impaired earning would properly be described as "undeniable accessions to wealth, clearly realized and over which the taxpayers have complete dominion," and this constitutes income in the eyes of the court. This rationale seems never to have been implemented further.

Substantial tax advantages are recognized by the IRS in Rev. Rule 79-220 and Rev. Rule 79-313. These rulings also provide the best available guidelines for structuring annuity-funded periodic payments.

XVII. LAWS RELATED TO PERIODIC PAYMENTS

Recent laws have been enacted, or presently are being proposed, that appear to further restrict and diminish the plaintiff's "day in court." One such law is the Model Periodic Payment of Judgments Act, which has been recommended for enactment in all states and proposes to restrict in many ways the immediate payment of large verdicts. The court stated in the 1972 case of *Frankel* v. *U.S.* [321 F. Supp. 1331, affirmed 166 F.2d 1226 (3rd Circ. 1972)] that periodic payment for large future damages would achieve "in all cases justice through just compensation, no more, no less." However, the court did not approve such payments for lack of statutory authority. Articles favoring and opposing the model act have been published [*ABAJ* (June 1980) and *ABAJ* (January 1981)] and are of sufficient importance to warrant study at the first opportunity.

XVIII. OTHER STATUTORY USES OF PERIODIC PAYMENT OF JUDGMENTS

Present statutory uses of periodic payment of judgments include workers' compensation, most small-claim-court-ordered payments based on defendant's ability to pay monthly, and periodic payment releases of auto damages to allow a debtor to avoid suspension of license.

XIX. PROPOSED OR ENACTED LEGISLATION

The Motor Vehicle Basic Protections Insurance Act (known as the BPI) is the basic no-fault insurance law. The Uniform Motor Vehicle Accident Reparation Act (known as UMVARA), proposed by the National Committee for Uniform Laws, follows the basic plan of BPI calling for installment payment of judgments. Both of these plans exempt most tort actions. About one-half of the states have no-fault concepts in some fashion—for example, Conn. Gen. Stat. 38.333, Fla. Stat. 627.736, and Kan. Stat. 40.3110. Some no-fault laws provide judgments to be paid as benefits accrue—for example, Ark. Stat. Ann. 66.4021, Colo. Rev. Stat. 10-1-708, and Ga. Code 56-34-6B; others do not specify a payment period, such as Delaware, South Dakota, and Virginia. Some are limited to three or five years total recovery, and others limit payment of income loss to one or more years (Arkansas, Colorado, Illinois, and New Jersey).

Of greater concern are states that have adopted laws to regulate payments to cover large judgments including malpractice and/or products liability—for example, Ala. Code 6-5-186, Alaska Civil Procedure Code 677-7, and Del. Code Ann. 18-6864. A California law regulating medical malpractice recovery was recently declared unconstitutional by reason of equal protection [*Am. Bank Trusts* v. *Community Hospital*, 104 Cal. App. 3d 219 (1980)]. More than a dozen states have laws permitting damages in civil cases to be periodically paid if the verdict exceeds a set amount—for example, Alabama, $100,000; Florida, $200,000; Wisconsin, $25,000; New Hampshire, $50,000; and California, $50,000.

XX. CONCLUSION

Hopefully this section has provided a brief summary of, as well as a fresh look at, the complex status of structured settlements. The material is not intended to be a comprehensive view of this topic, but merely represents this attorney's overview of his experience in the field.

VII

TRIAL AND APPEAL

After all that is said and done in the pleadings, discovery, and negotiation of a lawsuit, the moment of truth is the modern ordeal by fire known as the trial. Unresolvable conflicts on issues of the applicable law and the relevant facts are illuminated, and final decisions are made by the judge and jury. The exact process of the trial is in the form of a carefully ordered sequence of acts, played according to established rules of procedure and orchestrated by the judge. Section 27, Pretrial Motions, suggests how the first acts tend to set the stage and shape attitudes toward what subsequently transpires in the courtroom. The interpersonal relationships between the judge and the attorneys often crystallize and serve to color all further behavior and key rulings from the bench. The judge's early decisions may severely limit or expand the drama to be presented by each attorney.

Jury selection is the first direct personal contact between the attorneys and jurors (fact finders) and is the scene where first and lasting impressions are made. Section 28, Jury Selection, provides instructive thoughts on how to select a jury that is relatively free of bias and prejudice. A jury should be impartial and fair in its evaluation and deliberation of the facts that are presented to it in the courtroom. This is an area frequently underestimated in its importance.

Section 29, Expert Testimony by Engineers, is directed at the prospective expert witness and illustrates the kind of information, reasoning, and directions that might be given to any expert who is not entirely familiar with the role of the expert witness. It indicates some of the factors that the trial lawyer should consider in utilizing engineers as expert witnesses in automotive litigation.

Actual examples of the results of lawsuits are included in Significant Verdicts, Section 30. Theory is translated into more meaningful terms by actual case summaries. The reader is given the bare essence of what happened in the accident, the type of legal action undertaken, the key issues, the results, and the case identification (should further information be desired). The wide range of actionable defects presented should be helpful to lawyers who attempt to identify actionable defects and to engineers who attempt to prevent defects from becoming manifest. The concluding section, The Appeal Process, includes an actual Trial Brief dealing with significant issues in automotive engineering and litigation. It should be instructive on the form, character, and content of what is required in a meaningful appeal process.

27

Pretrial Motions

PAUL A. ROSEN, J.D.
Attorney at Law
Detroit, Michigan

Paul Rosen received a J.D. from Wayne State University Law School in 1964. He has been the senior trial attorney on numerous million-dollar product liability cases, including a landmark $10 million verdict. He is a member of and has practiced before the Fifth, Sixth, and Seventh Circuit Courts of Appeals and before the United States Supreme Court in the case of Palmer v. Thompson. *He has written articles and lectured on power presses and product safety. He has lectured at Wayne State University and before the Tennessee, Florida, Kentucky, and New York State Bar Associations. In 1978 he served as a faculty member at a seminar on product liability in Kansas City, Missouri, sponsored by the National Conference of State Legislatures, and as a faculty member at the Seventh Annual Conference on Product Safety in Washington, D.C., sponsored by the Consumer Product Safety Commission. His professional organizations include the Michigan Trial Lawyers Association (of which he was President, 1981–1982, and of which he is currently an Executive Board member), the American Trial Lawyers Association, and the State Bar of Michigan. In his law practice Rosen specializes in product liability with emphasis on industrial machinery. He is a partner in the firm of Goodman, Eden, Millender & Bedrosian, 3200 Cadillac Tower, Detroit, Michigan 48226-2889 (313-965-0050).*

I. INTRODUCTION

Pretrial motions are of extreme importance because they often shape the nature of trial, the method of advocacy, and, of course, the outcome.

First, as used here, a pretrial motion means a pleading filed after discovery has been completed and before, usually just before, the process of selecting the fact finder. However, a pretrial motion need not be made at that stage and good trial strategy may dictate otherwise. For example, where judges control their own dockets, the timing of a motion will be based on your knowledge of the issue as compared to that of your adversary and the character of the judge. Where a general docket system is used, the personality of the pretrial judge or motion judge will play an even more substantial role than an individual docket situation. If the pretrial judge is sensitive to you or your position, it may be very prudent to think about pretrial motions being filed before him or her.

II. MOTIONS IN LIMINE

In automotive supply and design cases, the motion in limine is most often used to limit testimony. Its purpose is to eliminate prejudicial allegations, be it questions or answers, before the fact finder ever hears them. For example, suppose there is a claim that the plaintiff lost control of defendant's designed vehicle due to a defect in the steering apparatus and assume further that defendant claims that the loss of control had more to do with the alcohol in plaintiff's blood than in a steering defect. Unless the defendant can establish a foundation for this claim, the evidence is not admissible. Absent a motion in limine, the defendant in its voir dire, opening statement, questions to witnesses, etc., may continually refer to the usage of alcohol. In the jury's mind, the use of alcohol may be synonymous with being drunk or impaired, when in fact the defendant only has very minimal evidence of drinking. A motion in limine should be filed to prevent reference to either alcohol or drunkenness until defendant demonstrates an arguable foundation and substantive testimony that will support this claim. In the case of death, the blood alcohol level is not enough to prove a claim that the deceased had been drinking. Defendant must show a complete chain of evidence that demonstrates that what purports to be the decedent's blood is his or her blood. Each person involved in the process, from the taking of the blood to its analysis and inventory, must vouch for the identity of it and the purity of tests used to analyze it. In large metropolitan areas, this chain of evidence is difficult to produce because of the constant change of personnel in coroner's offices. Other areas where motions of limine may be used are as follows:

1. Where the defendant has denied knowledge or the ability to retrieve data from testing during discovery. A motion in limine should be brought to foreclose the presentation of any data or related material at trial.
2. Negative evidence, i.e., defendant does not know of prior claims regarding the defect in design or manufacture, should be excluded unless defendant demonstrates that its organization established a procedure to determine claims or accident history.
3. Introduction of public studies and findings will play an important role in the outcome or conduct of the trial. For example, the National Highway Transportation Safety Administration has done numerous studies of the Ford transmission, Firestone "500" multipiece wheels, etc. Such evidence may be admissible—see Federal Rules of Evidence 803(8). In many jurisdictions such evidence is not admissible. The admissibility of that evidence, or the lack of admissibility, will have a substantial effect on the presentation of other testi-evidence and perhaps the outcome of the case.
4. Testimony of investigative police officials, who were at the scene or who have investigated the product generally, may have a tremendous impact on the trial. If the police official is not qualified to give an opinion, an allusion to their testimony in opening statement may not be forgotten because of a sustained objection or motion to strike it later. If you are on solid ground relative to the qualifications of the police official, file a pretrial motion to exclude reference to an opinion until the judge has ruled on it in absence of the jury.
5. Settlement with other parties should be excluded by a motion in limine. Also, pleadings that refer to such parties should be excluded by motion. Suppose plaintiff has settled with the driver of a car for policy limits, even though plaintiff claims the cause of the crash was defective design or manufacture by the manu-

facturer. If the settlement with the driver becomes an issue in the case, the defendant will be able to point the finger at the driver.

6. Receipt of collateral benefits by the plaintiff should be excluded by a motion in limine.

This list is not exhaustive, but it does represent frequent areas of controversy that may be ripe for legal resolution before trial.

Often we think that prejudicial and excludable evidence will never come before a jury. We know it is hearsay or without foundation, but perhaps our opponents do not agree. Let the trial judge decide the issue of admissibility of potential prejudicial evidence before the jury hears it. If you are wrong in your judgment regarding admissibility of the evidence, an early ruling will help you decide strategy concerning settlement, trial, voir dire, opening statements, witnesses, and closing argument. For example, think of the effect of a ruling excluding the failure to wear seat belts as contributory negligence in a crashworthiness case, as such ruling relates to the conduct of the trial. If a ruling eliminating such defense comes before jury selection, it will alter the entire conduct of the trial and may effectuate a settlement. However, if the court's decision to eliminate the defense comes during the instruction stage of the trial, the impact will have far less significance because all the evidence regarding seat belts has come before the jury.

The best rule to follow regarding motion in limine is that *its use be guided by judicial temperament, importance of issues, economy, and trial tactics.*

III. MOTIONS CONCERNING CONDUCT OF TRIAL

Motions concerning conduct of trial deal with the procedure regarding the trial of the case. For example, a motion to bifurcate liability and damages should be brought before the beginning of trial. A motion to bifurcate the trial is best presented after discovery is completed because the logical basis for such a motion may then be presented to the court.

Under the federal rules and most state rules, the court has power, in its discretion, to bifurcate a trial. However, such rulings cannot be made absent a showing of prejudice or unreasonable delay.

Typically, a motion to bifurcate involves the separation of liability and damage issues for jury consideration. However, a bifurcation can involve separating different plaintiff's claims or perhaps the responsibility of different defendants, cross-defendants, third-party defendants, etc. Typically, the basis for the motion to bifurcate may be one or more of the following:

1. Separating the trials will save time for both court and jury.
2. The damages are so overwhelming/underwhelming as to influence the outcome of the liability claim.
3. Evidence, such as insurance or settlement, etc., will create prejudice in judging one of the issues but not the other issue. Where the evidence only pertains to the issue that will not be prejudiced, bifurcation may be appropriate.

Usually, the defendant manufacturer wants to separate plaintiff's claims regarding liability and damages. This is especially true where there is a claim for substantial damages. Often the opposite motive is present where damages are minimal and liability is good. There the defendant does not wish to separate the liability and damage issues. All too often judges are persuaded that the substantial nature of the injuries will sway the jury to plaintiff's side. (These same jurists will allow in evidence the most horrendous photographs of the decedent in homicide cases, but they have great reluctance in civil cases to follow the same course.) The defendant usually tries to detail how the sympathies of jurors will create an unfair advantage for the plaintiff in the jury's evaluation of liability. However, those who oppose bifurcation of liability and damage issues should always keep in mind that the question of damages and liability may not be separable. For example, in crashworthiness cases the mechanism of injury is often determined from the nature of the injury. Medical and lay testimony detailing the nature of the injury is important and cannot be separated into compartments called liability and damages. A compression fracture to the spine may indicate where on the body the plaintiff has struck and the direction of force. In other cases, plaintiff's conduct or reliability—before, during, and after the original insult—may be called into question. Damage witnesses should be permitted to testify regarding plaintiff's conduct and reliability. Thus, to separate at trial would cause confusion and a substantial waste of time.

A motion to bifurcate must be accompanied with a very detailed explanation of the claimed prejudice or delay. A list of evidentiary items that will result in prejudice or delay should be set forth along with a clear demonstration that separation will not affect the ability of the party to present each claim satisfactorily. The best way to approach the subject is to develop discovery and pretrial orders in a fashion that narrows the liability issues and focuses them away from damages. Also, stipulation of certain damage issues may avoid the claim that the damage portion of the trial will be too time-consuming if tried separately.

Do not be caught napping on the issue of bifurcation. Often the issue is raised just before a trial begins. If you are unprepared for the motion, your response to it may be weak. If you do not think about it at length, before you raise the issue, the chances of success are minimized.

Motions regarding voir dire and challenges to the jury must be made at the pretrial stage. The conduct of the voir dire examination is extremely critical to both plaintiff and defendant. In cases involving great publicity and notoriety, such as the Pinto gas tank, Ford transmission cases, etc., the defendant may request and need separate, individual examinations of prospective jurors. Of course, the rationale for such a request is to avoid tainting the rest of the jury panel because questions and answers of individual jurors could result in prejudicial remarks. Individual voir dire of jurors may be very dangerous because it allows a broader latitude on the part of the examiner. In examining an individual juror, an attorney can say and do things without fear of what others listening may think of him or her.

Of more importance is the nature of the questions on voir dire examination and who asks them. Frequently, judges believe that voir dire examination is not important and is an area for attorney abuse.

It is critical in automobile cases involving claims of defective design and manufacture that a full and searching voir dire examination be conducted. Except for delicate areas of inquiry, which should be handled by the court, a motion concerning voir dire should request that the attorney be allowed to conduct the examination. This is a far better approach because it allows for follow-up questions. The judge is not in a position to know what the evidence in the case will be. The attorneys are hopefully in that position and thus can conduct a fair and thoughtful voir dire examination. Depending upon the judge, it might be a good idea to provide an outline of proposed questions along with your request for personal examination of the jurors. Such an outline will convince the court of the serious nature of your inquiry and the thoughtfulness of your examination. It may eliminate the judge's fear of attorney abuse during a voir dire examination.

There are many preconceived public notions concerning product liability cases—generally and specifically, automobile design and manufacturing cases. Prospective jurors must be examined about those preconceived notions. Questions concerning the attitude of the juror toward product liability cases, and specifically dealing with prospective juror's knowledge of or prejudice toward the manufacturer, product, or alleged defect, must be thoroughly examined.

Even if the judge decides that he or she will conduct the voir dire inquiry, a motion dealing with that subject may have the effect of expanding the judge's inquiry, making it far more searching and revealing to the parties.

Motions to sequester the witnesses are frequently used by both parties and are brought before the trial begins. The claim is that a witness will rely on or be influenced by the testimony of previous witnesses and not on what a witness himself knows. In the automobile design and manufacture case, there is usually a battle of experts. The credibility of an expert's opinion will depend on the factual predicate for it. For example, if the claim is that a metallurgical defect caused the car to go off the road, rather than driver error, the eyewitnesses' report of the car's travel before leaving the road will support the expert's claim. If the witnesses' testimony is that the car traveled normally and went off the road without warning, the expert's opinion that there was a defect in the steering assembly is supported and the defendant's expert's opinion that the defect occurred as a result of the impact may be attackable on the facts.

The issue for the trial lawyer concerning a motion to sequester is whether a fact witness will or will not be influenced by hearing testimony of others. If he/she will be influenced, is this good or bad? Sometimes we want a witness to be impacted by other testimony. A weak witness may fade when hearing others testify. A witness more concerned about his or her importance than the actual facts may be brought back to reality by hearing other witnesses who come to an opposite conclusion concerning what they heard or saw.

Experts may also be influenced by what they hear from factual witnesses and other experts. If they are present during the testimony of factual witnesses, an expert may make more realistic judgments about which testimony he or she will rely on for purposes of basing an opinion.

Thus, your decision regarding a motion to sequester witnesses must be based on at least two factors: (1) Will sequestering witnesses highlight the importance of testimony of each witness? (2) Will your better witnesses be adversely influenced by hearing others? I have had witnesses say to me, after listening to others testify, that they are more certain of their testimony because (1) they believe the other witnesses' consistent testimony, or (2) they disbelieve the others' inconsistent testimony.

We often assume that if a party makes a motion to sequester, the court will automatically grant the request. This is not necessarily true. An adequate and reasonable response to a motion to sequester can be made. Sequestering witnesses causes delay, and often the solitude of being out in the courthouse hallway is coercive. These factors should be pointed out to the trial court if you oppose a motion to sequester.

IV. MOTIONS REGARDING JURY VIEW EXPERIMENTS AND MOTION PICTURES

In automobile design and manufacture cases, sometimes it is important that the jury view the area where the incident occurred or view the automobile involved. Sometimes the area has been so changed or the automobile so altered that such a view would be prejudicial. It is important for the parties to raise, by a pretrial motion, the request for a jury review of the accident site or accident vehicle. Of course, if one anticipates that the opposition will make an unreasonable request for jury view before the jury, a motion in limine should be brought to exclude reference to such activities until the judge has ruled on the propriety of such view. A pretrial motion regarding view should establish similarity of conditions and the reason and rationale for the jury view. I believe that it is often prudent to raise the issue of jury view before the trial begins, so as to avoid the claim of unfair prejudice if the issue is raised during the course of trial. Further, it is wise to demonstrate in the motion that appropriate arrangements have been made to allow the jury to view the scene of the incident or the vehicle involved. Sometimes by raising the issue of jury view at the pretrial state, potential objections can be eliminated. For example, if there has been a change in roadway markings, an arrangement might be made to eliminate the alterations in the signing for the brief period of the view. This can be done, but sufficient advance warning to highway authorities must be provided.

Experiments before the jury are often used in automobile design and manufacture cases. Again, a foundation must be established for the experiments to demonstrate that they accurately reflect that which they purport to represent. The discussion of the jury view above is relevant here and should be followed.

The use of motion pictures to demonstrate causation or injury may be the subject of a pretrial motion. Again, the reason for this is to convince the trial judge that your opposite party has had enough time to digest what it is you are proposing and not be in a position to claim the need for time to object. Further, if there are reasonable objections, these can be dealt with at the pretrial motion and corrected in sufficient time so that the evidence can be presented at trial.

28

Jury Selection

GEORGE A. PETERS
Peters & Peters
Santa Monica, California

George A. Peters is the senior partner in the law firm of Peters & Peters, Santa Monica, California. Dr. Peters is a licensed psychologist, has been elected a Fellow of the American Association for the Advancement of Science (AAAS), and was awarded the 1972 Kraft Award by the Human Factors Society (HFS). He is a Certified Safety Professional (CSP) and a Certified Reliability Engineer (ASQC-CRE). He is the author of the book Product Liability and Safety *(Coiner, 1971), co-author of the books* Sourcebook on Asbestos Diseases *(Garland, 1980) and* Asbestos Litigation Reference Manual *(Garland, 1984), and co-editor of the book* Safety Law *(ASSE, 1983). He can be reached at Peters & Peters, 1460 Fourth Street, Santa Monica, California 90401 (213-395-7117).*

I. INTRODUCTION

The basic purpose of jury selection procedures is to provide some measure of assurance that the trial jury will be relatively free of bias and prejudice. A fair and impartial jury is a prerequisite for justice. The jury selection process attempts to eliminate from a group of prospective jurors (the jury panel or veniremen) those who manifest such bias or prejudice that they could not be expected to achieve reasonable fairness and impartiality in evaluating the facts of the lawsuit, as presented in the evidence introduced at the time of trial and applying the applicable law as they are instructed or charged by the judge.

It is the time during which prospective jurors begin to satisfy their curiosity as to the "human drama" aspects of the lawsuit and the resulting conflict that they may be called upon to resolve. They are in an unfamiliar environment, uncertain as to their responsibilities, seeking guidance and direction, having some need for peer group approval, and carrying with them some inaccurate perceptions of various aspects of the law; but they are in a situation that encourages receptive, adaptive, socially desirable, and conforming behavior. Thus, it is the kind of situation in which the judge and the trial lawyers can play a major role in determining the final outcome of the lawsuit.

Prospective jurors may be selected from voter registration lists, telephone directories, or other lists according to local practice. The source of such jurors may not reflect a true cross section of the general population. This initial selection bias may be compounded by those officials who, when they assemble the jury panels, exercise their discretion in arbitrarily excusing certain categories of prospective jurors. The result might be a panel that is biased for or against one party in a lawsuit. Thus, the trial lawyers must diligently and intelligently exercise their very important duty of determining possible juror prejudices or biases, during the questioning of prospective jurors and prior to the final impaneling of the jury for a particular case.

The jury voir dire is the first time the jurors see, hear, and react to the lawyers for each side. The lawyer may believe that he is getting to know the jury, but the jury is also getting to know the lawyer. Jurors may form lasting impressions of each lawyer's appearance, behavior, mannerisms, personality, competency, and believability, as well as of the possible merits of the case. In other words, there may be some quick first impressions by the jurors as to whether they like or dislike a lawyer, trust or distrust a lawyer, or feel a sense of rapport or suspiciousness of the plaintiff or the company representative. First impressions may be lasting impressions that flavor everything that subsequently transpires. Some lawyers believe that some cases have been won or lost by a lawyer's performance during the selection of the jury.

The first contact with the jury may be perceived as an opportunity to inform the jury; that is, while the lawyer is becoming informed about each juror by the questioning, he can use the questions to "sell" or influence the jury as to his version of the facts or even the applicable law. This approach may be argumentative, and objections, by other counsel or on the court's own motion, may be sustained. Such objectionable behavior may reflect adversely on the lawyer propounding such arguments and make more difficult his subsequent task of convincing the jury as to the merits of his version of the facts. While the jury should be convinced about the significance of the case—that they have the opportunity to tell a manufacturer that a product is safe or unsafe, and that the principles involved are bigger than the parties—it is equally important that the lawyer be perceived as being honest, sincere, knowledgeable, warm, and comfortable in terms of jury rapport, attentiveness, and credibility.

It is essential that the questions be carefully selected and worded to reveal possible juror bias or prejudice. Some questions are ineffective because they invite answers that facilitate concealment of possible bias or prejudice if the juror desires to serve on the jury or fears to speak out. Spontaneous lines of questioning may become somewhat aimless (without a specific defined objective) and reflect poorly on the lawyer. Each question should be designed or framed in such a manner as to elicit worthwhile responses (including behavior such as body language), without being offensive or objectionable. Some lawyers use the opportunity simply to demonstrate that they are nice, cheerful, and the "good guys." They may simply rely upon the information elicited by the judge, from jury books or jury services, from investigative reports of prospective jurors, or by categorization of individuals into general groups that "statistically" favor or tend to vote in a particular manner in terms of liability, damages, or stereotypes. Some lawyers are so concerned with their questions that they simply fail to give sufficient attention to the actual responses of each venireman.

The jury selection sheet should be utilized in a predetermined fashion for a particular case so that good use is made of the information that is derived.

The trial lawyer seeks the most alert, intelligent, and objective jurors to hear his case. The selection probably should be made by the attorney who will have to communicate to these same jurors during final argument. Despite the fact that the jurors will make the final decision on the outcome of the case, after the lawyers have spent a great deal of time and effort to prepare the case, jury selection often remains a neglected step in trial preparation. Decisions may be based on intuitive beliefs about stereotypes, rather than on the individual attributes of the person being questioned in the jury panel.

The first step in the jury voir dire process occurs in a pretrial meeting in the judge's chambers. The judge may or may not furnish a list of general voir dire questions to each attorney. At this meeting, oral or written supplemental questions can be given to the judge. In some courts, the questioning of the jury panel may be accomplished by the judge alone. In other courts, the judge may ask the first questions, then allow counsel to finish the questioning. In a few courts, the lawyers ask all the questions. The exact procedure to be followed, the scope of the questioning, and the duration of the jury voir dire should be determined from the court.

The selection of the jury is actually accomplished by a process of elimination, each side being allowed to challenge or to attempt to disqualify various prospective jurors. Each side can challenge "for cause", that is, for a good reason such as lack of competency or capacity to render a fair verdict, preconceived and inflexible attitudes or opinions, a financial interest in the outcome of the trial, or for other grounds established by statute or case law in that jurisdiction. There must be a reasonable basis for any challenge for cause; it cannot rest merely on some vague suspicion. If the challenge is sustained, at the discretion of and by the trial judge, the prospective juror is "excused" by the judge. It should be ascertained from the court, by the trial lawyers, whether challenges for cause should be made immediately (when the relevant information arises during the jury questioning) or whether such challenges should await the completion of all questioning.

After the attorneys "pass for cause," they may utilize a specified number of peremptory challenges (rejection of jurors on a basis not requiring any specific reason or cause). These challenges are used to eliminate prospective jurors that seem least desirable, for example, where a challenge for cause has failed. The exact number of peremptory challenges for each party should be ascertained from the court. The challenge should be phrased politely (such as, "We ask the court to excuse Mr. _____ at this time."), not as a "challenge" that could be misinterpreted by his friends remaining on the jury. It may be appropriate for the attorney to consult his client prior to using up all of the peremptory challenges.

After the jury has been examined, all challenges made and each side passing, the jury and alternate jurors have been "accepted" on the basis of elimination of those least desirable in the eyes of each party to the lawsuit. At this time it might be wise to have a stipulation, by and between counsel, that defines what will happen in the event that some jurors are unable to continue serving during trial. In a federal court, requiring a unanimous verdict, this may involve decisions regarding the number of remaining jurors acceptable from an original group of 6 or 12, plus alternates. In a state court, the stipulation may read that the trial will continue as follows: if 11 jurors remain, 9 will be necessary to render a verdict; if 10 remain, 8 will be required to render a verdict.

Before asking specific questions, the trial lawyer will introduce himself, co-counsel, and his clients to the jury. He may briefly mention the type of case being litigated so that the prospective jurors will have a general understanding why he may ask certain questions. He will attempt to question each and every juror so that there is some personal contact or communication between them. He will use their names (by referring to a jury list or from memory) and will look at each juror, attempting to make eye contact. He apologizes if he is required to ask personal questions, and his inquiries are polite, not in the nature of cross-examination. He avoids prolonged or technical questioning. While he may not attempt an "exchange" argument (that is, if we prove this fact, will you give us that), he often attempts to seek a "commitment" that the jury will decide the issues in the case on the basis of the facts and the law, not on the basis of sympathy or prejudice.

While it is true that questions that permit only a yes or no answer will permit the lawyer to maintain control over the voir dire process, will they reveal anything about the true feelings and beliefs of the jurors? Would a particular juror or jury reveal more if asked, "What are your feelings about lawsuits involving injuries from products?"; "How do you feel about the fact that a jury, composed of citizens of this community sitting in this court, can tell a corporate manufacturer, by their jury verdict, that the manufacturer has marketed an unsafe product?"; or "What have you heard on television or read about that pertains to product liability lawsuits?"

II. SAMPLE QUESTIONS

Many attorneys believe that the trial actually commences when the court calls the case, the counsel announce "ready," and the judge tells the clerk to "swear in the panel" and "call the jury." After the jury panel has been sworn and seated, the judge will attempt to explain some of the court procedure and initiate the questioning of the prospective jurors (veniremen) so that the final jury can be selected. Although each court may follow a different procedure and use different language, the following introductory remarks illustrate what could occur. The judge might turn to the jury panel and say:

I am now going to question the prospective jurors, who are seated in the jury box, concerning their qualifications to serve as jurors in this case. However, all members of this jury panel should pay close attention to my questions, remembering the answers you would give if these questions were put to you personally. When other members of this panel are called to the jury box, they will be asked to give their answers to these questions. In the event any juror is excused, he or she should get his or her slip from the Bailiff and return with it to the jury assembly room. In the trial of this case, the parties are entitled to have a fair, unbiased, and unprejudiced jury. If there is any question why any of you might be biased or prejudiced in any way, you must disclose such reason when you are asked to do so. It is your duty to make this disclosure. This trial may take _____ days to complete, although it could take longer. Will any of you find it difficult or impossible to participate for this length of time? The nature of this case is as follows: _____ _____. This is a concise statement of the facts and should not be considered as evidence by you. It is given to you now merely to help the Court and counsel in this voir dire or questioning of the jury panel. Most of the questions I am about to ask you will be phrased in such a manner that your silence will indicate a negative answer. In the event you do desire to answer in the affirmative, you should raise your hand. If the question calls for more than a yes or no answer, you should answer it in a concise manner.

A good trial lawyer will carefully select what he believes to be the most revealing topics for interrogation (jury voir dire) and the relevant specific questions that could assist him in selecting a jury. Then, he will phrase each question so that it is "in tune" with the kind of prospective jurors available in that court; in effect, he is attempting to tailor the form of the question so that it will be in consonance with the local style of language and with the lawyer's own personal mannerisms in the hope of establishing positive communication with the jurors. The "sample questions" in the text that follows will be illustrative to those unfamiliar with court procedure. These specific questions could also serve as a checklist or refresher for those attempting to formulate questions for jury voir dire.

A. Personal Relationships

A friendship or social relationship with either party, key witnesses, or the attorneys could give rise to bias, prejudice, or patterns of thought that might influence how the evidence is perceived by the juror. For example, if one of the lawyers is a former attorney for a juror, this may not be challenged (if disclosed) on that ground; yet the relationship may have created a present state of mind or implied bias worthy of further inquiry and challenge. Pertinent questions could be phrased as follows:

Do you know Mr. _____, the attorney for the Plaintiffs in this case, or any member of his firm, _____, _____ and _____? Do you know Mr. _____ the attorney for the Defendant, _____ Corporation, or any member of his firm, the law firm of _____, _____, and _____? Do you know any of the parties involved in this case? Are you acquainted with any of the following people, who are witnesses who may be called to testify in this case? 1. _____ 2. _____ 3. _____ 4. _____, etc.

B. Business Relationships

Those who have a direct pecuniary interest in a party to the action (such as stockholders, bondholders, agents, present employees, and possibly debtors and creditors) may be challenged for cause. This may not apply to a taxpayer interest in a lawsuit against a public entity. Questions may be phrased as follows:

Do you or any of your close family members have any type of ownership interest in _____ Corporation, such as stocks or bonds? Have you or any of your close family members ever been employed by _____ Corporation or by any of their subsidiaries or divisions? If so please tell us (a) when you or your family member was so employed, (b) where you or your family member was so employed, (c) you or your family member's duties while so employed, (d) if you or your family member were ever involved in the design, test, or engineering of automobiles or trucks, and (e) whether you or your family members were involved in the manufacture or assembly of automobiles or trucks. Do you know anyone who is presently employed by _____ Corporation, or by a division or subsidiary of _____ Corporation? If so, please tell us (a) where he or she works, (b) his or her job capacity and duties, and (c) whether or not you have ever discussed any aspect of his or her employment duties or responsibilities, and if so, what those discussions were about. Do any of you have any belief or feeling for or against corporations or companies that might prevent you from being a completely fair and impartial juror in this case?

C. Insurance

The existence of insurance may not be brought to the attention of the jury. However, questions to prospective jurors concerning their possible connection with the insurance industry may be proper if done in good faith and not merely to infer the presence of insurance coverage (unless there exists some evidence of a specific insurance company relationship). Questions may be phrased as follows:

Do you know anyone who is employed as a claims adjuster, claims manager, or investigator? If so, do you discuss with him or her the nature of his or her work?

When questions are asked about the jurors' occupations, some may be found to be employed by insurance companies. Those who have an identified interest in the insurance industry, such as agents of liability insurance companies, should be challenged for cause and disqualified.

D. Ability to Award Appropriate Damages

It may be regarded as prejudice or preconceived opinion if a prospective juror would refuse to award a large verdict, even if justified by the damages that could be proven. Questions may be phrased as follows:

Do you have a limit in your own mind of so many dollars beyond which you would not render a verdict, regardless of the evidence? Would you reduce the total verdict just because, when the elements are added up, it seems like a lot of money? How do you feel about awarding a large sum of money in a lawsuit like this? If you find that the Plaintiff is entitled to a verdict in this case, would any of you have any quarrel with awarding damages for both loss of economic support and for a loss of love, companionship, comfort, affection, society, solace, or moral support that has been suffered by _____?
Do you feel that loss of love, companionship, comfort, affection, society, solace, or moral support is of any less importance than purely financial losses, such as loss of economic support? If the Plaintiff proves his (her) case and you find that he (she) is entitled to your verdict, would you award damages commensurate with the financial and emotional losses suffered, even though that would require a verdict in a very substantial amount? Do you believe in the reality of pain? Do you have any objections to the law that states that a person may recover monetary damages for pain and suffering? Do you believe that a person can sustain mental or emotional injury in the same sense that a person can be physically injured? Do you have any preconceived ideas on the subject of damages?

E. Bias Toward Client

The trial lawyer is entitled to know whether a prospective juror could be fair and impartial about the parties, witnesses, and evidence presented during the trial. Any prejudice, bias, peculiarities, ill will, preconceived opinions, or unfavorable attitudes toward any party may be the subject of challenge for cause or peremptory challenge by the object of the bias. Questions may be phrased as follows:

Is there anything about the nature of this case that would make you hesitate to sit on this jury? If there is, it is your duty and responsibility at this time to disclose any such hesitation. Do you have any belief or feeling toward any of the parties that might be regarded as bias or prejudice for or against any of them? Will you be prejudiced against the plaintiff merely because he was driving a _____? Do you believe that a _____ person is entitled to just as much consideration as a _____ person? Certain parties or witnesses in this case may belong to a particular ethnic group. Would that fact cause you to give any lesser or greater weight to their testimony than you would give to the testimony of any other persons?

F. Experience with the Law

The trial attorney should attempt to learn the prospective juror's prior experience with the law, for example, the personal satisfaction or ill feeling that may have resulted. Jurors who have served in prior trials (involving some of the same parties, attorneys, and issues) may be challenged for cause. Questions may be phrased as follows:

Have you ever been a witness in a lawsuit? If so, please tell us about that situation. Have you or your family been involved in any type of lawsuit? If so, please tell us about it. Did it terminate in a manner that was satisfactory to you? Do any of you have any prior jury experience? If so, when was it and was it a civil or a criminal trial? Have any of you ever suffered the loss of a loved one as a result of a motor vehicle accident? If so, would you briefly describe your understanding of the event and tell us whether or not a claim or a lawsuit was ever filed as a result of that event. Have you or any members of your family ever suffered injuries as a result of any kind of an accident? If so, would you please tell us about it, and would you also tell us whether or not a claim was made and whether a lawyer was retained to represent you or your family member. Has anyone ever made a claim against you as a result of an accident or other situation? If so, could you briefly explain the nature of that claim? If you were injured in an accident because of the fault of another person, and you could not get a fair result, would there be any hesitation on your part in filing a lawsuit in an attempt to get justice? Why not? Did your experience with any claim or lawsuit affect your ability to be a fair and impartial juror?

G. Acceptance of the Law

Jurors should be willing to accept the law, as given to them by the judge, and apply it to the facts of the case. Some prospective jurors may believe that the law is wrong or have such preconceived, fixed, unconditional, and tenaciously held opinions that they should be challenged for cause. A juror's attitudes toward crucial issues of the law, in the case at bar, may be determinative of the outcome regardless of the weight of the evidence presented or the jury instructions given by the judge. Questions may be phrased as follows:

Even though you may disagree with what the law is, as the Judge instructs you, can you assure us that you will follow it and apply it to the facts of this case? Each case must be decided upon its own facts, and, according to the law, will you keep your mind open until you have heard all of the evidence and the law? Do you understand that the trial of a lawsuit is not a personality contest and that the case must be decided on the law and the evidence that is presented to you and not upon the personalities of the attorneys involved? In criminal cases, the requirement as to the degree of proof is different from what it is in a civil case such as this. In a criminal case, the prosecution has the burden of proof. It must convince the jury beyond a reasonable doubt that the defendant is guilty. In a civil case, the plaintiff has a lesser burden and need prove his case only by a preponderance of the evidence. Will you follow and apply the law in this case as the Court instructs you, particularly as to the degree of proof, even if you disagree with it? Do you have any objections as to the law which states _____

_____ [do not misstate
the law]? Will you consider all the evidence and try to reach a fair conclusion? Can you disregard _____ and decide the case on the basis of _____ [legal theory]? Will you observe the witnesses very carefully to see if their testimony is worthy of acceptance and belief, and not merely worthy because of the witnesses' professions, or the fact that they are sworn in before testifying, or that there may be disagreements between opinions? It is important that I have your assurance that you will, without reservation, follow my (or the Judge's) instructions*

and rulings on the law and will apply that law to this case. To put it somewhat differently, whether you approve or disapprove of the Court's rulings or instructions, it is your solemn duty to accept as correct these statements of the law. You may not substitute your own idea of what you think the law ought to be. Is there anyone who will not follow the law as given to you by me (or the Judge) in this case?

H. General Background

Sufficient personal information should be elicited so the trial lawyer can make an informed decision as to each prospective juror. The inquiry should neither be offensive nor invade the privacy of the juror. Questions may be phrased as follows:

Would each of you please give us the following information: (a) your name, (b) where you live or the area of your residence, present and past, (c) your marital status (whether married, single, widowed, or divorced), (d) the number and age of your children, if any, (e) your present occupation and any prior occupations that you may have had, (f) if you are married, your spouse's occupational history and present employer, if any, and (g) the occupation of any adult children. This we will call your personal data. Please begin with juror number one.

I. Occupational Bias

This is an important area. Questions may begin with the following:

Have you or any members of your immediate family ever been employed as _____ [Plaintiff's occupation]? If so, please tell us (a) when and where you or your family member was so employed, (b) you or your family member's duties or responsibilities as a _____ [occupation], and (c) did you ever see or witness _____ _____ [critical event]? Have you or any of your family members ever been involved in the design, test, manufacture, or assembly of products? If so (a) what kind of product or products were involved, (b) what was the nature of the work performed, and (c) who was the employer at that time? Do any of you have any background, training, education, or experience in the field of engineering? If so, what kind did you have? Do you have any lawyers or physicians (osteopaths, chiropractors, etc.) in your

*family? If so, could you please tell us the nature of their practice?
Do you or any members of your immediate family have any
training or experience in nursing or the health care sciences?*

J. Product Knowledge

*Is there anyone here who does not drive an automobile? If not,
why not? Have you or any of your immediate family members
ever owned a _____ Corporation automobile or truck
(or other product) in the recent past, or driven one in the course
of your employment? If so, please tell us (a) what the make,
model, and year of the vehicle or product was, (b) how long you
or your family member owned the vehicle or product, and
(c) whether the vehicle or product was a _____ (or
experienced) a _____ [critical trial
issue]. If so, please tell us what happened and if anyone was
injured?*

K. Other Topics

*Have you heard of or have you any knowledge of the facts,
events, or circumstances of this case other than what you have
heard in this courtroom today? Do you believe that a case of this
sort should not be brought into court for determination by a
jury? Are you or any members of your immediate family under
the care of a physician or health care provider, for any reason,
at this time? Have you or any member of your immediate
family been hospitalized, for any reason, for a period of time in
excess of one week? Do you have any prejudice with respect to
the use of intoxicants? Are you familiar with the places mentioned in this case; if so, will you disregard your familiarity
with the location and only consider the evidence produced in
court?*

L. Subsequent Jurors

When a new juror is seated, he may be asked:

*Have you heard all the questions the Court (and the counsel) has
asked the other prospective jurors? Would your answers be
substantially different from those we have heard from the other
prospective jurors? Do you know of any reason you could not sit
on this case, hear the evidence, and give both sides a fair trial
and arrive at a fair verdict? Do you have any opinion about*

this case at this time? May I have your personal data, please? Please give me any information called for by the questions asked the other jurors. Do I have your assurance that, if selected, you will give both sides a fair trial?

III. AFTER THE QUESTIONING

After all legal challenges for cause and the peremptory challenges, the jury and alternates may be impaneled and sworn. Excess jurors will be excused and told to report to a jury assembly location. The court then welcomes the jury, wishes it a pleasant and rewarding experience, and instructs them to remember the "admonition," which may be as follows:

Ladies and gentlemen of the jury, you are admonished that it is your duty not to converse among yourselves or with anyone else on any subject connected with this trial, or to form or express any opinion thereon until the cause is finally submitted to you.

The judge may go further and explain to the jurors that, from the very nature of these proceedings, the jurors should understand that it is important that they should have no contact with any of the witnesses, parties, or attorneys. Thus, they are not to speak to any of them, except for a hello or a nod of recognition.

The judge will attempt to explain to the jurors some of his court rules, based on the assumption that each and every juror is inexperienced and must receive some preliminary guidance from the judge. He will explain where the jury is to meet each day, the hours the court is in session, the nature of any recesses, and the reasons for any court interruptions. He may say that they do not have a window in the jury room. Therefore, if any juror objects to smoking in the jury room, there will not be any smoking. He may ask, "Is there any juror who would find it unpleasant if any juror smokes in the jury room? If so, there will be no smoking."

As to the conduct of the lawyers, the judge may inform the jury that from time to time counsel, for any party, may object to the introduction of evidence or object to some other legal matter. The court will either sustain or overrule the objection. If the court overrules the objection, this does not mean that counsel is being criticized for making an objection. It is his duty to make an objection when he feels he should do so. In addition, from time to time the court may ask counsel to approach the side bench. This is done to take up matters outside the hearing of the jury. The jury should be admonished to break their concentration and not attempt to overhear conversations at the side bench.

The judge should instruct the jurors that they are not to conduct a private investigation of any kind. They are not to visit the scene of the accident, nor do any reading on the subjects involved in the case, nor converse with anyone about the case or any of its circumstances or events. He may tell the jury that the court does not encourage questions from the jury because it tends to delay the trial and it is sometimes difficult for counsel to object to improper questions if asked by the jurors. However, if jurors feel so troubled by a matter that a question is necessary, they should write it out, sign their name, and give it to the bailiff, who will present it to the court. They should be told that the question, if it pertains to a witness, should be presented before the witness is excused, as it may be difficult or impossible to have the witness return.

Finally, the judge will tell the jurors that, at the conclusion of this case, it will be submitted to them for their deliberations. But no deliberations should take place until all the jurors are present: if the jurors should adjourn for an evening recess and arrive the next morning to continue their deliberations, they should not commence their deliberations until all of the jurors are present.

During and after jury selection, settlement demands and offers are often made. The plaintiff's attorneys may or may not appear ready for trial on all of the issues; if bluffing, they may be amenable to a "low ball" offer. The defense may have finally completely understood and fully evaluated the case, thus becoming more amenable to an appropriate demand. However, the defense may use the possibility of a settlement or some low offers only as a trial tactic to divert the energy of the plaintiff's counsel at a critical time or to influence the judge who may wish to conserve precious courtroom time by forcing a settlement at any price. Both sides may become more realistic as the day of judgment approaches with greater certainty. There are pressures for settlement created by the expense of a long trial, the ever present uncertainties that exist for both sides (such as the threat of a defense verdict or an extremely high verdict for the plaintiff), the demands upon the trial lawyers created by the ongoing accumulation of caseload work in their offices, the need to finally resolve the case at hand, and the plaintiff's fears, time required, and financial burdens. Some lawsuits may not be amenable to settlement because of embittered personality conflicts or personal ego problems among the lawyers or their clients, attempts to create new law or gain a measure of notoriety, beliefs that only a trial verdict can bring about social justice or prevent future similar accidents, clients who want to demonstrate or send a signal that they will fight every inch right down to the goal line, and the use of selected cases as trial balloons or sampling devices to explore the parameters of jury verdicts when insurers are faced with a series of similar claims that need "experience" for proper evaluation and resolution. Caution is advised as to structured settlements because of the limited time for their evaluation, determination of tax consequences, and possible legal ramifications (see Section 26, Structured Settlements). If a settlement is reached, it may be advisable to have the litigants consent in open court on the record and have the terms of the settlement also made a matter of record (including who will bear each party's costs and the jury fees, when payment will be made, and the nature of the dismissals).

IV. OBJECTIVITY

Survey research may be used to assist in jury selection, to forecast jury results, or to help prove an allegation. For jury selection, most trial lawyers seem to rely upon intuition, vague subjective criteria, and some personal beliefs about class attitudes and attributes in their attempt to impanel jurors who might be sympathetic or even biased in favor of their client. For example, defense counsel generally favors the selection of accountants, engineers, scientists, nurses, businessmen, salesmen, farmers, school teachers, building trades workers, military persons, and close relatives of law enforcement officers; those of Christian Scientist, Seventh Day Adventist, fundamentalist, or evangelist religious beliefs; those of Swedish, Welsh, Norwegian, German, Finnish, Japanese, and Chinese national origin; and those who are registered Republicans (who are assumed to have conservative attitudes). On the other hand, plaintiff counsel often favors the selection of blacks, Hispanics, musicians, artists, and blue-collar "working people"; those of Jewish, Roman Catholic, and Quaker religious beliefs; those of Spanish, Italian, French, and Irish national origin; and registered Democrats (who are assumed to have liberal opinions). However, as most trial lawyers have found out by personal experience, there are far too many individual variations within any such category or group for it to be appropriately predictive of a person's behavior and ultimate opinions if and when impaneled as a juror. Whether or not such criteria have marginal utility, they do reflect the trial lawyer's attempt to find some more "objective" process to assist in jury selection.

Surveys can be conducted on a representative sample or demographic cross section of the local population pool from which veniremen will be drawn. This should be accomplished by interviews having questions that deal with the specific issues of the case and are reasonably calculated to reveal hidden attitudes regarding the issues of and parties to the lawsuit. The objective of the survey is to provide the trial lawyer with a written profile describing those types of persons who might harbor strong inflexible prejudices for or against a party or issue, those who might have some modifiable biases, and those who appear neutral or reasonably impartial in respect to the issues. This information may guide the trial attorney during jury selection and provide him with a better understanding of what he must do to communicate effectively and establish rapport with the jurors.

Survey research may be performed to "test" or determine the effectiveness of warnings that may be in issue. It has been used to show the effect of advertising representations. It can be used to provide proof of "consumer expectations." Such surveys must be experimentally (scientifically) and statistically valid if they are to be used as evidence to support a key issue in the trial of a lawsuit. In other words, a "survey expert" may be required to "design," conduct, and interpret the results. Otherwise, the survey could be discredited if it simply consisted of leading questions that appear certain to evoke predetermined answers, had data incorrectly analyzed in terms of inferential statistics, was performed on a population having little similarity to that required by the contested issues, had its data edited, selected, or interpreted to produce a desired result, or was performed by someone without appropriate credentials. Since such survey research must withstand attempts to discredit it, careful planning, pretest reviews, and formal protocols are advised. These might be quite different than the "quick-and-dirty," informal, and novel approaches to survey research that may be appropriate to the personal jury selection needs of a trial attorney.

Mock juries may be used during pretrial preparation to rehearse various presentations and uncover the flaws in various arguments. Since mock juries should be representative of the population from which the actual jury will be drawn, the impressions and opinions of such mock jurors may be quite helpful in selecting the real jurors.

Shadow juries, which sit in the courtroom during trial and report their impressions each evening, serve a valuable guidance role for litigators. The number of shadow jurors may vary, depending on the case complexity, its relative importance, the available financing for such an expense, and the availability and unobtrusiveness of seating for such observers. If such role-playing jurors are not representative of the real jurors, they may not be "in tune" with how the actual jurors are interpreting and reacting to the evidence, the witnesses, the lawyers, and the judge. When they are representative of the real jurors, they can also provide the lawyer with valuable insight useful in future jury selection. Their usefulness can be enhanced by checklists that systematically focus their attention on key observational areas of interest to the trial attorney, the use of structured and unstructured interviews, and talk throughs of any problem aspects emerging in the case.

After the trial, jurors may be interviewed by the trial lawyers. If investigators are used for the posttrial interviews, the interviews must be carefully structured to avoid interpretative conclusions. This is an opportunity to gain "experience" that might be useful in future jury selection. In some cases, the hidden bias of a juror may not be revealed for several years, until prompted by some remarks at a social event. Thus, there are many ways in which the trial lawyer gradually accumulates the kind of knowledge that may be helpful in jury selection. Whether or not that knowledge becomes useful may depend upon its objective character, as opposed to experience retention in the form of a collection of vague subjective impressions and self-serving superficial conclusions.

Appropriate jury selection may be the key to success or failure, despite the apparent strength of the case and the diligence of the attorneys in all other phases of the case.

29

Expert Testimony by Engineers

BARBARA J. PETERS
Attorney at Law
Peters & Peters
Santa Monica, California

Dr. Peters is a practicing attorney and a partner in the firm of Peters & Peters. She is the co-author of the book Sourcebook on Asbestos Diseases (*Garland, 1980*), *a frequent lecturer on products liability, and the author of articles published in periodicals such as the* Journal of Products Liability, Hazard Prevention, Trial, *and* Professional Safety. *She is a former Executive Secretary of the System Safety Society and is an active member in various law associations. She may be contacted at Peters & Peters, 1460 Fourth Street, Santa Monica, California 90401 (213-395-7117).*

I. INTRODUCTION

It is just not enough to be right! Most attorneys agree that PREPARATION is a prerequisite to success in any lawsuit. This means preparation by everyone concerned, including the expert witness. However, to understand what must be done to prepare for the litigation experience, it is vital to have an understanding of the *purpose* of the expert's testimony, the *role* of the expert in relationship to others in the courtroom, and the *techniques* and the *process* generally described as cross-examination. This holds true whether you are involved in the initial analysis, deposition testimony, or trial testimony. Literally, you should know what you are doing as an expert witness, from the cradle to the final disposition of the case and from the beginning to the end of your experience as a witness.

II. THE ROLE OF CROSS-EXAMINATION

You should begin with an understanding of cross-examination. Often, litigation is the "battle of the experts" and the "credibility of fact witnesses," each presenting somewhat divergent facts and opinions. Because there is a conflict in opinion and fact, juries may have several divergent versions of what caused an injury. It is through the process of cross-examination that the believability or lack of credibility is exposed so that only one of these beliefs is determined to be the correct one in the minds of the jurors. By understanding what can happen in this final stage of an expert's testimony, you will understand which cases you may want to decline, which kinds of information you will need to testify, what kinds of tests or data you will need to compile, what kinds of seminars you may need to attend, and what your orientation should be.

III. QUALIFICATIONS FOR AN EXPERT

To "qualify" as an "expert," you must be testifying to matters that are beyond common experience, that will assist the jury, and that are based upon special knowledge, skill, training, or education. Moreover, this special knowledge must have some relationship to the facts and issues of the case being tried. Thus, you can expect to be asked about your college degrees, licenses, peer certifications, professional experience, courses you have taken or have taught, publications you have written or have read, patents, committees on which you have worked, and prior testimony. But just as these facets of your experience may result in being hired by the attorney, who believes that you are qualified to testify, they may also be your downfall. This is particularly true if you overstate your qualifications, have taken a different view of similar facts on other occasions, or become oversensitive and overreact to inquiry into your background.

Therefore, at the outset, you will want to be both accurate and circumspect in stating your particular qualifications to handle a specific case. Further, you should be prepared for the fact that your background, to some extent, will be checked. If you mislead others in the statements about your qualifications, you may not know that they have done their homework until the time for cross-examination arrives. I can recall one expert who stated he had a university degree, which, when checked, was not a degree but a certificate from a course given by a professional organization. If something embarrassing or overstated is uncovered, you can expect to hear about it at trial. By the same token, you may need to broaden your educational experience in order to handle the case. There is nothing wrong with this, so long as you follow through and take the seminars, perform the research, or do the testing necessary.

Moreover, when you prepare your resumé or place advertisements to solicit business, you may wish to consider the impression you create in terms of your credentials. Remember that the attorneys who may be cross-examining you may also see the advertisement. If you overstate your qualifications in your advertisements or resumés, do not be surprised to see a photographic enlargement of your advertisement in the courtroom. Or if you claim expertise in a large number of areas for an extremely broad number of unrelated products or problems, you may also hear yourself referred to by counsel as a "jack-of-all-trades, master of none."

Even though it may seem as if you are being personally attacked, you should avoid anger, sarcasm, or attempts at self-justification—if and when qualifications are challenged. While this may seem to be a simplistic statement, imagine your own reaction to a question like, "Have you ever been convicted of perjury?" For most people the answer is no, and the emotional reaction is one of righteous indignation. But those who cannot keep calm are more likely to be disbelieved or, far worse, to be baited just before a key area of substantive cross-examination is undertaken.

You will find cross-examination much less demanding if you stay within your area of expertise. Many veterans of the courtroom can tell you about the time an expert witness testified outside his or her area of expertise or was baited outside his or her area of expertise by not wishing to appear unknowledgeable in response to the opponent's questions. The effect can be disastrous. If you try to discuss something that may be beyond your qualifications and get caught, the jury may believe that you do not know much about any of the subjects about which you testified. In preparing for your cross-examination, you can never begin too early in defining your area of qualification—the areas about which you can or cannot testify as an expert. This means that at the preliminary stage of accepting a case or of identifying your qualifications to the attorney who may retain you, clearly define your role and its limits.

On the other hand, do not define your qualifications and the information upon which you rely so narrowly that you cannot testify at all. One expert, who was in possession of the autopsy report, was asked whether the defect in the product had caused the death of the product user. Not wishing to intrude upon an area requiring medical expertise, he replied, "I don't know." The causation of injury by a defect in the product was a key issue in the case. If this had been the only expert retained in the lawsuit, it would have had tragic results for the plaintiff. The expert can rely upon documents that customarily are used in his profession. Be prepared for causation questions since these can be asked of you as an engineering expert witness. If there is additional evidence that will be needed to draw the conclusion or additional experts who will be needed to establish causation, tell the attorney early in case preparation so that he will not rely upon you to give opinions that you feel you are not able to give.

IV. PREPARATION OF TESTIMONY

In preparing your testimony, you are going to be giving what is known as opinion testimony. You may be asked to give one of the following kinds of opinion: whether a defect was present in a given product, whether the defect caused or contributed to the injuries, and whether defendant or plaintiff performed some act that caused the injury. In rendering your opinion, you will be basing it on several kinds of foundational information: your experience as an expert with similar types of product failures, your personal knowledge of various facts, and the types of information upon which experts may reasonably rely.

Thus, you may be asked to examine failed parts, design drawings, photographs, or visit scenes of accidents. Those kinds of things that give you some measure of direct, personal knowledge—things that you can see, feel, touch, hear, or smell —are one element of your testimony. But be prepared for the inevitable cross-examination that will ask you to remember the tools you used to measure, including the sizes, colors, shapes, accuracy, and calibration. Literally, any of the facts that were gathered, how they were gathered, the accuracy of your perception, and what inferences could be drawn from the facts that you gathered can be the subject of examination. The attorney may attempt to find out how long you examined the object, what you were looking for, and whether you had any impediment to seeing the object to determine if there is some basis for believing that you did not see what you claim, whether you had some preconceived idea or bias prior to your initial observation, or whether the length of time you had to observe was inadequate. This is particularly true in the pretrial discovery deposition stages. Any weakness in the deposition testimony may be exhibited during your courtroom appearance. For example, if the conditions changed between the time of the injury and your inspection, if there was a high degree of variability in the types of measurements taken, if there were errors in obtaining or recording data, and whether the measurement instruments were properly calibrated are all issues about which you may expect questions at the time of trial. There may also be an attempt to test how clearly you can recall these facts or how clearly you can express yourself in the courtroom.

One difficult question may pertain to the subject matter on which experts reasonably rely in giving an expert opinion. This is a term of art in the law, but one that is unclear to the layman. It is not enough that you are experienced, knowledgeable, and have an opinion. You are required to have a customary and reliable basis for your opinion.

In fact, you should not be surprised to hear the questions, "On what did you rely in forming your opinion?"; "Is the Jones treatise relied upon by other experts in the field?"; and "Is it authoritative?" The attorney may be building support for his expert on the basis of your opinions or attempting to introduce something to undermine the logic of your opinion. Just what kinds of information can an expert reasonably rely upon? He can rely upon the reports of other experts; publications he has read; the text and history of a voluntary standard; information revealed in patents, advertising brochures, and design drawings; information supplied by the other party in the form of interrogatory answers and deposition testimony; statistical studies; designs of competitors; treatises; texts; consensus publications; accident reports; governmental documents; and testing that the expert may have performed.

Each of these sources of information, however, should be carefully examined. If you testify based upon the reports of other experts, you should be prepared to answer questions that may arise as to the accuracy of the report upon which you have relied. Any methodological error made by the person who gathered the data can become your error. In relying upon treatises, texts, or periodicals, be certain you have selected someone whose statements are within the range of acceptability in the scientific community. If you rely upon someone whose concepts are badly received by his peers, this fact may be raised upon your cross-examination. You should also be wary of the question "Did you consider, or rely upon, this treatise?" The purpose of the question, is to make "this treatise" *the* basis for your testimony. Knowing the purpose of this question, you should be able, in each case, to make a correct, ethical, and appropriate answer to the question. Be wary of those who may attempt to read the document to you and then ask for an *instant analysis*. Technically, you are supposed to have *read and relied* or *read and considered*.

If you are relying upon a statistical compilation, you should be aware that where someone else gathers the statistical data, some courts are skeptical of the reliability of the documents and may not permit you to testify from or about them. The court is only seeking to assure that the jury is hearing valid and accurate information. Where one source of information you had relied upon is ruled by the judge to be of a type not reasonably relied upon by experts or an impermissible basis for testimony, the effect is not devastating if there are other reliable bases from which you can testify and if the information from which you are permitted to testify can still reasonably support your opinion or conclusions.

You can rely upon a wide variety of information, such as advertisements and manufacturer's brochures. But there are some categories of information that are impermissible. Generally, you cannot testify from articles in generally circulated publications, such as the *Reader's Digest*. Courts do not consider these to be of the same caliber, weight, and accuracy as professional publications that are peer reviewed, authoritative in their field, and customarily relied upon by technical specialists. In general, the popular and daily publications are available to the jury and are not of special aid in understanding the issues.

Be sure that you are correctly reading the information that you have gathered. Keep in mind that your sources may be checked and anything that you cite the publication for will be verified. If you are inaccurate in your statement as to what the document contains, the opposing counsel can be expected to infer that your opinions may be just as inaccurate. If you think that this is specious or patently ridiculous, you should be aware that some attorneys have been known to prepare a notebook of all the documents that the expert claims to have relied upon, to have had those present either at deposition or trial, and to have asked which specific page the information came from. In one case, the attorney was chagrined when the expert was prepared for this tactic. He could not find the information she cited, until a cross-reference made by a footnote was explained by her. Her preparation, in fact, caused an otherwise stressful or embarrassing examination to become a victory of her own.

Be sure that the information upon which you rely is properly applied. Any logical inconsistency or inappropriate application of the theoretical knowledge upon which you rely may be commented upon at the time of cross-examination.

In performing testing on your own, your test must be of the type that is customarily used by your peers and other experts. You should utilize the tools used by other experts in an appropriate manner. You may be examined on your skill and experience in using the tool or on the acceptability of a tool. For example, there are specialized tools to measure coefficient of friction (Sigler machine) developed by the National Bureau of Standards. Some courts and some attorneys seem to attribute greater credibility (technically justified or not) to this machine and *may* feel that a jury should give lesser weight to other tests, particularly using one's own shoe to get a rough estimate of coefficient of friction. Some lawyers would tend to believe that a person experienced in using the machine would acquire a much more accurate measurement on which to formulate an opinion in spite of any controversy within the field as to whether these actually make accurate measurements. Thus, the tools you use should be accepted by your peers or you may find yourself trying to defend the tool that you used to make the measurements. If you are unfamiliar with how the tool is used, you may find yourself being asked to make measurements in the courtroom. Be sure that the conditions are the same as they were on the date of the injury. For example, for coefficient of friction measurements, the roadway surface should not have been repaved or have different surface conditions or your data and your conclusions may not be admitted into evidence.

More elaborate tests, such as an automotive crash test, must be similar in circumstances to the actual crash. If there are differences (even if you do not believe them to be significant or relevant), you can expect that your test *may* not be admitted by the judge. If the test is the only basis for your testimony, you may be excluded from testifying. Remember that a test, in the sense of a technically accurate re-creation or replication of the accident circumstances, may not always be justified and has a great many risks. You should identify such factors when you, and the attorney with whom you are working, decide on what kind of preparation needs to be done for trial.

The depth of your knowledge and the aptness of the information about which you testify will, in some measure, influence the degree of credibility that you have with the jury. Thus, a thorough knowledge of the field is more likely to stand up under cross-examination. The more accepted the theories you use and the more accepted the accident reconstruction technique, the less uncomfortable you may feel under cross-examination. For example, if you are using an automobile accident reconstruction technique that is not used by your peers or which your peers have rejected, this fact may be brought out on cross-examination. Remember, it is not just the pronouncement that something is defective or not defective that will resolve the controversy. You are going to have to show that you have a logical, reasonable, and generally accepted basis for your opinion.

Another important factor, always to be remembered, is that your role in the courtroom is not the same as an attorney or advocate. Your presence in the courtroom is as an unbiased witness. This is true even though your presence in the courtroom was desired by one of the litigants because what you have to say may help them to win their lawsuit. Like any other witness, you may be questioned to determine your credibility, bias, or tendency to fabricate testimony. Thus, the fact that you testify solely for a plaintiff, or solely for a defendant, or solely for one attorney may become the basis for a question on cross-examination. Further, the amount of compensation that you receive may also be the basis for a cross-examination question. While the amount received is fair game, it is sometimes framed in an improper way: "Were you paid for your testimony here today Mr. Jones?" Obviously, you were paid for your time and for sharing your opinion, not for your testimony. You should, as a good impartial witness, make this point clear. Don't get indignant! The unfairness of the question, when explained, should be enough to penalize the attorney who asks the question.

Likewise, there may be attorneys who will ask whether you could bend your testimony. While the best of intentions may be present, either in your desire to help or in the attorney's desire to preserve a good case, you might be led down a gangplank and, in the future, may have to explain why you took a different position in that case. You must exercise your professional discretion and ethics as to what testimony you can give.

Further, you have ethical obligations not to destroy evidence, generate false evidence, or misplace evidence. Anyone who suggests otherwise is not a worthy candidate for your services. When destructive testing is contemplated, you should be sure that you have the permission of all parties and the court to proceed. In some cases, destructive testing may be necessary, but to avoid the appearance of destroying evidence, you should secure the proper permission. Otherwise, you may be asked on cross-examination if you performed a destructive test, why you did not secure the court's permission to do so, and why you "destroyed the evidence."

In giving your testimony, you should be aware that the jurors neither are stupid nor are they engineers, since in most cases these are categories that lawyers seek to eliminate during their jury selection. You should simplify your testimony as much as possible, without losing the accuracy or the point you intend to make. You should be aware of the effect that each statement you intend to make will have on the jury. For example, if you are a design engineer who is called to testify on behalf of the safety of a company's product design, you may wish to consider that the testimony you give, as to the magnitude of the risk or as to the cost-benefit of a given design, may have an undesired jury reaction. For example, in some automobile product liability cases, the jury found body counts and the assignment of dollar values to various types of injuries to be repugnant. The impact on the jury of what you say should be considered!

Further, where you are employed by the company and are called upon *to defend* a product, you have a natural appearance of bias. No one likes to admit that something his or her company manufactured may have caused injury. Thus, the more substantive information and the more authoritative information upon which you rely, the more believable your testimony. Moreover, any appearance of callous indifference has to be avoided. Your role is not an easy one, but the more objectively you approach testifying in a courtroom, the more likely that you will be believed.

The "professional testifier" has his or her advantages and disadvantages. While someone who has courtroom savvy may be desirable because that person is more predictable in performance, knows what kinds of examination to expect, and knows how to expeditiously present an opinion, that particular individual may also be open to attack as someone who is not a "working engineer" in the reality of the industry being discussed or is simply a "hired gun." For the person who wants to make a career of expert testimony, this method of attack on credibility should be expected. Most often, the expert takes only those cases he or she "deems to be meritorious," "where his or her experience is such that it really bears upon the issues of the case," and "this usually works out to an even distribution between plaintiff and defendant cases." But if these statements are not true, be prepared for a litany during cross-examination of the cases and the parties for whom you have worked.

It is not always what you say, but also how you say it that sometimes is crucial. There are some words that may arise during the course of your testimony that have a different meaning to you than they do in the eyes of the law. If you attempt to testify that something is "possible," your testimony may be excluded as speculative. However, if you were to phrase the same statement using the words "it is more probable than not," your testimony would be allowed. The difference is in the degree of certainty. There may be times that you cannot be absolutely certain or scientifically certain, but you can be reasonably certain. The law does not require that you be absolutely certain, since there are very few things in life that have that degree of certainty. But you can be expected to testify to those things that are 50 percent plus a little extra, in terms of their certainty.

V. FEES FOR SERVICES

Finally, the financial aspect of expert testimony is important. This should be taken into account from the very beginning of the case. You should provide your attorney with your list of hourly or *per diem* fees, ask for the financial limits that the attorney expects you to place on the case, and provide periodic billings or statements of the services you have rendered. Where you are requested to appear at a deposition by the opposing attorney, you have a right to expert witness fees where the attorney intends to inquire into your opinion testimony. You should make inquiry at the beginning of the deposition as to who will pay and arrive at an understanding of what your reasonable fee is before you begin testifying.

VI. SUMMARY

Obviously, each case has its own specific requirements so that it is not possible to discuss individual cases. Hopefully, this discussion has given you a sufficient understanding of what goes on in the courtroom and what expert testimony is about so that you will be better able to prepare yourself for the litigation experience. Knowing what the opposing attorney is attempting to achieve, appreciating your role in the litigation, and deciding early in the litigation what information you are able to convey should give you a sufficient foundation on which to prepare and should enable you to be more comfortable in acting as an "expert witness" and to render your professional services in a worthy manner.

REFERENCES

1. M. M. Belli, Sr., "The Expert Witness." *Trial*, Vol. 18, No. 7, pp. 35–37 (July 1982).
2. J. W. Cotchett and A. B. Elkind, "Expert Opinions," in *Federal Courtroom Evidence*. Los Angeles: Parker, 1982, Chapter 19.

3. E. O. Delaney, "Evidentiary Issues in Products Liability Actions." *Defense Law Journal*, Vol. 24, pp. 341–367 (1975).
4. "Evidence—Use of Learned Treatises." *Defense Law Journal*, Vol. 25, pp. 133–142 (1976).
5. "Expert Evidence." *Defense Law Journal*, Vol. 26, pp. 432–449 (1977).
6. *Federal Rules of Evidence*, Nos. 702–705.
7. B. S. Jefferson, "Expert and Lay Opinion Testimony," in *California Evidence Benchbook*, 1972 (and 1978 supplement). Berkeley: California Continuing Education of the Bar, Chapter 29.
8. T. O. Lambert, "Admissibility of Expert Testimony." *Journal of the American Trial Lawyers Association*, Vol. 34, pp. 351–352 (1972).
9. E. Low, "Technical Experts," in *California Personal Injury Proof* (and supplement). Berkeley: California Continuing Education of the Bar, 1978, Chapter 5.
10. J. H. Newman, "Instructions on How to Testify at Depositions and in the Courtroom," presented at the Fifteenth Annual Fire Seminar on the Cause and Origin of Fires and Explosions, in Chicago.
11. G. A. Peters, "Expert Testimony," in *Product Liability and Safety*. Washington, D.C.: Coiner Publications, 1971, Chapter 3.
12. G. A. Peters, "The Engineer–Lawyer Interface." *Hazard Prevention*, Vol. 14, No. 3, pp. 14–15 (January/February 1978).
13. G. A. Peters, "Preparation for Your Court Appearance." *Hazard Prevention*, Vol. 14, No. 7, pp. 27–29 (September/October 1978).
14. H. M. Philo and L. M. Atkinson, "Products Liability: The Expert Witness." *Trial*, Vol. 14, No. 11, pp. 37–41 (November 1978).
15. E. M. Swartz, "Cross Examination of an Adverse Technical Expert in a Hazardous Products Case," presented at the 1982 Annual Convention of the Association of Trial Lawyers of America, in Toronto, July 17–23, 1982. Published in *Proceedings*, 1982, pp. 229–268.
16. V. L. Traster, "The Ultimate Issue Rule in State and Federal Courts." *Defense Law Journal*, Vol. 27, pp. 306–357 (1978).

30

Significant Verdicts

GEORGE A. PETERS
Peters & Peters
Santa Monica, California

*George A. Peters has been active in the trial of product
liability lawsuits for the past twenty years: first as an
expert witness and then as a trial attorney in personal
injury lawsuits throughout the United States. He is a
registered professional engineer (P.E.) who has served as
President of the System Safety Society (SSS), as a national
Vice President of the American Society of Safety Engineers
(ASSE), and as Chairman of the Product Liability Committee of the American Society for Quality Control (ASQC).
He is a member of the Society of Automotive Engineers
and the Phi Kappa Phi honor society, is Vice President
of the Americas for the World Safety Organization, and has
held many other positions with various engineering and law
associations. Dr. Peters has written and lectured on the subject of product liability in many countries. He is the senior
partner of the law firm of Peters & Peters, 1460 Fourth
Street, Santa Monica, California 90401 (213-395-7117).*

I. INTRODUCTION

There have been thousands of product liability lawsuits involving automotive products and services. Jury verdicts are quickly reported, on a weekly or other periodic basis, by various attorneys services: for example *Verdictum Juris*, published semimonthly, covering personal injury jury verdicts in six southern California counties. These services usually present short summaries that are intended to aid the trial attorney in assessing the "value of cases" (estimating what might be a reasonable plaintiff demand or defense offer for certain injuries), evaluating how juries might respond in a given court to a particular type of case, and in learning something about issues, experts, judges, and opposing counsel. Some attorney services publish jury verdict trends and other statistical data that might help in determining the probability of a successful outcome, in various jurisdictions, for various types of cases. Some services may be oriented toward plaintiff counsel and others may be a "confidential" service for defense counsel. Such services can only supplement the more direct knowledge personally acquired by experienced trial attorneys. There are many subjective and unpublished factors in almost every claim or lawsuit that determines how and when a case may be settled or tried to a jury verdict. In this section, we will present a selection of cases that are both illustrative in nature and unique in some manner.

II. TRIAL LAWYERS' PERCEPTIONS OF JURY VERDICTS

The following cases are presented *in the words and perspective of the attorneys* who participated in the trial of the lawsuit.

A. Automobile Seat Retention System

The attorney for the Plaintiff was Browne Greene, of the law firm of Greene, O'Reilly, Agnew, & Broillet, 1122 Wilshire Boulevard, Los Angeles, California 90017.

> The type of case was a motor vehicle incident on January 1, 1973; the product was a Ford Motor Company 1968 Ford Cortina; the defect or unsafe condition was an alleged unsafe seat retention system for the bucket seat for the

right front passenger; and the Cause of Action was Product Liability and Defective Design of the seat retention system and its inability to sustain a moderate or low impact.

The injuries were a neck fracture of C-6 and C-7, causing quadriplegia to a 21-year-old Plaintiff.

The verdict was for the Plaintiff in the sum of $3.9 million on May 8, 1981.

The basic facts were as follows: Plaintiff, David Espino, was a passenger in the right front passenger seat of a 1968 Ford Cortina vehicle. The vehicle was involved in a frontal collision whereby the front of the vehicle impacted a light pole on the side of the road at approximately 25–30 miles per hour. Evidence at the trial adduced the fact that due to the collision, the Plaintiff's body was thrown forward and thereafter the seat in which he was located was allowed to come up off its moorings and to strike the Plaintiff in the upper back/neck area, rendering his exposed body in a position for a neck fracture, which occurred.

The theory of design herein involved the fact that the Ford Motor Company used a piece of plastic on the floor for its seat retention instead of using metal for this purpose. Due to the fact that the plastic was used, over a period of time through heat and wear and tear, this plastic became unable to effectively be used for seat retention. Hence, the plastic was unable to retain the seat at the time in question, thereby allowing the seat to come up and fracture the neck of the Plaintiff.

The unusual issues in the case involved the following:

a. A severe statute of limitations issue herein, in which original attorneys handling Plaintiff's case failed to file a lawsuit against the Ford Motor Company within the statutory period of one year under the statute of limitations laws of California. Thereafter, this case was dismissed at the trial court level and was appealed to the Supreme Court and reversed under the statute of limitations law of California. The trial herein involved a three-stage (or trifurcated) trial in which the first stage involved the issue as to whether or not the statute of limitations had expired. The jury herein found unanimously that the statute of limitations had not been violated and thereafter the case went to the second issue.
b. The issue of defective design. The jury found in favor of the Plaintiff on that issue and thereafter.

c. The issue of damages. The jury awarded a third verdict in the sum of $3.9 million.

d. The issue of failure to wear seat belts. Evidence at the trial adduced the fact that the Plaintiff was not wearing seat belts at the time and substantial evidence was adduced to the effect that the comparative statistics of drivers at the time in question, 1973, for short residential rides, showed that 90 percent of drivers in California fail to wear seat belts. The issue of comparative negligence was found in the Plaintiff's favor therein.

e. The issue of drinking. Evidence in the case adduced the fact that on the prior evening, New Year's Eve, a substantial amount of liquor was imbibed by both Plaintiff and the driver, and on the day of the accident in question, further drinking took place prior to the accident in question. Again, the issue of drunk driving was found in favor of the Plaintiff on the issue of comparative negligence.

f. The issue of design. Plaintiff adduced the fact that the Ford Motor Company, subsequent to the date of the design of the plastic part in question, substantially modified the design and employed a much more substantial metal-based retention system. In California that evidence was admissible under the *Ault vs International Harvester Company Doctrine.* Said admissibility was, of course, materially effective in proving the issue of defective design herein.

The caption of the case was *David Espino, Plaintiff,* v. *Ford Motor Company, et al., Defendants,* Los Angeles Superior Court, Case Number C 75215.

B. Automobile Fuel System (Fire)

The attorney for the Plaintiffs was Jack B. Cowley, 2017 Cedar Springs Road, Dallas, Texas 75201.

The case involved a product liability suit against the Ford Motor Company arising from a defectively designed fuel system in a 1966 Ford Mustang automobile.

The driver and passenger in the Mustang received burn injuries to their face and hands when the Mustang caught on fire following a rear end impact by a full-sized Plymouth automobile. However, both the driver and passenger survived the accident by climbing from the burning Mustang through the passenger window.

After six days of trial, the case was settled for a total of $420,000.

The accident occurred at night on a major Dallas expressway when the Mustang was struck from the rear by a full-sized Plymouth automobile. Testimony revealed that the Mustang, at the time of the collision, was traveling between 45 and 55 miles per hour, and while experts from Ford Motor Company suggested a speed differential between the two cars of 50 miles per hour or more, the experts called by Plaintiffs suggested that the speed differential was approximately 35 miles per hour. The Mustang contained what is known as the "drop-in flange-mounted fuel system," where the top of the gas tank also serves as the trunk floor. The fuel tank is located approximately 5 inches from the rear bumper and contains a rear center filler pipe that connects to the gas tank, within the trunk itself, by a rubber hose and clamps. The experts called to testify by the Plaintiffs agreed that the fuel system was defective, and unreasonably dangerous for the following reasons: (a) the filler cap and filler pipe were located in the center at the rear of the vehicle and were particularly vulnerable to a rear end impact; (b) the filler pipe was connected to the gas tank, within the trunk itself, by a rubber hose and clamps, and which hose would separate from the fuel system upon rear end impact; (c) the fuel system was actually located within the trunk, rather than beneath the frame of the vehicle, without any fire wall between the trunk and passenger compartment; (d) these fuel systems tend to fail where the speed differential between the colliding vehicles equals or exceeds 20 miles per hour.

Ford contended that due to the severity of the impact, the rear window of the Mustang shattered or blew out and that the fire entered the vehicle through the rear window. Ford further contended that due to the severity of the impact, no fuel system in any American vehicle would have maintained its integrity during the impact. At the time the Mustang in question was manufactured, there were no governmental standards relating to fuel system integrity.

The case was styled *"Christopher J. Stilley and Paul Ingram* v. *William Frank Lovelace and Ford Motor Company*, in the United States District Court for the Northern District of Texas, Dallas Division, Civil Action No. CA-3-79-9493-G." The case was tried in October 1980. The collision, made the basis of the suit, occurred in 1977.

C. Automobile Steering Lockup

The attorney for the Plaintiff was David R. Gamble, Smith & Gamble, Ltd., 502 North Division Street, Carson City, Nevada 89701.

The case involved a single car rollover of a 1977 Datsun B-210 and was caused by an unspecified defect which caused the steering to lock, resulting in loss of control by the driver.

The case was originally filed with causes of action sounding in strict liability in tort under Section 402(a) of the Second Restatements of Torts, misrepresentation under Section 402(b) of the Second Restatement of Torts, and negligence under a theory of res ipsa loquitur. All causes of action were dismissed against the dealer Defendant, Carson City Datsun AMC Jeep, following the completion of the Plaintiff's case. All causes of action against the manufacturer Nissan Motor Corporation in U.S.A. were dismissed following completion of Plaintiff's case with the exception of the cause of action for strict liability for a defective product. This is the sole theory which went to the jury. The dismissals came under Rule 41(b) of the Federal Rules of Civil Procedure.

The 19-year-old female Plaintiff suffered permanent paraplegia, her spinal cord being severed at the T-9 level. Special damages, including past and future medical expenses and appliance maintenance, past wage loss, and future lost earning capacity, totaled approximately $675,000.

Prior to trial Plaintiff demanded $2.2 million, and through the trial, the Defense offered zero. After a six-day jury trial and approximately eight hours of deliberation, the jury returned a verdict in the amount of $3,775,000 in favor of the Plaintiff.

In August of 1977, the Plaintiff, Elizabeth Stackiewicz, purchased a new Datsun B-210 automobile from the Defendant, Carson City Datsun AMC Jeep. She and several of her friends had driven it a total of approximately 2,000 miles by October 17, 1977. On that date, at approximately 12 noon, Elizabeth was driving her mother, Veronica Wright, and a friend, Kimberly Seames, north from Carson City, Nevada to Reno, Nevada, along U.S. Highway 395. Between Carson City and Reno, Highway 395 is a four-lane freeway with the two northbound lanes separated from the two southbound lanes by a median approximately

50 feet in width which forms a shallow trough between the lanes.

While proceeding north along the right-hand lane of the northbound lanes of 395, Elizabeth attempted to pass a slower vehicle. In order to do this, she moved her car into the left-hand northbound lane, and when she attempted to straighten the car back out, the steering had locked. She announced the problem to her mother prior to the car leaving the highway, and the mother, sitting in the right-hand front seat, attempted to pull the wheel and also found that the wheel had locked and would not steer the automobile.

The vehicle proceeded off the left side of the northbound lanes at a very gradual angle, and in spite of the Plaintiff's attempts to slow the vehicle down, it eventually descended further into the bottom of the median, spun around, and rolled over. The Plaintiff and the passenger in the rear seat were ejected from the vehicle. The mother, who was strapped in with lap belt and shoulder harness, remained in the vehicle and was not severely injured. The other passenger was not injured at all except for a few bumps and bruises. The Plaintiff and her mother both informed witnesses and the highway patrolman of the locked steering mechanism. The highway patrolman on the scene checked the steering at the scene and found that it was operating relatively normally. The vehicle was later tested by the highway patrol after the tires had been inflated, and the low-speed testing in a parking lot again showed no problem with the steering. Following the accident, Plaintiff's counsel employed several automotive engineering experts to attempt to find the cause of the locked steering mechanism and to attempt to duplicate it on a similar 1977 Datsun B-210 automobile. Certain potentially lethal defects were found, but none which any of the experts could testify could reasonably have caused the accident.

Specifically, the front wheel bearings were found to be burned beyond the stage where they should have been considering the age of the automobile. A series of nicks and scratches were found on the universal joint on the steering column, which one expert theorized could have been caused by a rock or other object having become lodged between that universal joint and the fender well, which was approximately 3/8 of an inch from the universal joint. Testimony concerning this alleged defect was stricken by the trial court as being speculative.

The Defense also had one expert examine the car, and he found and testified that no defect existed anywhere in the steering mechanism and that the car had been operating normally at the time of the accident.

The most unusual aspect of this case was probably that the Plaintiff went to trial lacking proof of a specific defect other than one which was stricken by the trial court. Appended to this report is a series of case citations dealing with the availability to Plaintiff of a cause of action based on a general unspecified defect in a product.

Following the trial, the Defense filed a motion for judgment notwithstanding the verdict or, in the alternative, a motion for a new trial. Approximately eight months after the trial, the trial court ruled in favor of the Defendants on the motion for judgment notwithstanding the verdict and further ordered that if the Nevada Supreme Court reversed the order for judgment notwithstanding the verdict, that the Plaintiff accept remittitur to a total verdict of approximately $2.2 million or a new trial would be ordered.

The court's order has been appealed by counsel for the Plaintiff. The appeal is being handled by counsel for the Plaintiff and Leonard Sacks of 8949 Reseda Boulevard, Suite 217, Northridge, California 91324.

The case was captioned No. 79-1828, Dept. No. 4, in the Second Judicial District Court of the State of Nevada in and for the County of Washoe, *Elizabeth Stackiewicz, Plaintiff*, v. *Nissan Motors Company in U.S.A., a California corporation, Carson City Investors, a Nevada corporation, dba Carson City Datsun AMC Jeep, Black Corporation, White Corporation, and John Does I–V, Defendants.*

The Complaint [was] filed March 8, 1979, and the trial [was] held June 22, 1981.

The applicable case law (unspecified defect) included: *Rocket* v. *Chevrolet*, 334 N.E.2d 764 (Ill. App. 1975); *Tweedy* v. *Wright Ford*, 357 N.E.2d 449 (Ill. 1976); *Dunham* v. *Vaughn & Bushnell Mfg. Co.*, 247 N.E.2d 401, 403 (Ill. 1969) (86 Nev. at p. 413, 470 P.2d at p. 138); *Moraca* v. *Ford Motor Co.*, 332 Atl.2d 599 (N.J. 1975), affirming 332 Atl. 607 (N.J. App. 1974); *Vaner* v. *Kirby*, 450 P.2d 778 (Ore. 1969); *Dennis* v. *Ford Motor Co.*, 332 F. Supp. 901 (W.D. Pa. 1971), aff'd 471 F.2d 733 (3d Cir. 1973); *Stewart* v. *Ford Motor Co.*, 553 F.2d 130 (D.C. Cir. 1977); *Markle* v. *Mulholland's, Inc.*, 509 P.2d 529, 533-534 (Ore. 1973); *Farmer* v. *International Harvester Co.*, 553 P.2d 1306 (Ida. 1976); *Harrell Motors, Inc.* v. *Flannery*, 612 S.W.2d 727 (Ark. 1981); and *Brownell* v. *White Motor Corp.*, 490 P.2d 184 (Ore. 1971).

D. Motor Home Carbon Monoxide

The attorney for the Plaintiff was Elliot G. Wolfe, of the law firm of Langerman, Begam, Lewis & Marks, 111 West Monroe, Suite 1400, Phoenix, Arizona 85003.

The type of case was a wrongful death; the product was an Escape motor home manufactured by Skyline Corporation; the defect was that it was designed and/or manufactured so as to allow carbon monoxide from an auxiliary generator, housed in the motor home's rear compartment, to pass through the walls of the motor home into the living compartment; and the cause of action was strict liability in tort.

The injury was the death of Robert Cave Wood, a 63-year-old farmer, and the settlement was in the amount of $200,000 (October 1981).

The basic facts were as follows: On November 15, 1978, the Plaintiff's husband, Robert Cave Wood, his adult son, and three friends were using one of the friend's Skyline motor home on a hunting trip in northern Arizona. The motor home was equipped with an auxiliary gasoline-powered Onan generator that was housed in the middle of three wooden compartments in the rear of the vehicle.

Three of the hunters went to sleep in the motor home and two others in a camper that they had brought along with them on the trip. The Onan generator was operated through the night to provide heat to the interior compartment and a window was left open near the front of the motor home. In the early morning hours of November 16, 1978, one of the hunters who had been sleeping outside in the camper became cold and decided to spend the rest of the night in the motor home. When he entered, he closed the previously opened window. The one hunter who remained in the camper outside the motor home found all four of his friends dead of carbon monoxide poisoning several hours later.

The Plaintiff's experts testified that the carbon monoxide had entered the interior of the motor home through cracks in the rear wooden cabinets.

It was their opinion that those cracks developed as a result of normal wear and tear and by virtue of the fact that the manufacturer used no sealant to prevent the entry of the gas into the living quarters. Skyline defended on the theories that the motor home was more than seven years old, had been altered by five or six previous owners, and had developed cracks in the rear compartments as a result of misuse of the motor home in having it towed from the mud on the day before the fatal incident.

The unusual issues in the case included (a) whether or not the decedents' consumption of alcohol before going to sleep on November 15, 1978, was a contributing factor to their deaths by reason of the synergistic effect of alcohol and carbon monoxide; and (b) whether or not the Defendant Onan adequately warned the purchasers of its auxiliary generator to place it in a vapor-tight compartment.

The full caption of the case was *Gladys Raye Wood, surviving spouse of Robert Cave Wood, deceased, on her own behalf and for and on behalf of Robert Wayne Wood and Harvey Cave Wood, the surviving children of Robert Cave Wood, Plaintiff,* v. *Skyline Corporation, an Indiana corporation; Arizona State Trailer Sales, Inc., an Arizona corporation; Skyline Homes, Inc., a California corporation; Onan Corporation, a Delaware corporation, Defendants.* No. C-389780 in the Superior Court of the State of Arizona in and for the County of Maricopa.

E. Truck Tire Blowout

The Plaintiff attorney (lead counsel) was John Judge, of the law firm of Judge & Brown, American National Bank Building, P.O. Box 9045, Amarillo, Texas 79105.

The type of case was a products liability action involving a General Highway Brand 8-ply 10-22 tire mounted on the left steering axle of a Peterbilt truck that blew out while the truck was operating at approximately 55 miles per hour. The truck went out of control; crossed oncoming lanes of traffic; and finally collided with a culvert, causing injury to the operator.

The tire failed due to a manufacturing defect (inadequate adhesion between the plys) resulting in heat buildup within the body of the tire; molecular destabilization or "reverse vulcanizing"; and culminating in the tread separation and catastrophic blowout.

The Plaintiffs pitched their cause of action on §402a, RESTATEMENT OF TORTS SECOND; breach of implied warranty of fitness; and negligent manufacture. Jury issues were submitted only on the §402a rationale.

The driver, Jack Moore, suffered injuries to his right knee and right elbow. He developed osteoarthritis in his right knee, rendering him unable to perform the usual and ordinary tasks of a truck driver.

The jury verdict was for $183,000 personal injury damages, together with approximately $36,000 property damage.

This was a classic confrontation between the manufacturer's expert, who claimed that the tire failed due to overdeflection (overloaded or underinflated) operation, and the Plaintiff's proof that the tire was improperly manufactured, causing the destabilization, tread separation, and blowout. Plaintiff's trial counsel was able, on cross-examination, to require the manufacturer's expert to admit that the critical issue in the case was the credibility of his theory as opposed to the credibility of the Plaintiff truck driver's testimony that he had consistently maintained air pressure in the tires at or about 95 psi. The jury, obviously, chose to believe the truck driver.

The unusual issues: Plaintiffs sought inspection of the manufacturing facility in Waco, Texas. This was resisted by Defendants, who claimed trade secrets existed within the facility. Subsequent inspection, however, revealed nothing unusual, unique, or new in the manufacturing process.

The case was styled as *Jackie R. Moore and Dwight Cheek Trucking Co.* v. *General Tire and Rubber Co.*, Case No. CA 2-77-110 United States District Court, Northern District of Texas, Amarillo Division, and was tried in October 1980.

F. Wheel Spider

The Plaintiff's trial attorney was Lawrence P. Grassini, of the law firm of Hurley & Grassini, 11313 Weddington Street, North Hollywood, California 91601.

Eldon Plum, a 45-year-old machinist, purchased a 1973 Model 350 Ford pickup truck in 1973. He used the truck in his business and also used it to carry an in-bed Lance camper. When purchased in 1973, the truck was equipped with riveted steel rims which were manufactured by Kelsey Hayes for use on this model Ford pickup. In July of 1976, Mr. Plum was traveling on Interstate 15 outside of Beaver, Utah. It was raining and had been raining for some time. As he was traveling on a relatively straight stretch of road, he felt the vehicle start to slowly veer to the left with no steering response. After the truck traveled in this mode for a fairly substantial period of time, it left the pavement into the center meridian, turned sideways, and finally flipped and rolled over several times. The impact crushed the camper, destroyed the truck, and bent the rear axle.

At the scene, the spider or inner portion of the Kelsey Hayes rim on the left rear wheel was found still attached by the lug nuts to the brake drum. The remainder of the rim and tire were some distance past the final resting place of the truck.

The Plaintiff proceeded on a products liability theory, claiming that the wheel manufactured by Kelsey Hayes was defective in that the rivets which attached the spider to the rim stretched through usage and finally failed, causing the tire and rim to leave the vehicle, which in turn caused the truck to overturn.

The camper and truck were substantially damaged, and the Plaintiff, Mr. Plum, suffered a back injury. Medical testimony at trial showed that he had had a positive myelogram which indicated that he had a bulging intervertebral disc at the L-5/S-1 level. His property damage was approximately $8000 and his medical expenses were $3000.

The jury awarded Mr. Plum the sum of $317,000. During the course of the seven-week trial, the Defendants brought forth four engineers and a metallurgist to show that it was impossible for the rivets to separate the way the Plaintiff alleged they had. The Defendants also performed extensive impact testing on exemplar wheels to show that the rim would separate from the spider in a rollover exactly as it had, according to them, in the Plum accident. However, the physical evidence such as scrape marks, gouge marks, and the placement of the rim and wheel found at the accident scene by the investigating police officer and used in the reconstruction of the accident by the Plaintiff's expert overcame the technical testimony and testing of the defense experts.

The case was captioned *Elden Plum* v. *Ford Motor Company, Kelsey Hayes, Wray Brothers Ford and Gateway Ford, Los Angeles*, Central Case No. C 174713, Los Angeles Superior Court, October 1981.

G. Fraudulent Misrepresentation
The Plaintiff attorney was David H. Gold, 12th Floor, Roberts Building, 28 West Flagler Street, Miami, Florida, 33130.

The lawsuit involved auto dealer liability for fraudulent misrepresentation of the accident history of the car and deceptive and unfair trade practice.

The facts were as follows: The Plaintiff, a 34-year-old Florida International University administrative assistant, went to Sun Chevrolet on September 30, 1978, to purchase a car. She testified that the Defendant's salesman represented the car with 6333 miles as a "demonstrator." Plaintiff testified that she observed the hood was misaligned, that paint on the passenger's side was mismatched, and that some areas under the hood on the passenger's side were unpainted. Plaintiff asked whether the car had been in an accident or wreck, and the salesman assured her the hood and paint problems were typical factory defects. Plaintiff subsequently discovered that the Defendant first sold the car in March, 1978, and that the first purchaser was involved in an accident on August 28, 1978. The car was towed to Sun Chevrolet and repaired by Defendant's body shop at a cost of $1400. There was no mechanical or frame damage. The first purchaser picked up the car on September 26, 1978, and brought it back on September 28, 1978, as a trade-in. Defendant's used-car appraiser testified that he appraised the car on September 28, 1978, and was not aware that the car had been involved in a wreck.

Defendant denied misrepresenting the accident history of the car and relied on sales documents reflecting that Plaintiff had purchased a used car. Defendant further claimed that its salesman had no actual or constructive knowledge of the car's previous repairs because the dealer's service and sales department are separate entities and because the first purchaser's name had been misspelled on the repair bill. At the time of trial, the car had 39,000 miles and was still being driven by the Plaintiff.

The verdict was for $46,000 ($1000 compensatory; $45,000 punitive; plus $8000 attorney's fee awarded by court under Florida Deceptive and Unfair Trade Practices Act).

The case caption was *Irene Manos* v. *Sun Chevrolet, Inc.*, Dade County Circuit Court No. 80-20159, 3 June 1981.

H. Co-employee Liability (Bulldozer Rollover)

The Plaintiff attorney was Lanny S. Vines, of the law firm of Emond & Vines, 1800 City Federal Building, Birmingham, Alabama 35203.

This was a wrongful death action involving a Model D-8H Caterpillar bulldozer that overturned on a 42-degree strip mine embankment and crushed the operator. A lawsuit for failure to provide rollover protection was instituted against the manufacturer and the board chairman of the corporate employer of the bulldozer operator (a co-employee under the Alabama Extended Manufacturers' Liability Doctrine).

The jury returned a verdict of $350,000 against the manufacturer and $150,000 against the named company officer.

The Supreme Court of Alabama held that the offering of a rollover protected structure (ROPS) did not abrogate the manufacturer's duty to provide a known and needed safety device.

The case was *Ford* v. *Caterpillar Tractor Co.*, Jefferson County Circuit Court No. 42858, Alabama, November 1979.

I. Police Vehicle Warning Systems

The Plaintiff attorney was Richard P. St. Clair, 501 Shatto Place, Los Angeles, California 90020.

A police vehicle struck a bicycle occupied by two minors. The cause of action was founded on the negligent operation [of] a police vehicle, including failure to use the warning systems.

The minor passenger on the bicycle was killed and the minor driver of the bicycle incurred brain damage and psychiatric injury. There was a settlement of $50,000 for the wrongful death and a structured settlement with an approximate value of $2,775,000 for the minor driver of the bicycle.

The police vehicle was allegedly responding at 56.5 mph, in a 30-mph zone, to a possible shot-fired call after dark on the 4th of July, failed to activate its siren or red lights, struck and seriously injured two children who allegedly suddenly emerged from an alley into the middle of the street on an unlicensed bicycle which was not equipped with lights or reflectors as required by law.

A driver of an "emergency vehicle," as defined by statute (California Vehicle Code, §165), must sound a siren as reasonably necessary and display a lighted red lamp visible from the front as a warning to other drivers (California Vehicle Code, §21055) to be exempt from the provisions of the California Vehicle Code. When he fails to do so, the common law standard of care governs his conduct and does not include a consideration of the emergency circumstances attendant upon his response to an "emergency" call [*Grant* v. *Petronella* (1975) 50 C.A.3d 281, 289; 123 Cal. Rptr. 399].

The California Vehicle Code, §17004 gives immunity to a public employee from civil damages resulting from his operation of an authorized emergency vehicle in the line of duty while responding to an emergency call. Whether the situation was an emergency was a triable issue of fact. The police recording device for dispatch and reception of police radio transmissions was not working on the night of the accident, but a recording of same was obtained via a neighboring city's police department operating on the same waveband.

The caption of the case was Maria Concepcion Lopez, Hector Lopez by his Guardian Maria Concepcion Lopez, Los Angeles Superior Court Case No. SEC 21807, November 29, 1979.

J. Passenger Compartment Integrity

The attorneys for the Plaintiffs were Larry S. Stewart and Gary D. Fox, One Biscayne Tower, Miami, Florida 33131

The case involved an automobile intersection collision, with a products liability action alleging uncrashworthiness of the passenger compartment of a 1972 Honda AN600, the failure of the passenger compartment to maintain structural integrity, and the failure of the safety features of the vehicle. These failures allowed the Plaintiff, even though he was wearing his seat belt, to strike his head on the forward portions of the passenger compartment, resulting in brain damage.

The Plaintiff received severe brain damage. He also received orthopedic injuries from which he substantially recovered. His brain damage resulted in his being unable to continue in any employment. Prior to the injury he was an engineer working for McDonnell Douglas Corporation at Cape Kennedy in connection with the Skylab space program.

The jury verdict was for $5,825,000.

The Plaintiff was proceeding to work in heavy morning rush hour traffic. After passing through a series of signalized intersections he came to the accident intersection. A Ford LTD at the intersection, heading in the opposite direction, was waiting to make a left turn in front of him. As Dorsey approached the intersection, the other vehicle moved into his lane of traffic. At the time of impact the Ford was either stopped or barely moving and Dorsey was proceeding at about 30 mph.

The two vehicles struck left front to left front. There was only minor damage to the Ford, but the left front of the passenger compartment of the Honda collapsed inward approximately 10 inches. Although Dorsey was wearing his seat belt and shoulder harness at the time of the incident, due to the crush of the passenger compartment, the inherent stretch of his seat belts, and the failure of the seat track of his seat, Dorsey struck the left front portion of the passenger compartment with his head.

Documents produced by Honda revealed that Honda was aware of both the small size and insufficient strength of the passenger compartment. Honda was also aware of the probability of seat track failure in an accident of this magnitude and of the stretch capabilities of the seat belts. Notwithstanding its knowledge, Honda went ahead and marketed the AN600.

Of the jury award, $5 million was for Honda's reckless conduct in marketing the AN600 with knowledge of its dangerous characteristics and without warning of those characteristics. On posttrial motions, the trial judge reversed that award and entered judgment for Honda on the issue of punitive damages. Plaintiff appealed that order to the Fifth Circuit Court (now the Eleventh Circuit Court of Appeal). At the time of the appeal, the largest single punitive damage award which had been sustained on appeal was $1 million. The Eleventh Circuit Court of Appeals reversed the trial judge and ordered reinstatement of the punitive award. Honda had cross-appealed the award of compensatory damages and the Court of Appeals affirmed that order. *Dorsey* v. *Honda Motor Co.*, 655 F.2d 650 (5th Cir.).

The caption of the case was *Dorsey* v. *Honda Motor Company*, Case No. 76-388-Orl-Civ-R, United States District Court for the Middle District of Florida, Orlando Division; *Dorsey* v. *Honda Motor Company*, Case No. 79-3845, United States Court of Appeals for the Eleventh Circuit.

K. Door Latches

The attorney for Plaintiff was Gerard E. Mitchell of the law firm of Stein, Mitchell & Mezines, 1800 M Street, N.W., Washington, D.C. 20036.

This is a "second collision" products liability action against the manufacturer and importer of an automobile equipped with a defectively designed door latch system. The product was a 1967 Fiat 600D sedan, which was substantially unchanged from 1964 through 1967. The defect is the absence of longitudinal linkage in the door latch system, thereby permitting the doors to spring open upon the application of stretching forces to the sides of the car.

The cause of action was for damages sustained by the Plaintiff when he was ejected from the vehicle during a low-speed intersection collision between his Fiat and a Ford van. The Plaintiff sustained skull fractures and organic brain damage which affected his cognitive functioning, especially for more sophisticated tasks.

The jury verdict in the amount of $650,000 was returned on May 15, 1981.

The Plaintiff was operating his 1967 Fiat with seat belts unfastened when his vehicle collided with a Ford van which had failed to yield the right-of-way in violation of a stop sign. Both vehicles were estimated to be traveling approximately 25 miles per hour. The Fiat was distorted from left to right, causing the vehicle to spin 180° in a clockwise direction. During this spin, the driver's door popped open and the Plaintiff was ejected.

Fiat contended that the fractures, which were mainly in the area of the right temporal bone, were caused by impact upon the Plaintiff by the passenger in the Plaintiff's vehicle. Fiat presented expert testimony that the blow to Plaintiff's skull was in the area of the temporal bone behind the right ear, whereas Plaintiff's experts testified that the blow was to the left and top of the skull with fractures commencing in the area of outbending toward the base of the skull.

The main legal issues in the case concerned admissibility of seat-belt testimony to show that the vehicle was reasonably safe despite the absence of a door latch providing longitudinal linkage. However, because Fiat failed to proffer that it had not installed the seat belts, the evidence was excluded. This and numerous other issues have been appealed by Fiat to the United States Court of Appeals for the District of Columbia Circuit. The Plaintiff-Appellee's brief is included, in its entirety, in the section The Appeal Process (Section 31).

This case was captioned *Wyllie Gatewood* v. *Fiat, S.p.A.*, *et al.*, United States District Court for the District of Columbia, Civil Action No. 78-0277.

L. Auto Rental Agency Liability

The Plaintiff's attorney was James Krueger, Wailuku Town-house, 2158 Main Street, P.O. Box T, Wailuku, Maui, Hawaii 96793.

American International Rent-a-Car employed a lot boy named Bascar. On July 8, 1979, Bascar went to the rent-a-car lot and with questionable permission took a vehicle from it. He took it on a Sunday, giving as his reason later that he wanted to use it to come back to work on Monday. On that Sunday, with some other young friends, he went joy riding and, while doing so, permitted his automobile to cross the center line of a highway and crash into a vehicle driven by the Plaintiff, a 34-year-old realtor. As a result of a collision, the Plaintiff became a comatose quadriplegic. At the time of the collision, the Plaintiff was divorced but was very close to his 10-year-old son from the marriage and over whom he had joint custody. He was also survived by his parents who were economically dependent upon him.

The facts revealed that the rent-a-car operation maintained keys in each car on the lot, and when a car had to be taken to a nearby airport for delivery to a patron, the lot was left unattended.

A lawsuit was filed against Bascar, the employee, as well as against the rent-a-car company, for negligent maintenance of its premises in addition to a master–servant relationship with Bascar.

The National Union Insurance Company hired a lawyer to defend the rent-a-car operation. National Union failed to obtain a lawyer for Bascar. Defense counsel for the rent-a-car operation wrote to National Union and advised that it ought to get three lawyers: one for Bascar, one for the rent-a-car, which it had already gotten, and one to file a declaratory relief action in view of National Union's position that there was no coverage to cover Bascar because of the fact that he had allegedly taken the vehicle without permission.

Rather than heed their chosen defense counsel's admonition, National Union did not hire an attorney for Bascar but did hire another law firm to pursue a declaratory relief action. Thus, no attorney was hired for the defendant driver, Bascar.

In fact, a declaratory relief action was instituted by the insurer, National Union. Their proceeding was based upon the contention that Bascar did not have permission to operate the automobile. Under the then existing law, a permissive user was not a basis for disclaiming coverage and the Plaintiff prevailed in the declaratory relief action.

Subsequently, default judgments were obtained in the amount of $1 million for the minor son and $4.2 million in favor of the comatose quadriplegic, John Harvey.

Subsequently, a new law firm was hired by National Union to come into the original tort case to set aside the default judgments. However, in the interim, the Plaintiff obtained an assignment from Bascar providing him with his rights against National Union for its failure to defend him. The trial judge refused to set aside the default judgments inasmuch as the new lawyers for National Union failed to provide any reason why National Union did not defend Bascar originally.

Since that time, the insurer has filed a notice of appeal in the tort case, alleging that the trial court erred in refusing to set aside the default judgments.

It is anticipated that the insurance company will likewise appeal the adverse decision it received in the declaratory relief action which was adjudicated on motion for summary judgment in the Plaintiff's favor.

A third case has been filed, a collection case. However, before doing so, a settlement was reached with the rent-a-car's excess carriers for $400,000. Thus, the prime focus is on National Union, the primary carrier. This proceeding has been filed in a state court and, curiously, the insurer has now removed it to federal court. Whereas the trial courts might not have been terribly scrutinizing about mainland law pertaining to bad faith cases, there being no Hawaii cases in point, certainly the federal judges will apply applicable federal law which may be harsh for the insurer in this case.

The caption of the case was *Harvey* v. *Bascar, et al.*, Civil No. 4539, Second Circuit Court, Hawaii, 8 June 1981.

III. ILLUSTRATIVE CASE SUMMARIES

A. Tanker Truck Working Surface

A chemical loader fell from the top of a tanker truck at a loading facility and was injured. In a product liability action it was alleged that the truck manufacturer and truck owner were negligent in failing to install a flat working surface on the top of the cylindrical tanker truck. A 4-foot work platform was present at the fill hole, but the tanker was called unsafe because the work platform did not extend the length of the tanker top. Defendants denied any defect and alleged that the proximate cause was an antiquated loading rack furnished by the Plaintiff's employer. After an eight-day trial, the jury returned a verdict for the Defense. *O'Neil* v. *Widing Transportation Company and Fruehauf Corporation*, Case No. SOC 43032, Long Beach, California, 16 June 1981.

B. Auto Door Opens

A real estate salesman was driving his 1964 Lincoln Continental at about 35 mph. His 2½-year-old son was playing with the right rear door handle, his father warned him to stop, the door opened, the son fell out, and the injuries resulted in the amputation of the left leg below the knee. Plaintiffs claimed that the rear hinged doors were defective. Jury verdict was for $295,000 for the son. The father and another son had claimed emotional distress from witnessing the accident, and the jury awarded $125,000 to the father (who netted $6,200 because he was found 95 percent negligent) and $2,500 to the other son. *Bateman et al.* v. *Ford Motor Co.*, Case No. EAC-20916, Pomona, California, 12 March 1981.

C. Auto Transmission (Park to Reverse)

A 1977 Ford automobile was stopped in a driveway (in the "park" position, with the engine running); the driver got out and walked to the rear to close the driveway gate; the vehicle went into reverse, struck the driver, and killed her. Plaintiff alleged that the FMX transmission was designed so that the rooster comb had too flat a hill or gatepost between the park and reverse detents, that the spring load on the detent plunger was too weak, and that the linkage was susceptible to door slamming or vibrations that could cause the transmission to self-shift from a false or apparent park position into reverse. Evidence was presented of notice (728 accidents), inaction, and a safer feasible alternative design costing 3 cents per vehicle. The jury verdict was for $400,000 compensatory damages and $4 million punitive damages. The case was appealed and upheld by the Texas

Supreme Judicial Court. *Ford* v. *Nowak*, Tex. App. 30 June 1982.

D. Pickup Truck Tailgate

A young carpenter leased a Toyota pickup, sat on the tailgate, it failed, and he suffered a herniated disc. The Plaintiff alleged defective welds on the tailgate; the Defense claimed the welds were strong enough even though they did not meet specifications. The Defense also claimed a prior injury caused disability. The jury verdict was for the Defense. *English* v. *Toyota Motor Sales of U.S.A., et al.*, Case No. C-205-985, Los Angeles, Superior Court, Central, California, 27 July 1982.

E. Fire Without Collision

A 914 Porche caught fire and burned up after only four months (4500 miles). The Plaintiff claimed a defective fuel system and sued under theories of warranty, bad faith, and punitive damages. The Plaintiff demanded three new 914 Porches. The jury verdict was for $44,600. *Gomez* v. *Century Porche-Audi, et al.*, Case No. C-159-857, Los Angeles, Superior Court, Central, California, 9 April 1981.

F. Spare Tire Mount

A passenger was asleep in the cargo area behind the rear seat of a 1970 Chevrolet Suburbia when the vehicle struck a steel utility pole. The passenger (Plaintiff) alleged that the spare tire mount was defective and allowed the tire to hit him in the back, resulting in paraplegia. The jury verdict was for the Defense. *Prochaska* v. *General Motors*, Case No. 78-4714 WNB and 77-4764 WNB, Federal Court, Los Angeles, California, 3 August 1982.

G. Motorcycle Brakes

The brakes of a motorcycle failed and an auto body shop repaired them. Two days later (200 miles) they failed again, so brake fluid was added at a gasoline service station. When the motorcyclist applied his brakes, the brake fluid geysered out of the cylinder and allegedly caused an accident. Plaintiff claimed that the master cylinder cap was not attached properly, in a lawsuit against the service station, the oil company, and the auto body shop. Defendants claimed the master cylinder cap came off in the accident and that a leak in the master cylinder caused the brakes to fail. The injuries included a severely fractured leg and internal injuries. The jury returned a verdict for $1,200,000 against the service station. *Cynko* v. *Mike Lloyd Chevron, et al.*, Case No. C-244,880, Los Angeles, Superior Court, Central, California, 7 July 1982.

H. Cement Mixer Step

A worker was riding on the "J" step of a cement mixer truck, the step broke, he fell, and the rear wheels killed him. The employer had 99 identical trucks and 50 had step failures. Plaintiff and employer (owner of the truck) sued the truck manufacturer alleging defective design and failure to test. The jury verdict was for $500,000 gross, with Plaintiff 10 percent negligent, so the net was $450,000. Employer was held 30 percent negligent, and the manufacturer was held 60 percent negligent. *Diaz* v. *Conrock Company and International Harvester*, Case No. C-153,109, Los Angeles, Superior Court, Central, California, 30 March 1981.

I. Stuck Throttle

A 71-year-old driver and his 57-year-old wife were driving their new 1979 Cadillac Coupe De Ville when the throttle stuck. The auto went through his garage wall, then went into reverse and into his home. He suffered brain damage from subdural hematomas. In a lawsuit against the manufacturer and dealer, it was alleged that the sound deafener panel caused the throttle rod to stick. The trial resulted in a hung jury in May 1982, but a retrial resulted in a jury verdict of $1,140,000 to the man and $75,000 to his wife for loss of consortium. The Plaintiff had demanded $500,000 and the Defense had offered only $100,000. *Kappler, et al.* v. *General Motors Corp., et al.*, Case No. C-341,555, Los Angeles, Superior Court, Central, California, 3 August 1982.

J. Structured Settlement

A Honda struck a bicycle at a blind intersection, resulting in fractured legs and massive brain damage to the 8-year-old bicycle driver. It was alleged that massive vegetation created the blind intersection. The medical bills, between 1977 (the date of the accident) and 1982 (the date of trial), were in excess of $600,000. After four weeks of trial, a settlement was reached that had a present value of $4,015,000 and a total gross value of $23,051,000. The structured payment, for 28 years, guaranteed to the child and/or her parents was $180,000 per year, plus a substantial takeout every five years. *Brobeck* v. *City of Laguna Beach*, Case No. 29-32-33, Orange County, California, 10 September 1982.

K. Trailer Fire

A fifth-wheel travel trailer was purchased July 20, 1977, loaded with personal possessions, and driven away. The next morning, the trailer generator was turned on to power the refrigerator. Fifteen minutes later the Plaintiffs heard a "poof," and the trailer became engulfed in flames. Plaintiffs claimed no vent on the propane and generator compartment doors, failure to separate the generator and propane compartments, and substandard installation allowing vapors to ignite. It was also claimed that the fire extinguisher was inaccessible and the truck release lever would not release. The damage was the destruction of a 1977 Ford truck, an Ardon Travel Trailer, and all the personal belongings of the Plaintiffs ($39,961.75 for the personal belongings and $36,597.40 for the truck and trailer as a fire loss subrogation). The Defendants alleged that the fire did not originate in the trailer. The jury verdict was for $107,841.42 (including prejudgment interest, attorney's fees, and costs). *Brockman et al.* v. *Ardon Mobile Corp. et al.*, Case No. 286784, Orange County, Superior Court, California, 19 August 1981.

L. Auto Wheel Alignment Rack

An automobile moved off a wheel alignment rack, crushed a mechanic against a wall, and he was asphyxiated. The rack had been equipped with removable stops on the front to prevent the cars from rolling forward, but these stops were stored in the parts department. In a lawsuit against the rack manufacturer, it was alleged that the failure to have permanently affixed front wheel stops was a design defect. The jury found the decedent 5 percent negligent and returned a verdict for $326,610 (net). *Hutchins* v. *Manbee Equipment Co. and Pacific Telephone Co.*, Case No. C-178-287, Los Angeles, Superior Court, Central, California, 30 October 1981.

M. Fan Blade

Decedent was looking at his automobile engine and was killed when a fan blade broke off and entered his chest. It was alleged that the fan blade was susceptible to metal fatigue when installed on the engines of certain passenger automobiles. Because the seller could not be identified, the jury was instructed on negligence but not strict liability, and returned a Defense verdict. The case was appealed and it was held that strict liability applies to those Defendants who played an integral part in placing a defective product into the stream of commerce (such as one who designs but does not sell or manufacture a product). A motion for a new trial was granted. *Taylor* v. *General Motors, Inc.*, 537 F. Supp 949 (E.D. Ky. 1982).

N. Apportioning Injury due to Defects

A driver crashed into the rear of a parked car, struck the steering wheel, and ruptured his aorta. A product liability action was brought against the retailer and manufacturer of the 1972 Chrysler Dodge Colt alleging enhanced injuries caused by insufficient collapsing of the steering column and malfunctioning of the seat belt. The case was dismissed by the trial court for failure to prove what the injuries would have been if the automobile had not had the claimed defects. This was reversed by the Idaho Court of Appeals, which held that the Plaintiff is only required to show that the defect was a substantial factor in causing the injury. It further held that the Defendant had the burden of apportioning injury. *Fouche* v. *Chrysler Motors Corp.*, 646 P.2d 1020 (Idaho App. 1982).

O. Forklift Maintenance

A forklift operator was crushed against the steering wheel when an overhead guard collapsed. The overhead guard had been attached to the mast and body of the lift, the tilt cylinder became separated, the mast went forward, and the guard fell on the operator. The Plaintiff alleged a connection between the cylinder and mast was improperly designed, maintained, or repaired. The Defense claimed that the Plaintiff's employer had been warned by the maintenance company to get a new factory installed guard. The jury returned a defense verdict for the manufacturer, found the employer 35 percent negligent, and found the maintainer 65 percent negligent with damages of $87,000. *Burns* v. *Towmotor Corp.*, Case No. C-209-853, Los Angeles, Superior Court, Central, California, November 1982.

P. Jack Stand (Misuse)

An automobile mechanic was killed when a Cadillac fell off four tripod jack stands. It was alleged that there was a weak side of the safety jack stands and that the vehicle's axle did not fit the saddle of the jack stand, so only 100 pounds of lateral force could topple the vehicle. The Plaintiff alleged a failure to warn (proper positioning of jack stands and not to use them on rectangular axles). The Defense alleged misuse, the judge instructed the jury on misuse, and a Defense verdict was returned. The appellate court ruled that misuse is not an affirmative defense (but is an issue that arises with causation and the unreasonably dangerous criterion) and the instruction should not be given where foreseeability has been uncontradicted. Note: Illinois Pattern Instruction No. 400.08 (no misuse instruction should be given). *Illinois State Trust Co.* v. *Walker Manufacturing Co.*, 392 N.E.2d 70 (Ill. App. 1979).

Q. Crashworthiness (Roof Design)

A 1969 Chevrolet Impala roof collapsed during a rollover, rendering the driver a quadriplegic. After a jury verdict of $1,140,000, the Defense appealed, contending that defects based on conscious design choice should be judged on an engineering malpractice (negligence) standard. The Texas Supreme Court formulated the following jury instruction for design defect cases: "By the term 'defectively designed' as used in this instruction is meant a product that is unreasonably dangerous as designed, taking into consideration the utility of the product and the risk involved in its use." While risk-benefit factors should not be specifically enumerated, evidence "necessary to address the appropriate elements of balancing criteria should be overtly advanced by both parties." *Turner* v. *General Motors Corp.*, 584 S.W.2d 844 (Texas 1979).

R. Side Impact Crashworthiness

A policeman lost control of his patrol car, as he was responding to a burglar alarm, when the vehicle slid on a wet highway. The 1974 Dodge Monaco struck a steel pole, which penetrated between the front and rear seats, crushing the police officer against the roof. He was rendered a quadriplegic. It was alleged that the vehicle was defectively designed by having a two-part frame that made it vulnerable to side impacts. At trial there was testimony that a continuous frame with a cross-member would have prevented the intrusion and Plaintiff's injuries. The jury returned a verdict for $2,064,683 and $60,000 for loss of consortium, to which $399,287 was added in prejudgment interest. This was upheld by the Third Circuit Court of Appeals, in *Dawson* v. *Chrysler Corp.*, 630 F.2d 950 (3rd Cir. 1980).

S. Steering Loss

A 1971 Chevrolet Impala went out of control, allegedly because a stone jammed the steering coupling. The Plaintiffs claimed that the manufacturer had delayed notice of the defect (to the owners, in accordance with the federal Motor Vehicle Safety Act), inadequately warned, and failed to provide enough corrective shields to the dealers. The Plaintiff had received a recall notice prior to the accident; but all the dealerships (13) he contacted had no shields. The jury was instructed that violation of the MVSA constituted negligence. The jury found for the Plaintiff in the amount of $500,000. The Defendants argued that this implied a private cause of action, a new trial was granted, and the case was appealed to the Fifth Circuit Court of Appeals. It was held that violation of the MVSA may constitute negligence per se, under Alabama law, that such safety requirements are a minimum standard of care, that violation is evidence in a state-created cause of action, and that the jury verdict should be reinstated. *Lowe* v. *General Motors Corp.*, 624 F.2d 1373 (5th Cir. 1980). See also *Richardson* v. *Ford Motor Co.*, Case No. 51959, Mobile County Circuit Court, Alabama, 27 March 1980, dealing with an award for punitive damages for fraudulent misrepresentation (at the time of sale) and fraudulent concealment (after the sale) in delaying and limiting a recall pertaining to defective steering.

T. Brake Cable

An automobile mechanic was removing a parking brake cable from a 1977 Buick Electra when a retainer clip fractured and lacerated the cornea of his right eye. The mechanic alleged that the retainer clip was too brittle and unsuitable for use. Defense claimed the clip broke because of improper tools and procedures. Prior to trial, the Plaintiff demanded $25,000 (plus satisfaction of workmen's compensation lien of $5,192) and the Defense offered $1000. After a five-day trial, the jury returned a verdict of $101,120 gross. Since it also found the Plaintiff 10 percent negligent and the employer 20 percent negligent, the Plaintiff netted

$85,860. *Wilson* v. *General Motors Corporation*, Case No. NEC-27900, Pasadena Superior Court, California, 24 August 1982.

U. Motorcycle Crash Bar

A 1972 Harley Davidson Sportster motorcycle was struck by an automobile on its right side, and the motorcyclist's leg had to be amputated. In an action against the motorcycle manufacturer it was alleged that there was inadequate leg protection; i.e., no crash bar. The Defense argued that a crash bar would not have protected the driver's leg and that it would have resulted in higher "g-forces" being transmitted to the head, neck, and upper torso of the motorcyclist (i.e., trading-off head and neck injuries for leg protection). The Plaintiff made a demand of $1 million prior to trial; the Defense offered nothing. There was $412,620 in future lost earnings, $66,770 in past lost earnings, and $63,240 in medical payments. After a ten-day trial, the jury returned a verdict for the Defense. *Dennis* v. *Harley Davidson Motor Corp.*, Case No. SWC 43878, Torrance Superior Court, California, 14 June 1982.

V. Gas Tank Fire

The driver of a 1963 Ford F-100 pickup truck made a sudden turn onto an on ramp; the pickup overturned and caught on fire within seconds. Plaintiffs (the four burned occupants) alleged the following design defects: a gas tank located behind the driver, a filler cap that could come off during impact, and a fuel filler hose that could easily be torn or ruptured. Before trial, the Plaintiffs demanded $3.5 million and subsequently raised this to $13.9 million. The Defense offered $2 million. The jury returned a verdict for the Defense. *Ornelas, Munoz, Castro, and the Munoz Baby* v. *Ford Motor Company*, Case No. C-209,950, Los Angeles, Superior Court, Central, California, 7 August 1981.

31

The Appeal Process

GEORGE A. PETERS
and
BARBARA J. PETERS
Peters & Peters
Santa Monica, California

I. INTRODUCTION

After a jury verdict there is usually at least one dissatisfied
party who thinks immediately about the advantages and disadvantages of appealing various questions of the law. The
losing defendant may file an appeal just to obtain sufficient
negotiating leverage to reduce the value of an adverse jury
verdict; that is, a lesser settlement may be achieved if the
plaintiff and his attorneys do not wish to go through the cost of
an appeal process, do not wish to risk a retrial, and would like
some money immediately. The losing plaintiff may use the
appeal process to get a second chance with a "better jury,"
although it is the judge's decisions that are being criticized by
those seeking appellate relief from trial court "errors."

In preparing the appellate brief, a rigorous review of the
applicable case law is necessary on each relevant issue. The
review is usually with greater precision than found in most
pretrial preparation efforts or trial motions. The priority and
sequence of issues must be carefully considered. The lawyer
may ask himself, "What is the appellate court likely to do in a
case of this type?"; "Is this issue ripe for determination?"; and
"How can I quickly convince the reviewing judge that the
opposing side is presenting outworn law from outdated cases;
'bad law' or erroneous law that needs clarification; internally

inconsistent legal theories leading to inconsistent results; and improper applications of the law to the facts, circumstances, or jury instructions in this case?"

When faced with the time limits and unique procedures for the appeal process, added to the pressures of a legal practice that requires some catch-up after a long trial, the trial attorney may turn to a legal specialist in appellate practice. However, the attorney still needs to expend some time and effort to clarify the issues, of the specific case, for the appellate attorney.

In some instances, the trial lawyer quickly searches for a similar appellate brief to give him or her a rough idea of appropriate format, presentation, issues, cases, and argument. This is a good starting point in terms of economy of effort, useful ideas, and early orientation in the "right direction."

The following appellate brief is an example of a well-written appellate brief that provides good presentation of one advocate's perception of the facts and applicable law in one jurisdiction. It highlights forensic engineering issues that should be of considerable interest to nonlawyers involved in automotive product liability litigation, as they relate to the technical issues, the legal tactics, the earlier appeals, and the general "history" of the lawsuit.

II. THE APPEAL BRIEF

IN THE UNITED STATES COURT OF APPEALS
FOR THE DISTRICT OF COLUMBIA CIRCUIT

```
WYLLIE GATEWOOD,                        :
                                        :
              Plaintiff-Appellee,       :
                                        :
    vs.                                 : Nos. 81-1967 and
                                        :      81-2004
FIAT, S.p.A., et al.,                   :
                                        :
              Defendants-Appellants.    :
```

ON APPEAL FROM THE
UNITED STATES DISTRICT COURT FOR THE
DISTRICT OF COLUMBIA

     Certificate required by Rule 8(c) of the General Rules
of the United States Court of Appeals for the District of Columbia
Circuit:

     The undersigned, counsel of record for appellee, certifies
that the certificate filed by the appellant is true and accurate
to the best of appellee's knowledge.

     These representations are made in order that the Judges of
this Court may evaluate possible disqualifications or recusal.

```
                              _____
                              Gerard E. Mitchell
                              STEIN, MITCHELL & MEZINES
                              Suite 1060-N
                              1800 M Street, N. W.
                              Washington, D. C.   20036
                              (202) 737-7777
                              Counsel for Appellee
```

Dated: January 19, 1982

TABLE OF CONTENTS

TABLE OF AUTHORITIES

6A _Moore's Federal Practice_ ¶59.05[5] (1979) 20

B. Phillips, _Seat Belt Usage Among Drivers_, at xvii (U.S.
Department of Transportation, 1980) 34

C. Stowell & J. Bryant, _Safety Belt Usage: Surve of the
Traffic Population_ 4-5 (U.S. Department of Transportation
1978) 29, 34

* Cases or authorities chiefly relied upon are marked by
asterisks.

STATEMENT OF ISSUES PRESENTED FOR REVIEW

1.   Whether defendants' motion for judgment n.o.v.
or, in the alternative, for a new trial was properly denied
where there was overwhelming evidence from which the jury
could reasonably conclude that the plaintiff's injuries were
caused by Fiat's defective door latch system.

2.   Whether the trial court properly refused to admit evidence regarding seat belts for the purpose of determining
(a) if plaintiff's vehicle was reasonably safe, since the
plaintiff's Fiat lacked seat belts when sold by defendants,
and (b) if the plaintiff failed to mitigate damages.

3.   Whether testimony regarding Federal Motor Vehicle
Safety Standard No. 206, which merely codified existing
practices, was admissible to prove the state of the art one
year prior to the effective date of that standard.

4.   Whether, where the Fiat 600D, Version 140, was made
for distribution in the United States, evidence of door latch
designs used on U. S. vehicles was admissible to prove the state
of the art for door latch systems.

5.   Whether, where the complaint was filed and Fiat, S.p.A.'s
designated representative was served within sixteen months of
the product's failure, the trial court properly denied defendant
S.p.A.'s motion to dismiss on the ground that the plaintiff's
claim was barred by the statute of limitations.

6.   Whether Fiat Motors of North America, Inc., the distributor of the plaintiff's vehicle, was properly retained as a
defendant on the strict liability and breach of warranty counts.

7.   Whether the trial court properly allowed the jury to consider claims based on the "Second Collision" theory approved in
Knippen v. Ford Motor Co.

8.   Whether the jury was properly permitted to consider plaintiff's probable loss of future wages as an item of damage.

9.   Whether the trial court properly refused to reduce the judgment against defendants based on defendants' alleged right to
contribution from absent "Joint Tortfeasors."

RULE 8(b) STATEMENT

Pursuant to Rule 8(b) of the General Rules of the United States Court of Appeals for the District of Columbia Circuit, counsel for the appellee certifies that the Rule 8(b) Statement filed by counsel for appellant makes note of any and all related cases.

STATEMENT OF THE CASE

Introduction

In an article published in 1964 Enzo Franchini, head of
defendant Fiat, S.p.A.'s Dynamic Test laboratory, observed
that the trend for some years among auto manufacturers was
to install door latch systems providing fore and aft linkage
so that car doors did not open unnecessarily and allow
occupants to be ejected in motor vehicle collisions. In
that same year Fiat began to import into the United States
its 600D series. The 600D door latch system had been
unchanged since 1951. It offered no fore and aft resistance
to forces tending to open the car doors during impact. In
1967, when Fiat manufactured plaintiff's vehicle for sale in
the United States, the door latch system in the 600D was
twelve years behind the state of the art in this country.

On October 23, 1976 an accident occurred which served
to illustrate perfectly the necessity and importance of
reasonably safe door latch design. A low speed intersection
collision caused mild stretching forces to be applied to the
driver's side of plaintiff's Fiat. A reasonably good latch
in keeping with the 1956-1967 state of the art would have
kept the door closed. Like the other four occupants of the
two vehicles, plaintiff would have suffered no serious
injury if he had stayed in the car.

In this case, however, because of the outmoded and
dangerous latch system on the 1967 600D, plaintiff was

ejected from his vehicle and landed head first on the
pavement. As a result of his head striking the pavement,
plaintiff suffered severe and permanent brain damage.

Proceedings Below

Suit against the Fiat defendants was filed in the
District Court on February 17, 1978, sixteen months after
the accident of October 23, 1976. On February 23, 1978,
service was made upon C. Ferrari, S.p.A.'s designated
representative for service of process under the National
Traffic and Motor Vehicle Safety Act of 1966.

The District Court granted defendants' motion to
dismiss for lack of personal jurisdiction on April 21, 1978,
but made no ruling on the motion of Fiat, S.p.A. to dismiss
for insufficient service of process. This Court reversed
the lower court on January 24, 1980. With the motion based
on alleged insufficient process still pending, plaintiff on
February 12, 1980 served Fiat, S.p.A. by mailing process to
Fiat, S.p.A.'s president in Torino, Italy. Fiat, S.p.A. on
March 3, 1980 filed a motion to dismiss on the ground that
the claim against Fiat, S.p.A. was barred by the applicable
three year statute of limitations. The motion was denied on
April 16, 1980. Fiat then filed a similar motion on July
17, 1980. Over plaintiff's opposition, the District Court
granted that motion on August 8, 1980. Plaintiff's first
motion for reconsideration was denied on August 22, 1980.
Plaintiff filed a renewed motion for reconsideration on

November 26, 1980, which the District Court granted on
December 1, 1980.   In a written opinion Judge Robinson ruled
that the statute of limitations was tolled by the filing of
the complaint, but that Fiat, S.p.A. would have leave to
file a motion to dismiss pursuant to Rule 41(b).   Such a
motion was filed on December 15, 1980 and denied on January
6, 1981.

Trial on this matter began on Monday, May 4, 1981, and
concluded on Wednesday, May 13, 1981.   Jury deliberations
began shortly after 2:00 p.m. on Tuesday, May 12, 1981.   The
jury returned a verdict at 3:24 p.m. on Wednesday, May 13,
1981. On that date the District Judge entered judgment on
the verdict in the sum of $650,000.00, plus costs.

On May 20, 1981 the defendants filed a motion to amend
the judgment on the ground that the defendants were entitled
to a pro rata credit by reason of the alleged negligence of
so-called joint tortfeasors.   On May 26, 1981 plaintiff
filed an opposition to the defendants' motion to amend the
judgment.   On May 27, 1981 the defendants' motion was
denied.

On May 26, 1981 the defendants filed a motion for
judgment n.o.v. or, in the alternative, for a new trial.
The defendants did not seek a remittitur.   Plaintiff's
opposition to the motion was filed June 1, 1981.   A
supplemental memorandum in opposition to the defendants'

motion for a new trial was filed on July 10, 1981, following
argument on defendants' motion. Defendants then filed two
supplemental memoranda in support of their motion. On July
28, 1981 the District Judge entered an order denying the
motion for judgment n.o.v. or, in the alternative, for a new
trial. In its order the court stated:

> (1) There is no basis for entering a
> judgment notwithstanding the verdict pursuant
> to Fed.R.Civ.P. 50(b). The above captioned
> case is not one where the Court must conclude,
> without weighing the credibility of the witnesses
> or otherwise considering the weight of the evi-
> dence, that the only verdict that reasonable
> persons could have reached was one for the De-
> fendants. There was sufficient evidence to
> support Plaintiff's case.

> (2) There is no basis for ordering a new
> trial pursuant to Fed.R.Civ.P. 59. The verdict
> was not against the weight of the evidence suffi-
> cient to order a new trial and it would not be in
> the interests of justice to do so. (Joint Ap-
> pendix, hereinafter "J. App.", at 3).

STATEMENT OF FACTS

A. <u>The Collision</u>

The parties stipulated to basic facts concerning the
collision which resulted in plaintiff's injuries. On the
afternoon of October 23, 1976, the plaintiff, while
operating a 1967 Fiat 600D sedan, collided with a Ford van
at the intersection of Peabody and Seventh Street, N. W.,
Washington, D. C. The plaintiff's Fiat had been travelling
northbound on Seventh Street. The Ford van had been
travelling eastbound on Peabody Street. The driver side

-4-

door of the Fiat opened following impact, and plaintiff was
ejected from the vehicle (Trial Transcript, hereinafter
"Tr.," at 756-57).

There was one eyewitness to the collision. Robert
Wayne Harris, then age 15, was standing at the entrance of
an alley less than half a block from the point of the
collision. According to his testimony, both vehicles were
proceeding at approximately 25 miles per hour (Tr. 765).[1/]
The Ford van failed to stop for a stop sign and entered the
intersection in the path of the plaintiff's Fiat (Tr. 766,
775). The left front of the Fiat struck the van on the
forward right side, causing the Fiat to spin in a clockwise
direction approximately 180° (Tr. 776). The driver door
fully opened at 150° of the turn (Tr. 779). The eyewitness
then testified as follows:

> Q. Can you describe what happened to
> the driver as he came out?
>
> A. He sort of pivoted out and he landed
> on his head and sort of toppled and came to a
> rest right there.
>
> Q. What part of the head did he land on?
>
> A. It looked like the left. About the
> left side of his head.
>
> Q. Can you show us where on your head
> that was or that you believe he hit on the head?
>
> A. About right here (indicating).
>
> Q. Pointing to the left top of your
> head?

[1/] Compare Fiat Brief, at 2 ("a speeding Ford van").

A.   Right.

Q.   And sort of above the ear, is that right?

A.   Right.

Q.   Did you see the driver's head hit anything other than the pavement?

A.   No.   He didn't hit nothing other than the pavement.

Q.   Could you see whether the driver hit the roof of the car as he came out?

A.   No.   The driver came out, out of the car.   The door came open and he came right out of the car.

Q.   What did you mean when you said that the driver pivoted?   That his body was pivoted?

A.   It was like he was catapulted.   He came out head first, sort of slumped over.   (Tr. 776-77).[2/]

Robert Wayne Harris went over to the Fiat following the collision (Tr. 779).   He noticed that the driver's door window was down (Tr. 779), and that there were no broken windows (Tr. 785).   He observed that the right front seat passenger in the Fiat, Anthony Copeland, was conscious and had only facial bruises (Tr. 785-787).

Albert Fonda, one of plaintiff's expert mechanical engineers, after viewing photographs of the vehicles,

---

[2/] Defendants have tried to convey the impression that the plaintiff flopped out of the car in a manner suggesting that he was clearly unconscious.   However, the eyewitness, who testified through his deposition, stated: "It was real fast.   He came out instantaneously and fell on the ground" (Tr. 796).   The witness again described the plaintiff as having been "catapulted" (Tr. 797).

examining an identical 600D vehicle, and visiting the scene
of the accident, described the collision as a "nose-wipe"
plus "side-slap" type of accident (Tr. 278-79). He
described the mechanics of the collision as entailing
movement of the front of the Fiat to the right, distorting
the shape of the vehicle. As the front of the vehicle was
rotated in a clockwise direction, relatively mild
stretching forces were applied to the left side of the
vehicle (Tr. 283-84, 968). Because of the absence of fore
and aft linkage in the door latch assembly the door
separated from the so-called "B" post and flew open (Tr.
284, 294). The extent of the deformation of the door at the
"B" post is depicted in plaintiff's exhibits 11 and 13 (J.
App. 52, 54). The relationship of the car door to the "A"
and "B" posts is also shown on plaintiff's exhibits 18 and
21 (J. App. 58, 61).

Based on his examination of the photographs, Mr. Fonda
testified that the driver door of the Fiat opened one or two
feet upon impact and then struck the side of the van (Tr.
293). This had the effect of pushing the door closed
momentarily, but the door then opened again and allowed the
plaintiff to be spilled onto the pavement (Tr. 294).

B. **The Defect**

(1) **State of the Art.**

One of the prime objectives of a door latch system is
to hold the door shut in the event that there are forces on

the car tending to open the car door (Tr. 220, 964). This proposition was never disputed at trial, and was conceded by Henry W. Wessells, III, Fiat's automotive engineering expert (Tr. 964). The rationale for designing a door latch that would tend to keep doors closed during a collision was established during the 1950's. According to Albert G. Fonda, one of plaintiff's expert engineers, a landmark paper in the field of automotive design was published at Cornell University in August, 1954. A Study of Automobile Doors Opening Under Crash Conditions, by John O. Moore and Boris Tourin, concluded that the risk of moderate to fatal injuries was more than doubled when vehicle occupants were ejected due to accidental door opening (Tr. 236-37; Pl. Ex. 52). Subsequent studies showed that ejection increased the risk of injury and fatality fivefold as compared with being retained in the vehicle (Tr. 238). As pointed out by Mr. Fonda, Fiat's awareness of the greater hazards presented by ejection was demonstrated in a 1964 paper by Enzo Franchini entitled Catapult Crash Testing, and more specifically in a section of that paper entitled "Accidental Door Openings" (Tr. 239; Pl. Ex. 51). Having testified that he considered Mr. Franchini's views to be reliable as well as indicative of Fiat's knowledgeableness, Mr. Fonda read the following statements into evidence in accordance with Rule 803(18) of the Federal Rules of Evidence:

> Statistics have shown that the ejection
> of occupants as a result of accidental door

openings is responsible for a high percentage
of injuries (bibl. ref. 11). Since some years,
the trend of manufacturers has shown preference
for door locks with three direction linkage (1st
transversal; 2nd vertical; 3rd longitudinal) to enhance safety with regard to accidental openings
instead of the previous two direction type (1st
and 2nd). (Tr. 240; J. App. 91).[3/]

Door latch designs providing fore and aft linkage were
adopted in the United States in 1955-56 by Ford, General
Motors, Chrysler and Studebaker (Tr. 234). There were
several different types or designs. Mercedes by 1953 had
employed a cone type of latch which afforded resistance to
stressing forces tending to open car doors (Tr. 259-60; J.
App. 66). A second type of design, the rachet latch, was
used by General Motors from 1955 through 1964 (Tr. 263-64;
J. App. 68). The third type of design, the pin latch, has
been employed by major manufacturers from 1962 until the
present time (Tr. 261-62; J. App. 67). According to Mr.
Fonda, there was no reason whatsoever why one or more of
these protective latches giving longitudinal linkage could
not have been adapted to a car of the size and nature of the
Fiat 1967 600D (Tr. 273).

There were no significant changes in the state of the
art for door latch systems from 1963-66 through January 1968
(Tr. 272; see Tr. 928). On January 1, 1968, Federal Motor

[3/] Studies demonstrating the hazards of door latch
systems lacking longitudinal linkage are referenced in
footnote 11 of Mr. Franchini's paper. (J. App. 116)(see
Tr. 301-02).

Vehicle Safety Standard No. 206 for passenger car door latch
systems became effective (Pl. Ex. 55). According to Mr.
Fonda, Standard No. 206 codified accepted practices (Tr.
352). Fiat's expert, Henry Wessells, agreed that the
principles for longitudinal linkage in door latch design
were known for many years prior to January, 1967, when Fiat
manufactured the plaintiff's vehicle (Tr. 928).

(2) The Fiat 600D Door Latch Provided Zero
Longitudinal Linkage.

Two highly qualified mechanical engineers -- Albert G.
Fonda, with bachelor's and master's degrees from Cornell
University and experience in a dozen door latch cases (Tr.
212-14), and Charles B. Watkins, Jr., Ph.D., Professor and
Chairman of the Department of Mechanical Engineering at
Howard University (Tr.634) -- testified that the 1967 Fiat
600D was unreasonably dangerous because its door latch
system provided no fore and aft resistance to door openings
in the event of a collision (Tr. 219; 639). A lucid
description of this defect was provided by Dr. Watkins:

> In my opinion, the door latch design
> in the model 600D Fiat as I investigated was
> deficient inasmuch as it does not provide
> any means of restraint in the fore and aft
> direction, that is, the direction of travel
> of the automobile; and in the circumstances of
> a fairly, kind of ordinary collision, this can
> allow the automobile door to open and the occu-
> pant to be ejected (Tr. 639).

After explaining in detail, with the aid of a large diagram,
the principles and concepts embodied in door latch design
(Tr. 640-47; Pl. Ex. 35), Dr. Watkins testified that the

-10-

latch used in the 1967 Fiat 600D "would allow the door to
pop open under certain accident conditions which would not
be all that severe, that is, in a fairly minor collision"
(Tr. 648). Mr. Fonda testified that the latch has no
strength in the longitudinal direction so that zero
stretching forces are resisted at the latch during a
collision (Tr. 342-43).

C. The Causal Relationship Between The Defect And
Plaintiff's Injury.

Both Mr. Fonda and Dr. Watkins testified that a
reasonably good door latch adapted to the Fiat 600D would
have kept the plaintiff's door shut during the course of
this collision (Tr. 294, 651, 687). Both experts cited the
relatively mild deformation of the door frame, which was of
no greater magnitude than one-half inch (Tr. 295-97, 651;
see Pl. Ex. 11 & 13, J. App. 52, 54). According to Mr.
Fonda's measurements, the Fiat latch overlapped the striker
by no more than three-eighths of an inch, so that fore and
aft stretching of only three-eighths of an inch would open
the car door (Tr. 299-300). Mr. Fonda and Dr. Watkins
expressed the opinion, based on reasonable engineering
certainty, that the door opening on plaintiff's car was
caused by the defective latch system (Tr. 302, 650).

Plaintiff also provided several expert opinions that
plaintiff would not have suffered a significant blow to the
head if the door latch system had not failed. According to
Mr. Fonda, if the door had stayed shut, the force of the

-11-

impact would have been upon the plaintiff's shoulder rather than upon his head, which would then have struck nothing (Tr. 310-11). Dr. Watkins also testified that if the door had remained closed, there would have been no significant blow to plaintiff's head (Tr. 653). Further support for this view was given by John T. Legowik, M. D., a board certified clinical and forensic pathologist on the staff of the Armed Forces Institute of Pathology (Tr. 492). Dr. Legowik, who testified that he had investigated several thousand cases involving the biomechanics of head injury and who was accepted as an expert in the biomechanics of head injury (Tr. 497-98), testified that the plaintiff would have suffered no appreciable injury if the car door had remained closed in this accident (Tr. 505).

Plaintiff's engineering experts expressly excluded the possibility that the plaintiff was struck in the head by the passenger, Anthony Copeland. According to Mr. Fonda, the forces involved in this collision would not cause the passenger's forehead to strike the plaintiff behind the right ear, as Fiat claimed (Tr. 317-18). Dr. Watkins also testified that the passenger could not have impacted the driver because they would have been travelling in parallel paths (Tr. 664-65). He testified further that their trajectory would not have been affected by their posture in the vehicle because of the overwhelming dynamics of the collision forces in a typical automobile accident (Tr. 665-66).

Lastly, there was evidence from medical experts that a blow to the left top of the plaintiff's head was responsible for the injuries which plaintiff suffered. Plaintiff's treating neurosurgeon, Guy W. Gargour, M. D., a board certified neurosurgeon with nineteen years of training and experience in his specialty (Tr. 386-87), testified that the plaintiff's injuries were caused by a single blow to the top or vertex of the head (Tr. 391). Dr. Gargour explained that the patient had no surface lacerations or black and blue marks on the right side of his head (Tr. 417), and stated that the bogginess that he noted in that area two days after the collision was due to bleeding from the fractures rather than a direct blow to that location.[4/]

James C. King, M. D., a board certified otolaryngologist, performed surgery on plaintiff's right ear. Under an operating microscope, he lifted up the skin on the right side of the plaintiff's head and viewed the plaintiff's fractures (Tr. 471). Having directly examined the fractures in the area where Fiat claims the blow was

---

[4/] Fiat continues to make every effort to portray Dr. Gargour's trial testimony as inconsistent with his deposition (Fiat Brief, at 11). In fact, the re-direct examination of Dr. Gargour makes it perfectly clear that Dr. Gargour's opinions at deposition and trial were consistent, and on both occasions he concluded that the more likely site of the blow suffered by the plaintiff was the top of his head (Tr. 421-23).

struck, Dr. King testified that the blow was actually received "from the opposite side" (Tr. 487). Based on his observing that the fracture was a shear type of fracture (Tr. 486), Dr. King concluded that the point of impact was approximately three inches above the left ear (Tr. 488-89).

John T. Legowik, M.D., a board certified pathologist specializing in head and neck injuries, testified that the blow was received to the plaintiff's left superior parietal area (Tr. 501, 565). Dr. Legowik stated that the direction of the blow was downward and to the plaintiff's right (Tr. 566). He explained that a blow to the top of the head causes inbending at the point of impact with outbending away from the impact point (Tr. 525). The fracture begins at the outbended area and the accumulated stress tends to be relieved by fracture lines at the base of the skull (Tr. 525-26). Dr. Legowik, agreeing with Dr. Gargour, stated that the bogginess was from fracture bleeding rather than direct impact (Tr. 566).

Ayub Khan Ommaya, M. D., who was described by defense counsel as "an internationally known brain surgeon" (Tr. 449), was employed at the National Institutes of Health in Bethesda, Maryland from 1961 until 1980, where he was Chief of Applied Research in Neurosurgery (Tr. 587). In 1980 he entered private practice and became Medical Advisor to the National Highway Traffic Safety Administration (Tr. 587). In addition, he has authored 140 articles and books in his particular field of interest, damage to the brain and nervous system (Tr. 589). He was accepted without challenge as an expert in the field of neurosurgery, particularly in the biomechanics of head injuries (Tr. 590).

Dr. Ommaya testified that the point of impact was at the top of plaintiff's head, slightly to the rear and to the left (Tr. 591-92). The direction of the blow was downward, into the neck (Tr. 592). He testified that a vertex impact was the only way to explain all of the fractures exhibited by the plaintiff (Tr. 594). He reiterated the fracture mechanism described by Dr. Legowik: that a blow with a blunt instrument causes inbending at the point of impact and outbending at some distance from that point; that the fracture begins at the outbending; and that fracture lines are drawn towards the base of the skull (Tr. 606-607). "That explains why you can get very severe fractures in the base of the skull with blows at the top of the head" (Tr. 607).

The plaintiff's medical experts emphatically rejected the defense theory that the blow was struck to the plaintiff's right ear. As grounds for excluding that explanation, Dr. Legowik pointed to the absence of neck and spinal cord damage that would be associated with a blow to that area (Tr. 527-28), the absence of lacerations over the ear area (Tr. 528), the inability of a blow to the right side to account for the epidural hematoma in the upper left

-15-

portion of the plaintiff's head (Tr. 529), and the absence
of any depression fractures at the point of alleged impact
(Tr. 529). Dr. Legowik specifically rejected x-ray analysis
of soft tissue swelling as a valid means of making a
diagnosis of the impact point (Tr. 555). According to Dr.
Legowik, x-ray evaluation of soft tissue swelling is
"notoriously inaccurate" and "would be a probable disaster"
(Tr. 553). Dr. Legowik also testified that the compression
fracture of plaintiff's first cervical vertebra was due to a
downward impact from the left side rather than from a
lateral impact from the right side (Tr. 523-24). Asked
about Fiat's theory on the mechanics of injury, Dr. Legowik
stated that there was no possibility that the plaintiff's
injuries were inflicted by his being struck by Mr. Copeland
(Tr. 503). Dr. Ommaya added that a right side blow could
not explain the fracture to the left side of the plaintiff's
skull or the small epidural hemorrhage located near the
vertex, left of the midline on the skull (Tr. 595-96; 600).

SUMMARY OF ARGUMENT

The design of the door latch system on the 1967 Fiat
model 600D was defective and unreasonably dangerous because
it provided no resistance to fore and aft stretching such as
frequently occurs even in minor collisions. Although the
latch system was designed in 1951, Fiat did not begin to
export the 600D to the United States until 1964. By the

time plaintiff's vehicle was manufactured in January, 1967,
the vehicle's latch system was nearly twelve years behind
the state of the art.

Fiat manufactured and sold the plaintiff's vehicle
without seat belts installed. There was no testimony
linking Fiat to the unidentified third party who installed
lap belts in the plaintiff's Fiat. Like over 90% of male
drivers, plaintiff was not wearing the lap belt on the date
of the accident. He had no knowledge at that time that the
Fiat door latch system would allow the car door to pop open
even in a relatively minor collision.

The trial court properly denied defendants' motion for
judgment n.o.v. or, in the alternative, for a new trial,
because there was abundant evidence to support the
plaintiff's claim that he was injured as the result of
ejection due to door latch system failure. Plaintiff
presented eyewitness and expert testimony that he struck the
roadway on the left top of his head after being thrown head-
first from his vehicle following a low speed intersection
collision.

Fiat's liability depends on whether the 600D was unreasonably dangerous at the time that it was placed into the
stream of commerce by the defendants. Where plaintiff
proved that the vehicle was unreasonably dangerous on
account of a defective door latch system installed by the
manufacturer, the defendants cannot be relieved from

-17-

liability by evidence of seat belt installation by an
unidentified third party. Although the court did permit
Fiat to introduce evidence of the existence of lap belts and
their non-use at the time of the accident, such non-use was
not admissible to show that the plaintiff was contributorily
negligent or that he failed to mitigate damages.

Where there was testimony that door latch design
principles apply equally to small as well as large vehicles,
the trial court properly allowed plaintiff to introduce
evidence regarding U.S. vehicles in order to show the state
of the art for door latch systems. Likewise, testimony
regarding the subsequently enacted Federal Motor Vehicle
Safety Standard No. 206 was properly admitted as relevant to
the state of the art one year earlier, where there was ample
evidence that Standard 206 merely codified accepted
principles and practices.

ARGUMENT

    I. DEFENDANTS' MOTION FOR JUDGMENT N.O.V.
        OR, IN THE ALTERNATIVE, FOR A NEW TRIAL
        WAS PROPERLY DENIED BECAUSE THERE WAS
        OVERWHELMING EVIDENCE FROM WHICH THE
        JURY COULD REASONABLY CONCLUDE THAT THE
        PLAINTIFF'S INJURIES WERE CAUSED BY
        FIAT'S DEFECTIVE DOOR LATCH SYSTEM.

Most of the defendants' brief is a republication of
their unsuccessful jury argument. Buoyed by the District

Judge's apparent endorsement of their theory of the case[5]/
the Fiat defendants present a one-sided version of the record in the hope that this Court will override the jury's
verdict. As plaintiff's recitation of facts above makes
clear, however, there was ample and really overwhelming evidence before the jury in support of every aspect of the
plaintiff's case. The District Judge therefore correctly
ruled on July 28, 1981 that there was no basis for entering
a judgment notwithstanding the verdict pursuant to Fed.R.
Civ.P. 50(b) or for ordering a new trial pursuant to
Fed.R.Civ.P. 59.

It is not surprising that the defendants omit any
reference to the legal standards applicable on appeal from
denial of motions for judgment n.o.v. or new trial. It is
well established in this jurisdiction that entry of judgment
n.o.v. is improper unless the evidence, together with all
inferences that can reasonably be drawn therefrom, is so
one-sided that the only verdict that reasonable persons
could have reached was one for the moving party. Vander Zee
v. Karabatsos, 191 U.S. App. D.C. 200, 589 F.2d 723, 726
(1978), cert. denied, 441 U.S. 962 (1979); Luck v.
Baltimore & Ohio Railroad, 166 U.S. App. D.C. 283, 510 F.2d
663 (1975). As the trial court properly observed in the

---

[5]/   See Tr. of July 10, 1981, proceedings on post-trial
motions. However, Judge Robinson emphatically refused to
set aside the verdict on the basis of his own views (J. App.
3).

order denying the motion for judgment n.o.v., there was sufficient evidence to support the plaintiff's case (J. App. 3).

Nor is the law more favorable for Fiat on appeal from denial of a motion for new trial. As this Court noted with approval in Taylor v. Washington Terminal Co., 133 U.S. App. D.C. 110, 113, 409 F.2d 145 (1969): "In this jurisdiction particularly, District Court judges have given great weight to jury verdicts." Particularly when a verdict is challenged on the ground that it is against the weight of the evidence, this Court is reluctant to interfere with the constitutionally protected right to jury trial. Id. at 113 n.13. As the Supreme Court admonished in Tennant v. Peoria & Pekin Union Railway, 321 U.S. 29, 35 (1944):

> Courts are not free to reweigh the evidence and set aside the jury verdict merely because the jury could have drawn different inferences or conclusions or because judges feel that other results are more reasonable.

Here the trial judge denied the motion for new trial, ruling that the verdict was not against the weight of the evidence sufficient to order a new trial and that it would not be in the interests of justice to do so (J. App. 3). Such a conclusion is not to be upset on appeal absent an abuse of discretion. 6A Moore's Federal Practice ¶59.05[5] (1979) (citing cases).

There was no reason in this products liability case for the trial court to adopt the more critical jury review standard which has been approved to some degree in certain patent and antitrust cases. No products liability case has been cited by defendants which adopts a different standard for review than is applicable in tort actions generally. Judge Robinson at the conclusion of the trial commented that the evidence had been "laid out clearly" (Tr. 1180). His application of the traditional test under Rule 59 should not be disturbed.

A. Plaintiff's Injuries Were Caused By Ejection From The Vehicle.

Much of Fiat's brief repeats factual allegations which are either unsupported by the record or completely outweighed by the plaintiff's evidence. Fiat contends, for example, that plaintiff's injuries were so clearly proved to be due to impact by the passenger's forehead as to mandate entry of judgment n.o.v. (Fiat Brief, at 17). In fact, there was no testimony, lay or expert, that the passenger's forehead struck the plaintiff. The defendants do not and cannot give a record reference for such testimony because it was never presented to the jury. That theory is completely the hypothesis of defense counsel. The defendants presented the testimony of a mechanical engineer, John W. Melvin, Ph.D., but never was Dr. Melvin asked for his opinion on whether the passenger's forehead was propelled against the right side of plaintiff's head. Plaintiff, on the other hand, presented the testimony of three experts that such an event did not occur and was not even possible (Tr. 317-18, 503, 653).

Another typical Fiat contention is the argument that the plaintiff would not have had amnesia with respect to the initial collision if he had really suffered the injury when he hit the pavement (Fiat Brief, at 18). The record, however, shows that the plaintiff had retrograde amnesia for all events after he entered his vehicle in Landover, Maryland (Tr. 99). Fiat's attempt to correlate the onset of amnesia and the moment of secondary impact has absolutely no evidentiary basis, either lay or expert.

Fiat's effort to reconstruct the record is illustrated by defendants' representation that the eyewitness, Robert Wayne Harris, testified that the plaintiff "'toppled' out of the car as 'the Fiat came to a rest.'" (Fiat Brief, at 18). Fiat cites the transcript at page 776. In fact, the actual testimony at that page gives a much different impression:

> He sort of pivoted out and he landed on
> his head and sort of toppled and came
> to a rest right there. (Tr. 776, lines
> 24-25).

Fiat chooses to ignore the repeated references in the testimony of Mr. Harris to the fact that the plaintiff was "catapulted" out of the car (Tr. 777, 797). Likewise, Fiat mentions the eyewitness' statement that plaintiff landed on the left side of his head (Fiat Brief, at 19), without adding that the witness pointed to the left top of his head and so acknowledged in his testimony (Tr. 777).

Four doctors (two neurosurgeons, one pathologist, and one otolaryngologist) testified that the plaintiff suffered impact upon a blunt surface at the top or left top of his head (Tr. 390-91, 487, 501, 591-92). Undaunted, Fiat argues that "the only conclusion that can be reached from the medical testimony is that plaintiff suffered a blow to the right side of his head while inside the car" (Fiat Brief, at 21)(emphasis added).

Fiat presented a single witness on this point. That witness, a radiologist, admitted that he had never been specifically asked regarding the mechanics of a head injury prior to this case (Tr. 1035), and that he gave his opinions in this case without first becoming acquainted with the deposition testimony of the eyewitness, the operating neurosurgeon, or the operating otolaryngologist (Tr. 1036-38). The witness also admitted that Alicia Gurdjian, M.D., is a specialist in the mechanics of head injury and that Dr. Gurdjian's writings are authoritative in this field (Tr. 1019). On cross-examination, the witness, David Davis, M.D., agreed with several propositions advanced in Dr. Gurdjian's works which were completely consistent with the plaintiff's theory of how this injury was inflicted. Dr. Davis agreed that linear fractures begin at the outbended area away from the point of impact (Tr. 1026-27); that blows to the top rear of the head cause fractures extending toward the petrous bone, adjacent to the ear (Tr. 1028); and that

-23-

fractures from the outbended areas extend towards other
areas of stress concentration, such as areas of unusual,
bony, or irregular formation (Tr. 1033-34).[6] When asked
repeatedly concerning the views of the reknowned Dr.
Gurdjian, Dr. Davis responded, "How can I disagree with
someone like Dr. Gurdjian?" (Tr. 1034). One might as easily
inquire how anyone could rationally argue for judgment
n.o.v. or for a new trial on such a record.

   B.   The 1967 Fiat 600D was Defective and
        Unreasonably Dangerous.

   1.   Alternative Latches

Fiat contends that it is absolved from responsibility
for installing a latch providing fore and aft linkage
because none of the latches made by other manufacturers
would fit without modification in the Fiat 600D (Fiat Brief,
at 25). However, plaintiff's expert engineer testified that
latch designs in existence when this Fiat was manufactured
could have been adapted to the space available in the door
of the Fiat so that radical changes in the vehicle were not
necessary (Tr. 339-40). Asked by Fiat's counsel whether the
car frame would have to be modified in order to install a
door latch system having a longitudinal component, Mr. Fonda
testified that the manufacturer had the option either way
(Tr. 340).

   6/ According to plaintiff's experts, including Dr.
Ommaya, the fracture lines in this case were drawn to the
buttresses at the base of the skull, where severe fractures
are frequently encountered as a result of blows to the top
of the head (Tr. 607).

The extent of the modifications to the 600D necessary
to accommodate a latch providing longitudinal linkage was
illustrated by testimony concerning the 1971 Fiat 750.
After being cross-examined on the nature and extent of the
modifications that would be required, Mr. Fonda on redirect
examination testified that the 1971 Fiat, with a door
virtually the same size as the door on the 600D, and with
even less distance between the window tracks and the edge of
the door, permitted installation of a latch providing
longitudinal linkage (Tr. 355-58).[7] He testified further

---

[7] Fiat implies that this testimony was presented on
direct examination (Fiat Brief, at 29), but at that time Mr.
Fonda merely identified two exhibits as being doors from
1971 Fiats (Tr. 316-17). No questions on direct examination
concerned the nature of the latch system employed in those
doors. On cross-examination, however, Mr. Fonda was asked
whether any of the latches that he brought to court could
have been installed in the 600D (Tr. 338); whether such
latches were too big to fit the 600D (Tr. 339); what latch
that was in existence in 1967 could have been adapted to the
600D (Tr. 339); whether the door frame would have required
modification in order to put in a latch system having a
longitudinal component (Tr. 340); and whether such a latch
would entail changes in the whole unibody construction of
the Fiat (Tr. 341). At that point the feasibility of
modifications to the 600D had clearly been raised on cross-
examination, so that the plaintiff was properly permitted by
the trial judge to inquire on re-direct examination regarding the remedial changes in the 1971 model (Tr. 355-56).
See Fed. R. Evid. 407. Mr. Fonda was entitled on redirect
examination to show, based on a comparision with the 1971
door, that the adaptation of a longitudinal latch system to
the Fiat 600D door did not entail significant changes in the
dimensions of the door and was not impractical by reason of
door size and shape (Tr. 355-58). Mr. Fonda testified that
the 1971 Fiat latch was very similar in design to the 1956
Ford latch, one of the latches about which Fiat's counsel
had inquired on cross-examination (Tr. 358).

that a properly designed "striker," the portion of the latch
system attached to the B post, could be easily adapted to
the 600D so as to afford longitudinal protection (Tr. 358).

The testimony in this case clearly permitted the jury
to assess the reasonableness of Fiat's failure to adopt a
safer door latch system. An expert engineer testified that
adaptation of better design principles was basically no
different for small cars than large cars. Other
manufacturers had made the switch to superior designs. And
the 1971 Fiat door latch incorporated the safer concepts
while maintaining door appearance virtually
indistinguishable from the 1967 600D. Moreover, no
representative of Fiat appeared to testify regarding the
burden of adopting a safer design. Mr. Wessell's estimate
of the number of machine hours needed to make the change
told the jury nothing of the real cost to Fiat, particuarly
when Mr. Wessells admitted unfamiliarity with whether the
other Fiat models in 1967 offered longitudinal linkage in
their door latch systems (Tr. 947). In sum, there was ample
testimony from which the jury could perform its traditional
function of "balancing the likelihood and gravity of harm
against the burden of effective precautions." Knippen v.
Ford Motor Co., 178 U.S. App. D.C. 227, 546 F.2d 993, 999
(1976).

2. Effect of a Superior Latch in this Case.

Fiat argues that because no witness computed the
longitudinal forces that were applied to the plaintiff's
Fiat during this accident, there could be no basis for the
jury's finding that a properly designed latch would have
prevented plaintiff's ejection (Fiat Brief, at 26). As the
Fiat brief notes, however, Mr. Fonda did specifically
testify that reasonably good contemporary latches adapted to
the 600D would have withstood the effects of the collision
without allowing the door to open (Tr. 294). In addition,
Dr. Watkins testified that the deformation to plaintiff's
door was so slight that it was not necessary to calculate
the pounds of force involved in the collision (Tr. 665). He
concluded that a door latch with the traditional fore and
aft linkage would have retained the plaintiff in his vehicle
(Tr. 651). As Dr. Watkins put it:

> I base that conclusion on the photographs
> which show an apparently very mild deforma-
> tion of the door frame area, which leads me
> to believe that the forces involved in the
> collision which acted to open the door frame,
> expand the door frame area, would not be that
> great; and, therefore, a different kind of door
> latch would likely have helped. (Tr. 561).

Because Fiat presented no contrary testimony, the jury
really had no choice but to find that a latch designed in
accordance with the state of the art could have prevented
plaintiff's door from opening in this low speed collision.
There is simply no basis, on this record, for overriding the
jury's verdict.

-27-

II. THE TRIAL COURT PROPERLY REFUSED TO ADMIT
EVIDENCE REGARDING SEAT BELTS FOR THE PUR-
POSE OF DETERMINING (A) WHETHER PLAINTIFF'S
VEHICLE WAS REASONABLY SAFE, SINCE THE
PLAINTIFF'S FIAT LACKED SEAT BELTS WHEN
SOLD BY DEFENDANTS, AND (B) WHETHER THE
PLAINTIFF FAILED TO MITIGATE DAMAGES.

The defendants argue that the trial court erroneously
refused to admit evidence of plaintiff's non-use of his seat
belt in consideration of whether the Fiat was unreasonably
dangerous and in mitigation of damages (Fiat Brief, at 37).
The trial court did in fact permit evidence that the
plaintiff had a lap belt in his vehicle but was not using it
at the time of the collision (Tr. 206). One is left to
speculate what further evidence regarding seat belts the
defendants wanted to introduce at trial, since there was
never a clear offer of proof as required by Rule 103 of the
Federal Rules of Evidence. Consideration of the transcript
references provided in Fiat's Brief at page 38 confirms the
absence of an adequate offer of admissible evidence.

Since the trial court did allow proof of the presence
of lap belts and their non-use, the only issue is whether
the defendants were denied a fair opportunity to show (a)
that plaintiff's vehicle was reasonably safe or (b) that the
plaintiff failed to mitigate damages. An analysis of these
twin objectives shows that lap belt non-use was not
admissible for either purpose and that Fiat's requested
instruction on seat belt non-use would have been error.

A. In Determining Whether the Fiat 600D As A Whole Was Defective And Unreasonably Dangerous, No Special Consideration Should Be Given To Lap Belts Which Were Not Included In The Vehicle At The Time The Defendants Placed The Vehicle Into The Stream Of Commerce.

Even if defendants had made an adequate offer of proof regarding the advantages of lap belts,[8] the issue of whether the 1967 Fiat 600D was unreasonably dangerous should be determined as of the time the vehicle was sold by the defendants and not in light of subsequent improvements added by third parties. The question here is not whether the vehicle must be assessed "as a whole."[9] The question (assuming, arguendo, an adequate proffer was made) is whether the manufacturer and importer of a vehicle may rely on a safety feature, lap belts, which were not included in

---

[8] It is not enough to boast about seat belts generally. Lap belts are inferior to other types of seat belts, McCord v. Green, 362 A.2d 720, 724 (D.C. 1976), citing Kleist, The Seat Belt Defense -- An Exercise In Sophistry, 18 Hastings L.J. 613 (1967), and are worn less frequently. C. Stowell & J. Bryant, Safety Belt Usage: Survey of the Traffic Population 4-5 (1978).

[9] Defendants complain that the trial court did not instruct the jury, as set forth in defendants' requested instruction number 5, that the car should be considered as a whole in determining whether the vehicle was unreasonably dangerous (Fiat Brief, at 45). This is incorrect. The court instructed that it was for the jury to determine "whether or not the Fiat as a whole was unreasonably dangerous." (Tr. 1288).

-29-

the vehicle at the time that defendants placed it into the
stream of commerce.[10]/

Defendants remark in a footnote in their brief that the
vehicle at the time of sale only had "stantions (sic) to
which belts could be attached" (Fiat Brief, at 40). The
full extent of the evidence at trial concerning the origin
of seat belts in this vehicle is contained in the Fiat 600D
Instruction Book (Def. Ex. C; J. App. 182). At page 6 of
that 50 page book, the following text appears, without any
photographs to illustrate the changes needed for the
installation of seat belts:

SAFETY BELT ANCHORAGES

The car is provided with the necessary arrangements for the application of safety belts for the
front seat occupants.
For the anchoring of diagonal type belts use
the holes drilled in floor at both sides of
tunnel while below rear quarter windows -- in
right and left side panels -- drill four 12 mm
(.47") holes in reference dimples (be careful to
clear the threads of the underlying welded blocks).
For the anchoring of lap type belts use said holes
at tunnel sides and the holes already drilled in
floor near doors, behind front seats. Floor holes
are blanked by rubber plugs and covered by rubber
matting. (J. App. 182).

10/ This case is easily distinguished from Wilson v.
Volkswagen of America, Inc., 445 F.Supp. 1368 (E.D. Va.
1978) (Virginia law), where VW designed and sold a vehicle
with seat belts installed. Also, the Fiat defendants never
sought an instruction on the defense of misuse such as was
given in Melia v. Ford Motor Co., 534 F.2d 795 (8th Cir.
1976). Plaintiff notes that Melia did not rule on the
propriety of allowing the jury to consider whether failure
to use a seat belt constituted misuse, contrary to the
representation in Fiat's brief at 39-40. See 534 F.2d at
799 n.6.

Prior to trial the judge heard argument on whether
Fiat should be permitted to present the defense that lap
belts made the vehicle reasonably safe despite the defective
door latch system (Tr. 32-35). At that time the defendants
were challenged by plaintiff's counsel to make a proffer
concerning their role in the provision of seat belts in this
vehicle (Tr. 32-34).[11/] None was made.[12/] After Fiat failed
to make an adequate proffer, the trial court properly
concluded that "seat belts have nothing to do with this
case."(Tr. 75).

In determining whether a vehicle is unreasonably
dangerous the courts in the District of Columbia have
focused upon the condition of the vehicle at the time it
left the seller's hands. E.g., Cottom v. McGuire Funeral

[11/] Plaintiff's counsel noted in open court that a
"very sensitive legal issue" would be posed if the
defendants "can proffer that at the time they sold the car
it had a seat belt in it"(Tr. 32); that the issue would be
whether the provision of a seat belt could, in the minds of
a jury, offset the unreasonable dangers created by a
defective door latch system (Tr. 33); that there are two
bands of potential protection in a car, the latch system and
the seat belt system (Tr. 33); and that the defendants,
having failed to provide normal door latch protection or to
advise the user that the door latch system was inadequate,
should not expect the user to compensate by employing the
lap belt instead (Tr. 33).

[12/] By contrast, plaintiff made a specific proffer of
testimony that a lap belt would not foreseeably protect
against head injury. Where the door latch is defective, the
operator remains free in a lap belt to pivot with his torso,
so that after the door swung open and hit the passing van
and closed again, the door could act like a guillotine and
inflict an even more serious injury than plaintiff
encountered by striking the pavement (Tr. 34-35).

Service, Inc., 262 A.2d 807, 809 (D.C. 1970)(strict liability imposed if product defective when placed into stream of commerce).   In Stewart v. Ford Motor Co., 179 U.S. App. D.C. 396, 553 F.2d 130 (1971), this Court approved, as an accurate statement of D. C. law, a jury instruction which cautioned that the automobile's failure must be "due to an obvious or hidden defect in the car which existed at the time it left Ford Motor Company."   553 F.2d at 138.   Accord, Hall v General Motors Corp., 207 U.S. App. D.C. 350, 353, 647 F.2d 175, 178 (1980).   This is the focus provided by §402A of the Restatement (2d) of Torts.   Comment g to §402A articulates the rule that a product is defective when "the product is, at the time it leaves the seller's hands, in a condition not contemplated by the ultimate consumer."   See Young v. Up-Right Scaffolds, Inc., 637 F.2d 810 (D.C. Cir. 1980)(strict liability in tort under §402A applicable in D.C.)

A manufacturer or distributor is not responsible for modifications after sale which render a product unreasonably dangerous.   E.g., Verge v. Ford Motor Co., 581 F.2d 384 (3rd Cir. 1978)(Ford not chargeable for absence of back-up warning device where cab and chassis were built by Ford but unit was later converted to a garbage truck by another company).   If a manufacturer cannot be held liable for defects resulting from modifications made subsequent to the time the product left its control, so the manufacturer should not be entitled to defend an otherwise unsafe product on the basis of an unused safety feature added by some third party. When a vehicle occupant, without knowledge of a defective door latch system, fails to use a lap belt installed by a third party, the manufacturer's position in a suit by the injured user should be no different than if the lap belt had never been installed.[13]

B. District of Columbia Law Forbids Consideration of Lap Belt Non-Usage On The Issue Of Contributory Negligence Or Mitigation of Damages.

After thoroughly reviewing statistics and analyses on both sides of the seat belt debate, the District of Columbia Court of Appeals ruled in McCord v. Green, 362 A.2d 720 (D.C. 1976), that the so-called seat belt defense does "violence to such well-settled principles of tort liability as proximate causation, foreseeability, and the standard of care exercised by a reasonably prudent man." 362 A.2d at 722. There is no logic to the defendants' contention that the rule of McCord v. Green should not be applied to a second collision case.

Non-use of a seat belt can constitute evidence of contributory negligence only if the plaintiff was under a

---

[13] This is particularly true where, as here, there was no testimony regarding trade custom or practice for installation of seat belts. Compare Verge v. Ford Motor Co., supra, 581 F.2d at 387-88. No evidence was presented, for example, that Fiat had made arrangements for a third party such as a retail dealer to install the belts.

duty to wear a seat belt. McCord, supra, 362 A.2d at
724-25. Negligence consists of conduct from which the
reasonably prudent man in the exercise of ordinary care
would refrain. 362 A.2d at 724. To hold that failure to use
a seat belt amounts to negligence assumes that the usual
practice of car drivers and passengers is to use seat belts,
an assumption which is refuted by all pertinent statistical
studies, especially those concerning lap belts. 362 A.2d at
725. According to a 1978 study prepared for the U.S.
Department of Transportation, only 10.4% of drivers of
vehicles equipped with lap belts made use of them, and the
percentage of men using lap belts was even lower. C.
Stowell & J. Bryant, Safety Belt Usage: Survey of the
Traffic Population 4-5 (1978). In subsequent years lap belt
usage has declined to 8.1%. B. Phillips, Seat Belt Usage
Among Drivers, at xvii (U.S. Department of Transportation,
1980).[14/] The plaintiff simply cannot be required to do
that which the reasonably prudent man in the exercise of
ordinary care does not do.

[14/] These studies were cited in plaintiff's trial
brief at page 12. Additional studies are cited by Chief
Judge Reilly in McCord v. Green, supra, 362 A.2d at 725.

For the same reasons, non-use of a lap belt is not admissible in mitigation of damages under the doctrine of avoidable consequences.[15] As explained by Chief Judge Reilly in McCord, the doctrine of avoidable consequences only comes into operation after the plaintiff has been made aware of the defendant's wrongful acts and has an opportunity to avoid the consequences in whole or in part. McCord v. Green, supra, 362 A.2d at 725. Plaintiff therefore could be penalized for failure to mitigate damages only if he had the opportunity to do so after becoming aware of the defendant's wrongful act. Accord, Vizzini v. Ford Motor Co., 569 F.2d 754, 764-68 (3rd Cir. 1977)(evidence of seat belt non-usage properly excluded); Miller v. Miller, 273 N.C. 228, 160 S.E.2d 65 (1968).

In the instant case, the plaintiff was not aware of defendants' defective door latch system prior to the "second collision." Since the plaintiff was under no duty to utilize the seat belt when he began his journey, it would be thoroughly inconsistent to find that he later had a duty to engage in the lap belt device.

15/ Defendants' requested jury instruction number 2 essentially directed a verdict on the issue of mitigation of damages. Defendants requested that the jury be instructed that "in the event that you find either defendant liable for enhanced injuries, such liability must be diminished by the amount of enhanced injuries that you determine would have been avoided if plaintiff had been wearing his seat belt." (Emphasis added). None of the cases cited in defendants' brief supports this extreme position.

III.   THE TRIAL COURT PROPERLY ADMITTED EVIDENCE
       CONCERNING FEDERAL MOTOR VEHICLE SAFETY
       STANDARD NO. 206 AS EVIDENCE OF THE STATE
       OF THE ART ONE YEAR PRIOR TO THE EFFECTIVE
       DATE OF THAT STANDARD.

The trial court admitted oral testimony concerning
Federal Motor Vehicle Safety Standard No. 206 for passenger
vehicle door latch systems as bearing on the standard of
care for a reasonable man at the time that the plaintiff's
car was manufactured and sold by the defendants (Tr. 40,
45). The question of the admissibility of evidence
regarding Standard 206 was considered in the parties' trial
briefs and was the subject of argument prior to trial.
On the basis of two cases decided by this Court, Curtis v.
District of Columbia, 124 U.S. App. D.C. 241, 363 F.2d 973
(1966), and Edmonds, Inc. v. Vojka, 118 U.S. App. D.C. 109,
332 F.2d 309 (1964), Mr. Fonda's testimony regarding the
standard was admitted as relevant to the state of the art
(Tr. 250).[16] The written standard itself was not offered
into evidence (Pl. Ex. 55).

The defendants attempt to distinguish Curtis and
Edmonds on the ground that the premises in each case
remained under the control of the defendants after the

_____
[16] Under the rule of Curtis and Edmonds the Fiat
defendants were entitled to a special instruction, if
requested, limiting the effect of the evidence regarding
subsequently enacted standards. Judge Robinson invited such
a request by indicating awareness of the difference between
setting a mandatory minimum standard, on the one hand, and
reflecting the state of the art, on the other (Tr. 251).
However, no such special instruction was requested.

regulations were enacted. However, one seaches in vain in those decisions for any indication that continued control over the premises was an element in the outcome. Curtis dealt with a D.C. building code provision setting standards for the paving over of vaults on public sidewalks. Although enacted subsequent to the date plaintiff fell when walking over defendant's vault, the regulation was deemed admissible as relevant to determining the common law standard of care. 124 U.S. App. D.C. at 243. Similarly, the Court in Edmonds permitted the introduction of a subsequently enacted building code provision governing handrails as relevant to accepted architectural practice. 118 U.S. App. D.C. at 111.

In the instant case, the proper foundation for the admission of the subsequently implemented standard was laid by plaintiff's expert engineer, Albert G. Fonda.[17] Asked whether there had been any appreciable change in the state of the art from the 1963-1966 period until January, 1968, the effective date of Standard 206, Mr. Fonda testified that there had been "refinements, but no change" (Tr. 272). On cross-examination he stated that the standard merely codified accepted practices (Tr. 352).

---

[17] The defendants did not object to the specific questions asked of Mr. Fonda at trial. Preliminary objections to admissibility of the DOT evidence, in the nature of a motion in limine, is not adequate to preserve the question of admissibility for appellate review. Fed.R.Evid. 103(a)(1); Vergie M. Lapelosa, Inc. v. Cruze, 407 A.2d 786 (Md. App. 1979).

The DOT standard was passed into law in 1967, taking effect in January, 1968 (Tr. 272-73). The effect of Standard 206 was to establish a requirement that there be certain strength in the fore and aft direction at the latch and striker components of door latch systems (Tr. 273). Fiat's witness on the engineering questions, Henry W. Wessells, III, conceded that the principles underlying fore and aft linkage requirements were known for many years prior to 1967 (Tr. 938). It is obvious, therefore, that the testimony concerning Standard 206 was properly admitted as relevant to accepted engineering practice among manufacturers of automobile door latch systems as of January, 1967.[18]

The Fiat defendants also argue that introduction of evidence of the DOT standard was improper because the standard was not reflective of the "state of the art in Europe" at that time (Fiat Brief, at 47). Certainly Fiat's Enzo Franchini made no distinction between European and American state of the art when he wrote in December, 1964 that "since some years the trend of manufacturers" showed

------

[18] Exclusion of such evidence would have been error. See General Motors Corp. v. Turner, 567 S.W.2d 812 (Tex. 1978), rev'd on other grounds, 584 S.W.2d 844 (trial court erred in excluding evidence of subsequently enacted Federal Motor Vehicle Safety Standard No. 216 pertaining to vehicle roof structures where expert witnesses testified that the state of the art had not appreciably changed between the manufacture of the roof and the issuance of the federal standard).

preference for longitudinal linkage for reasons of occupant
safety (Tr. 240; J. App. 91). Defendants cite no authority
for the proposition that the European state of the art
governs liability questions regarding a vehicle manufactured
for sale in the United States.

Nevertheless, the record shows that in 1967 there was
substantial use among European manufacturers of door latch
designs that incorporated longitudinal linkage. Mr.
Wessells, Fiat's expert witness, testified that to the best
of his knowledge, there may have been some models of
European cars which had a longitudinal component to prevent
ejection in 1967 (Tr. 909). Mr. Fonda testified that the VW
Beetle implemented longitudinal linkage in April, 1965 (Tr.
335). Although the Mercedes had latches with longitudinal
linkage as early as 1953 (Tr. 259-60; App. 66), Mr. Fonda
indicated that foreign-made cars generally did not have
latches with a longitudinal component until the mid-60's
(Tr. 336). There was ample testimony that the principles of
fore and aft linkage were equally applicable to small cars
as to large cars (Tr. 273, 653).

A related Fiat contention is that the evidence
concerning Standard 206 should not have been admitted in the
absence of a showing that a latch designed to meet this
requirement would have prevented the plaintiff's door from
opening. Analytically the argument fails because evidence
was offered to show the state of the art, not a causal

connection between a breach of Fiat's duty of care and the injury to the plaintiff. Factually the argument also fails, since there was much testimony that compliance by Fiat with the prevailing state of the art for door latch systems would have sufficed to prevent plaintiff's door from opening (Tr. 294, 651, 687).

Lastly, the defendants urge that they were prejudiced when evidence regarding the Society of Automotive Engineers' Recommended Practice was "allowed to creep into the testimony of plaintiff's witnesses" (Fiat Brief, at 49).[19/] That testimony, however, first came during the course of cross-examination by Fiat's counsel (Tr. 347, 352). The only other reference to the SAE standard was not consciously elicited by plaintiff's counsel's questions, but came out innocuously during direct examination of Dr. Watkins (Tr. 681). Fiat was not prejudiced, and no curative instruction was requested.

19/ The SAE Recommended Practice, Passenger Car Side Door Latch Systems - SAE J839b (1962), called for fore and aft linkage in vehicle door latch systems. The SAE test, as modified in 1965, was codified in January 1968 as Federal Motor Vehicle Safety Standard No. 206 (Tr. 40). Because the SAE recommendations had become "accepted practices" (Tr. 352) they should have been admitted to show the state of the art of door latch design. E.g., Anderson v. Heister Co., 385 N.E.2d 690 (Ill. 1979); see Annot., 58 A.L.R.3d 148 (1974). However, the trial court ruled the evidence inadmissible (Tr. 45).

IV. WHERE THE FIAT 600D, VERSION 140, WAS MADE
     FOR DISTRIBUTION IN THE UNITED STATES, THE
     COURT DID NOT ERR IN ADMITTING EVIDENCE OF
     VEHICLES MANUFACTURED IN THE UNITED STATES AS
     RELEVANT TO THE STATE OF THE ART FOR DOOR
     LATCH SYSTEMS.

The trial court properly admitted evidence concerning

the state of the art for vehicles sold in the United States,

whether manufactured here or not. The Fiat 600D, Version

140, was made for distribution in the United States. (Def.

Ex. C; see Defendants' Answers to Plaintiff's Second

Interrogatories, Ans. to Int. No. 2). When Mr. Fonda

testified regarding the state of the art for door latch

systems, he defined the state of the art as being for

vehicles sold in this country, including imported vehicles

as well as vehicles manufactured in the United States (Tr.

231). Both of plaintiff's engineering experts testified

that the principles of door latch design and door latch

safety were equally applicable to small cars and that there

was no reason whatsoever for declining to apply those

principles in the manufacturing of small cars (Tr. 273,

653).

Dreisonstok v. Volkswagenwerk, A.G., 489 F.2d 1066 (4th

Cir. 1974)(Va. law) cited by the defendants, merely ruled

that a plaintiff cannot hold all vehicles, regardless of

their intended use, to the safety features of the standard

American passenger car. In the instant case, unlike

Dreisonstok, plaintiff did not restrict his proof to

American-made vehicles. Plaintiff introduced excerpts from

a 1964 article by Fiat's Enzo Franchini to the effect that the trend for some years among automobile manufacturers (without geographical qualification) was for use of latches providing longitudinal linkage. Plaintiff also cited at least two large European manufacturers, Volkswagen and Mercedes, who provided longitudinal linkage prior to the date of the manufacture of plaintiff's vehicle, January, 1967. Moreover, the jury was specifically instructed to consider factors such as the size, weight, and purpose of the vehicle in determining whether the vehicle as a whole was unreasonably dangerous (Tr. 1288).

    V.   WHERE THE COMPLAINT WAS FILED AND FIAT, S.p.A.'S DESIGNATED REPRESENTATIVE WAS SERVED WITHIN SIXTEEN MONTHS OF THE PRODUCT'S FAILURE, THE TRIAL COURT PROPERLY DENIED DEFENDANT S.p.A.'S MOTION TO DISMISS ON THE GROUND THAT THE PLAINTIFF'S CLAIM WAS BARRED BY THE STATUTE OF LIMITATIONS.

Fiat, S.p.A. claims that it is entitled to dismissal of the complaint on the ground that process was not properly served until February 5, 1980, more than three years after the accident of October 23, 1976. On the basis of Varela v. Hi-Lo Powered Stirrups, Inc., 424 A.2d 61 (D.C. 1981), the trial court determined that the filing of the complaint on February 17, 1978 tolled the applicable three year statute of limitations.

The statute of limitations was tolled in this case regardless of whether the Varela doctrine is deemed applicable. Even if Varela were deemed prospective only,

District of Columbia law prior to _Varela_ clearly provides
that the statute of limitations is tolled by the filing of a
complaint and the delivery of process to the marshal or the
U.S. Postal Service. _Hall v. Cafritz_, 402 A.2d 828, 832
(D.C. 1979); _Criterion Insurance Co. v. Lyles_, 244 A.2d 913
(D.C. 1968). Process in the instant case was promptly
delivered to the U. S. Postal Service, and service upon
Fiat's designated agent for receipt of process pursuant to
the National Traffic and Motor Vehicle Safety Act of 1966
was accomplished on February 23, 1978, sixteen months after
the date of the accident. (Affidavit of Service of Process,
filed March 23, 1978).

On March 14, 1978, Fiat, S.p.A. contested the validity
of service upon its designated agent, but the trial court
made no initial determination on that issue. Instead, the
court on April 26, 1978 granted the defendants' motion to
dismiss for lack of personal jurisdiction, and the case then
came before this Court on that issue. After this Court on
January 24, 1980 reversed and found that the trial court
possessed jurisdiction over the Fiat defendants under the
District of Columbia Long Arm Statute, plaintiff, without
waiting for a ruling on the defendant's motion challenging
sufficiency of process, effected service in Italy upon Fiat,
S.p.A.'s president on February 12, 1980.

Fiat, S.p.A. claims that the plaintiff was guilty of
"willful disregard for the legal requirements to effect

valid service and its (sic) obligation to act with due
diligence" (Fiat Brief, at 52 n.25). However, it was hardly
a lack of diligence to rely on the literal language of the
National Traffic and Motor Vehicle Safety Act of 1966, 15
U.S.C.A. §1399(e), or the Department of Transportation
Regulations promulgated thereunder, 49 C.F.R. §551.45(c).[20/]
Moreover, the only decided federal case on point at the time
was a products liability action which upheld the validity of
service of process under the Act. Bollard v. Volkswagenwerk, A.G., 313 F.Supp. 126 (D. Mo. 1970). Even if it were
assumed, arguendo, that service under the Act was not
effective, plaintiff's reliance on service under the Act did
not amount to a lack of diligence where this means of
effecting service was not patently unreasonable and had not
been rejected by the trial court.

The instant case is clearly distinguishable from the
class of cases where the plaintiff is responsible for
unexplained and unreasonable delay in making service of
process. E.g., Joseph Muller Corp. v. Societe Anonyme, 508
F.2d 814 (2nd Cir. 1974)(cited in Fiat Brief, at 52); Rouse
v. National Seating Co., Inc., 244 A.2d 491 (D.C.
1968)(delay in accomplishing service occurred when the

20/ The Act, 15 U.S.C. §1399(e), describes the
designated agent of a foreign automobile manufacturer as
follows: "An Agent upon whom service of all administrative
and judicial processes, notices, orders, decisions, and
requirements may be made for or on behalf of said
manufacturer." (Emphasis added).

defendant had never been served, not when the defendant had been served but challenged sufficiency thereof); Bailey v. Washington Motor Truck Trans. Employees Pension Trust, 240 A.2d 133 (D.C. 1968)(plaintiff failed to serve unincorporated association until 14 months after complaint was filed, and then served wrong complaint); Steele v. General Baking Co., 101 A.2d 845 (D.C. Mun. App. 1954) (unexplained failure to accomplish service until 32 months after complaint filed). Here the delay in serving Fiat's president occurred at a time when the defendant's designated agent under a broad federal statute had been served, where the propriety of service had been questioned but not ruled upon, and where the entire case was on appeal on an unrelated issue.

In summary, the statute of limitations either was tolled in accordance with Varela when the complaint was filed, or was tolled in accordance with Hall v. Cafritz when process was initially delivered into the hands of the U.S. Postal Service. Dismissal under either Rule 12 or Rule 41 would have been plainly unjustified.

VI. AS THE DISTRIBUTOR OF THE PLAINTIFF'S VEHICLE, FIAT MOTORS OF NORTH AMERICA, INC. WAS PROPERLY RETAINED AS A DEFENDANT ON THE STRICT LIABILITY AND BREACH OF WARRANTY COUNTS.

The argument that Fiat Motors of North America, Inc. ("FMNA") should have been dismissed as a party defendant can be disposed of quickly. Counsel agreed during the

conference concerning jury instructions that FMNA should not
be retained under the negligence theory. Accordingly, when
the trial court instructed the jury on negligence, the
instruction was limited to the manufacturer, Fiat, S.p.A.
(Tr. 1286-87).

With respect to the theories of strict liability and
implied warranty, the law in the District of Columbia is
settled that an injured consumer has a cause of action
against all parties who participated in placing the
defective product into the stream of commerce. The leading
case in the District of Columbia is Cottom v. McGuire
Funeral Service, Inc., 262 A.2d 807 (D.C. 1970), where the
court held that a pallbearer injured by a defective casket
was entitled to recover against the manufacturer,
wholesaler, and retailer. The principles outlined in Cottom
were affirmed in Berman v. Watergate West, Inc., 391 A.2d
1351 (D.C. 1978), where the court stated that "the law is
clear that the consumer has a cause of action against all
who participated in placing the [defective] product into the
stream of commerce. . . ." 391 A.2d at 1352. Cases from
other jurisdictions limiting the liability of so-called
middlemen do not represent the law of the District of
Columbia.

The defendants seek to carve out an exception from the
Cottom and Berman principles for "latent" defects. There is
no basis in Cottom and Berman for such an exception,

-46-

especially since <u>Cottom</u> involved a defective casket handle
that would be more "latent" than a door latch which to the
trained eye obviously lacked longitudinal linkage.

Moreover, there is nothing in the record in this case to
substantiate the suggestion that the defect in the Fiat's
door latch system was latent. No representative from either
Fiat defendant testified that the defect in the door latch
system was unknown or hidden from discovery in the routine
inspection and distribution of vehicles.[21/] Viewed from the
perspective of Fiat's exclusive North American importer,
there is no way on the record in this case to conclude that
the defect on the 600D was "latent" as a matter of law.

Since no instruction was requested to distinguish between
latent and non-latent defects on the strict liability and
implied warranty claims, FMNA has waived any objection to
its inclusion in the instructions on those claims.

> VII.   THE TRIAL COURT DID NOT ERR IN RE-
> FUSING TO DISMISS PLAINTIFF'S CLAIMS
> ON THE THEORY THAT THE DISTRICT OF
> COLUMBIA DOES NOT RECOGNIZE "SECOND
> COLLISION" LIABILITY.

Defendants raise for the first time on this appeal the
contention that "second collision" liability is not

[21/] The defendant attempts to show through excerpts
from the deposition of Paolo Nervo that the importer would
not have observed the door latch system during the course of
distribution of the 600D vehicle (Fiat Brief, at 55).
However, the deposition excerpts were not offered into
evidence. Mr. Nervo testified on deposition that he was not
employed by FMNA until 1971, so he had no personal knowledge
concerning whether FMNA representatives observed the door
latch design on vehicles sold from 1964 through 1967.

recognized in the District of Columbia. The law on this question was announced in Knippen v. Ford Motor Co., 178 U.S. App. 227, 546 F.2d 993 (1976). Holding that an automobile manufacturer owes a duty to highway users to avoid unreasonably dangerous features in automobile design which may enhance injuries received in a highway collision even though the collision itself is not caused by the vehicle's design, the Court in Knippen adopted the line of authority represented by Larsen v. General Motors Corp., 391 F.2d 495 (8th Cir. 1968). The court specifically declined to follow the line of authority represented by Evans v. General Motors Corp., 359 F.2d 822 (7th Cir. 1966), cert. denied, 385 U.S. 836 (1967).[22]

22/ Fiat fails to advise the Court that the Seventh Circuit expressly overruled Evans in Huff v. White Motor Corp., 565 F.2d 104 (7th Cir. 1977). Noting that most of those jurisdictions which adopted Evans have now rejected Evans in favor of Larsen, the Seventh Circuit adopts the Larsen rule:
> One who is injured as a result of
> a mechanical defect in a motor vehicle
> should be protected under the doctrine
> of strict liability even though the
> defect was not the cause of the collision
> which precipitated the injury. There
> is no rational basis for limiting the manu-
> facturer's liability to those instances where
> a structural defect has caused the colli-
> sion and resulting injury. This is so
> because even if a collision is not caused
> by a structural defect, a collision may
> precipitate the malfunction of a defective
> part and cause injury. In that circum-
> stance the collision, the defect, and the
> injury are interdependent and should be
> viewed as a combined event. Such an event
> is the foreseeable risk that a manufacturer
> should assume. Since collisions for what-
> ever cause are foreseeable events, the scope
> of liability should be commensurate with the
> scope of the foreseeable risks.

565 F.2d at 109.

The defendants attempt to characterize the defective
door latch system as a "passive" defect which did not itself
cause injury. The distinction between "active" and
"passive" defects was not made in the Knippen decision,
however, and is inconsistent with Knippen's focus on whether
product design is unreasonably dangerous in terms of the
likelihood and gravity of harm and the burden of effective
precautions. 546 F.2d at 999. It is also an illogical and
unfair distinction to make in this case, where the evidence
showed that the absence of a reasonably competent door latch
system did not literally "enhance" the plaintiff's injuries
but was responsible for the full extent of the permanent
injuries that the plaintiff sustained. As Dr. John Legowik
testified, if the door had stayed shut the plaintiff would
have perhaps suffered bruises, but no permanent injuries
(Tr. 505-506). The defendants are unable to cite a single
case which has treated a defective door latch as a "passive
defect" so as to exempt the manufacturer or distributor
from liability for injuries sustained as a result of
ejection from the vehicle.

VIII. THE JURY WAS PROPERLY PERMITTED TO
       CONSIDER PLAINTIFF'S PROBABLE LOSS
       OF FUTURE WAGES AS AN ITEM OF DAMAGE.

Under the law of the District of Columbia, loss of
future earnings is an allowable item of damages if properly
proved. District of Columbia v. Barriteau, 399 A.2d 563,
567 (D.C. 1979). In this jurisdiction a distinction is made
between the measure of proof necessary to establish the fact
of damage and the measure of proof necessary to enable the
jury to fix the amount. Abraham v. Gendlin, 84 U.S. App.
D.C. 307, 172 F.2d 881 (1949). Accordingly, an award for
future lost earnings has been allowed where the only
testimony in support of work disability consisted of
testimony by the plaintiff, an economics student, regarding
occasional back pain (and related doctor's visits) due to a
bullet lodged in his spine. Spar v. Obwoya, 369 A.2d 173,
179 (D.C. 1977). Assessment of future lost wages
necessarily involves some uncertainty, but in the District
of Columbia the risk of that uncertainty has always been
borne by the wrongdoer rather than the victim of his
wrongdoing. McDermott v. Severe, 25 App. D.C. 276, 291
(1905).

In this case the plaintiff produced abundant evidence
that he was medically disabled from his job as a crypto-
telecommunications specialist at the Pentagon. His treating
neurologist, Andrew J. Armer, M.D., testified that he was
100% disabled from his Pentagon job (Tr. 384). The

plaintiff was described by Dr. Armer as suffering a
permanent post-traumatic seizure disorder, residual
dysphasia, and an organic brain syndrome with broad effects
on his ability to work (Tr. 370, 375, 379). The plaintiff's
supervisor, Milton Nash, described the plaintiff as "so
disoriented that he just cannot be given anything" (Tr.
725). His assessment of the plaintiff's post-accident
performance was as follows:

> For the past three years, I have
> recommended to him that he put in for
> a medical retirement -- three years ago.
> And every single performance appraisal
> I had to tell him that because he would
> not have got a "satisfactory" rating if
> I had judged him like any other person
> because he was not up to efficiency.
>
> His efficiency was not 50 percent of that
> that I expected of a step 10. A step 10
> is over and above a supertech.
>
> And he is classified as a supertech,
> but he is not 50 percent of that now.
>
> And he would have got an unsatisfactory
> efficiency rating and he would have been
> fired had he not been medically handi-
> capped. (Tr. 725)

Both Mr. Nash and the plaintiff's vocational rehabilitation
expert, Karen van Dyke, testified that the plaintiff's work
capability was limited to that of a common laborer or
minimum wage worker (Tr. 728, 803).

Defendant's first point on the matter of lost earnings
is that the plaintiff should not have been permitted to make
a claim for future lost earning capacity because he was
still in his Pentagon job at the time of trial. At that

time, however, plaintiff also had a pending application for
medical disability from his Pentagon position (Tr. 147).
Mr. Nash, plaintiff's supervisor with over 35 years of
Pentagon experience, indicated that a determination of
disability was expected by June, 1981 (Tr. 729). The jury
was therefore entitled to find that plaintiff would be out
of his Pentagon job and eligible to take any other position
for which he was qualified. Accordingly, the jury was
properly instructed, without objection, that they could
award as damages "any loss of earnings that will probably
occur in the future" (Tr. 1291).

Fiat's position that plaintiff may not recover future
lost wages because still employed at the time of trial is
grossly unfair. It was fortuitous that plaintiff had a job
where he was tolerated for a time on account of his
disability,[23]/ but this should hardly exculpate Fiat from
responsibility for plaintiff's lost earning capacity in the
future. Under Fiat's theory the injured plaintiff either
must forego temporary employment benefits such as sick pay
or special disability status (lest he lose his right to sue)
or forever remain a burden upon the taxpayers in a job that
he cannot perform and that may be harmful to him. In this

---

[23]/ Earnings while medically disabled are more in the
nature of sick pay than actual compensation for work done.
Although such earnings might be deemed a collateral source,
like sick pay or welfare benefits, plaintiff did not claim
lost wages for the period after he returned to work in his
medically disabled state.

case, for example, there is evidence that the plaintiff was the butt of complaints by co-workers (Tr. 717), that he was frequently frustrated at his inability to do his job (Tr. 704), and that he hated being given only menial tasks (Tr. 818-19). In sum, there was clear and uncontradicted evidence that the plaintiff was disabled from his present job and was suffering from his persistent efforts to perform it. Fiat's solution -- to prohibit recovery for future lost earnings -- would add insult to injury.

Fiat's second argument is that an award for future lost earnings must take into account plaintiff's actual earning capacity based on a minimum wage occupation (Fiat Brief, at 60). This is exactly what happened in this case, in complete accord with District of Columbia v. Barriteau, 399 A.2d 563, 567 n.6 (D.C. 1979).

Plaintiff introduced testimony that he was probably limited to minimum wage occupations, based on the assessment of a qualified vocational rehabilitation and evaluation expert (Tr. 803). In order to allow the jury to deduct the value of probable future earnings, the plaintiff first proved the present discounted value of earnings in the Pentagon position ($423,570)(Tr. 844), and then proved the present discounted value of earnings in a minimum wage occupation ($120,237)(Tr. 845), as well as in a higher paid type of job in case the plaintiff could eventually qualify for such a position ($201,893) (Tr. 846-47).

Dr. Ransford Palmer, plaintiff's economic expert, wrote these figures on plaintiff's Exhibit 95 (Tr. 849-50). Defendants complain that this exhibit assumed that plaintiff would not engage in any meaningful productive activity for the next 27 years (Fiat Brief, at 61), but this construction is neither reasonable nor necessary. The exhibit portrayed the following information:

Present Job	$423,570
Minimum Wage Job	$120,237
$13,500 Job	$201,893
Present Job Minus $13,500 Job	$221,677
Present Job Minus Minimum Wage Job	$303,333

There is no way to arrive at the net loss of earnings without first showing the present value of the Pentagon earnings, but this is not an invitation to the jury to award damages on the assumption that there will be no future employment. Plaintiff's counsel, in his argument to the jury, did not make an appeal for an award based on no future employment, but specifically urged the jury to assess lost wages on the assumption of minimum wage employment (Tr. 1208).[24]/

---

[24]/ The net loss figure of $303,333 is actually overly conservative. Plaintiff assumed that minimum wage work would be available 52 weeks a year. However, according to the testimony of Fiat's economic expert, Herman Miller, a minimum wage worker can only expect employment 70% of the year (Tr. 1130-31). In other words, the deduction for future miminum wage earnings overstated actual earnings by approximately 30%.

The last point urged by the defendants is that the jury should not have been permitted to project lost earnings on the assumption that the plaintiff would have continued working at the Pentagon until age 70 (Fiat Brief, at 61). The plaintiff himself testified that prior to being hurt he had no plans to retire until reaching the mandatory retirement age (Tr. 208). There was testimony from plaintiff's economic expert that the mandatory retirement age for government workers was age 70 (Tr. 843), but in fact the Age Discrimination in Employment Act, 29 U.S.C. §631(b), forbids imposition of any mandatory retirement age for federal employees. Plaintiff did not make the assumption that he would continue working for the balance of his life expectancy, which was slightly in excess of age 70 (Tr. 837).

Defendant would have required the jury to limit its assessment of the plaintiff's working life to the average work-life expectancy for all American males as of 1970, or 20.6 years (Tr. 856-57). As Fiat's economic expert conceded on cross- examination, however, those statistics antedated amendments to the Age Discrimination in Employment Act, so that private employers can no longer compel retirement of workers prior to age 65. 29 U.S.C. §631(b). In light of the changes in the law, and the trend towards later retirement in this country, the jury was certainly not required to assume that the plaintiff would retire after

20.6 years of further service rather than upon reaching age
70. The jury was left free to determine, based on the
plaintiff's prior work history and personal situation,[25]
what the reasonable work life expectancy for the plaintiff
would be.

IX.   THE TRIAL COURT PROPERLY REFUSED TO
      REDUCE THE JUDGMENT AGAINST DEFENDANTS
      BASED ON A CREDIT FOR PRO-RATA CONTRIBU-
      TION BY ALLEGED JOINT TORTFEASORS.

Fiat filed a motion to amend the judgment on or about
May 20, 1981. Following receipt of plaintiff's opposition
to defendants' motion, the trial court on May 27, 1981
entered an order that "there is no basis for reducing the
judgment in this case on account of the alleged negligence
of an absent tortfeasor." Defendants' appeal on this point
is based on a complete misunderstanding of the law governing
contribution among joint tortfeasors in the District of
Columbia.

---

[25] The plaintiff was unmarried but responsible for the
care of a minor son (Tr. 89). In 1976 plaintiff also took a
second job, driving vehicles to and from National Airport
for Avis Rent-a-Car (Tr. 88). No consideration was given to
the second job in projecting the plaintiff's future earning
losses as a result of the accident, although he was forced
to give up that job (Tr. 89). The fact that he obtained
additional work would be relevant to assessing whether
plaintiff was the type of person who would remain in the
active work force rather than seek early retirement.

The basic principles applicable to contribution among alleged joint tortfeasors can be simply stated:

1.   Each of several joint tortfeasors is responsible for all of the victim's damages. "It is no defense for wrongdoers that others aided in causing the harm. Each is responsible for the whole." McKenna v. Austin, 77 U.S. App. D.C. 228, 233, 134 F.2d 659 (1943).

2.   A defendant may file a claim, including a third-party claim, for contribution against any other joint tortfeasor, regardless of whether that other tortfeasor has been sued by the plaintiff. Hall v. General Motors Corp., 207 U.S. App. D.C. 350, 647 F.2d 175 (1980); Jones v. Schramm, 141 U.S. App. D.C. 169, 171, 436 F.2d 899 (1970); Knell v. Feltman, 85 U.S. App. D.C. 22, 174 F.2d 662 (1949).

3.   Where a defendant pleads and proves a claim against a joint tortfeasor, the defendant is entitled to contribution for amounts paid by the defendant in excess of his pro rata share of the damages awarded. Knell v. Feltman, 85 U.S. App. D.C. 22, 27, 174 F.2d 662 (1949).

4.   A joint tortfeasor is entitled to a credit against the plaintiff's judgment on account of the concurrent negligence of a second tortfeasor only (a) where the second tortfeasor has settled with the plaintiff and therefore "bought his peace" from any further payment or contribution, as in McKenna v. Austin, 77 U.S. App. D.C. 288, 134 F.2d 659 (1943), Otis v. Thomas, 104 U.S. App. D.C. 343, 262 F.2d 232

(1958), Martello v. Hawley, 112 U.S. App. D.C. 129, 300 F.2d
721 (1962), Snowden v. D.C. Transit System, Inc., 147 U.S.
App. D.C. 204, 454 F.2d 1047 (1971), and Rose v. Associated
Anesthesiologists, 163 U.S. App. D.C. 246, 501 F.2d 806
(1974), or possibly, (b) where the second "tortfeasor" is an
employer liable only under the workers' compensation laws
and therefore immune from any common law liability for
contribution, as in Murray v. United States, 132 U.S. App.
D.C. 91, 405 F.2d 1361 (1968), and Dawson v. Contractors
Transport Corp., 151 U.S. App. D.C. 401, 467 F.2d 727
(1972). The common thread throughout both sets of cases is
the immunity of the second tortfeasor from contribution
which the first tortfeasor is normally entitled to claim.
See McKenna v. Austin, supra, 77 U.S. App. D.C. at 234, 134
F.2d at 665, Martello v. Hawley, supra, 112 U.S. App. D.C.
at 131-32, 300 F.2d at 723-724, and Dawson v. Contractors
Transport Corp., supra, 151 U.S. App. D.C. at 403, 467 F.2d
at 729. Since the litigating tortfeasor is foreclosed as a
matter of law from obtaining contribution from the second
wrongdoer, the courts recognize a credit against the
plaintiff, who after all has the benefit of his settlement
or workers' compensation remedy.

Applying these principles to the instant case, the Fiat
defendants stand fully responsible for the entire judgment
of $650,000.00. The Fiat defendants were fully entitled to
assert a claim against the so-called joint tortfeasors,

Rayfield and Pryor, for contribution, but declined to do so.
Neither the owner nor the operator of the Ford van was made
a party to this litigation, either as a defendant, cross-
defendant, or third-party defendant. If the Fiat defendants
pay the entire judgment, they are presumably entitled to
pursue a claim for contribution against Rayfield and Pryor
to the extent of payments in excess of Fiat's pro rata
share. However, the Fiat defendants are not entitled to a
credit on account of the alleged concurrent negligence of
Rayfield and Pryor, since the plaintiff has not settled or
agreed to settle any claim he may have against Rayfield and
Pryor, and of course neither Rayfield nor Pryor is an
employer of the plaintiff.

The statement that the plaintiff has "in effect"
settled with the alleged joint tortfeasors is nonsense. As
defendants point out in their Rule 8(b) Statement, the
action against the owner and driver of the van is stayed
indefinitely pending the outcome of the instant case (Fiat
Brief, at xiii). The affidavit of counsel filed below in
opposition to the defendants' motion to amend makes it clear
that there have been no settlement discussions between
Richard W. Galiher, Sr., counsel for Rayfield and Pryor, and
the plaintiff (Affidavit of Gerard E. Mitchell, filed May
26, 1981). Moreover, if the judgment against the Fiat
defendants is sustained, the case against Rayfield and Pryor
will have practically no value since they will be entitled

to a credit for any payments by the Fiat defendants. See
<u>Hall v. General Motors Corp.</u>, 207 U.S. App. D.C. 350, 647
F.2d 175 (1980). Plaintiff therefore intends to dismiss the
pending claim against Rayfield and Pryor if Fiat's appeal in
this case is unsuccessful.

    Lastly, the defendants claim that the plaintiff has
failed to join an indispensable party. The law is clear in
the District of Columbia that an action may be brought
against any one of several possible joint tortfeasors
without joining others. <u>E.g.</u>, <u>Ewald v. Lane</u>, 70 App. D.C.
89, 104 F.2d 222, <u>cert. denied</u>, 308 U.S. 568 (1939); <u>Gale v.
Independent Taxi Owners Ass'n</u>, 65 App. D.C. 396, 84 F.2d 249
(1936). Plaintiff was therefore under no duty to make
Rayfield and Pryor parties to this litigation.

CONCLUSION

    For the foregoing reasons, the judgment below should be
affirmed, including the award of costs.

Respectfully submitted,

Gerard E. Mitchell
STEIN, MITCHELL & MEZINES
1800 M Street, N.W.
Suite 1060 North
Washington, D.C. 20036
(202) 737-7777

Attorneys for Appellee

Dated: January 19, 1982

CERTIFICATE OF SERVICE

I hereby certify that on the 19th day of January, 1982, two copies of Appellee's Brief were mailed, postage paid, to R. Kenly Webster, Esquire, SHAW, PITTMAN, POTTS & TROWBRIDGE, 1800 M Street, N. W., Suite 900 South, Washington, D. C., 20036.

_____
Gerard E. Mitchell

Author Index

Subject Index

568, 571
pure, 615, 616
reduction, 552, 553, 560, 576
risk-benefit, 552, 557, 558, 565, 568
safety criterion, 560–562, 564, 565, 566, 572
severity, 622
social utility, 552
speculative, 615, 616
Risk-benefit factors not enumerated, 771
Risk evaluation, 601, 607, 617
Risk management, 612, 613
Risk reduction, 576, 578, 579, 591, 612, 616, 618, 632
Risk-taking behavior, 379, 382
River marks, 242
Rivet failure, 219
Road, 563
bumps, 224
change in markings, 714
curves, 226
driver's headway, 363
environment, 360
factors in accident reconstruction, 222
gravel on road, 223
hazards, 376
headlight illumination time, 364
maintenance, 563
similarity of accident studies, 360
users, 360
see also Highway
Roadside hazards, 376
Roll bars, 552, 558, 564, 565, 572
Rollover, 213, 226, 566, 758
accidents, 417, 453, 454, 503, 516, 530
bulldozer, 759
crane, protection, 154
fire spread, 134
fuel system fire case, 773
gasoline truck, 225, 226
recreational vehicles, 180, 186
seat belt injuries, 107, 108
Roll stability, 62
Roof, 494, 517
crashworthiness, 771
Rotational injuries, 473, 474, 476, 479, 487, 491, 492, 495, 506, 510, 530

Rubber, aging, 84
Rugs, 17

SAE standards, 597, 603
warnings, 586, 587
Safe, driver's interpretation, 364
Safety devices, 560, 562
in crane litigation, 169–171
cranes, 143–173
duty to provide, 760
Satellite navigation systems, 26
Scare campaigns, 364
School bus warnings, 587
Scratches, metal, 237
Seals in recreational vehicles, 199
Seat belts, 552, 558, 561, 563, 565, 566, 572, 578, 580, 581, 582, 583, 612
acceptability, 380
admissibility as reasonable safety, 763
adverse effects, 103, 108
age, 99, 111
anchorages, 816
cost, 666
defense, 815
failure, 687, 688
at 35 mph, 220
failure to wear, 750
frequency of use, 364
hazards created by, 90, 96–101, 106
inherent stretch of belts, 762
injuries
abdominal, 101, 109, 111, 516, 523
balance against alternative injury, 111
burns, 107
head contact, 97
hyperextension-hyperflexion, 96, 97, 98
internal bleeding, 107
neck, 96–98, 111
statistics, 104–106
thoracic, 99, 100, 107, 109, 111
issues, 377
malfunction, 770
mandated, 90, 95, 97, 103, 379, 382